Stanley Gibbons

# Great Britain

Specialised Stamp Catalogue

Vol. 2

Retail Price

45s. (£2.25)

Stanley Gibbons

# Great Britain

Specialised Stamp Catalogue

Volume 2
King Edward VII
to King George VI

By Appointment
to H.M. the Queen
Stanley Gibbons Ltd.
Philatelists

Stanley Gibbons Ltd  391 Strand London WC2R OLX
Telephone 01-836 9707

1st Edition—February 1967
Reprinted—April 1967
2nd Edition—July 1970
Printed in England by The Anchor Press Ltd Tiptree Essex
Bound by the Leighton-Straker Bookbinding Co Ltd NW10

# Preface

It is now more than three years since the First Edition of this work was published and a great deal has happened in the interval. For one thing there has been a tremendous demand for the middle issues of Great Britain which this volume covers. This has forced up prices faster than we can recollect for any comparable period in the past. We believe that by and large the prices now shown are realistic and fully in accord with the present state of the market.

The prices are expressed in decimal currency since this will be in force within a few months of publication. Further information about decimal pricing and conversion tables are given on pages 11 and 12.

Pricing apart there is a wealth of new information in this edition particularly in the field of Die Proofs, Essays, Colour Trials, etc. Mr. J. T. Clarke was of great assistance in amplifying our listing of this material in the Edward VII period and Mr. P. J. Slingsby covered the King George V typographed issues and the help that he and his colleagues gave, provided much new data. Mr. Marcus Samuel was also particularly helpful in checking over and adding to our listing of the " Specimen " and " Cancelled " stamps.

Mr. J. O. A. Arkell allowed us to inspect his collection of the first 1911–12 issues of King George V, the Downey Heads, which enabled us to fill a number of gaps in our listing. He, and others, also provided further evidence of the interesting cuts and dots Plate Markings resulting in a few corrections and a number of additional items.

We thank Major F. R. B. Whitehouse, C.B.E., for providing material for a relisting of the more prominent varieties of the King George VI Coronation Stamp which made it possible for us to make a new enlarged composite illustration embodying all the listed flaws.

To Mr. H. W. Fisher, co-ordinator of research work within the Great Britain Society, we are greatly indebted for much help and advice in various fields.

Finally, the coincidence of our disposal of the unrivalled Maximus Collection during the period when we were working on this volume, has enabled us to list or record many items for the first time and to illustrate some of those already included.

At the end of the volume we have introduced a tabulated index to assist readers in quickly finding the page on which any particular stamp is listed.

We look forward to having the continued help of specialists on which we rely so much for making further improvements in successive editions of these catalogues.

STANLEY GIBBONS LTD.

# The Stanley Gibbons
# Great Britain Specialised Catalogue

## Volume 1—Queen Victoria

The authoritative Catalogue of the Victorian issues in a new, completely revised edition embodying over fifty extra pages and 900 new illustrations.

In the Line-Engraved stamps the chapter relating to Die Proofs, Essays and Colour Trials, etc. has been completely rewritten and many recently discovered constant varieties in these issues are listed for the first time. Much new material added to the Surface-Printed issues, particularly in the Die Proofs, etc. derived from research at the National Postal Museum and study of the famous Maximus Collection. This new edition also contains much additional historical data and we have added a General Index as well as tabulated tables of all issues, giving essential descriptions of each stamp together with its Specialised and S.G. catalogue numbers and page reference.

3rd Edition. July 1970. Uniform binding. 269 pages.
**Price 45s. (£2·25).** Postage extra.

## Volume 3—Queen Elizabeth II

This new publication covering the present reign completes the Specialised Catalogue. The definitive issues (Wilding, Machin and Regional) are classified value by value, dealing in turn with the changes in watermarks, papers, and the various colour reactions of the phosphor bands, with all cylinder blocks listed in conjunction with the various perforation types. Booklets, Booklet Panes and Cylinder Numbers and Coils and Coil Joins are fully recorded and the Special (Commemorative) issues are listed in great detail.

Listed varieties are fully illustrated in all Sections and in addition minor constant flaws are recorded and the interesting sheet markings are given in detail for each stamp. Information is also given of Presentation Packs, First Day Covers, withdrawal dates and quantities issued.

1st edition. Publication in August 1970. Uniform binding. Over 300 pages.
**Price 30s. (£1·50).** Postage extra.

# Contents

# Notes

The aim of this catalogue is to classify in specialised form the stamps of Great Britain, to give distinguishing numbers to them and to quote prices which are current with the Publishers at the time of going to press and at which they will supply if in stock.

## To Order from this Catalogue

Always quote the *Specialised Catalogue* number, mentioning *Vol. 2, 2nd* Ed., and where necessary specify additionally the precise item wanted.

All *Specialised Catalogue* numbers in the basic catalogue (except for Essays, Proofs, Colour Trials, etc.) include a prefix letter or letters, shades have a number in brackets where there is more than one and subsequent varieties have letter identifications. Once the principle of arrangement and numbering is understood, specific identification of items is simple, as the following example demonstrates:—

**1913 (JANUARY). ½d. GREEN, TYPE N6**

| Cat. No. | S.G. No. | Wmk. | | | Shades | Unused | Used |
|---|---|---|---|---|---|---|---|
| N14 | 351/56 | W.14 Simple Cypher | | | (1) Green | 5 | 5 |
| a. | Doubly printed | .. | .. | £500 | (2) Deep green | 15 | 15 |
| b. | No watermark | .. | .. | 4·00 | (3) Pale green | 50 | 8 |
| c. | Watermark inverted | .. | 15 | 10 | (4) Very pale green (1919) | 2·50 | 1·00 |
| d. | Watermark reversed | .. | 1·50 | 1·50 | (5) Very deep green (1919) | 6·50 | 4·00 |
| e. | Watermark inverted and | | | | (6) Bright green | 8 | 5 |
| | reversed | .. | .. | 75 | 75 | (7) Deep bright green | 75 | 15 |
| f. | "New Moon" flaw | .. | .. | 25·00 | 25·00 | (8) Yellow-green | 1·00 | 25 |
| g. | Cracked plate | .. | .. | 6·00 | | | |

*Example:* "N14(1)c" is watermark inverted in the commonest shade. If a scarcer shade were requested, the price would be proportionally higher. Naturally the varieties listed will not necessarily exist in all shades shown.

In the Appendices, there are prefix letters to identify the watermark varieties in Appendix G and the Booklets in Appendix K. In the Plate Markings listed in Appendix J it is necessary to describe the basic stamp and quote the Plate number and any particular control piece desired, remembering that all prices quoted are for the cheapest control. The Booklet Pane Advertisements listed in Appendix L are numbered. In ordering cylinder numbers from Booklets in Appendix M and from Sheets in Appendix N it is necessary to quote the basic catalogue number, followed by the cylinder number stating whether with or without dot, and where necessary giving the Perforation Type.

## Symbols

†   = Does not exist.

—   = Exists, but price cannot be quoted (also blank in used price column).

\*   = One of the Photogravure "Abnormals"
(See Section N2, General notes).

(F)   = after colours means fluorescent
(See Section M, General notes).

/   between colours means "on" and the colour following is that of the paper on which the stamp is printed.

"From"   = Where stamps or varieties are grouped, prices are generally the same for each, but there are exceptions, particularly where "From" appears. In "basic" lists prices quoted are for the cheapest plate, control or cylinder number, etc.

N.P.M. = National Postal Museum.

## Watermark Illustrations

These are always shown as seen from the *front* of the stamp. This is important to remember when classifying sideways watermarks which also exist sideways inverted.

## Terms of Business

Cash with order, except where clients have accounts. Prices "postage extra". We reserve the right to alter prices without notice.

*Want Lists* for stamps priced at £1 or over will have the careful attention of our special Great Britain Dept.

Our *Approval Dept.* always has available a wide range of Great Britain selections including stamps priced at less than £1.

## How to Remit

Remittances must be made free of costs, preferably by cheque, payable on a Bank in the United Kingdom or by Banker's Draft. Cheques, Money Orders and Postal Orders should be made payable to "Stanley Gibbons Ltd." and crossed "Lloyds Bank Ltd." Foreign cheques will be sold, and the proceeds only credited to the customer.

In their own interests customers in the U.K. are advised not to send currency notes or coin. Foreign Bank Notes should be registered, any that our bankers are unable to negotiate will have to be returned to the customer.

Remittances from abroad *apart* from the British Commonwealth (except Canada), Iceland, the Irish Republic, Jordan, Kuwait, Libya, the Republic of South Africa, South West Africa and Western Samoa should be made by International Money Order or by Banker's Draft. Before remitting by any other method than a Money Order, it is advisable to consult a banker.

## Guarantee

Every effort is made to ensure that all stamps sold by us, unless otherwise described, shall be in all respects genuine originals and they are offered for sale as such. If not as described, and if returned to us by the purchaser within six years, we undertake to refund the price paid to us and our liability in respect thereof shall be limited accordingly. If any stamp is certified as genuine by the Expert Committee of the Royal Philatelic Society, London, or of the British Philatelic Association Ltd., the purchaser shall not be entitled to make any claim against us in respect of any error, omission or mistake in such certificate.

All purchases from us are to be deemed to be subject to the above conditions.

*N.B.—The above form of guarantee is that approved by the Royal Philatelic Society and by the British Philatelic Association Ltd.*

## Examination and Identification of Stamps

We do not give opinions as to the genuineness of stamps, nor do we identify stamps or number them by our Catalogues.

## Our Addresses and Hours of Business

**HEAD OFFICE—**

STANLEY GIBBONS LTD.
391 STRAND,
LONDON, WC2R OLX.

*Telephone:* 01-836 9707.
*Telegrams:* Philatelic, London, W.C..
*Cables:* Stangib, London, W.C.2.
*Code:* A.B.C. (6th Edition).

**SHOP DEPARTMENT—**

Our only retail shop is at
391 Strand, WC2R OLX.

Open from Monday to Friday 9 a.m. to 5.30 p.m. and on Saturday 9.30 a.m. to 12.30 p.m.

**RARE STAMP DEPARTMENT—**

ROMANO HOUSE,
399 Strand, WC2R OLX

Opening hours as for Shop Department

**EDITORIAL, ACCOUNTS AND AUCTIONS—**

STANLEY GIBBONS LTD.
DRURY HOUSE,
RUSSELL STREET,
DRURY LANE,
LONDON, WC2B 5HD

*Telephones:*
01–836 4136 (Editorial and Publishing)
01–836 2005 (Retail Publications)
01–836 7941 (Auctions)
01–836 9707 (Stamps and all Depts.)

**WHOLESALE PUBLICATIONS AND ACCESSORIES—**

STANGIB HOUSE, Sarehole Road, Hall Green, Birmingham, 28.

**NEW YORK BRANCH—**

STANGIB LTD,
STANGIB BUILDING,
595 FIFTH AVENUE,
NEW YORK,
N.Y. 10017, U.S.A.

*Telephone:* 212–PL8–2210.
*Cables:* Stangib, New York.

# Decimal Pricing

As explained in the Preface, prices are quoted in decimal form. During the period when shillings and pence are still in use the procedure when making remittances is to add up the amounts in decimals and convert *the total only* into pounds, shillings and pence. Naturally only the figures after the decimal point have to be converted and this can be done by reference to the Conversion Table given below:—

| New pence | s. | d. |
|---|---|---|
| 5 | 1 | 0 |
| 8 | 1 | 7 |
| 10 | 2 | 0 |
| 12 | 2 | 5 |
| 15 | 3 | 0 |
| 20 | 4 | 0 |
| 25 | 5 | 0 |
| 30 | 6 | 0 |
| 35 | 7 | 0 |
| 40 | 8 | 0 |
| 45 | 9 | 0 |
| 50 | 10 | 0 |
| 55 | 11 | 0 |
| 60 | 12 | 0 |
| 65 | 13 | 0 |
| 70 | 14 | 0 |
| 75 | 15 | 0 |
| 80 | 16 | 0 |
| 85 | 17 | 0 |
| 90 | 18 | 0 |
| 95 | 19 | 0 |
| 1·00 | 20 | 0 |

To make the addition of prices simple we have quoted them in multiples of 5 new pence with the exception of the 8 and 12 pence prices as it was felt here that a gap of 5 pence between prices would be too wide. 5 new pence is now the minimum price, the equivalent of one shilling. It costs us at least this much in overheads to supply such low value stamps; this must therefore be regarded as a *handling charge* as it does not necessarily represent the actual value of a stamp. By way of compensation, stamps formerly priced at 1s. 3d. have been converted to 5 new pence except where they would have been increased in the course of price revision. Prices below £1 are expressed as given in the table above and prices above £1 in the price columns are shown as pounds followed by a decimal point and new pence or zeroes as the case may be up to 95·00. For £100 and upwards the pound sign is used and there is no decimal point followed by zeros.

*The old and new ways of showing prices are given in the U.S. dollar conversion table on the next page.*

# Conversion of Expression of Old £sd Prices to New £p Prices with U.S. Dollar Equivalents

The £1 sterling is converted at the rate of $2.40 rounded off to avoid awkward equivalents. When ordering from U.S. dollar countries, the sterling prices should be added up and the total converted at the current rate of exchange.

£sd currency: 12 pence = 1 shilling. 20 shillings = £1 (pound).
£p currency: 100 new pence = £1 (pound).

| £sd | £p | U.S. | £sd | £p | U.S. |
|---|---|---|---|---|---|
| 1 0 | 5 | 12 | £19 | 19·00 | 46·00 |
| 1 9 | 8 | 20 | £20 | 20·00 | 48·00 |
| 2 0 | 10 | 25 | £21 | 21·00 | 51·00 |
| 2 6 | 12 | 30 | £22 | 22·00 | 54·00 |
| 3 0 | 15 | 35 | £23 | 23·00 | 56·00 |
| 4 0 | 20 | 50 | £24 | 24·00 | 58·00 |
| 5 0 | 25 | 60 | £25 | 25·00 | 60·00 |
| 6 0 | 30 | 75 | £26 | 26·00 | 62·50 |
| 7 0 | 35 | 85 | £27 | 27·00 | 65·00 |
| 8 0 | 40 | 1·00 | £28 | 28·00 | 67·50 |
| 9 0 | 45 | 1·10 | £29 | 29·00 | 70·00 |
| 10 0 | 50 | 1·20 | £30 | 30·00 | 72·00 |
| 11 0 | 55 | 1·35 | £32 | 32·00 | 80·00 |
| 12 0 | 60 | 1·50 | £35 | 35·00 | 85·00 |
| 13 0 | 65 | 1·60 | £38 | 38·00 | 92·00 |
| 14 0 | 70 | 1·70 | £40 | 40·00 | 96·00 |
| 15 0 | 75 | 1·80 | £42 | 42·00 | $100 |
| 16 0 | 80 | 2·00 | £45 | 45·00 | $110 |
| 17 0 | 85 | 2·10 | £48 | 48·00 | $115 |
| 18 0 | 90 | 2·20 | £50 | 50·00 | $120 |
| 19 0 | 95 | 2·30 | £55 | 55·00 | $135 |
| 20 0 | 1·00 | 2·40 | £60 | 60·00 | $145 |
| 22 6 | 1·10 | 2·75 | £65 | 65·00 | $155 |
| 25 0 | 1·25 | 3·00 | £70 | 70·00 | $170 |
| 27 6 | 1·40 | 3·50 | £75 | 75·00 | $180 |
| 30 0 | 1·50 | 3·75 | £80 | 80·00 | $195 |
| 32 6 | 1·60 | 4·00 | £85 | 85·00 | $205 |
| 35 0 | 1·75 | 4·25 | £90 | 90·00 | $220 |
| 37 6 | 1·90 | 4·50 | £95 | 95·00 | $230 |
| 40 0 | 2·00 | 5·00 | £100 | | $240 |
| 42 6 | 2·10 | 5·25 | £110 | | $265 |
| 45 0 | 2·25 | 5·50 | £120 | | $290 |
| 47 6 | 2·40 | 5·75 | £130 | | $315 |
| 50 0 | 2·50 | 6·00 | £140 | | $340 |
| 55 0 | 2·75 | 7·00 | £150 | | $360 |
| 60 0 | 3·00 | 7·50 | £160 | | $385 |
| 65 0 | 3·25 | 8·00 | £170 | | $410 |
| 70 0 | 3·50 | 8·50 | £180 | | $440 |
| 75 0 | 3·75 | 9·00 | £190 | | $460 |
| 80 0 | 4·00 | 10·00 | £200 | | $480 |
| 85 0 | 4·25 | 10·50 | £225 | | $540 |
| 90 0 | 4·50 | 11·00 | £250 | | $600 |
| 95 0 | 4·75 | 11·50 | £275 | | $660 |
| £5 | 5·00 | 12·00 | £300 | | $720 |
| 110 0 | 5·50 | 13·50 | £325 | | $780 |
| £6 | 6·00 | 15·00 | £350 | | $840 |
| 130 0 | 6·50 | 16·00 | £375 | | $900 |
| £7 | 7·00 | 17·00 | £400 | | $960 |
| 150 0 | 7·50 | 18·00 | £425 | | $1020 |
| £8 | 8·00 | 20·00 | £450 | | $1080 |
| 170 0 | 8·50 | 21·00 | £475 | | $1140 |
| £9 | 9·00 | 22·00 | £500 | | $1200 |
| 190 0 | 9·50 | 23·00 | £550 | | $1325 |
| £10 | 10·00 | 24·00 | £600 | | $1450 |
| £11 | 11·00 | 27·00 | £650 | | $1600 |
| £12 | 12·00 | 30·00 | £700 | | $1700 |
| £13 | 13·00 | 32·00 | £750 | | $1800 |
| £14 | 14·00 | 34·00 | £800 | | $2000 |
| £15 | 15·00 | 36·00 | £850 | | $2100 |
| £16 | 16·00 | 40·00 | £900 | | $2200 |
| £17 | 17·00 | 42·00 | £950 | | $2300 |
| £18 | 18·00 | 44·00 | £1000 | | $2400 |

# SECTION M
# King Edward VII Issues, 1902-1913

## General Notes

**INTRODUCTION.** King Edward VII came to the throne on 22nd January 1901. Discussions on the new series of stamps began immediately, and the printers, De la Rue & Co., prepared sets of Essays. These were "paste ups" of the "Jubilee" issue values ½d. to 1s. (except the 4½d.) and the 1d. lilac. With the exception of the ½d., 1d., 2½d. and 6d. values, the final designs closely resembled the Victorian "Jubilee" issue. De la Rue & Co. printed the stamps until 1910, when the contract passed to Harrison & Sons.

**ARRANGEMENT.** Each value has been dealt with in turn, through its changes of colour, perforation and printer.

**PLATES AND PRINTING.** After the designs had been approved, dies were engraved for all sixteen values. The values 1½d., 2d., 4d., 5d., 9d., 10d. and 1s. were printed from head and duty plates, and as the designs were similar to the 1887 "Jubilee" issue, it was possible to utilise the Victorian dies for the duty plates (frame plate in the case of the 1s.).

The plates were prepared by the electrotype process adopted by De la Rue for the surface-printed Victorian issues, and they were surfaced with steel. When part of a plate became defective it was the practice to cut out the defective stamp image and insert another in its place. Instances are known of plates having these substituted clichés. They can be identified by the fact that the level of the substituted cliché does not correspond exactly with the level of the adjoining impression (see illustration).

## LAYOUT
**Values ½d., 1d., 2½d., 3d., 4d. (orange), 6d. and 7d.** Each sheet consisted of 240 stamps arranged in two panes of 120, one above the other. Each pane contained 10 horizontal rows of 12 stamps, separated from one another by a horizontal gutter, known as the inter-pane gutter. The whole sheet was surrounded by a marginal line which crossed over the interpane gutter. The interpane gutter was filled with 48 vertically lined pillars.

The marginal lines are often referred to as Jubilee lines, as it was during the 1887 Jubilee issue that they first made their appearance. They are known technically as "Printer's Rule" and formed part of the printing plate. Their use was to take the initial shock of the inking roller, and thus prevent damage to the stamp images. We shall therefore use the term "marginal rule".

There were two types of marginal rule:

(1) *Continuous*  An unbroken line (sometimes with certain breaks) round the pane or panes.
(2) *Co-extensive*  Lines broken opposite the margins where the stamps were perforated.

These lines were usually also broken above the top pane and below the bottom pane opposite the centres of the 6th and 7th stamps, but not opposite the margins between them. Exceptions are Plates 25, 26 and 27 of the ½d. value. Here the breaks were filled in, and a break opposite the margins between them was substituted. This is known as the 6-7 rule variety.

**Values 1½d., 2d., 4d. (green and brown), 5d. and 1s.** These sheets were arranged in two panes of 120 stamps each as before. Each pane was surrounded by a marginal rule which did not cross the interpane. The interpane gutter was without the vertically lined pillars. There were three different types of marginal rule:—

    (1) *Continuous.*
    (2) *Co-extensive.*
    (3) *Short bars* approximately the width of, or the length of the value tablets, and opposite to them. This type was used only for some of the 2d. and 5d. duty plates.

The 1s. sheets were cut through the interpane gutter into two halves before delivery to the Post Office, thus leaving half a margin to each half sheet.

**The 9d. Value.** Sheets consisted of 160 stamps arranged in eight panes in pairs side by side. The panes contained 4 horizontal rows of 5 stamps each and were surrounded by marginal rules which did not cross the interpane gutters.

The vertical interpane gutter between each pair of panes was filled with a series of short horizontal lined pillars, five to the height of a stamp, and the horizontal gutters between the upper two pairs and the lower two pairs of panes contained four long horizontal lined pillars. The central horizontal gutter was left blank. These lined pillars in the interpane gutters did *not* form part of the plate.

The sheets were cut into two halves before delivery to the Post Office.

For reference purposes the eight panes have been designated by letters as follows:—

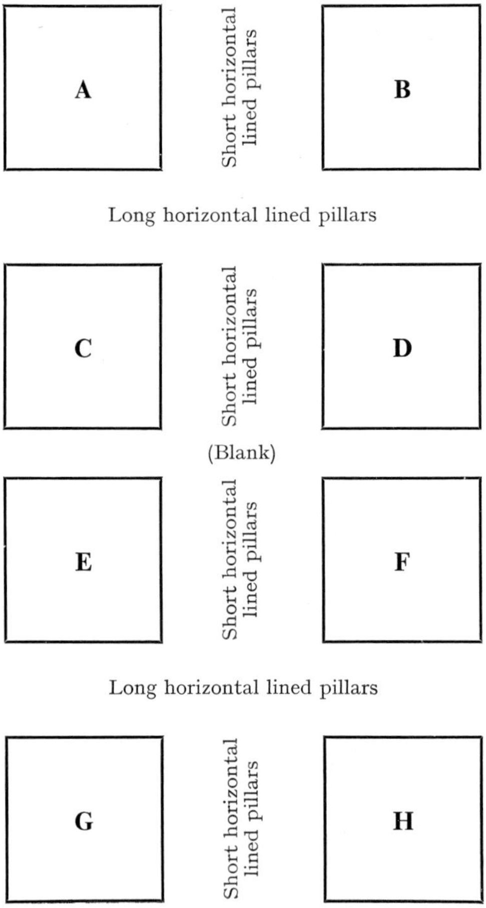

A    Short horizontal lined pillars    B

Long horizontal lined pillars

C    Short horizontal lined pillars    D

(Blank)

E    Short horizontal lined pillars    F

Long horizontal lined pillars

G    Short horizontal lined pillars    H

**The 10d. Value.** The sheets consisted of 192 stamps, arranged in four panes one above the other. The panes contained 4 horizontal rows of 12 stamps each, and were surrounded with marginal rules that did not cross the interpane gutters.

The horizontal interpane gutters between the two upper and the two lower panes were filled in with long horizontal lined pillars, between which was a series of vertical lined pillars four to the width of each stamp. The central horizontal gutter was left blank. These lined pillars in the interpane gutters did *not* form part of the plate.

The sheets were cut into two halves before delivery to the Post Office.

For reference purposes the four panes have been designated by letters as follows:—

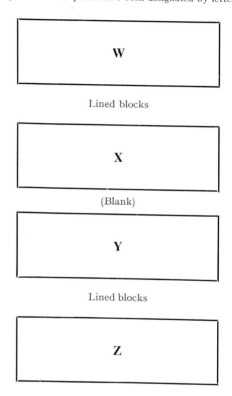

Lined blocks

(Blank)

Lined blocks

**Values 2s. 6d., 5s. and 10s.** Each sheet consisted of 112 stamps arranged in two panes one above the other. The panes contained 7 horizontal rows of 8 stamps and were surrounded by a marginal rule which crossed the interpane gutter. The interpane gutter was filled with vertical lined pillars, four to the width of a stamp.

The sheets were cut into two halves before delivery to the Post Office.

**The £1 Value.** The sheet consisted of 80 stamps arranged in two panes one above the other. Each pane contained 10 horizontal rows of 4 stamps and was surrounded by a marginal rule which crossed the interpane gutter. The interpane gutter was filled with vertical lined pillars, eleven to the width of a stamp.

The sheets were cut into two halves before delivery to the Post Office.

**Booklet Plates.** Special plates were made for the issue of stamps in booklets, so as to facilitate the stitching.

The first three vertical rows were upright, rows 4 to 6 inverted, rows 7 to 9 upright and rows 10 to 12 inverted. There was a gutter margin between rows 6 and 7 for stitching. This layout results in half of the stamps having inverted watermarks. A similar special plate was made for the ½d. stamps having the St. Andrew's Cross. In this case the sheet contained 200 stamps and 40 crosses.

## THE PROVISIONAL PRINTINGS

**(a) By Harrison & Sons Ltd.** Harrison & Sons secured the contract for stamp printing on January 1st, 1911. As far as is known they had never previously printed any postage stamps, so that the award of the contract to them occasioned some surprise. Their task was a novel one, and as they had only a few months for preparation their early work fell short of the high standard of De la Rue.

It was hoped that they would be able to commence work on the new Georgian series without making any printings from the old Edwardian plates. Philatelists would have missed an interesting field for study if this had been possible, but it was soon clear that supplies of the De la Rue printings would not suffice until the issue of the new series. It was then announced that the 6d. stamp and the values from 2s. 6d. upwards would be printed by the Stamping Department of the Board of Inland Revenue at Somerset House, while the stamps of the remaining denominations would be produced by Harrison and Sons. In actual fact Harrisons only printed ½d., 1d., 2½d., 3d. and 4d. stamps, and the remaining values were provisionally printed at Somerset House.

The Harrison printings of the ½d. and 1d. stamps from the old Edwardian plates were heavily printed, and the design was very blurred and smudgy in consequence. The stamps were, in many cases, badly centred as regards the perforation, and a number of badly perforated " freak " sheets were issued, owing to insufficient care in checking. Later printings of Edwardian stamps were fairly satisfactory, though they never reached the De la Rue level of technical excellence.

The alteration of the horizontal perforation from 14 to 15 for Great Britain stamps was made to coincide with the first Georgian issue in June 1911. The Georgian stamps were not well received by the public, and in the period when the original dies were being redrawn, further printings of the Edwardian stamps were made. These printings can be distinguished by the perforation (15 × 14).

**(b) By Somerset House.** Until the expiration of the De la Rue contract few people suspected the existence of the well equipped Government stamp-printing establishment at Somerset House, and the announcement that postage stamps would be printed there aroused considerable curiosity in philatelic circles. If, in the printing of the Edwardian stamps, they failed to reach at once the high standard set by De la Rue, this is largely explained by the unsatisfactory surface of the paper on which they had to work.

One of the most interesting features in connection with the Somerset House printings was their novel way of plate marking. When it became necessary to identify the plates, the marginal rules were naturally chosen for the purpose. Throughout the De la Rue period they had been used by the printers for marking the different plates (q.v.). In this case they were again used, but for the different purpose of recording the date of printing. Thus the cuts under the 11th or penultimate stamp of the bottom row represent 1911, and under the 12th or last stamp 1912. These cuts are of great assistance in establishing the various printings. Marginal dots were also added above and below the marginal rule on many plates, but the reason for this is not understood.

## MARGINAL MARKINGS ON THE PLATES.

All the Edwardian plates were made by De la Rue & Co.

In the marginal rule of nearly every plate, cuts or in some cases dots, other than the normal breaks were made. These markings are the printers' private marks of identification.

Many of the plates of the ½d. and 1d. values, which were first put to press with a single cut or series of cuts, were taken from the press for some reason, and before being put back, had further cuts added. In the lists in Appendix J, the adding of cuts or other changes has been indicated by the addition of the letters a, b, c, d, etc., after the plate number.

**The numbering of the plates is arbitrary, as there is no evidence to show the actual order in which the plates were made.** The lists in this catalogue follow the numbering given by Major Beaumont and C. G. Shaw. Certain values of the stamps printed in one colour had the printings made from two plates simultaneously. The additional markings mentioned above occurred when one plate was transferred to the other side of the printing bed.

The original plate markings made by the De la Rue printers were always in the marginal rule below the bottom row of the lower pane. In the descriptions given, " cut below 1st " always means the cut below the first stamp in the bottom row. The only exception is on the head plates of the 9d. value, where cuts were made in the top row of the pane.

The added cuts on the ½d. and 1d. were usually in the bottom rule, and only occasionally in the side rules. However, when the plates were handed over to Harrison & Sons, they made extra markings in the marginal rule on the right side of the last four rows of the sheet.

After plates were handed over to Somerset House in 1911, further cuts or dots were added. Most of these consisted of double cuts in the marginal rule below the last but one or the last stamp in the bottom row of the lower pane, sometimes in the upper pane also. These cuts are not plate markings but marks to show the period of printings (1911 or 1912 respectively).

**THE IDENTIFICATION OF THE PLATES.** Our descriptions are as brief as possible, and usually refer only to the deliberate markings made by the printers. It is sometimes possible to plate a marginal piece from a different part of the sheet from that which is indicated, by knowledge of characteristic flaws in the marginal rule.

For fuller descriptions of these, see *The Stamps of Great Britain, Part III,* published by the Royal Philatelic Society.

**HOW TO DISTINGUISH BETWEEN THE PRINTINGS.** The provisional printings were made from the plates handed over by De la Rue & Co., so that the task of distinguishing between the two sets of printings is chiefly one of colour. Notes on these differences in colour are given under their respective values. In general, the colours used by De la Rue varied little from that of the 1887 Jubilee issue, and the stamps on ordinary paper should be compared with this set.

The " ordinary " paper used by De la Rue was of high finish in contrast with that used by the other printers. Only very late printings at Somerset House on " plate glazed " paper come up to the standards of De la Rue's work.

With the exception of the 6d. stamp all values on chalk-surfaced paper are from the De la Rue printings.

The printings show marked differences, as in addition to the blotchy and heavy early printings of some values, there is a coarseness about the finer lines of the design in most of the provisional printings which is absent from the stamps printed by De la Rue.

The paper on which they had to work seems to have been one of the greatest handicaps to the provisional printers. This was due to the inferior printing surface of the paper and also to the Crown watermark which made an appreciable difference in the thickness of those portions where it appeared. When they came to the actual printing of the stamps, the printers appear to have been in a quandary. Were they to use heavy pressure in order to get the colour well into the lines of the watermark, and risk blurring the fine lines of the design, or should they use less pressure and have insufficient colour along the lines where the paper was thinned by the watermark? Specimens showing the result of each of these methods will be found, the heaviest inking being chiefly in the early Harrison printings, while in the later and lighter printings, of both Somerset House and Harrison, white specks will be seen which are particularly noticeable on the background of solid colour to the left of the head, in the stamps where this is found. On holding such stamps up to the light and looking through them from the front, it will be noticed that these specks follow the lines of the watermark. In the case of the 2d. and 5d. stamps printed at Somerset House, with the portrait on a white background, this defect is hardly noticeable, and they have therefore the most finished appearance of any of the early provisional printings. In the De la Rue printings the white specks practically never occur, probably owing to some difference in the preparation of the paper for printing.

In the De la Rue issues generally speaking, the gum is yellowish, opaque and fairly plentiful, while in the provisional issues it is hardly apparent being transparent, colourless and thinly applied. In stamps with the latter gum the mesh of the paper is usually very distinct, and the watermark stands out more clearly than in specimens with the yellowish gum. A very good idea of the appearance of the gum and paper of the provisional printings may be obtained from the Harrison stamps with the 15 × 14 perforation. Complaints by the public over the lack of gum resulted in certain stamps being issued " doubly gummed ". This gum is easily recognized being thick, yellowish and very shiny.

**FLUORESCENCE.** Certain stamps from the provisional printings show a marked degree of fluorescence, under the quartz lamp. By fluorescence we mean that the colours give a golden emission. We have noted this phenomenon where it occurs with an (F), but it must be emphasized that the colour descriptions we give are the result of daylight study in a good North light. The reaction of colours to ultra violet or any other kind of light is not within the scope of this catalogue.

**THE CONTROLS.** The system of controls which was started on the ½d. and 1d. Victorian stamps continued with these values of the Edwardian issues. The control did not form part of the printing plate, but was screwed into the margin before a printing began, and removed when the printing had ceased.

Controls A and B were each in use for twelve months. Controls C to D 10 inclusive were each in use for a period of six months, the figure representing the year, and the letter signifying the particular half. The only control used by Harrison was A 11.

The controls are listed under their respective values in the catalogue. The dates shown are the dates when the controls were first noted by collectors. It is presumed that the controls were brought into use by the printers on the 1st January or the 1st July of each year.

**IMPRIMATURS.** One sheet of each value was placed in the records of Somerset House. With the exception of the ½d. blue-green and the 1d. they are imperforate. Unlike the Victorian imprimaturs, no copies seem to have come on the market.

**" SPECIMEN " AND " CANCELLED " STAMPS.** From time to time for various reasons such as circularization of information to postmasters or the presentation of sets to foreign governments, certain stamps were overprinted " Specimen ". Stamps overprinted " Cancelled " are very much scarcer and come from official records. We have not listed varieties which have only been seen in official archives. The overprints were in numerous different types and these types are illustrated in Appendix H. For the information that has permitted us to make a full and correct listing of these issues we are indebted to Mr. Marcus Samuel.

**PAPER.** The paper was manufactured by R. D. Turner & Co. Ltd., in mill sheets equal in size to four Post Office sheets. The gum was applied before printing.

In addition to the 960 Imperial Crown wmks. (or 448 Anchor wmks. in the case of the values 2s. 6d., 5s. and 10s.), the mill sheet bore other watermarks.

Each Post Office sheet had the watermark " POSTAGE " in the four margins, and in each corner were vertical and horizontal lines in the form of an " L ". Each mill sheet also had 18 cross watermarks in two sizes arranged as follows:—

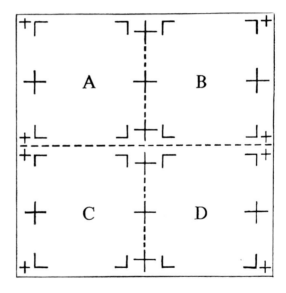

The Post Office sheet of the 9d. value also had the watermark " POSTAGE " in the gutter between the upper and lower halves. In some cases two plates side by side were printed from simultaneously on the upper or lower half of the mill sheet. This method was only used on the values ½d., 1d., 2½d., 3d., 4d. orange and 6d.

After the division of the mill sheet, the four Post Office sheets show the crosses in each of the four corners, and also in the margins opposite the interpane gutter. Since the small crosses appeared only in the side margins of the mill sheet, they indicate the relative positions of the two plates when they were printed from simultaneously.

In 1905 De la Rue took to printing some of the values on chalk-surfaced paper. This paper may be recognized by the extreme smoothness of the surface, and the shine of the coating when viewed obliquely. In nearly all cases, the chalk-surfaced paper appears thicker and heavier than the ordinary paper. The watermark also is not so immediately apparent.

In 1913 Somerset House used an experimental coated paper believed to have been supplied by John Dickinson. This was not a chalk-surfaced paper as it does not respond to the silver point test. Further details are given under the 6d. stamp heading.

Somerset House also used paper which had been subjected to a process known as " plate glazing ". This process produced a very smooth surface, and printings made on this paper gave excellent impressions.

**WATERMARKS.** The values ½d. to 1s. all have the Imperial Crown watermark. The values 2s. 6d., 5s. and 10s. have the Anchor watermark and the £1 value has three crowns in the watermark.

**Imperial Crown**

**Anchor**

**PERFORATION.** The gauge of the perforation was 14 throughout, the exception being the Harrison provisional printings late in 1911 which were 15 horizontally by 14 vertically.

**De la Rue** used horizontal comb machines which gave an extension hole in each margin, and perforated the sheets from bottom to top. Examples of reverse feeds (i.e. perforated from top to bottom) are known on the ½d., 1d., 5d. and 6d. values. In addition De la Rue used vertical comb machines on the ½d. and 1d. values (also a few 4d. sheets printed in green and brown). These were set to perforate the sheets from left to right (or right to left).

**Harrison & Sons** used both horizontal and vertical comb machines with both feeds, top to bottom, bottom to top, left to right and right to left.

**Somerset House** used vertical comb machines only on the values 1½d. to 10s., perforating sheets from left to right or right to left. The £1 value was perforated by horizontal comb machines, either from bottom to top or top to bottom.

For convenience of reference the various types have been given numbers and are illustrated in Appendix I. The illustrations indicate clearly how to tell the difference between the various types.

# Essays, Proofs and Colour Trials

Series A                                Series B

## 1901 "Paste up" of the Victorian "Jubilee" Issue

The ½d. to 1s. values (except 4½d.) and the 1d. lilac. The portrait of the Queen was cut from the design and a lithographed head (in appropriate colour) of King Edward VII substituted.

Price

Series A  ½d. to 1s.  Mounted on card with a three-quarter face likeness of
        K.E. VII facing left. 12 values exist .. .. .. .. *Each* 50·00
Series B  As above, but with a quarter-face likeness facing left  .. *Each* 50·00

In addition, the frame and likeness of the 1d. lilac stamp exists in three other states.

Aa   As in series A, but portrait reversed .. .. .. .. .. .. 60·00
Bb   As in series B, but portrait reversed .. .. .. .. .. .. 60·00
C    Similar to A but portrait engraved instead of lithographed .. .. £100

*Transitional Essays.* These show hand painted alterations to the Victorian stamps. The values known are the 1½d., 2d., 3d., 4d., 5d., 9d., 10d. and 1s. They all had a crown superimposed above the Queen's head.


The portrait for the issued stamps was executed by Emil Fuchs, an Austrian artist who also prepared a new design for the ½d., 1d., 2½d. and 6d. stamps. The remaining values of the issues were similar in design to their Victorian predecessors, but with the incorporation of the Crown above the head.


## 1901 Proofs of the Suggested Design for the ½d., 1d., 2½d., and 6d. Stamps

Frames produced from temporary copper plates and pasted on card.
(1) Proof in black of the frame, inscribed "POSTAGE : REVENUE". A photograph of the King's head inserted .. .. .. .. .. .. 80·00
(2) As above, but inscribed "POSTAGE & REVENUE". An engraved head
inserted .. .. .. .. .. .. .. .. .. .. 80·00
(3) As above, but the King's head differently placed in the oval .. .. 80·00
(4) As above, but printed in various colours. Red, green, or purple on pink. *Each* 70·00

Eight different essays were prepared for the 2½d. stamp, differing in the design of the value tablets. Photographic frames with heads inserted. Mounted on card dated "July 10th 1901 " .. .. .. .. .. .. .. *Each* 40·00


## Essays for 2s. 6d., 5s., 10s., £1 and £5

Artist's sunken sketches. Head and Crown from a proof, and backgrounds similar to the issued design hand painted in black and white .. *Each from* £100

It was originally intended to have a £5 stamp, but no plate was made, and the value passed from currency.

£5 Die proof in black on white glazed card
    Endorsed " BEFORE HARDENING 11 MAR 1902 " .. .. .. £400
      „ " AFTER HARDENING 13 MAR 1902 " .. .. .. .. £400
      „ (M/S) " Proof of Die prepared but not registered as it was resolved
        to discontinue the £5 stamp/1902 " .. .. .. .. .. £400

# Die Proofs

Extra Large Head　　　Large Head　　　Small Head　　　Head and Frame

## Approved Head

Die Proof of extra large size head which was adopted in reduced size .. .. 50·00

Die proof of the large head in black on white glazed card (used for the values ½d., 1d., 2½d., 6d., 7d., 2s. 6d., 5s., 10s. and £1)

　　Endorsed " BEFORE HARDENING 27 JUNE 1901 " .. .. .. 50·00
　　　　" AFTER HARDENING " and (M/S) " 27/6/01 " and initials .. 50·00
　　As above but no date .. .. .. .. .. .. 50·00

Die proof of the small head on solid background in black on white glazed card (used for the values 1½d., 3d., 4d., 9d., 1od. and 1s.) .. .. .. .. 40·00

　　As above but (M/S) " After Hardening " .. .. .. .. 40·00
　　As above but endorsed " 5 SEP 01 AFTER HARDENING " .. .. 40·00
　　As above, but no background to head (used for the values 2d. and 5d.) .. 40·00

## Approved Frame-value Tablet Blank

Die proof on white glazed card

　　Without marking .. .. .. .. .. .. .. .. 35·00
　　Endorsed " AFTER HARDENING 1 AUG 1901 " .. .. .. .. 35·00

The dies for the ½d., 1d. and 6d. were made from this master die, also the 2½d. value with modifications.

## Approved Head and Frame Without Value

Die Proof of complete design except the value (used for the ½d., 1d. and 6d.) .. 50·00

　　Endorsed in reverse " ORIGINAL DIE " above and " P6 " below .. .. £100
　　Endorsed " 1 AUG 01 BEFORE HARDENING " .. .. .. .. 70·00

## Complete Die Proofs

These are listed under their respective values in the catalogue. They are known without markings, marked " BEFORE HARDENING ", " AFTER HARDENING " etc. The prices given are for these varieties. Proofs with designers' and other official instructions in manuscript, if not quoted separately, are worth more.

## "Transvaal Essays"

Some months after the first Edwardian stamps were issued, further essays were prepared at the request of the King, who it is believed favoured the design of the Transvaal stamps to that of the ½d., 1d., 2½d. and 6d. of Great Britain.

Type 1　　　　　　　Type 2

Essays were prepared in the above design of which there are two types.
(1) No line between the oval for the King's head and the frame
(2) With line between the oval and frame.

### Type 1 (Oct. 1902)

*Price*

Die proof in black on white glazed card .. .. .. .. .. .. 75·00

Printed from a small plate of six images. No wmk. Perf. 14.

　1d. red, green, ultramarine, lake or brown-purple .. .. *Each* 50·00

Printed from new plates with head in black and frame in colour.

　1d. black and brown-purple or black and red .. .. .. .. *Each* 50·00

Examples of all the above are known pasted on card, with a line of colour painted in the space between the oval for the head and the frame. The line of colour approximates to that of the frame but is different in shade.

## Type 2

Imperf.

1d. black .. .. .. .. .. .. .. .. .. .. 60·00

No wmk. Perf. 14.

1d. red, copper red, carmine, green, blue, purple, dull lilac, lilac or black   *Each* 50·00
1d. centre in black; frame in red, green, ultramarine or purple   ..   *Each* 50·00

Three of the above are known pasted on card and numbered 1, 2 and 3. The value tablets and crown were touched in by hand with white paint.

No. 1 for 1d.  Black and red   ..   ..   ..   ..   ..   ..  ⎫
No. 2 for 1d.  Red ..   ..   ..   ..   ..   ..   ..   ..  ⎬ *Each* 75·00
No. 3 for 1d.  Copper-red ..   ..   ..   ..   ..   ..   ..  ⎭

## 1903 The "Canada Head" Essays

Design similar to the " Transvaal " essay but with both top corners blacked in, and value tablets altered to the duty in white on a black background.

The accepted head die design was cut out, and the head used in the Canadian issue of 1903 was inserted ..   ..   ..   ..   ..   ..  *Each* 50·00

## Photographic Essays

The frames of the 2d., 4d., 9d. and 1s. values mounted on card, with the head of the King inserted. This head was a smaller edition of that used for the 1903 issue of Canada. Touched in by hand in white paint ..   ..  *Each* £150

## 1909 Essays

In this year a new value, the 7d. was proposed, and trials were being made to produce the 1½d., 2d. and 4d. stamps from single plates.

The 4d. made its appearance in November 1909 and the 7d. on 4th May, 1910, two days prior to the King's death. The 2d. in a new design was due to be issued about this time, but owing to the death of the King the project was abandoned. The existing stock of bicoloured stamps, however, was not enough to meet requirements, and further printings from the head and duty plates were made in July 1910. The 1½d. value was not proceeded with.

### 1909 Essays for the 7d. value

Printed on very highly glazed paper. Four different designs, similar to the issued stamp.

*Price*

Two with value tablets at top in indigo and deep green. Two with value tablets at foot in claret and brown ..   ..   ..   ..   ..   ..  *Each* 60·00

The design in deep green was chosen, and a proof is known in this colour showing the lines in the four margins (also on highly glazed paper) ..   .. 60·00

### Colour Trials of the 7d. value

16 different on white paper. Watermark Crown. Perf. 14

Black, red-brown, mauve, Tyrian plum, lavender-violet, slate-green, brown, olive-brown, sage-green, pale blue, olive-bistre, cinnamon, blue, claret, dull orange-brown, yellowish buff ..   ..   ..   ..   ..   ..   ..   ..  *Each* 25·00

## 1909 Colour Trials

Printed from special temporary plates, on white paper. Watermark Crown. Perf. 14. Three values, 1½d., 2d. and 4d. known in the following colours:

| | | | | |
|---|---|---|---|---|
| Carmine-lake | Violet | Dull blue-green | Sage-green | Yellow-orange |
| Rose-carmine | Lavender-violet | Slate-grey | Olive-brown | Orange |
| Tyrian plum | Deep blue | Brown | Deep brown | *Each* 25·00 |

In addition the 4d. value is also known in yellow and in chrome.

As above on yellow paper, watermark Crown. Perf. 14. Three values, 1½d., 2d. and 4d., known in the following colours:

| | | | | |
|---|---|---|---|---|
| Dull purple | Purple | Carmine | Dull blue-green | *Each* 25·00 |

On tinted paper with white back. Chalk-surfaced. No watermark. Perf. 14. Three values, 1½d., 2d. and 4d., known in the following colours:

| | | | | |
|---|---|---|---|---|
| Carmine on blue | Brown on blue | Dark green on red | Dark green on crimson | |
| Purple on blue | Purple on red | Purple on rose-red | | *Each* 25·00 |

## 1911 Colour Trials by Harrison & Sons

In 1911 colour trials were made for the new Georgian stamps. One series of trials was made with a K.E. VII cliché and Georgian sketch die *se-tenant*, the object being to demonstrate the appearance of the Georgian stamps in the Edwardian colours. No watermark and imperforate.

(*a*) In the K.E. VII Colours

Ungummed paper

| | |
|---|---|
| ½d. green | 4d. orange |
| 1d. scarlet | 6d. dull purple |
| 2½d. ultramarine | 7d. slate-grey |
| 3d. purple on yellow | |

(*b*) In the proposed K.G. V Colours

Gummed paper

| | |
|---|---|
| ½d. bright green | 4d. sage-green |
| 1d. rose-red | 6d. violet |
| 2½d. indigo | 7d. pale blue |
| 3d. bright orange | |

| | | | | | | | |
|---|---|---|---|---|---|---|---|
| Edwardian clichés only | .. | .. | .. | .. | .. | *Each* | 50·00 |
| *Se-tenant* pairs of K.E. VII and K.G. V | .. | .. | .. | .. | .. | *Each* | £120 |

# SECTION M
## King Edward VII Issues, 1902-1913

For watermarks in this section, see page 19.

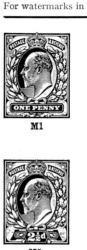

M1

M2

M3

M4

M5

M6

M7

M8

M9

M10

M11

M12

M13

M14

M15

M16

| Cat. No. | S.G. No. | Perf. | Paper | Shades | Unused | Used |
|---|---|---|---|---|---|---|

**1902 (JANUARY 1). ½d. BLUE-GREEN, TYPE M1. PERF. 14. DE LA RUE**

| | | | | | | |
|---|---|---|---|---|---|---|
| M1 | 215/16 | 14 | Ordinary | (1) Dull blue-green | 10 | 5 |
| *e.* | Substituted cliché (Pl. 20, | | | (2) Blue-green | 10 | 5 |
| | R. 20/12) corner pair　.. | 45·00 | | (3) Deep blue-green | 20 | 8 |
| *i.* | Split frame (Pl. 20, R. 11/8) | 6·00 | 3·00 | | | |
| *j.* | Minor frame breaks *From* | 1·25 | 50 | | | |
| *s.* | "Specimen", Type 15　.. | 4·00 | | *t.* "Cancelled", Type 18　.. | 6·00 | |

**Perforation 14** (Nos. M1 and M2).

Types  H1 and H1A  
V1 (controls A to E5)

V2 and V2A (controls C to J10)  
V2 (a) (control E5 only)

**Plates.** 64 plates have been identified.

**Die Proofs** in black on white glazed card :—

| | | | | |
|---|---|---|---|---|
| Without marking | .. | .. | 30·00 | Endorsed " 22 AUG 01 AFTER |
| Without marking but initialled | | | | HARDENING "　..　.. | 30·00 |
| " EF " (E. Fuchs)　.. | .. | 40·00 | Endorsed (M/S) " Working Die |
| Endorsed (M/S)　" 25/VI/1901 | | | No. 17 26–9–01 "　..　.. | 40·00 |
| Emil Fuchs "　.. | .. | 50·00 | Endorsed (M/S) " Jan 1907 |
| Endorsed (M/S) " 21 Aug EF " | | 40·00 | After Striking "　..　.. | 35·00 |
| Endorsed " 21 AUG 01 BEFORE | | | | |
| HARDENING "　.. | .. | 30·00 | | |

Endorsed " AFTER STRIKING " with signatures dated:—  
" 7 JULY 03 ", " 12 APR. 05 ", " 15 APR. 05 ", " 10 AUG. 05 ", " 21 FEB. 06 ",  
" 5 APR. 06 ", " 3 APRIL 08 ", " 23 JUN. 08 ", " 23 DEC. 08 ", " 3 MAR. 09 ",  
" 2 APR. 10 ", " 1 DEC. 010 "　..　..　..　..　..　..　..　..　.. *Each* 35·00

**Plate Proofs.** No watermark, imperf.

| | | | | | |
|---|---|---|---|---|---|
| Blue-green on yellowish paper | .. | .. | .. | .. | 5·00 |
| Ditto, diagonally overprinted " CANCELLED " | .. | .. | .. | 5·00 |
| Blue-green on thick surfaced card | .. | .. | .. | .. | 5·00 |

**1904 (NOVEMBER 26). ½d. YELLOW-GREEN, TYPE M1. PERF. 14. DE LA RUE**

| | | | | | | |
|---|---|---|---|---|---|---|
| M2 | 217/18 | 14 | Ordinary | (1) Pale yellowish green | 8 | 5 |
| *a.* | Watermark inverted　.. | 40 | 40 | (2) Yellowish green | 8 | 5 |
| *b.* | Raised crown in watermark | | | | | |
| | (corner block of 4)　.. | 6·00 | | *f.* Right frame broken (Pl. ?, | | |
| *c.* | With St. Andrew's Cross | | | R. 10/12)　..　.. | 8·00 | 4·00 |
| | attached .. | 12·00 | 10·00 | *g.* Split left frame (Pl. ?, | | |
| *ca.* | Ditto watermark inverted | 12·00 | 10·00 | R. 1/5)　..　.. | 8·00 | 4·00 |
| *d.* | Doubly printed　.. | £500 | | *h.* Left frame broken (Pl. ?, | | |
| | The bottom rows of one | | | R. 4/3)　..　.. | 11·00 | 8·00 |
| | sheet with control H9 | | | *i.* Bottom frame broken (Pl. | | |
| | showed 13 stamps with | | | 33, R. 20/5)　.. | | |
| | partial or full doubling. | | | *j.* Minor frame breaks *From* | 1·00 | 50 |
| *e.* | Substituted cliché (Pl. 20, | | | *s.* "Specimen", Type 17　.. | 2·00 | |
| | R. 20/12) corner pair　.. | 35·00 | | *t.* "Cancelled", Type 20　.. | 6·00 | |

Many cracks and breaks in the frame lines are known.　We illustrate and catalogue four major examples.

M1*i*　　　　M2*f*　　　　M2*g*　　　　M2*h*

**Proofs**

    In issued colour on poor quality buff paper    ..    ..    ..    ..    1·25

**Issued for use in stamp booklets (1 June, 1906)**

| | | |
|---|---|---:|
| MB1 | Booklet pane of 6 with watermark upright .. .. .. | 1·50 |
| MB1a | Booklet pane of 6 with watermark inverted .. .. .. | 1·75 |

*Booklet pane containing St. Andrew's Cross*

    In order to provide the required quantity of ½d. stamps one of the ½d. panes had only 5 stamps, the dummy being filled with a St. Andrew's Cross. For this a special plate had to be made (see 15).

| | | |
|---|---|---:|
| MB2 | Booklet pane of 5 with watermark upright .. .. .. | 12·00 |
| MB2a | Booklet pane of 5 with watermark inverted .. .. .. | 12·00 |

    All the above panes exist overprinted "Specimen", Type 17.

*Die Proof*

The St. Andrew's Cross in black on white unglazed card dated 24 JAN. 06   20·00

    It is probable that the plates which were handed over to Harrison & Sons were resurfaced before use. The lines in the veining of the leaves, and the lines on the King's neck are noticeably strengthened.

    The Harrison printings, with the exception of the two bright green shades, have a very flat appearance when compared with the De la Rue issues. There is less white in the design, and the shading extends well up to the sides of the Crown. The pale green shade (No. M3(5)) is the nearest approach to the De la Rue colour, but is bluer. The bright green shades are distinct ; on No. (7) the design is rather spotted (Plate 64b).

| Cat. No. | S.G. No. | Perf. | Paper | Shades | Unused | Used |
|---|---|---|---|---|---|---|

**1911 (MAY 3). ½d. YELLOW-GREEN, TYPE M1. PERF. 14. HARRISON**

| Cat. No. | S.G. No. | Perf. | Paper | Shades | Unused | Used |
|---|---|---|---|---|---|---|
| M3 | 267/71 | 14 | Ordinary | (1) Dull yellow-green | 25 | 8 |
|    a. | Watermark inverted .. | 2·00 | 2·00 | (2) Dull green | 30 | 8 |
|    b. | Watermark sideways .. | | | (3) Deep dull green | 1·00 | 75 |
|    c. | No watermark .. .. | | | (4) Deep dull yellow- | | |
|    d. | Imperf. (pair) .. .. | | |     green (very blotchy | | |
|    e. | Misplaced perforation (parts | | |     print) | 6·00 | 4·00 |
| |   of 4 designs on one stamp) | 5·00 | | (5) Pale bluish green | 1·25 | 1·00 |
|    f. | With St. Andrew's Cross | | | (6) Bright green (fine im- | | |
| |   attached .. .. .. | 15·00 | 20·00 |     pression) (June 1911) | 20·00 | 15·00 |
|   fa. | Do. watermark inverted .. | 15·00 | 20·00 | (7) Deep bright green | 15·00 | 7·50 |
|    g. | Gash in Crown (Pl. ?, R. | | | | | |
| |   12/11) .. .. .. | 35·00 | 25·00 | | | |
|    h. | Major frame breaks (Pl. 64b, | | | *i.* Minor frame breaks | *From* 1·00 | 50 |
| |   R. 18/10) .. .. | 35·00 | 20·00 | | | |

**Perforation 14**

    Types H2 (a, c, d and e)                          H2A (c, d and e)
              V1 and V1A

**Issued for use in stamp booklets**

| | | |
|---|---|---:|
| MB3 | Booklet pane of 6 with watermark upright .. .. .. | 8·00 |
| MB3a | Booklet pane of 6 with watermark inverted .. .. .. | 10·00 |

    Booklet pane containing St. Andrew's Cross

| | | |
|---|---|---:|
| MB4 | Booklet pane of 5 with watermark upright .. .. .. | 15·00 |
| MB4a | Booklet pane of 5 with watermark inverted .. .. .. | 18·00 |

**1911 (OCTOBER 30). ½d. GREEN, TYPE M1. PERF. 15 × 14. HARRISON**

| Cat. No. | S.G. No. | Perf. | Paper | Shades | Unused | Used |
|---|---|---|---|---|---|---|
| M4 | 279/9a | 15 × 14 | Ordinary | (1) Dull green | 1·25 | 1·25 |
| | | | | (2) Deep dull green | 2·00 | 2·50 |
|    g. | Gash in Crown (Pl. ?, | | | (3) Deep dull green (very | | |
| |   R. 12/11) .. .. | 50·00 | 40·00 |     blotchy print) | 14·00 | 14·00 |
|    h. | Major frame breaks (Pl. | | | (4) Pale bluish green | 60 | 1·00 |
| |   64b, R. 18/10) .. | 35·00 | 30·00 | | | |

**Perforation 15 × 14**

    Types V3 and V3A

M3/4g

M3/4h

## CONTROL POSITIONS

The Control is beneath the 2nd stamp, bottom row in the Edwardian issues, except for the ½d. Nos. MC54/5 and MC60 when it is below the 11th stamp.

Perforated Selvedge with co-extensive Rule

Imperf. Selvedge with continuous Rule

The "marginal" rule is the coloured line extending round the pane outside the stamps. When this rule is unbroken it is described as "continuous", though in some plates the rule has occasional breaks. When the rule is composed of short pieces with gaps exactly opposite the spaces between the stamps, it is termed "co-extensive".

Controls are further sub-divided into "Imperf." and "Perf." according to whether the perforating head was used in such a way as to perforate the selvedge bearing the control letter. (See illustrations.)

**½d. Green Controls.**   Prices are for unused singles.

| Controls | | Date | I. | P. | Controls | | Date | I. | P. |
|---|---|---|---|---|---|---|---|---|---|
| Printed by De la Rue | | | | | MC67 | E 6 .. | .. June 1906 | 25 | — |
| | | | | | MC68 | F 6 .. | .. Aug. 1906 | 25 | 35 |
| (a) With continuous rule | | | | | MC69 | F 7 .. | .. July 1907 | 65 | 75 |
| Blue-green | | | | | MC70 | G 7 .. | .. Sept. 1907 | 25 | 25 |
| MC54 | A .. | .. Jan. 1902 | 25 | 30 | MC71 | G 8 .. | .. July 1908 | 25 | 40 |
| MC55 | B .. | .. Dec. 1902 | 25 | 30 | MC72 | H 8 .. | .. Oct. 1908 | 25 | 25 |
| MC56 | C .. | .. Dec. 1903 | 30 | 5·00 | MC73 | H 9 .. | .. Aug. 1909 | 30 | 50 |
| MC57 | C 4 .. | .. Feb. 1904 | 25 | 6·00 | a. Control and part stamp | | | | |
| MC58 | D 4 .. | .. April 1904 | 25 | 40·00 | | doubly printed | .. | | |
| Yellow-green | | | | | | | | | |
| MC59 | D 4 .. | .. Nov. 1904 | 7·00 | — | MC74 | I 9 .. | .. Nov. 1909 | 25 | 25 |
| | | | | | MC75 | I 10 .. | .. July 1910 | 25 | 25 |
| (b) With co-extensive rule | | | | | MC76 | J 10 .. | .. Oct. 1910 | 25 | 25 |
| Blue-green | | | | | | | | | |
| MC60 | B .. | ..March 1902 | 12·00 | † | | | | | |
| MC61 | C .. | ..March 1903 | 90 | — | | | | | |
| MC62 | C 4 .. | .. Jan. 1904 | 50 | 25·00 | Printed by Harrison | | | | |
| MC63 | D 4 .. | .. April 1904 | 25 | 25·00 | | | Perf. 14 | | |
| Yellow-green | | | | | | | | | |
| MC64 | D 4 .. | .. Nov. 1904 | 25 | 20·00 | MC77 | A 11.. | .. May 1911 | 50 | 35 |
| MC65 | D 5 .. | ..March 1905 | 25 | 10·00 | | | Perf. 15 × 14 | | |
| MC66 | E 5 .. | .. Sept. 1905 | 25 | 1·00 | MC78 | A 11.. | .. Oct. 1911 | 1·25 | 1·40 |

| Cat. No. | S.G. No. | Perf. | Paper | Shades | Unused | Used |
|---|---|---|---|---|---|---|

## 1902 (JANUARY 1). 1d. RED, TYPE M1.   PERF. 14.   DE LA RUE

| | | | | | | |
|---|---|---|---|---|---|---|
| M5 | 219/20 | 14 | Ordinary | (1) Scarlet | 10 | 5 |
| a. | Watermark inverted† .. | | 40   40 | (2) Bright scarlet | 10 | 5 |
| b. | Raised crown in watermark | | | (3) Deep bright scarlet | 20 | 8 |
| | (corner block of 4) .. | | 12·00 | (4) Rose-carmine | 2·50 | 75 |
| c. | Imperf. (pair) .. .. | | £500 | | | |
| d. | Imperf. margin at bottom | | | | | |
| | of top pane .. | | 25·00 | k. Minor frame breaks *From* | 1·00 | 50 |
| e. | Substituted cliché (Pl. 30, | | | l. Cracked plate (various) | | |
| | R. 20/12) corner pair .. | | 12·00 | *From* | 1·00 | 50 |
| f. | Substituted cliché (Pl. 51, | | | m. Dot before P of POSTAGE | | |
| | R. 20/12) corner pair .. | | 15·00 | (Pl. 14, R. 20/11) | 1·00 | |
| g. | Plug repair, N.E. of value | | | n. Dot under V of REVENUE | | |
| | tablet .. .. .. | | — 20·00 | (Pl. 50b, R. 20/11) .. | 90 | |
| h. | Plug repair below ON of | | | s. " Specimen ", Type 15 .. | 3·00 | |
| | ONE .. .. .. | | — 40·00 | t. " Specimen ", Type 16 .. | 6·50 | |
| i. | Frame broken at right (Pl. | | | u. " Specimen ", Type 17 .. | 1·50 | |
| | ?, R. 19/12) .. .. | | 15·00   8·00 | v. " Cancelled ", Type 19 .. | 6·00 | |
| j. | Flaw in E of ONE and P of | | | w. " Cancelled ", Type 20 .. | 6·50 | |
| | PENNY (Pl. 58, R. 20/8) | | 4·50 | | | |

†No. M5a. The prices are for booklet stamps. Inverted watermarks from sheets are worth much more but can only be differentiated by marginal copies or multiples differing from the booklet format of 3 × 2.

Many cracks and breaks in the frame lines are known on the 1d. value. We only list some of them. For further information see *Cracked Units on K.E. VII 1d.* by H. S. Doupé; published by the G.B. Philatelic Society.

M5g          M5i

### Perforation 14

Types  H1 and H1A

V1 (controls A to E5)
V2 and V2A (controls C to J10)

**Plates.**  72 Plates have been identified.

**Die Proofs** in black on white glazed card :—

| | |
|---|---|
| Without marking          30·00 | Endorsed " AFTER HARDEN- |
| Without marking but initialled | ING 20 AUG 01 "          30·00 |
| (M/S) " EF " ..          40·00 | Endorsed  " AFTER  STRIK- |
| Endorsed (M/S) " As approved | ING " (various dates)          30·00 |
| by Mr. Fuchs 19 Aug "          50·00 | Endorsed " Working Die No. 16 "  40·00 |
| Endorsed  " BEFORE  HARD- | |
| ENING 20 AUG 01 "          30·00 | |

**Plate Proofs.**  All imperf. and without watermark.

Pale or deep green on thin white card          .. .. .. .. .. .. *Each*  5·00
Carmine on thin white paper ..          .. .. .. .. .. .. ..  5·00

The above proofs are known with double, and with triple impressions *Each*  6·00

Bright scarlet on poor quality buff paper          .. .. .. .. .. ..  1·50
Bright scarlet on white wove paper ..          .. .. .. .. .. ..  8·00

**Colour Trials.**  Made from a special plate of 20 electros.

1901.  Watermark Crown, Imperf. or perf. 14.

Dull purple, black on red, purple on red          .. .. .. .. .. *From*  20·00

1906.  Watermark Crown.  Imperf. or perf. 14.  Trials for a suggested change of colour.

Blue-geranium, cerise, deep carmine and four different shades of carmine-red ..  *From*  20·00

### Issued for use in stamp booklets (16 March, 1904)

MB5   Booklet pane of 6 with watermark upright          .. .. ..  90
MB5a  Booklet pane of 6 with watermark inverted          .. .. ..  3·00
        Both panes exist overprinted " Specimen ", Type 17.

| Cat. No. | S.G. No. | Perf. | Paper | Shades | Unused | Used |
|---|---|---|---|---|---|---|

**1911 (MAY 3). 1d. RED, TYPE M1. PERF. 14. HARRISON**

| | | | | | | |
|---|---|---|---|---|---|---|
| M6 | 272/75a | 14 | Ordinary | (1) Rose-red | 35 | 12 |
| | | | | (2) Deep rose-red | 35 | 12 |
| *a.* | No watermark | .. .. | 25·00 | 25·00 | (3) Intense rose-red | 15·00 | 10·00 |
| (1) *b.* | Watermark inverted | .. | 3·00 | 3·00 | (4) Pale rose-carmine | 3·50 | 3·00 |
| (4) *b.* | Watermark inverted | .. | 5·00 | 5·00 | (5) Rose-carmine | 8·00 | 2·50 |
| (5) *b.* | Watermark inverted | .. | 12·00 | 12·00 | (6) Deep rose-carmine | 10·00 | 6·00 |
| (7) *b.* | Watermark inverted | .. | 16·00 | 12·00 | (7) Aniline rose (F) | 8·00 | 4·50 |
| *c.* | Misplaced perforation (parts of 4 designs on one stamp) | 5·00 | | (8) Aniline pink (F) | 20·00 | 10·00 |
| *d.* | Bottom frame broken (Pl. 61b, R. 20/9) .. .. | 4·50 | 3·00 | Some of the rose-red shades |
| *s.* | "Specimen", Type 22 .. | 4·25 | | show slight fluorescence. |
| *t.* | "Cancelled", Type 21 imperf. .. .. .. | 3·50 | | |

Some shades of this value are difficult to classify. The best method of checking M6 Nos. (4) (5) and (6) is to use the identical perf. 15 × 14 shades for comparison purposes. The rose-red shades of Harrison are quite different from the scarlet of De la Rue, and little difficulty should be encountered here. M5 (4) is brighter than M6 (5). The latter has less white in the design, and the shading extends well up to the sides of the crown.

The plates which were used for the provisional printings, like those of the Halfpenny value, were probably resurfaced before use.

### Perforation 14

Types   H2 (c, d and e)             H2A (b, c, d and e)
       V1 and V1A

### Issued for use in stamp booklets

| | | |
|---|---|---|
| MB6 | (1) Booklet pane of 6, with watermark upright .. .. .. | 10·00 |
| MB6a | (1) Booklet pane of 6, with watermark inverted .. .. .. | 21·00 |
| MB6 | (4) Booklet pane of 6, with watermark upright .. .. .. | 24·00 |
| MB6a | (4) Booklet pane of 6, with watermark inverted .. .. .. | 35·00 |
| MB6 | (5) Booklet pane of 6, with watermark upright .. .. .. | 55·00 |
| MB6a | (5) Booklet pane of 6, with watermark inverted .. .. .. | 80·00 |
| MB6 | (7) Booklet pane of 6, with watermark upright .. .. .. | 55·00 |
| MB6a | (7) Booklet pane of 6, with watermark inverted .. .. .. | £150 |

*Variety*

MB6b   No. 3 and No. 6 on the booklet pane showing substituted clichés   ..   40·00

**1911 (OCTOBER 5). 1d. RED, TYPE M2. PERF. 15 × 14. HARRISON**

| | | | | | | |
|---|---|---|---|---|---|---|
| M7 | 280/82 | 15 × 14 | Ordinary | (1) Rose-red | 4·50 | 4·00 |
| *d.* | Bottom frame broken (Pl. 61b, R. 20/9) .. .. | 6·00 | 4·00 | (2) Deep rose-red | 6·00 | 5·00 |
| | | | | (3) Rose-carmine | 50 | 35 |
| | | | | (4) Deep rose-carmine | 1·50 | 1·00 |
| | | | | (5) Pale rose-carmine | 40 | 30 |

### Perforation 15 × 14

Types   V3 and V3A

### 1d. Red Controls.  Prices are for unused singles.

| Controls | Date | I. | P. | Controls | Date | I. | P. |
|---|---|---|---|---|---|---|---|
| *Printed by De la Rue* | | | | C91 | F 6 .. .. Sept. 1906 | 25 | 25 |
| *(a) With continuous rule* | | | | C92 | F 7 .. .. July 1907 | 50 | 50 |
| C79 | A .. .. Jan. 1902 | 25 | 75 | C93 | G 7 .. .. Oct. 1907 | 25 | 25 |
| C80 | B .. .. Dec. 1902 | 25 | 2·00 | C94 | G 8 .. .. July 1908 | 25 | 25 |
| C81 | C .. .. Dec. 1903 | 40 | 5·00 | C95 | H 8 .. .. Oct. 1908 | 25 | 25 |
| C82 | C 4 .. .. Feb. 1904 | 25 | 2·50 | C96 | H 9 .. .. July 1909 | 25 | 25 |
| C83 | D 4 .. .. April 1904 | 25 | 5·00 | C97 | I 9 .. .. Oct. 1909 | 25 | 25 |
| C84 | D 5 .. .. July 1905 | 5·00 | — | C98 | I 10 .. .. July 1910 | 25 | 25 |
| | | | | C99 | J 10 .. .. Sept. 1910 | 25 | 25 |
| *(b) With co-extensive rule* | | | | *Printed by Harrison* | | | |
| C85 | C .. .. Dec. 1903 | 50 | 25·00 | | *Perf. 14* | | |
| C86 | C 4 .. .. Feb. 1904 | 50 | 20·00 | C100 | A 11(c) .. Sept. 1911 | 6·00 | — |
| C87 | D 4 .. .. April 1904 | 25 | 22·00 | C100a | A 11(w) .. May 1911 | 60 | 50 |
| C88 | D 5 .. .. June 1905 | 25 | 25·00 | | *Perf. 15 × 14* | | |
| C89 | E 5 .. .. Aug. 1905 | 25 | 25 | C101 | A 11(c) .. Oct. 1911 | 75 | 75 |
| C90 | E 6 .. .. July 1906 | 25 | 20·00 | | | | |

The Control is beneath the 11th stamp, bottom row. Examples occur where the control (e.g. I9) is repeated under the 10th, 9th, 8th, 7th, etc., stamps, each impression fainter than its predecessor. Such examples are always perforated by the Type V2A perforator with right feed. The variety is caused by the comb head picking up the ink from the control, which had not properly dried, and at each descent of the comb a progressively fainter control became printed in the bottom margin.

The Harrison control piece comes in two widths. In C100a the figures are 1½ mm. apart; in Nos. C100 and C101 the figures are 1 mm. apart.

| Cat. No. | S.G. No. | Perf. | Paper | Shades | Unused | Used |
|----------|----------|-------|-------|--------|--------|------|

**1902-05. 1½d. PURPLE AND GREEN, TYPE M2. PERF. 14. DE LA RUE**

**A.  1902 (MARCH 21).  Ordinary paper**

| | | | | | | |
|---|---|---|---|---|---|---|
| M8 | 221/22 | 14 | Ordinary | (1) Dull purple and green | 1·50 | 30 |
| *a.* | Watermark inverted | .. | — £150 | (2) Slate-purple and green | 1·75 | 30 |
| *b.* | Deformed leaf (Duty Pl. 2, R. 19/1) .. .. .. | | 50·00 | 25·00 | | |
| *s.* | "Specimen", Type 15 .. | | 2·50 | | | |

**B.  1905 (SEPTEMBER 6).  Chalk-surfaced paper**

| | | | | | | |
|---|---|---|---|---|---|---|
| M9 | 223/4 | 14 | Chalky | (1) Pale dull purple and green | 1·75 | 50 |
| *c.* | Frame broken at left (Pl ?, R. 6/4) .. .. .. | | 9·00 | 4·50 | | |
| *d.* | Cut through rule into stamp (Head Pl. 4, R. 5/1) .. | | 6·00 | 3·00 | (2) Slate-purple and bluish green | 1·50 | 50 |
| *e.* | Frame broken at top left | | 9·00 | 4·50 | (3) Deep slate-purple and bluish green | 3·25 | 1·00 |
| *s.* | "Specimen", Type 17 .. | | 3·50 | | | |
| *t.* | "Cancelled", Type 18 .. | | 5·00 | | | |
| *u.* | "Cancelled", Type 20 .. | | 5·00 | | | |

In the De la Rue printings, the uppermost line at the top of the fringe in the S.E. corner is faint.

| M8*b* | M9*c* | M9*e* | M10*f* | M10*g* |
|-------|-------|-------|--------|--------|

**Perforation 14**

Type H1 only

**Plates.**  De la Rue made 8 head plates, and 4 duty plates.

**Die Proofs** in black on white glazed card :—

Head plate only
Without marking .. .. 40·00
Endorsed " BEFORE HARD-
ENING 20 NOV 01 " .. 40·00
Endorsed " AFTER HARDEN-
ING 27 NOV 01 " .. .. 40·00
Endorsed " AFTER STRIKING
29 NOV 01 " .. .. .. 40·00

Duty plate only
A die proof of the duty plate is known, struck presumably from the 1887 die.
Endorsed "After Striking 19 APR 06" .. .. .. 30·00

**Colour Trials**

1909  Made from a special combined head and duty plate, for a proposed issue in monochrome.  For list of colours and price see page 23.

| Cat. No. | S.G. No. | Perf. | Paper | Shades | Unused | Used |
|---|---|---|---|---|---|---|

**1911 (JULY 13). 1½d. PURPLE AND GREEN, TYPE M2. PERF. 14. SOMERSET HOUSE**

M10    287/89    14    Ordinary
*f.*   Damaged frame at left   ..   15·00   15·00
*g.*   Cracked plate   ..    ..   6·00   6·00

(1) Reddish purple and bright green   3·50   3·00
(2) Reddish purple and yellow-green (Oct. 1912)   3·50   3·00
(3) Dull reddish purple and bright green (Sept. 1911)   1·00   60
(4) Dull reddish purple and green (1912)   1·00   60
(5) Dull purple and green (some F)   1·00   60
(6) Deep plum and deep green   1·00   60
(7) Slate-purple and green (F)   1·50   90

In the Somerset House printings, the uppermost line at the top of the fringe in the S.E. corner is thick, and sometimes broken. Many stamps show damage to the circle round the medallion, and the frame lines are sometimes pitted, as though the plate had suffered corrosion.

With the exception of No. (7) all shades of purple appear redder when placed side by side with stamps from the De la Rue printings. Some of the above shades of purple are met with again on the 5d., 6d., 9d. and 10d. values.

**Perforation 14**
Types V1 V1A

**1902-10. 2d. GREEN AND RED, TYPE M3. PERF. 14. DE LA RUE**
**A. 1902 (MARCH 25). Ordinary paper**

M11    225/26    14    Ordinary
*s.*   "Specimen", Type 16   ..   2·50

(1) Yellowish green and carmine   1·75   75
(2) Yellowish green and vermilion   9·00   6·00
(3) Grey-green and carmine (Mar. 1903)   2·00   75

**B. 1905 (SEPTEMBER 6). Chalk-surfaced paper**

M12    227/29    14    Chalky
*b.*   Deformed tablet (Pl. 1, R. 5/9)   ..    ..   60·00   50·00
*c.*   Distorted tablet ("Rhombus") (Pl. 2, R. 1/1)   ..   35·00   12·00
*s.*   "Specimen", Type 17   ..   3·50
*t.*   "Cancelled", Type 18   ..   5·00
*u.*   "Cancelled", Type 20   ..   5·00

(1) Grey-green and carmine   1·50   75
(2) Pale blue-green and carmine   10·00   3·00
(3) Grey-green and scarlet (July 1910)   3·00   1·00
(4) Deep grey-green and scarlet (July 1910)   3·00   1·00

The duty plates became very worn, and many minor varieties in the tablet are known. On duty plate 1 a coloured mark occurs in the base at the point of 2. Row 20/11.

**Perforation 14**
Type H1 only

**Plates.** De la Rue made 6 head plates and 3 duty plates.

**Die proofs** in black on white glazed card :—
Head plate only
Without marking    ..    ..   40·00
Endorsed " BEFORE HARDENING 19 DEC 01 "   ..   40·00
Endorsed " AFTER HARDENING 27 DEC 01 "   ..    ..   40·00
The Victorian die was used for the duty plate.

**Colour Trials**

1909 Made from a special combined head and duty plate for a proposed issue in monochrome. For list of colours and price see page 23.

M12/13*b*                    M12*c*

| Cat. No. | S.G. No. | Perf. | Paper | | Shades | Unused | Used |
|---|---|---|---|---|---|---|---|

**1911 (AUGUST 8). 2d. GREEN AND RED, TYPE M3. PERF. 14. SOMERSET HOUSE**

| | | | | | | | |
|---|---|---|---|---|---|---|---|
| M13 | 290/2 | 14 | Ordinary | | (1) Deep dull green and red | 1·25 | 1·00 |
| *b.* | Deformed tablet (Pl. 1, R. 5/9) .. .. .. | | 60·00 | 50·00 | (2) Deep dull green and carmine | 1·75 | 1·00 |
| *d.* | Frame damaged at bottom left (Pl. 4, R. 2/5) .. | | 4·50 | 3·00 | (3) Deep dull green and bright carmine (Dec. 1911) | 2·00 | 1·50 |
| | | | | | (4) Grey-green and bright carmine (11 Mar. 1912) | 1·25 | 1·50 |

The green shades are all deeper and duller than those of De la Rue. The carmine colour on Nos. (3) and (4) shows noticeably on the backs of the stamps.

**Perforation 14**

Types V1 V1A

**Prepared for use, but not issued.**

**1910 (MAY). 2d. TYPE M4. PERF. 14. DE LA RUE**

| | | | | | |
|---|---|---|---|---|---|
| M14 | 266a | 14 | Ordinary | Tyrian plum | £3500 |
| *s.* | "Specimen", Type 17 .. £350 | | | | |

One copy of this stamp is known used, dated 5th May, 1910, but owing to the death of the King on May 6th it was never issued to the public. The bulk of the stock was destroyed and only a few mint copies have survived.

**Essays** on glazed card :—

Two different rejected designs .. .. *Each* £200

**Die proofs** in black on white glazed card :—

Endorsed " BEFORE HARD-ENING 1 DEC 09 " .. £200

Endorsed " AFTER HARDEN-ING 2 DEC 09 " .. .. £200

In various colours on white glazed card :—

Without marking .. *Each* £200

On white wove paper. Imperf.

Various colours .. .. *Each* £200

**Colour Trials.** Watermark Crown.

Various colours (16 different) Perf. 14 Pale Tyrian plum and others .. *From* £200

Various colours Imperf. *From* £200

**1901 (DECEMBER). 2½d. TYPE M5, PERF. 14. DE LA RUE**

| | | | | | |
|---|---|---|---|---|---|
| M15 | — | 14 | Ordinary | Purple on blue | £1800 |

The Imprimatur sheet was registered at Somerset House on December 3, 1901. A few hundred sheets were printed and delivered to the Stamping Department, which were destroyed when the authorities changed their minds in favour of the adopted colour. Only a few copies have survived.

| Cat. No. | S.G. No. | Perf. | Paper | Shades | Unused | Used |
|----------|----------|-------|-------|--------|--------|------|

**1902 (JANUARY 1).  2½d. BLUE, TYPE M5.  PERF. 14.  DE LA RUE**

| | | | | | | |
|--|--|--|--|--|--|--|
| M16 | 230/31 | 14 | Ordinary | (1) Deep ultramarine | 1·00 | 12 |
| c. | Frame broken at right .. | | — 30·00 | (2) Ultramarine | 50 | 12 |
| d. | Minor frame breaks *From* | 4·00 | 2·00 | (3) Pale ultramarine | 50 | 12 |
| e. | Retouched background .. | | — 6·00 | | | |
| f. | Cracked plate .. *From* | 4·00 | 2·00 | | | |
| s. | "Specimen", Type 15 .. | | 2·50 | | | |
| t. | "Cancelled", Type 20 .. | | 5·00 | | | |

M16e

M16c

## Perforation 14

Type H1 only

**Plates.**  De la Rue made 8 plates.

**Die proofs** in black on white glazed card :—

| | | |
|--|--|--|
| Without marking .. .. | 40·00 | Endorsed " BEFORE HARD-ENING 28 NOV 01 " .. | 40·00 |
| Without marking but with (M/S) initials and date " 7 Sept 01 " .. .. .. | 40·00 | Endorsed " AFTER HARD-ENING 7 DEC 01 " .. | 40·00 |
| Endorsed " 7 SEP. 01 AFTER HARDENING " .. .. | 40·00 | Endorsed " Working Die No. 19 " | 50·00 |

## Plate Proofs.

On thick white paper.  No watermark, Imperf.

Ultramarine, violet-blue, deep ultramarine, steel blue  ..  ..  ..  .. *Each*  15·00

## Colour Trials

Prepared from a special plate of 20 electros.
1901.  Watermark Crown, Perf. 14.

Three shades of ultramarine (including issued colour), sky-blue, violet-blue, deep blue, greenish blue and two shades of dull blue  ..  ..  ..  .. *Each*  35·00

**1911 (JULY 10).  2½d. BLUE, TYPE M5.  PERF. 14.  HARRISON**

| | | | | | | |
|--|--|--|--|--|--|--|
| M17 | 276 | 14 | Ordinary | (1) Deep bright blue | 2·50 | 1·50 |
| a. | Watermark inverted .. | | 20·00 | (2) Bright blue | 1·75 | 1·50 |
| | | | | (3) Dull blue | 4·00 | 3·00 |

## Perforation 14

Types V1  V1A

G.S.C.(II)—3

| Cat. No. | S.G. No. | Perf. | Paper | Shades | Unused | Used |
|---|---|---|---|---|---|---|

**1911 (OCTOBER 14).  2½d. BLUE, TYPE M6.  PERF. 15 × 14.  HARRISON**

| | | | | | | |
|---|---|---|---|---|---|---|
| M18 | 283/84 | 15 × 14 | Ordinary | (1) Deep bright blue | 75 | 40 |
| b. | Imperf. between stamp and | | | (2) Bright blue | 50 | 25 |
| | left margin .. .. | | 15·00 | (3) Dull blue | 80 | 30 |
| g. | Frame broken at right (Pl. | | | | | |
| | ?, R. 19/12) .. .. | | 30·00 | 30·00 | | |
| h. | Frame broken at right .. | | 50·00 | 50·00 | j. Frame broken at right .. | 40·00 | 40·00 |
| i. | Frame broken at right .. | | 80·00 | 80·00 | k. Frame broken at right .. | 50·00 | 50·00 |

Shade No. (3) may be found with double gum.

M18*g*         M18*h*         M18*i*         M18*j*         M18*k* (1)         M18*k* (2)

The broken frame varieties exist in progressive states of wear ; we illustrate two states of variety k.

**Perforation 15 × 14**
    Types V3  V3A

**1902-06.  3d. PURPLE ON YELLOW, TYPE M6.  PERF. 14.  DE LA RUE**

**A. 1902 (MARCH 20).  Ordinary Paper**

| | | | | | | |
|---|---|---|---|---|---|---|
| M19 | 232/32a | 14 | Ordinary | (1) Dull purple on orange-yellow back, yellow front | 1·50 | 25 |
| s. | "Specimen", Type 15 .. | | 3·00 | (2) Deep purple on orange-yellow back, yellow shades front | 1·50 | 25 |

**B. 1906 (MARCH 31).  Chalk-surfaced paper**

| | | | | | | |
|---|---|---|---|---|---|---|
| M20 | 232b/34 | 14 | Chalky | (i) Orange-yellow surface and back | | |
| b. | Broken scroll (Pl. 5, R. 20/2) .. .. .. | | 28·00 | (1) Pale reddish purple | 6·00 | 1·00 |
| c. | Broken frame .. .. | | 8·00 | 4·00 | (2) Dull purple | 10·00 | 1·50 |
| d. | Broken corner .. .. | | 6·00 | 3·50 | (ii) Yellow surface, lemon back | | |
| s. | "Specimen", Type 17 .. | | 4·00 | (3) Dull reddish purple | 6·00 | 1·00 |
| t. | "Cancelled", Type 20 .. | | 6·00 | (iii) Lemon surface and back | | |
| | | | | (4) Pale purple | 1·00 | 60 |
| | | | | (5) Purple | 1·00 | 60 |

**Perforation 14**
    Type H1 only

**Plates.**  De la Rue made 5 plates.

**Die proofs** in black on white glazed card :—

| | | |
|---|---|---|
| Without marking .. .. | 40·00 | |
| Endorsed " BEFORE HARD-ENING 21 NOV 01 " .. | 40·00 | Endorsed " AFTER HARDEN-ING 25 NOV 01 " .. .. | 40·00 |

| Cat. No. | S.G. No. | Perf. | Paper | Shades | Unused | Used |
|----------|----------|-------|-------|--------|--------|------|

**1911 (SEPTEMBER 12). 3d. PURPLE ON YELLOW, TYPE M6. PERF. 14. HARRISON**

M21     277   14     Ordinary     (1) Purple on lemon   6·00   8·00
  *b.*   Broken scroll (Pl. 5, R. 20/2)  8·00     (2) Grey on lemon
  *e.*   Frame broken at right
      (Pl. 5, R. 9/12)   ..  35·00

**Perforation 14**
  Types  H2(c)   H2A(c)
         H2(d)   H2A(d)
         V1     V1A

**1911 (SEPTEMBER 22). 3d. PURPLE ON YELLOW, TYPE M6. PERF. 15 × 14. HARRISON**

M22     285/85*a*   15 × 14     Ordinary     (1) Purple on lemon   50   25
  *b.*   Broken scroll (Pl. 5, R. 20/2)  3·50   3·00     (2) Greyish purple on
  *e.*   Frame broken at right               lemon   50   25
      (Pl. 5, R. 9/12) ..   ..  18·00   14·00     (3) Grey on lemon   £300   £150
  *f.*   Frame broken at right (Pl.
      5, R. 8/12)   ..   ..  18·00   14·00     Variety *c* shows progressive states of
  *g.*   Broken crown   ..   ..  6·00   4·00     wear.
                                            Variety *f* is from the 1st vertical row of
                                          the sheet.

**Perforation 15 × 14**
  Types  V3   V3A

M20/2*b*              M21/2*e*          M22*f*           M22*g*

**1902-06. 4d. GREEN AND BROWN, TYPE M7. PERF. 14. DE LA RUE**

**A. 1902 (MARCH 27). Ordinary Paper**

M23     235/36   14     Ordinary     (1) Green and grey-brown   2·00   50
  *b.*   White centres to 4's *From*  3·00   1·00     (2) Green and brown   2·00   50
  *c.*   Damaged 4 (S.W. corner)   —   7·00     (3) Green and chocolate-
  *d.*   Cracked plate   ..   ..   —   10·00         brown   2·75   60
  *s.*   "Specimen", Type 16   ..  3·00

**B. 1906 (JANUARY 19). Chalk-surfaced paper**

M24     237/38   14     Chalky     (1) Green and chocolate-
  *c.*   Damaged 4 (S.W. corner)   —   7·00         brown   1·50   70
                                      (2) Deep green and choco-
                                          late brown   1·75   75

**Perforation 14**
  Type 1A
  A few sheets on chalky paper with Types 8A or 8B

**Plates.** De la Rue made 5 head plates and 2 duty plates.

**Die Proofs** in black on white glazed card :—

  Head Plate only
    Without marking   ..   ..   40·00     Endorsed " AFTER HARDEN-
    Endorsed " BEFORE HARD-                 ING 28 NOV 01 "   ..   ..   40·00
      ENING 28 NOV 01 "   ..   40·00

The Victorian die was used for the duty plate.

M23*d*                     M26/7*f*                     M23/4*c*

| Cat. No. | S.G. No. | Perf. | Paper | Shades | Unused | Used |
|---|---|---|---|---|---|---|

### 1909 (NOVEMBER 1).   4d. ORANGE, TYPE M7.   PERF. 14.   DE LA RUE

| M25 | 239/41 | 14 | Ordinary | (1) Brown-orange | 5·00 | 3·50 |
| *s.* | "Specimen", Type 17 | .. | 4·00 | (2) Pale orange | 75 | 50 |
| *t.* | "Cancelled", Type 20 | .. | 6·00 | (3) Orange-red | 75 | 50 |

**Perforation 14**
   Type H1 only

**Plates.**  De la Rue made 4 plates.

**Die proofs** in black on white glazed card :—

| Endorsed " BEFORE HARD-ENING 30 AUG 09 " .. | 40·00 | Endorsed " BEFORE STRIK-ING " .. .. .. .. | 40·00 |
| Endorsed " AFTER HARDEN-ING 2 SEP 09 " .. .. | 40·00 | Endorsed "After striking 8 OCT 09 " .. .. .. | 40·00 |

**Plate Proof.**  In orange on poor quality buff paper ..   ..   ..   .. 7·50

**Colour Trials.**  Various colours (see page 23)

### 1911 (JULY 13).   4d. ORANGE, TYPE M7.   PERF. 14.   HARRISON

| M26 | 278 | 14 | Ordinary | (1) Bright orange | 6·00 | 4·00 |
| *e.* | White space at foot of stamp between design and vertical lines of shading (R. 11/12).. .. .. | 16·00 | 8·00 | (2) Deep bright orange | 6·00 | 4·00 |
| *f.* | As *e,* but white space at left of stamp .. .. | 20·00 | 12·00 | | | |

**Perforation 14**
   Types H2(c)   H2A(c)   V1   V1A
          H2(d)   H2A(d)

### 1911 (NOVEMBER 22).   4d. ORANGE, TYPE M7.   PERF. 15 × 14.   HARRISON

| M27 | 286 | 15 × 14 | Ordinary | (1) Bright orange | 60 | 50 |
| *e.* | White space at foot of stamp between design and vertical lines of shading | 4·00 | 4·00 | (2) Deep bright orange | 60 | 50 |
| *f.* | As *e,* but white space at left of stamp .. .. | 8·00 | 8·00 | (3) Very deep orange | 2·00 | 2·00 |

The Harrison shades are much brighter than those of De la Rue.

**Perforation 15 × 14**
   Types V3   V3A

| Cat. No. | S.G. No. | Perf. | Paper | Shades | Unused | Used |
|---|---|---|---|---|---|---|

**1902-06. 5d. PURPLE AND BLUE, TYPE M8.   PERF. 14.   DE LA RUE**

**A. 1902 (MAY 14).  Ordinary paper**

M28   242   14   Ordinary   (1) Dull purple and ultra-
 b.  Broken frame at right   ..  10·00   7·00       marine   1·50   50
 c.  Damaged R.H. duty tablet   5·00   5·00   2) Slate-purple and ultra-
 s.  "Specimen", Type 16   ..  3·00       marine   1·50   50

**B. 1906 (MAY 19).  Chalk-surfaced paper**

M29   243/44   14   Chalky   (1) Dull purple and ultra-
 a.  Watermark inverted   ..  30·00       marine   1·75   75
 d.  Damaged head plate   ..  10·00   5·50   (2) Slate-purple and ultra-
 e.  Damaged L.H. duty tablet   2·50   2·50       marine   1·50   75
 s.  "Specimen", Type 17   ..  3·50
 t.  "Cancelled", Type 19   ..  6·00
 u.  "Cancelled", Type 20   ..  6·00

The value tablets vary from pale to deep ultramarine.

M28c   M29e

M28b

M29d

**Perforation 14**
 Types H1   H1A

**Plates.**  De la Rue made 5 head plates and 4 duty plates.  The Victorian die was used for the duty plates.

**Die proofs** in black on white glazed card :—
 Head plate only
  Without marking   ..   ..   40·00   Endorsed " AFTER HARDEN-
  Endorsed " BEFORE HARD-       ING " and (M/S) " 27 Dec 01 "  40·00
  ENING 20 DEC 01 "   ..  40·00

**Plate Proofs.**  In issued colours on poor quality buff paper   ..   ..   3·50

**1911 (AUGUST 7). 5d. PURPLE AND BLUE, TYPE M8.  PERF. 14.  SOMERSET HOUSE**

M30   293/94   14   Ordinary   (1) Dull reddish purple and
 f.  Broken harp strings (Pl. 5b,         cobalt blue   3·00   1·50
   R. 19/11)   ..   ..  6·00   4·00   (2) Dull reddish purple and
 g.  Damaged tablet (Pl. 5b,         bright blue   1·50   90
   R. 20/12)   ..   ..  4·00   3·50   (3) Deep dull reddish
 h.  Headless lion (Pl. 5c,         purple and bright
   R. 20/12)   ..   ..  18·00   18·00       blue   1·75   1·25
 i.  Damaged shield (R. 18/2)   25·00   20·00   (4) Deep plum and cobalt-
            blue   2·25   1·75

The value tablets became considerably worn and many minor varieties of breaks and missing lines may be found on both De la Rue and Somerset House printings. The two composite illustrations show examples of typical breaks.

M30*f*      Damaged value tablets      M30*h*

The Somerset House printings are clearly distinguishable by colour. The purple shades all show a distinctive reddish hue when placed side by side with the De la Rue printings. The deep plum shade is the nearest approach to the De la Rue slate-purple colour, and difficulty is encountered with classification as this was a later printing with a fine impression. The cobalt-blue of the value tablet is, however, quite different from the ultramarine of the De la Rue printing. A printing of No. (4) exists in fluorescent ink.

### Perforation 14
Types V1   V1A

| Cat. No. | S.G. No. | Perf. | Paper | Shades | Unused | Used |
|---|---|---|---|---|---|---|

**1902-05. 6d. PURPLE, TYPE M1. PERF. 14. DE LA RUE**

**A. 1902 (JANUARY 1). Ordinary Paper**

| | | | | | | |
|---|---|---|---|---|---|---|
| M31 | 245/46 | 14 | Ordinary | (1) Pale dull purple | 1·25 | 40 |
| s. | "Specimen", Type 15 | .. | 3·00 | (2) Slate-purple | 1·25 | 40 |

**B. 1905 (OCTOBER 1). Chalk-surfaced paper**

| | | | | | | |
|---|---|---|---|---|---|---|
| M32 | 247/48 | 14 | Chalky | (1) Pale dull purple | 1·25 | 40 |
| b. | Frame broken at right | .. | — 18·00 | (2) Dull purple | 1·00 | 40 |
| | | | | (3) Slate-purple | 1·75 | 1·00 |

### Perforation 14
Types H1   H1A

**Plates.** De la Rue made 11 plates.

**Die Proofs** in black on white glazed card :—

| | | |
|---|---|---|
| Without marking  ..  .. | 40·00 | Endorsed " 29 APR. 04 AFTER |
| Endorsed "28 AUG 01 BEFORE | | STRIKING "..  ..  ..  40·00 |
| HARDENING "  ..  .. | 40·00 | Endorsed " Working Die No. 18 "  50·00 |
| Endorsed " 7 SEP 01 AFTER | | |
| HARDENING "  ..  .. | 40·00 | |

### Plate Proofs
In grey-black on thick soft white paper ruled on both front and back within lines 10 mm. apart  ..  ..  ..  ..  ..  ..  ..  ..  ..  6·00
In black on thin white card  ..  ..  ..  ..  ..  ..  ..  ..  6·00

### Colour Trials
Watermark Crown. Imperf. on very thin paper
In buff, blue, dull purple, grey, slate, green, orange, carmine and bright rose  ..  *Each*  35·00

*Chalky Paper*
These were made on the selvedge of a British Colonial ½d. stamp on chalky paper. They are without watermark and show the green rule along the perforated edge either at top or bottom of the stamp. The other three sides are imperf. Eight different trials were made in the following colours:—
Deep red, red, slate-purple, grey-black and black  ..  ..  ..  ..  ..  *Each*  60·00

| Cat. No. | S.G. No. | Perf. | Paper | Shades | Unused | Used |
|---|---|---|---|---|---|---|

**1911-13. 6d. PURPLE, TYPE M1. PERF. 14. SOMERSET HOUSE**

**A. 1911 (OCTOBER 31). Ordinary paper**

| | | | | | | |
|---|---|---|---|---|---|---|
| M33 | 295, 297/300 | 14 | Ordinary | | | |

*ba.* Frame broken at bottom right (Pl. 2d, R. 11/12) .. 30·00 30·00
*bb.* Frame repaired (Pl. 2e, R. 11/12) .. .. 35·00 35·00
*c.* Frame broken at top right — 20·00
*d.* No top to crown (Pl. 9, R. 11/11) .. .. 18·00 18·00
*e.* Flaw below N of PENCE (Pl. 9, R. 20/6) .. .. 4·00 3·00
*f.* " J " flaw (Pl. 9, R. 10/12) 2·00 1·50
*s.* " Specimen ", Type 22 .. 2·50

| | | Unused | Used |
|---|---|---|---|
| (1) | Royal purple (31 Oct. 1911) | 3·00 | 4·00 |
| (2) | Reddish purple (Nov. 1911) | 1·25 | 50 |
| (3) | Very deep reddish purple (Nov. 1911) | 4·00 | 1·50 |
| (4) | Dull purple | 1·75 | 40 |
| (5) | Dark purple (March 1912) | 3·00 | 2·00 |
| (6) | Pale dull purple | 1·25 | 50 |
| (7) | Pale reddish purple (March 1913) | 1·75 | 1·00 |

Nos. (6) and (7) are very fine impressions on rather thinner plate glazed paper.

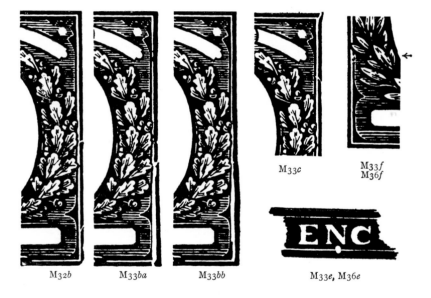

M33c   M33f M36f

M32b   M33ba   M33bb   M33e, M36e

When placed side by side with the De la Rue issues, the great majority of the Somerset House printings show the distinctive reddish purple tints as mentioned on the 1½d. value. The colours of Nos. (4) and (6) are sometimes confused with the De la Rue shades and classification can only be made with some experience. The coarse printings are always Somerset House, as also are the very clear printings on plate glazed paper.

**B. 1913 (MARCH). '' Dickinson '' coated paper**

| | | | | | Unused | Used |
|---|---|---|---|---|---|---|
| M34 | 301 | 14 | Coated | (1) Dull purple | 12·00 | 8·00 |
| | | | | (2) Dull reddish purple | 14·00 | 9·00 |

This paper, although coated, does not respond to the silver point test. Its use was experimental and some experience is needed to identify it.

The surface has the smooth glossy appearance associated with chalk-surfaced paper and an aid to its identification is the dead white appearance of the back of the stamp. Possibly the paper was coated both sides. As the paper is rather thick the watermark is not immediately visible. Printings on this paper were from Plates 10 and 11.

| Cat. No. | S.G. No. | Perf. | Paper | Shades | Unused | Used |
|----------|----------|-------|-------|--------|--------|------|

### C.  1911 (NOVEMBER).  Chalk-surfaced paper

M35  296  14  Chalky  Bright magenta  £300
   *s.*  " Specimen ", Type 22  ..  60·00

M36  303  14  Chalky  Deep plum (July 1913)  2·00  4·75
   *d.*  No top to crown (Pl. 9,
     R. 11/11)  ..  ..  25·00  25·00
   *e.*  Flaw below N of PENCE
     (Pl. 9, R. 20/6) ..  ..  3·50  6·00  .  "J" flaw (Pl 9, R. 10/12)  2·50  4·00

    This chalky paper was of a different kind from that used by De la Rue.  One does not encounter the rubbed appearance on the surface, so common to the De la Rue printings on chalky paper.  These two stamps are the finest and clearest of all the 6d. K.E. VII printings.
    The colour of M35 was considered unsatisfactory and nearly all the printed sheets were destroyed.  M36 has thick yellowish gum.

**Perforation 14**
   Types VI  VIA

### 1910 (MAY 4).  7d. GREY-BLACK, TYPE M9.  PERF. 14.  DE LA RUE

M37  249/49a  14  Ordinary  (1) Grey-black  40  35
   *s.*  "Specimen", Type 17  ..  3·50  (2) Deep grey-black  2·50  1·50
   *t.*  "Cancelled", Type 20  ..  6·00

**Perforation 14**
   Type H1 only

**Plates.**  De la Rue made 3 plates.

**Die Proofs** in black on white glazed card :—
   Endorsed " Die No. 89 "  ..  40·00      Endorsed " AFTER STRIKING
   Endorsed " BEFORE HARD-         12 MAR 10 " ..  ..  ..  40·00
     ENING 7 SEP 09 " ..  ..  40·00
   Endorsed " AFTER HARDEN-
     ING 12 SEP 09 "  ..  ..  40·00

**Colour Trials**  Various colours (see page 23)

### 1912 (AUGUST 1).  7d. GREY-BLACK, TYPE M9.  PERF. 14.  SOMERSET HOUSE

M38  305  14  Ordinary  (1) Deep slate-grey  2·50  2·50
       (2) Slate-grey  80  90
       (3) Pale grey (May 1913)  1·00  1·20

    No. (1) is on poorly surfaced paper which produced a coarse impression.  The later printings (Nos. 2 and 3) are on finely calendered paper, and it is difficult to distinguish between these and the De la Rue printings.
    All the Somerset House issues show a trace of olive in the grey—some more so than others, but always apparent to the keen eye.

**Perforation 14**
   Types VI  VIA

### 1902-05.  9d. PURPLE AND BLUE, TYPE M10.  PERF. 14.  DE LA RUE
### A. 1902 (APRIL 7).  Ordinary paper

M39  250/51  14  Ordinary  (1) Dull purple and ultra-
   *b.*  Damaged S.E. corner (Head         marine  3·00  1·25
    Pl. 1, 2nd stamp "D"      (2) Slate-purple and ultra-
    pane)  ..  ..  ..  6·00  4·00     marine  3·25  1·25
   *s.*  " Specimen ", Type 16  ..  3·00  (3) Slate-purple and deep
       ultramarine  4·00  2·00

### B. 1905 (JUNE 29).  Chalk-surfaced paper

M40  252/53  14  Chalky  (1) Dull purple and ultra-
   *s.*  " Specimen ", Type 17  ..  3·50     marine  3·25  2·00
   *t.*  " Cancelled ", Type 18  ..  6·00  (2) Slate-purple  and  pale
   *u.*  " Cancelled ", Type 20  ..     ultramarine  2·75  2·00
       (3) Slate-purple and ultra-
       marine  2·25  1·50
       (4) Slate-purple and deep
       ultramarine  4·00  2·50

**Perforation 14**
   Type H1 only

**Plates.** De la Rue made 3 head plates and 2 duty plates. The Victorian die was used for the duty plates.

**Die Proofs** in black on white glazed card :—

Head plate only
Without marking .. .. 40·00
Endorsed "BEFORE HARD-
ENING 10 DEC 01 " .. 40·00

Endorsed " AFTER HARDEN-
ING 10 DEC 01 " .. .. 40·00

| Cat. No. | S.G. No. | Perf. | Paper | Shades | Unused | Used |
|---|---|---|---|---|---|---|

**1911 (JULY 24). 9d. PURPLE AND BLUE, TYPE M10. PERF. 14. SOMERSET HOUSE**

| | | | | | | |
|---|---|---|---|---|---|---|
| M 41 | 306/08 | 14 | Ordinary | (1) Reddish purple and light blue | 7·00 | 4·00 |
| c. | Cracked head plate (Head Pl. 1, Pane G R2/4) .. | | 22·00  22·00 | (2) Dull reddish purple and blue (Oct. 1911) | 2·00 | 1·25 |
| | "Specimen" ,Type 22 .. | | 3·00 | (3) Deep dull reddish purple and blue | 2·00 | 1·25 |
| | | | | (4) Deep dull reddish purple and deep bright blue (Sept. 1911) | 6·00 | 3·75 |
| | | | | (5) Slate-purple and cobalt-blue (F) (March 1912) | 7·00 | 4·00 |
| | | | | (6) Dark plum and blue (July 1913) | 1·50 | 1·25 |

The purple colours are the same as for the 1½d. of these printers. An additional check on No. (1) is the light blue frame which colour was not used again.

The purple of No. (5) may be confused with the De la Rue No. (2) but the shades (of blue and ultramarine) are unmistakable. No. (6) is on plate glazed paper, and an extremely fine impression.

M41c                    M42/3c

**Perforation 14**
Types V1   V1A

**1902-05. 10d. PURPLE AND RED, TYPE M11. PERF. 14. DE LA RUE**
**A. 1902 JULY 3). Ordinary paper**

| | | | | | | |
|---|---|---|---|---|---|---|
| M42 | 254 | 14 | Ordinary | (1) Dull purple and car-mine | 3·25 | 1·50 |
| b. | No Cross on crown .. | | 25·00  20·00 | (2) Slate-purple and car-mine | 3·25 | 1·50 |
| c. | Damaged base to VEN of REVENUE .. .. | | 3·00  2·00 | (3) Slate-purple and car-mine-pink | 8·00 | 4·00 |
| s. | " Specimen ", Type 16 .. | | 3·00 | | | |

| Cat. No. | S.G. No. | Perf. | Paper | Shades | Unused | Used |
|----------|----------|-------|-------|--------|--------|------|

**B. 1905 (SEPTEMBER 6).   Chalk-surfaced paper**

| | | | | | | |
|---|---|---|---|---|---|---|
| M43 | 255/6 | 14 | Chalky | (1) Dull purple and carmine | 4·00 | 1·75 |
| (2) b. | No Cross on crown | | 18·00    15·00 | | | |
| (4) b. | No Cross on crown | | 20·00    18·00 | (2) Slate-purple and carmine | 3·75 | 1·50 |
| c. | Damaged base to VEN of REVENUE | | 5·00    2·50 | (3) Slate-purple and deep carmine | 20·00 | 12·00 |
| d. | Damaged head plate top left | | 5·00    2·50 | | | |
| e. | Damaged head plate bottom left | | 5·00    2·50 | (4) Dull purple and scarlet (Sept. 1910) | 5·00 | 3·00 |
| f. | Damaged head plate top and bottom left (R. 13/5) | | 8·00    3·00 | (5) Slate-purple and scarlet | 5·00 | 3·00 |
| g. | Break in frame at back of head | | 7·00    3·50 | | | |
| s. | " Specimen ", Type 17 | | 4·00 | | | |
| t. | " Cancelled ", Type 18 | | 6·00 | | | |
| u. | " Cancelled ", Type 20 | | 6·00 | | | |

Varieties *d, e* and *f* occur on many positions in the sheet.   We illustrate two typical examples.

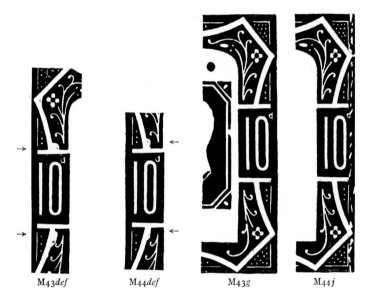

M43*def*          M44*def*          M43*g*          M44*f*

**Perforation 14**

Type H1 only

**Plates.**   De la Rue made 2 head plates and 1 duty plate.   The Victorian die was used for the duty plate.

**Die proofs** in black on white glazed card :—

Head plate only
Without marking    ..    ..    40·00        Endorsed " AFTER HARDEN-
Endorsed " BEFORE HARD-                         ING 28 NOV 01 "    ..    ..    40·00
ENING 27 NOV 01 "    ..    40·00

**Plate Proof** in issued colours on poor quality buff paper    ..    ..    ..    3·50

| Cat. No. | S.G. No. | Perf. | Paper | Shades | Unused | Used |
|---|---|---|---|---|---|---|

**1911 (OCTOBER 9).  10d. PURPLE AND RED, TYPE M11.  PERF. 14.  SOMERSET HOUSE**

| | | | | | Unused | Used |
|---|---|---|---|---|---|---|
| M44 | 309/11 | 14 | Ordinary | (1) Dull reddish purple and scarlet | 5·00 | 3·00 |
| d. | Damaged head plate top left | | | 5·00 | 3·50 |
| e. | Damaged head plate bottom left | | | 5·00 | 3·50 |
| f. | Damaged head plate top and bottom left (R. 16/5) | | | 8·00 | 6·00 |
| g. | Ditto but (R. 13/5) | | | 5·00 | 3·00 |
| h. | Damaged S.W. corner (shade 8) | | | — | 20·00 |
| i. | Mark after E of REVENUE | | | 6·00 | 5·00 |
| j. | Cracked duty plate (Pane X, R. 4/12) | | | 15·00 | |
| k. | No Cross on Crown (shade like (7)) | | | 30·00 | |
| s. | " Specimen ", Type 22 | | | 3·00 | |

Shades:
| | Shades | Unused | Used |
|---|---|---|---|
| (1) | Dull reddish purple and scarlet | 5·00 | 3·00 |
| (2) | Dull purple and scarlet | 4·00 | 2·25 |
| (3) | Deep dull purple and scarlet | 5·00 | 3·00 |
| (4) | Dull purple and deep scarlet | 15·00 | 9·00 |
| (5) | Dull reddish purple and aniline pink (F) | 25·00 | 20·00 |
| (6) | Dull reddish purple and carmine (May 1912) | 3·00 | 2·00 |
| (7) | Deep dull purple and carmine | 4·00 | 3·00 |
| (8) | Dark plum and carmine | 4·00 | 3·00 |

Nos. (1) to (7) may be distinguished quite easily from the De la Rue printings by the different shade of purple.  No. (8) is often confused with No. M42 (2 and 3).  It is printed on plate glazed paper, producing a clearer and sharper impression than the De la Rue print.

M44*i*

M46*e*

**Perforation 14**

Types V1   V1A

**1902-05.  1s. GREEN AND RED, TYPE M12.  PERF. 14.  DE LA RUE**

**A. 1902 (MARCH 24).  Ordinary paper**

| M45 | 257 | 14 | Ordinary | (1) Dull green and carmine | 2·50 | 75 |
|---|---|---|---|---|---|---|
| s. | " Specimen ", Type 16 | | 3·00 | (2) Dull green and bright carmine | 2·50 | 75 |

**B. 1905 (SEPTEMBER 6).  Chalk-surfaced paper**

| M46 | 258/59 | 14 | Chalky | (1) Dull green and carmine | 4·50 | 75 |
|---|---|---|---|---|---|---|
| d. | " Full beard " to portrait | | £120 | (2) Dull green and pale carmine | 5·50 | 1·00 |
| e. | Frame broken at left | | 7·00 | 4·00 | (3) Dull green and scarlet (Sept. 1910) | 2·00 | 75 |
| s. | " Specimen ", Type 17 | | 5·00 | (4) Deep dull green and scarlet | 3·00 | 1·50 |
| t. | " Cancelled ", Type 18 | | 7·00 | | |
| u. | " Cancelled ", Type 20 | | 7·00 | | |

**Perforation 14**

Type H1 only

**Plates.**  De la Rue made 2 head duty plates and 3 frame plates.

**Die Proofs** in black on white glazed card :—

Head plate only
Without marking .. .. 40·00
Endorsed " BEFORE HARDENING 4 DEC 01 " .. .. 40·00

Endorsed " AFTER HARDENING 10 DEC 01 " .. .. 40·00

| Cat. No. | S.G. No. | Perf. | Paper | Shades | Unused | Used |
|---|---|---|---|---|---|---|

**1911 (JULY 17).   1s. GREEN AND RED, TYPE M12.   PERF. 14.   SOMERSET HOUSE**

| | | | | | | |
|---|---|---|---|---|---|---|
| M47 | 312/14 | 14 | Ordinary | (1) Dark green and scarlet | 8·00 | 5·00 |
| a. | No watermark | .. | .. 50·00 | (2) Deep green and scarlet | | |
| b. | Watermark inverted | .. | 10·00 | (9 Oct. 1911) | 3·50 | 1·00 |
| c. | Watermark part of the word POSTAGE | .. | 20·00 | (3) Green and bright scarlet | 3·50 | 1·00 |
| s. | " Specimen ", Type 22 | .. | 3·00 | (4) Green and scarlet | 3·50 | 1·00 |
| t. | " Specimen ", Type 23 | .. | 6·00 | (5) Green and carmine | | |
| | | | | (15 April 1912) | 1·50 | 75 |

The green of the Somerset House printings is darker and more olive than that of De la Rue.

**Perforation 14**

Types VI VIA

**1902-05.   2s. 6d. PURPLE, TYPE M13.   PERF. 14.   DE LA RUE**
**A. 1902 (APRIL 5).   Ordinary paper**

| | | | | | | |
|---|---|---|---|---|---|---|
| M48 | 260 | 14 | Ordinary | (1) Lilac | 12·00 | 3·00 |
| b. | Watermark inverted | .. | 20·00 | (2) Slate-purple | 15·00 | 4·00 |
| s. | " Specimen ", Type 15 | .. | 6·00 | | | |
| t. | " Specimen ", Type 16 | .. | 2·00 | | | |

**B. 1905 (OCTOBER 7).   Chalk-surfaced paper**

| | | | | | | |
|---|---|---|---|---|---|---|
| M49 | 261/62 | 14 | Chalky | (1) Pale dull purple | 12·00 | 3·50 |
| b. | Watermark inverted | .. | 25·00    50·00 | (2) Dull purple | 12·00 | 3·50 |
| | | | | (3) Slate-purple | 12·00 | 3·50 |

**Perforation 14**

Type H1 only

**Plates.**  De la Rue made one plate only.

**Die Proofs** in black on white glazed card :—

| | | | |
|---|---|---|---|
| Without marking | .. | .. 50·00 | Endorsed " AFTER HARDEN- |
| Endorsed " BEFORE HARD- | | | ING 12 NOV 01 " .. .. 50·00 |
| ENING 8 NOV 01 ".. | .. | 50·00 | |

**Plate Proof** in issued colour on poor quality buff paper .. .. .. 8·00
As above, double impression   ..   ..   ..   ..   ..   ..   10·00

**1911 (SEPTEMBER 27).   2s. 6d. PURPLE, TYPE M13.   PERF. 14.   SOMERSET HOUSE**

| | | | | | | |
|---|---|---|---|---|---|---|
| M50 | 315/17 | 14 | Ordinary | (1) Dull greyish purple (F) | 25·00 | 8·00 |
| s. | " Specimen ", Type 22 | .. | 6·00 | (2) Dull reddish purple | | |
| t. | " Cancelled ", Type 24 | .. | 7·00 | (Oct. 1911) | 10·00 | 5·00 |
| | | | | (3) Dark purple | 12·00 | 6·00 |
| | | | | (4) Pale dull reddish purple | | |
| | | | | (18 Mar. 1913) | 10·00 | 5·00 |

Shades (2), (3) and (4) resemble the shades of certain 6d. values by the same printers.
No. (1) is very much like the De la Rue colour, but is printed in a fugitive ink which is fluorescent.
Some printings of No. (3) are very slightly fluorescent. No. (4) is a late printing on plate glazed paper giving a clear impression.

**Perforation 14**

Types VI VIA

**1902 (APRIL 5).   5s. RED, TYPE M14.   PERF. 14.   DE LA RUE**

| | | | | | | |
|---|---|---|---|---|---|---|
| M51 | 263/64 | 14 | Ordinary | (1) Bright carmine | 12·00 | 3·00 |
| s. | " Specimen ", Type 16 | .. | 2·00 | (2) Deep bright carmine | 15·00 | 4·00 |

**Perforation 14**

Type H1 only

**Plates.**  De la Rue made one plate only.

**Die Proofs** in black on white glazed card :—

| | | | |
|---|---|---|---|
| Endorsed " BEFORE HARD- | | | |
| ENING 22 NOV 01 " | .. | 50·00 | With   initials   and   (M/S) |
| Endorsed " AFTER HARDEN- | | | " 25.11.01 " ..   ..   .. 50·00 |
| ING 25 NOV 01 " .. | .. | 50·00 | |

**Plate Proof** in issued colour on poor quality buff paper .. .. .. 8·00

| Cat. No. | S.G. No. | Perf. | Paper | Shades | Unused | Used |
|---|---|---|---|---|---|---|

**1912 (FEBRUARY 29). 5s. RED, TYPE M14. PERF. 14. SOMERSET HOUSE**

| M52 | 318 | 14 | Ordinary | (1) Carmine-red | 17·00 | 7·00 |
|---|---|---|---|---|---|---|
| | | | | (2) Carmine | 15·00 | 7·00 |

An aid to identification in this difficult value is the back of the stamp. The ink used by De la Rue had a permeating quality which gives the appearance of an offset of the design on the back. No. (2) is the later printing with fine impression. A small printing of No. (1) exists in fluorescent ink.

**Perforation 14**

Types V1     V1A

**1902 (APRIL 5). 10s. BLUE, TYPE M15. PERF. 14. DE LA RUE**

| M53 | 265 | 14 | Ordinary | (1) Ultramarine | 25·00 | 15·00 |
|---|---|---|---|---|---|---|
| s. | "Specimen", Type 16 | .. | 3·00 | (2) Deep ultramarine | 30·00 | 18·00 |
| t. | "Specimen", Type 17 | .. | 6·00 | | | |

**Perforation 14**

Type H1 only

**Plates.** De la Rue made one plate only.

**Die Proofs** in black on white glazed card :—

| Without marking | .. | .. | 50·00 | Endorsed "AFTER HARDEN- | | |
| Endorsed " BEFORE HARD- | | | | ING 25 NOV 01 " | .. | .. | 50·00 |
| ENING 22 NOV 01 " | | .. | 50·00 | | | |

**1912 (JANUARY 14). 10s. BLUE, TYPE M15. PERF. 14. SOMERSET HOUSE**

| M54 | 319 | 14 | Ordinary | (1) Bright blue | 28·00 | 25·00 |
|---|---|---|---|---|---|---|
| | | | | (2) Blue | 25·00 | 20·00 |
| | | | | (3) Deep blue | 28·00 | 25·00 |

All the blues of Somerset House have a more violet tone, Nos. (2) and (3) being more akin to cobalt-blue.

**Perforation 14**

Types V1     V1A

**1902 (JULY 16). £1 GREEN, TYPE M16. PERF. 14. DE LA RUE**

| M55 | 266 | 14 | Ordinary | (1) Dull blue-green | £110 | 35·00 |
|---|---|---|---|---|---|---|
| s. | "Specimen", Type 16 | .. | 5·00 | | | |
| t. | "Specimen", Type 17 | .. | 10·00 | | | |

**Perforation 14**

Type H1 only

**Plate.** De la Rue made one plate only.

**Die Proofs** in black on white glazed card :—

| Without marking | .. | .. | 75·00 | | | |
| Endorsed " BEFORE HARD- | | | | Endorsed " AFTER HARDEN- | | |
| ENING 16 DEC 01 " | | .. | 75·00 | ING 13 MAR 02 " | .. | .. | 75·00 |
| Endorsed "AFTER HARDEN- | | | | | | |
| ING 19 DEC 01 " | .. | .. | 75·00 | | | |

**1911 (SEPTEMBER 3). £1 GREEN, TYPE M16. PERF. 14. SOMERSET HOUSE**

| M56 | 320 | 14 | Ordinary | (1) Deep green | £110 | 40·00 |
|---|---|---|---|---|---|---|
| a. | Imperf. | .. | .. | £400 | | |
| s. | " Specimen ", Type 22 | .. | | | | |

**Perforation 14**

Types  H2 (f or g)     H2A (f or g)

**£1 GREEN, THE "LOWDEN" FORGERY**

Produced by photo lithography, and usually found affixed to brown paper with a forged Channel Islands postmark. The watermark was impressed in the paper. The stamp is a good imitation of the Somerset House shade, but the impression is coarser than that of the original and the lines of shading are faint and broken. Price £50

# The Official Stamps

For introductory notes see Section L in Volume 1.

## 1.  Inland Revenue

**I.R.**          **I. R.**

**OFFICIAL**      **OFFICIAL**

L1                L2

| Cat. No. | S.G. No. | Date | | Stamp optd. | Description | Unused | Used |
|---|---|---|---|---|---|---|---|
| **(A) "I.R. OFFICIAL" TYPE L1 ON STAMPS OF 1902** | | | | | | | |
| MO1 | O20 | 4.2.1902 | | M1 | ½d. Blue-green | 50 | 15 |
| *s.* "Specimen", Type 15 .. | | | 2·00 | | | | |
| MO2 | O21 | 4.2.1902 | | M5 | 1d. Scarlet | 25 | 5 |
| *s.* "Specimen", Type 15 .. | | | 2·00 | | | | |
| MO3 | O22 | 19.2.1902 | | M16 | 2½d. Ultramarine | 15·00 | 5·00 |
| *s.* "Specimen", Type 15 .. | | | 4·00 | | | | |
| MO4 | O23 | 14.3.1904 | | M31 | 6d. Dull purple | £4000 | |
| *s.* "Specimen", Type 16 .. | | | £300 | | | | |
| MO5 | O24 | 29.4.1902 | | M45 | 1s. Green and carmine | 35·00 | 7·00 |
| *s.* "Specimen", Type 16 .. | | | 7·00 | | | | |
| **(B) "I.R. OFFICIAL" TYPE L2 ON STAMPS OF 1902** | | | | | | | |
| O6 | O25 | 29.4.1902 | | M51 | 5s. Carmine | £500 | £220 |
| *a.* Raised stop after "R" .. | | £550 | £275 | | | | |
| *s.* "Specimen", Type 16 .. | | 25·00 | | | | | |
| MO7 | O26 | 29.4.1902 | | M53 | 10s. Ultramarine | £2500 | £1700 |
| *a.* Raised stop after "R" .. | | £2750 | £2000 | | | | |
| *s.* "Specimen", Type 16 .. | | £250 | | | | | |
| MO8 | O27 | 20.4.1902 | | M55 | £1 Dull blue-green | £1200 | £500 |
| *s.* "Specimen", Type 16 .. | | | £120 | | | | |
| *Controls* | | | | | | | |
| MOC1 | ½d. Continuous | A | 2·00 | MOC3 | 1d. Continuous  A | 1·25 | |
| MOC2 | ½d. Continuous | B | 2·00 | MOC4 | 1d. Continuous  B | 1·25 | |

## 2.  Government Parcels

**GOVT**

**PARCELS**

L3

| "GOVT. PARCELS" TYPE L3 ON STAMPS OF 1902 | | | | | | | |
|---|---|---|---|---|---|---|---|
| MO9 | O74 | 30.10.1902 | | M5 | 1d. Scarlet | 1·50 | 1·00 |
| *s.* "Specimen", Type 16 .. | | | 2·00 | | | | |
| MO10 | O75 | 29.4.1902 | | M11 | 2d. Green and carmine | 5·00 | 2·00 |
| *s.* "Specimen", Type 16 .. | | | 2·00 | | | | |
| MO11 | O76 | 19.2.1902 | | M31 | 6d. Dull purple | 5·00 | 1·00 |
| *s.* "Specimen", Type 15 .. | | | 3·50 | | | | |
| MO12 | O77 | 28.8.1902 | | M39 | 9d. Purple and ultramarine | 10·00 | 3·00 |
| *s.* "Specimen", Type 16 .. | | | 4·00 | | | | |
| MO13 | O78 | 17.12.1902 | | M45 | 1s. Green and carmine | 20·00 | 5·00 |
| *s.* "Specimen", Type 16 .. | | | 7·00 | | | | |
| *Control* | | | | | | | |
| MOC5 | 1d. Continuous | A | 6·00 | | | | |

## 3. Office of Works

### O. W.

### OFFICIAL
**L4**

| Cat. No. | S.G. No. | Date | Stamp optd. | Description | Unused | Used |
|----------|----------|------|-------------|-------------|--------|------|

**" O.W. OFFICIAL " TYPE L4 ON STAMPS OF 1902**

| | | | | | | |
|---|---|---|---|---|---|---|
| MO14 | O36 | 11.2.1902 | M1 | ½d. Blue-green | 5·00 | 1·00 |
| s. | " Specimen ", Type 15 .. | | 2·00 | | | |
| MO15 | O37 | 11.2.1902 | M5 | 1d. Scarlet | 5·00 | 50 |
| s. | " Specimen ", Type 15 .. | | 2·00 | | | |
| MO16 | O38 | 29.3.1902 | M11 | 2d. Green and carmine | 12·00 | 3·00 |
| s. | " Specimen ", Type 16 .. | | 4·00 | | | |
| MO17 | O39 | 20.3.1902 | M16 | 2½d. Ultramarine | 14·00 | 4·00 |
| s. | " Specimen ", Type 16 .. | | 6·00 | | | |
| MO18 | O40 | 28.5.1903 | M42 | 10d. Purple and carmine | 65·00 | 35·00 |
| s. | " Specimen ", Type 16 .. | | 9·00 | | | |
| t. | " Cancelled ", Type 18 .. | | 20·00 | | | |

*Controls*

| | | | | | | | | |
|---|---|---|---|---|---|---|---|---|
| MOC6 | ½d. Continuous | A | 10·00 | | MOC8 | 1d. Continuous | A | 8·00 |
| MOC7 | ½d. Continuous | B | 10·00 | | MOC9 | 1d. Continuous | B | 8·00 |

## 4. Army

### ARMY      ARMY

### OFFICIAL      OFFICIAL
**L5**      **L6a**

**" ARMY OFFICIAL " TYPE L5 ON STAMPS OF 1902**

| | | | | | | | |
|---|---|---|---|---|---|---|---|
| MO19 | O48 | 11.2.1902 | | M1 | ½d. Blue-green | 8 | 5 |
| c. | Long leg to A and stop under R | 1·50 | 1·00 | h. | Long stroke to second F | 75 | 50 |
| d. | Short A in ARMY | 75 | 50 | i. | Long stroke to I .. | 75 | 50 |
| e. | Stop between legs of R | 1·50 | 1·00 | j. | Tall L .. .. | 75 | 50 |
| f. | Short Y .. .. | 75 | 50 | k. | Short and thin L .. | 1·00 | 75 |
| g. | Splayed Y .. .. | 1·00 | 75 | s. | "Specimen" Type 15 .. | 1·25 | |
| | | | | | | | |
| MO20 | O49 | 11.2.1902 | | M5 | 1d. Scarlet | 8 | 5 |
| a. | ARMY omitted .. | | | | | | |
| b. | OFFICIAI for OFFICIAL | | | g. | Splayed Y .. .. | 1·00 | 75 |
| c. | Long leg to A in ARMY | 1·50 | 1·00 | h. | Long stroke to second F | 75 | 50 |
| d. | Very short leg to A in ARMY | 75 | 50 | i. | Long stroke to I .. | 75 | 50 |
| e. | Stop between legs of R | 1·50 | 1·00 | j. | Tall L .. .. | 75 | 50 |
| f. | Short Y .. | 75 | 50 | s. | "Specimen" Type 15 .. | 2·50 | |
| | | | | | | | |
| MO21 | O50 | 23.8.1902 | | M31 | 6d. Dull purple | 4·00 | 3·50 |
| h. | Long stroke to second F | 3·00 | 2·00 | j. | Tall L .. .. | 4·00 | 2·50 |
| i. | Long stroke to I .. | 4·00 | 2·50 | s. | "Specimen" Type 16 .. | 5·00 | |

| ARMY | ARMY | ARMY | OFFICIAL | OFFICIAL |
|---|---|---|---|---|
| Var. *c* | Var. *f* | Var. *g* | Var. *h* | Var. *j* |

*Controls*

| | | | | | | |
|---|---|---|---|---|---|---|
| *MOC10* | ½d. Continuous | A | 1·00 | *MOC12* | 1d. Continuous | A | 1·00 |
| *MOC11* | ½d. Continuous | B | 1·00 | *MOC13* | 1d. Continuous | B | 1·00 |

### " ARMY OFFICIAL " TYPE L6*a* ON STAMP OF 1902

| Cat. No. | S.G. No. | Date | Stamp optd. | Description | Unused | Used |
|---|---|---|---|---|---|---|
| MO22 | O52 | –.9.1903 | M31 | 6d. Dull purple | 35·00 | 25·00 |

## 5.  Board of Education

BOARD

OF

EDUCATION

**L7**

### " BOARD OF EDUCATION " TYPE L7 ON STAMPS OF 1902

| | | | | | | | | |
|---|---|---|---|---|---|---|---|---|
| MO23 | O83 | 19.2.1902 | | | M1 | ½d. Blue-green | 2·50 | 50 |
| *s.* | " Specimen ", Type 15 .. | | 2·00 | | | | | |
| MO24 | O84 | 19.2.1902 | | | M5 | 1d. Scarlet | 2·00 | 30 |
| *s.* | " Specimen ", Type 15 .. | | 2·50 | | | | | |
| MO25 | O85 | 19.2.1902 | | | M16 | 2½d. Ultramarine | 14·00 | 3·00 |
| *s.* | " Specimen ", Type 15 .. | | 5·00 | | | | | |
| MO26 | O86 | 6.2.1904 | | | M28 | 5d. Purple and blue | 50·00 | 35·00 |
| *s.* | " Specimen ", Type 16 .. | | 15·00 | | | | | |
| *t.* | " Cancelled ", Type 18 .. | | 25·00 | | | | | |
| MO27 | O87 | 23.12.1902 | | | M45 | 1s. Green and carmine | £2200 | £1300 |
| *s.* | " Specimen ", Type 16 .. | | £250 | | | | | |

*Controls*

| | | | | | | | |
|---|---|---|---|---|---|---|---|
| *MOC14* | ½d. Continuous | A | 10·00 | *MOC 16* | 1d. Continuous | A | |
| *MOC15* | ½d. Continuous | B | 10·00 | *MOC 17* | 1d. Continuous | B | 7·00 |

## 6. Royal Household

Only the ½d. and 1d. King Edward VII issue were overprinted in 1902. These were for the use of Heads of the Royal Households in the various Royal Palaces. They were over-printed in black by De la Rue.

# R.H.

# OFFICIAL
### L8

### " R.H. OFFICIAL " TYPE L8 ON STAMPS OF 1902

| Cat. No. | S.G. No. | Date | Stamp optd. | Description | Unused | Used |
|---|---|---|---|---|---|---|
| MO28 | O91 | 29.4.1902 | M1 | ½d. Blue-green | 7·00 | 6·00 |
| s. | " Specimen ", Type 16 .. | 6·00 | | | | |
| MO29 | O92 | 19.2.1902 | M5 | 1d. Scarlet | 5·00 | 4·00 |
| s. | " Specimen ", Type 15 .. | 6·00 | | | | |

*Controls*
| MOC17 | ½d. Continuous | A | 15·00 | | MOC18 | 1d. Continuous | A | 12·00 |
|---|---|---|---|---|---|---|---|---|

## 7. Admiralty

These were for use in the various Admiralty Departments throughout the country and they were overprinted in black by De la Rue. The first overprint was made in 1903 (Type **L9**) but soon after it was found that this electro was damaged and it was remade using a thicker type in a slightly narrower setting (Type **L10**).

# ADMIRALTY          ADMIRALTY

# OFFICIAL          OFFICIAL
### L9                   L10

### " ADMIRALTY OFFICIAL " TYPE L9 ON STAMPS OF 1902

| | | | | | | |
|---|---|---|---|---|---|---|
| MO30 | O101 | 3.3.1903 | M1 | ½d. Blue-green | 1·00 | 40 |
| s. | " Specimen ", Type 16 .. | 3·00 | | | | |
| MO31 | O102 | 3.3.1903 | M5 | 1d. Scarlet | 50 | 25 |
| s. | " Specimen ", Type 16 .. | 3·00 | | | | |
| MO32 | O103 | 3.3.1903 | M8 | 1½d. Purple and green | 4·00 | 2·50 |
| s. | " Specimen ", Type 16 .. | 6·00 | | | | |
| MO33 | O104 | 3.3.1903 | M11 | 2d. Green and carmine | 6·00 | 3·50 |
| s. | " Specimen ", Type 16 .. | 6·00 | | | | |
| MO34 | O105 | 3.3.1903 | M16 | 2½d. Ultramarine | 3·50 | 3·00 |
| s. | " Specimen ", Type 16 .. | 6·00 | | | | |
| MO35 | O106 | 3.3.1903 | M19 | 3d. Purple on yellow | 6·00 | 3·00 |
| s. | " Specimen ", Type 16 .. | 6·00 | | | | |

*Controls*
| MOC19 | ½d. Continuous | A | 6·00 | | MOC21 | 1d. Continuous | A | 5·00 |
|---|---|---|---|---|---|---|---|---|
| MOC20 | ½d. Continuous | B | 4·50 | | MOC22 | 1d. Continuous | B | 3·00 |

**" ADMIRALTY OFFICIAL " TYPE L10 ON STAMPS OF 1902**

| | | | | | | | |
|---|---|---|---|---|---|---|---|
| MO36 | O107 | −.9.1903 | M1 | ½d. Blue-green | 1·00 | 40 |
| MO37 | O108 | −.11.1903 | M5 | 1d. Scarlet | 60 | 20 |
| MO38 | O109 | −.2.1904 | M8 | 1½d. Purple and green | 12·00 | 6·00 |
| MO39 | O110 | −.3.1904 | M11 | 2d. Green and carmine | 28·00 | 14·00 |
| MO40 | O111 | −.3.1904 | M16 | 2½d. Ultramarine | 45·00 | 30·00 |
| MO41 | O112 | −.2.1904 | M19 | 3d. Purple on yellow | 15·00 | 3·50 |

*s.* " Specimen ", Type 16 ..   7·00

*Controls*

| | | | | | | |
|---|---|---|---|---|---|---|
| MOC23 | ½d. Continuous | B | 6·00 | MOC24 | 1d. Continuous B | 5·00 |

## 6.  Board of Trade

This Department was the first to use official stamps.   Instead of overprinting current stamps they were perforated with a " Crown " over the letters " B.T.".   Unfortunately insufficient information or records exist to make a complete listing but all values from ½d. to 1s. were so perforated.   Collectors should be warned that no less than ten different forgeries have been recorded of this " perforated " variety.

## 7.  Crown Agents

In 1903 the 1d. Scarlet was overprinted in black with the letters " C.A." (4·5 mm. high 10·5 mm. long); later the 6d. Dull Purple also appeared with this overprint.   There are no records to show that either of these varieties were used for postal purposes.

## 8.  Stationery Office

Following the Board of Trade's practice in perforating current postage stamps for departmental mail, the Stationery Office perforated their supplies of postage stamps with a " Crown " over the letters " S.O.".   Similarly no official records have been seen to give complete details.

# SECTION N1
# King George V
## Typographed Issues, 1911-1934

## General Notes

**INTRODUCTION.** King George V came to the throne on 6th May, 1910, and in July the Postmaster General invited designs for a new series of stamps. Those selected were the work of two artists, G. W. Eve and Sir Bertram Mackennal. The ½d. and 1d. values of the proposed new series were issued on Coronation Day 1911, and they aroused a storm of criticism from the public on artistic and other grounds. The head, having been copied from a photograph by W. & D. Downey, was unsuited for the typographic process, and the majority of printed impressions were blotchy. In an effort to improve the appearance, the die was deepened and fresh plates were made, but the results were still not satisfactory. A new die was then prepared and stamps from this improved " Die 2 " were placed on sale on January 1st, 1912.

Finally, the " Downey " head was discarded, and a new set of stamps was prepared with the King's head in profile, taken from Mackennal's design for the Coronation medal. The issue of stamps in this series was not completed until August 1913, and these designs remained unaltered for the rest of the reign. Remarkably few varieties are found, and philatelic interest centres chiefly on the wide range of colours and in the identification of the plates.

**PRINTERS.** Harrison and Sons held the contract for printing the typographed stamps until 1924, and from 1924 until 1933 the stamps were printed by Waterlow and Sons.

Harrison and Sons, who regained the contract in 1934, were to have produced a new set of stamps by the photogravure process. They were, however, unable to get this process under way in time to supply the new stamps before the existing stock of typographed stamps would have become exhausted. In consequence Harrison's made provisional printings by typography, aided in the initial stages by Waterlow.

Preliminary printings of most values were made at Somerset House during 1912-13, and the government printers also were solely responsible for supplies of the 6d. value from 1913-33.

**ARRANGEMENT.** The issues of 1911-12 have been listed separately, under three headings: Die 1A, Die 1B and Die 2 (redrawn die). The issues of 1912-34 have been listed separately under two headings according to the watermark.

**PLATES AND PRINTING.** The plates were prepared by the Electrotype process as for the K.E.VII issues, but were nickel-surfaced.

Almost every plate, at some time during its use, carried a marking deliberately made in the marginal rule. These marks were made by the operators for their own guidance in plate identification.

Much research work has now made a fairly complete listing possible, but new discoveries are still being made, and our list may need to be amended from time to time. See Appendix J.

## LAYOUT.
### Harrison 1912 contract.

Each sheet consisted of 240 stamps arranged in two panes of 120; the panes contained 10 rows of 12 stamps, and were separated from one another by an interpane gutter.

The ½d. and 1d. plates of 1911-12 (Dies 1 and 2) and a few 2d. Die 1 plates had marginal rules as for the K.E.VII ½d. and 1d.; that, is co-extensive, with breaks at top above the 6th and 7th stamps and at bottom below the 6th and 7th stamps, with no break between them.

The issues of 1912-22 had co-extensive lines all round the panes.

### Waterlow 1924 contract.

Each plate contained 240 stamps in 20 rows of 12, with no divisions between the halves. There was an arrow in each side margin between the 10th and 11th rows.

When Waterlow took over the contract in 1924 they used several of the Harrison plates, modified so as to conform with the new layout. The interpane gutter was removed, and the two halves of the plate brought together.

### Somerset House 6d.

Until 1924 the arrangement was the same as for the Harrison 1912 contract. In 1925, this was changed to conform with the arrangement used by Waterlow.

**Booklet Panes.**

The same arrangement as given for K.E. VII on page 15. For the advertisement panes, a special plate was made having two vertical blanks on the binding edge of each pane. The advertisements were printed at a separate operation.

**PAPER.** Up to 1916 this was of a good standard and well calendered. From 1917 to about 1921 the quality varied and, as a result of poorer calendry, the printings assumed a coarser and duller appearance. In 1922 the general appearance of the stamps returned to the earlier high standards.

In 1911 an experimental printing of the 1d. stamp was made on chalk-surfaced paper. Chalk-surfaced paper was used for the 6d. value up to 1925 and again in 1936, for a short period in the Harrison printings.

## WATERMARKS

| Simple Cypher | Multiple Cypher | Block Cypher | |
|:---:|:---:|:---:|:---:|
| **W.14** | **W.13** | **W.15** | **W.16** |

Type **W.12** is the Crown watermark used for the K.E.VII issues; the marginal watermarks also remain unchanged.

Type **W. 14** described as Simple Cypher watermark, is found with three variations as illustrated in Appendix G:—

      I    as used for the issues of 1912–13
      II    in general use until 1917 and from 1922–24
      III    in general use from 1917–22

Type II reappeared as the general watermark in the later issues. It seems probable that the watermarks II and III are associated with the quality of paper. For example, the 8d. stamp on ordinary yellow paper is always Type II and the poorer quality granite paper, which appeared in 1917, is always Type III.

The best method of collecting these watermark types is to obtain specimens from either the top or bottom margin of the sheet. The watermark can then be seen more clearly.

A detailed list of watermark varieties is given in Appendix G.

Type **W.13** described as Multiple Cypher watermark, was used for a short time with the ½d. and 1d. values, Die 2. In 1913, stocks of this paper were used for making up vertical rolls of stamps for sale in slot machines, of the ½d. and 1d. values. Subsequently a sheet or part sheet of each value was found, and blocks of four are known of both values.

Type **W.15** described as Block Cypher watermark, was used solely by Waterlow and Harrison (1934 contract).

Type **W.16** is a variant of Type **W.15** and was used with an experimental paper by Waterlow in 1924–25.

**PERFORATION.** All stamps in this section are perforated 15 × 14, unless otherwise stated.

**SHADES.** The series of stamps issued during the years 1912–23 is notable for the wide range of colours and shades. In fact it is probable that no other series of stamps ever issued exhibits such an array.

The stamps issued in these years are treated as one issue, although ideally they should be separated into three groups.

     (a)    Issues of 1912–14
     (b)    The war period 1915–19
     (c)    Issues of 1920–24

The collection sorted in this manner reveals that the shades in groups (a) and (c) are fairly constant, and those in group (b) show great contrasts. However, for practical purposes the series has to be treated as one unit, as the colours of the three periods overlap and sharp lines of division cannot be drawn. The chief reason for the startling variations from the normal in group (b) is the fact that the World War of 1914–18 interrupted the supply of aniline dyes from Germany.

Early in 1916 experiments were carried out with British dyes, and printings of the ½d. and 1d. stamps are known in various shades of green and red overprinted " cancelled ".

The compilation of the check-list has been a job of the utmost difficulty, particularly with the naming of the colours. In general we have adhered to the terms most familiar to philatelists, and wherever possible have described the colours in such a manner as to make them self-evident.

The controls give an indication of the time of printing. The figure refers to the year, and the letter to the first or second half of the year, i.e. K 18 indicates use during the first six months of 1918 and L 18 indicates use in the second half of 1918.

Due to the length of time this issue was at press, it is only possible to list the shades in colour groups. The rarer shades, because of their brief appearances, are more precise and distinctive, but the basic shades that traversed the span of twelve years will show minor variations of hue in the published descriptions.

Wherever possible, a rough indication of the year or years when the shade was in use has been noted. This has been made possible by a study of the controls, which indicate the year the plate was at press. Where no dates are given, it must be taken that the colour group is generally spread over the entire issue.

**FUGITIVE INKS.** Experiments with fugitive inks seem to have been made during 1919 and 1920. Many of the values change their appearance when immersed in water, and used specimens of a diffused hue are usually from these printings. The ½d. olive-green of 1916 is also highly fugitive, and produces a bright yellow-green after immersion in water.

**COLOUR VARNISH.** Printings in a heavy thick glossy ink are known on some ½d., 1d., 5d. and 1s. values. These varieties are listed as " varnish ink ", and are probably caused by inadequate mixing of the pigments by the printer.

**PROVISIONAL PRINTINGS.** These are the printings made by both Waterlow and Harrison just prior to the issue of the photogravure stamps. For further information see *King George V. A Study of the Provisional Issues of 1934 and 1935* by J. B. M. Stanton and K. G. Rushworth (Stanley Gibbons Ltd).

**THE CONTROLS.** The system of controls was now extended to all values from ½d. to 1s. As before, the control was screwed into the margin before printing, and removed when printing had ceased. The Somerset House controls all had a stop after the letter which enable these printings to be distinguished.

The controls are listed after their respective values in the catalogue.

**Position.** The Control appears below the 2nd stamp, bottom row, except for the 1d. value, where it is beneath the 11th stamp.

Somerset House Controls with imperf. margins

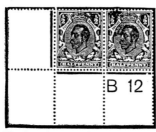

Harrison Control with perf. margin

L 18    Letters and figures with serifs. Used from L 18 onwards.

A 24    Small thick letters and figures, with serifs. Used with Block Cypher wmk.

**53**

**1911–12**

N1

N2

Ornament above P of HALFPENNY
has two thin lines of colour; beard
is undefined

Ornament has one thick line;
beard well defined

**Die 1A.**  The three upper scales on the body
of the right hand dolphin form a triangle.
The centre jewel of the cross inside the crown
is suggested by a comma.

**Die 1B.**  The three upper scales are incomplete.
The centre jewel is suggested by a crescent.

Die 1A       Die 1B

Nos. N1 to N13 were printed by Harrison & Sons except for the preliminary printings
at Somerset House, distinguishable only by the stop controls.

Cat. No.   S.G. No.   Watermark   Die          Shades                    Unused   Used

**1911 (JUNE 22).  ½d. GREEN, TYPE N1, WMK. CROWN.  DIE 1A**

| N1 | 321/23 | W.12 | 1A | (1) Green | 15 | 12 |
|---|---|---|---|---|---|---|
| a. | Watermark inverted | | | (2) Pale green | 30 | 15 |
| b. | Perforation 14 .. | .. | £400 40·00 | (3) Deep green | 60 | 60 |
| s. | " Specimen ", Type 22 | .. | 3·00 | (4) Bluish green | 10·00 | 4·50 |

**Perforation**

Types 1A, 2, 2A, 2C and 3 (rare).

**Plates.**  7 plates have been identified.

**Colour Essays.**  Marked by the colour makers' reference numbers—S.D. (Stamping Department), M.B.
(Manders Bros.), S.P. (Slater and Palmer), W. (Winston) or showing colour numbers only.

Fig. 1

Fig. 1 in various colours on white paper   ..   ..   ..   ..   ..   .. *From* 35·00

**Die Proofs of the accepted design**

Head and frame

Without value on thick glazed paper with reversed figure " 2 " above design:—
 In brown-red, pink or green   ..   ..   ..   ..   ..   ..   .. *Each* 80·00
Varying stages of engraving with value:—
 In black or green   ..   ..   ..   ..   ..   ..   ..   .. *Each* 75·00
Finished die, with figure " 5A " above design:—
 Three different colours   ..   ..   ..   ..   ..   ..   .. *Each* 75·00

Head only

With uncleared surround, in brown-red or violet   ..   ..   ..   .. *Each* 75·00
With cleared surround, in green or black   ..   ..   ..   ..   .. *Each* 60·00

**Plate Proofs**

Imperf. on thick paper in black   ..   ..   ..   ..   ..   ..   .. 15·00
Imperf. on thin card in green ..   ..   ..   ..   ..   ..   ..   .. 15·00
Imperf. in deep green on paper Wmk. Crown   ..   ..   ..   ..   .. 15·00
Perf. 14 on thick paper in green   ..   ..   ..   ..   ..   ..   .. 15·00

| Cat. No. | S.G. No. | Watermark | Die | Shades | Unused | Used |
|---|---|---|---|---|---|---|

**As last, but DIE 1B**

N2    324/26    W.12    1B
a. Watermark inverted    ..    1·00    75
b. Watermark sideways    ..    —    £500
c. Cracked plate    ..    ..    5·00    5·00
d. Gash in Crown, etc.    ..
e. Deep green in varnish ink ..    25·00

(1) Bright green    15    5
(2) Pale bright green    30    10
(3) Yellow-green    15    10
(4) Bright yellow-green    2·00    1·50
(5) Green    30    10
(6) Deep green    1·75    1·00
(7) Very deep green    14·00    8·00
(8) Bluish green    15·00    10·00

N2c

N2d

**Perforation**

Types 1, 1A, 2, 2A, 2C and 3.

**Plates.** 16 plates have been identified.

**Die Proof**

On thick paper in green    ..    60·00

**Plate Proof**

On thick paper in black    ..    15·00

**Booklet panes of six, Die 1B, Wmk. Crown**

NB1    ½d. Green (shades),
       Watermark upright    2·00

NB1a    ½d. Green (shades),
        Watermark inverted    6·00

**½d. Green Controls**

|  |  | I. | P. |  |  | I. | P. |
|---|---|---|---|---|---|---|---|
| NC231 | A 11 (w) Die 1A    .. | 50 | 40 | NC233 | A 11 (w) Die 1B    .. | 50 | 40 |
| aa | Perf. 14    .. | † | £750 | NC233a | A 11 (c) Die 1B    .. | 40 | 40 |
| NC231a | A 11 (c) Die 1A    .. | — | — |  |  |  |  |

(c) "close" and (w) "wide" refer to the space between the figures (1 mm. and 1½ mm. respectively).

**1912 (AUGUST).  ½d. GREEN, TYPE N1, WMK. SIMPLE CYPHER**

N3    334/35    W.14    1B
a. No watermark    ..    ..
b. Watermark inverted    ..    1·00    75
c. Watermark reversed    ..    12·00
d. Watermark inverted and reversed    ..    ..    ..    18·00
e. Deep green in varnish ink ..    20·00
s. "Specimen", Type 22    ..    3·00

(1) Green    60    40
(2) Pale green    60    40
(3) Deep green    3·00    3·00

**Booklet panes of six, Die 1B, Wmk. Simple Cypher**

NB2    ½d. Green (shades),
       watermark upright    4·00

NB2a    ½d. Green (shades),
        watermark inverted    8·00

**Controls**    NONE.    This issue was made for use in booklets only.

Cat. No.   S.G. No.     Watermark    Die      Shades           Unused   Used

**1912 (JANUARY 1). ½d. GREEN, TYPE N2, WMK. CROWN**

| | | | | | | Unused | Used |
|---|---|---|---|---|---|---|---|
| N4 | 338/40 | W.12 | 2 | (1) | Green | 15 | 5 |
| a. | Watermark inverted | .. 15·00 | | (2) | Pale green | 40 | 10 |
| b. | No cross on Crown | .. 4·00 | 2·25 | (3) | Deep green | 1·75 | 50 |
| c. | No cross on Crown and | | | (4) | Myrtle-green | 2·75 | 1·25 |
| | broken frame | .. .. 10·00 | 5·00 | (5) | Bluish green | 4·50 | 2·00 |
| s. | "Specimen", Type 26 | .. 3·00 | | (6) | Yellow-green | 20 | 8 |
| | | | | (7) | Bright yellow-green | 2·50 | 1·50 |

**Perforation**
   Types 1A, 2, 2A and 3

**Plates.** 24 plates have been identified.

**Die Proofs**
   Die 2 head only, with uncleared surround
     In blue-green, red or black .. .. .. .. .. .. .. .. *Each* 60·00
   Improved frame, but still showing the two curved lines at the left of the
   lower ornament, and the fronts of the dolphins' heads have a single line
   of shading as in Die I
     In black on thin card ..   .. .. .. .. .. .. .. .. 20·00
   Ditto. With amended head inserted
     In chestnut on glazed paper ..   .. .. .. .. .. .. .. £100
   Ditto. With Die II frame
     In green on glazed paper   .. .. .. .. .. .. .. .. 80·00
   Proofs are known of an amended die which was used for colour trials (q.v.)
     In black, as above, but single curved line at the left of the lower ornament .. .. 20·00
     In black, as above, but with lines of shading replacing the single line to the fronts of the
     dolphins' heads   .. .. .. .. .. .. .. .. .. 25·00
   Proofs are known of a modified die which is very similar to the approved Die II.
   Used also for colour trials (q.v.)
     Accepted die, in blue-green on thick paper   . .. .. .. .. .. 20·00

**Plate Proofs**
   On thick paper, in black (amended die) or green ..   .. .. .. .. *From* 15·00
   In green on paper Wmk. Crown (upright or sideways) ..   .. .. .. 15·00

**Colour Trials**
   No watermark, Imperf.
     In various colours from the amended die ..   .. .. .. .. *From* 50·00
     In various colours from the modified die ..   .. .. .. .. *From* 50·00
   Watermark Crown (upright or sideways), Imperf.
     In various colours from the amended die ..   .. .. .. .. *From* 50·00
     In various colours from the modified die ..   .. .. .. .. *From* 50·00

**1912 (AUGUST). ½d. GREEN, TYPE N2, WMK. SIMPLE CYPHER**

| | | | | | | Unused | Used |
|---|---|---|---|---|---|---|---|
| N5 | 344 | W.14 | 2 | (1) | Green | 15 | 15 |
| a. | No watermark | .. 20·00 | | (2) | Pale green | 20 | 8 |
| b. | Watermark inverted | .. 2·25 | 1·50 | (3) | Deep green | 35 | 15 |
| c. | Watermark reversed | .. 3·00 | 2·00 | (4) | Yellow-green | 1·00 | 25 |
| d. | Watermark inverted and re- | | | | | | |
| | versed | .. .. 1·00 | 1·00 | | | | |
| e. | No cross on Crown | .. 15·00 | 5·00 | s. | "Specimen", Type 26 .. | 3·00 | |
| ed. | Do. watermark inverted and | | | t. | "Cancelled", Type 24 .. | 3·00 | |
| | reversed | .. .. 30·00 | | | | | |

**1912 (OCTOBER). ½d. GREEN, TYPE N2, WMK. MULTIPLE CYPHER**

| | | | | | | Unused | Used |
|---|---|---|---|---|---|---|---|
| N6 | 346/8 | W.13 | 2 | (1) | Green | 10 | 10 |
| a. | Watermark inverted | .. 60 | | (2) | Pale green | 35 | 15 |
| b. | Watermark reversed | .. 70 | | (3) | Deep green | 50 | 25 |
| c. | Watermark inverted and re- | | | (4) | Yellow-green | 75 | 30 |
| | versed | .. .. 5·00 | | | | | |
| d. | Watermark sideways | .. † | £200 | | | | |
| e. | Crown missing in watermark | 9·00 | | g. | No cross on Crown .. | 20·00 | 7·00 |
| f. | Imperforate | .. .. 10·00 | | | | | |

**Perforation** (Nos. N5 and N6)
   Types 2 or 2A

### ½d. Green Controls, Die 2

Controls with a stop after the letter are from preliminary printings made at Somerset House.

| Wmk. Crown | I. | P. | Wmk. Simple Cypher | I. | P. | Wmk. Multiple Cypher | I. | P. |
|---|---|---|---|---|---|---|---|---|
| *NC104a*  B. 12 .. | — | — | *NC240*  B 12 (c) | 15 | 20 | *NC105a*  B.12 .. | 40·00 | 40·00 |
| *NC235*  B 11 .. | 20 | 30 | *NC240a*  B 12 (w) | 15 | 20 | *NC244*  B 12 (c) | 25 | 35 |
| *NC237*  B 12 (c) | 15 | 15 | *NC242*  B 13 .. | 15 | 20 | *NC244a*  B 12 (w) | 30 | 30 |
| *NC237a*  B 12 (w) | 45 | 35 | | | | | | |

Error. Complete bottom row of sheet (12 stamps):
·*NC239*  None .. 5·00  †

(c) " close " and (w) " wide " refer to the space between " B " and the serif of " 1 " (4½ mm. and 6 mm. respectively).

Watermark varieties.  The following controls are known:—

| Wmk. inverted | .. | .. | .. | NC244, NC244*a* |
|---|---|---|---|---|
| Wmk. reversed | .. | .. | .. | NC244 |
| Wmk. inverted and reversed | .. | NC240, NC240*a* | | |

**N3**

Lion unshaded

**N4**

Lion shaded

Die IA

Die 1B

**Die 1A.**  The second line of shading on the ribbon to the right of the crown extends right across the wreath.  The centre leaf below the right hand ribbon shows a vertical line at left.

**Die 1B.**  The second line of shading is broken in the middle.  The centre leaf shows a dot at left.

| Cat. No.  S.G. No. | Watermark | Die | Shades | Unused | Used |
|---|---|---|---|---|---|

**1911 (JUNE 22).  1d. RED, TYPE N3, WMK. CROWN.  DIE 1A**

| | | | | | |
|---|---|---|---|---|---|
| N 7   327/8 | W.12 | 1A | (1) Carmine-red | 25 | 10 |
| *a.* Experimental printing, Chalk-surfaced paper | .. | | (2) Pale carmine-red | 25 | 10 |
| | .. | 20·00 | (3) Deep carmine-red | 4·00 | 2·00 |
| *b.* No watermark | .. | .. 25·00 | (4) Carmine | 1·50 | 1·00 |
| *c.* Watermark inverted | .. | 30·00 | (5) Pale carmine | 50 | 15 |
| *d.* Perforation 14 | .. | £650 | (6) Rose-pink | 4·50 | 2·50 |
| *e.* No cross on Crown | .. | 22·00 | 22·00 | | |
| *f.* Deep carmine in varnish ink | 15·00 | | | | |
| *g.* White fleur-de-lis (Pl. 4, R. 16/1) | .. | .. 25·00 | 25·00 | | |
| *s.* " Specimen ", Type 22 | .. | 3·00 | | | |

**Perforation**

Types 1A, 2, 2A, 2C and 3

**Plates.**  13 plates have been identified.

**Colour Essays.**  Marked by the colour makers' reference numbers—S.D. (Stamping Department), M.B. (Manders Bros.), W. (Winston) or showing colour numbers only.

Fig. 2

Fig. 2 in various colours on white paper  ..  ..  ..  ..  ..  .. *From* 35·00

## Die Proofs

| | |
|---|---|
| Without value in pink or black on card .. .. .. .. .. .. | *Each* £175 |
| As above, but the lions more heavily engraved .. .. .. .. .. | *Each* £175 |
| Finished die in red, with uncleared surround .. .. .. .. .. | .. 80·00 |

## Plate Proof

| | |
|---|---|
| In red on white paper.  No watermark, imperf. .. .. .. .. .. | .. 15·00 |
| In carmine on white paper.  Watermark Crown, imperf .. .. .. .. | .. 15·00 |

## As last, but DIE 1B

| Cat. No. | S.G. No. | Watermark | Die | | Shades | Unused | Used |
|---|---|---|---|---|---|---|---|
| N8 | 329/31 | W.12 | 1B | (1) | Carmine | 15 | 5 |
| a. | Watermark inverted .. | 75 | 50 | (2) | Pale carmine | 20 | 5 |
| b. | No cross on Crown .. | 20·00 | 15·00 | (3) | Deep carmine | 40 | 10 |
| c. | Do. and damaged Crown | | | (4) | Bright carmine | 40 | 10 |
| | (No. 4 on booklet pane, with | | | (5) | Deep bright carmine | 2·00 | 1·00 |
| | wmk. inverted) .. .. | 25·00 | 25·00 | (6) | Carmine-red | 25 | 5 |
| d. | Do. with damaged frame | | | (7) | Pale carmine-red | 50 | 10 |
| | (No. 6 on booklet pane with | | | (8) | Rose-pink | 2·50 | 1·25 |
| | wmk. inverted) .. .. | 25·00 | 25·00 | | | | |
| e. | Damaged cross on Crown, | | | | | | |
| | and weak frame (No. 6 on | | | | | | |
| | booklet pane with wmk. up- | | | | | | |
| | right) .. .. .. | 22·00 | 22·00 | | | | |
| f. | Carmine, in varnish ink .. | 22·00 | | | | | |

N8*d*

## Perforation

Types 1, 1A, 2, 2A, 2C and 3

**Plates.**  16 plates have been identified.

## Die Proofs

| | |
|---|---|
| In carmine or rose-red on thick paper .. .. .. .. .. .. | *Each* £150 |
| In carmine-pink on paper Watermark Crown.  Two impressions on one piece .. | £250 |

## Plate Proof

| | |
|---|---|
| In carmine on Austrian enamelled paper.  No watermark, imperf. .. .. .. | .. 15·00 |

## Booklet panes of six, Die 1B, Wmk. Crown

| NB3 | 1d. Carmine (shades), water-mark upright | 3·00 | NB3a | 1d. Carmine (shades), watermark inverted | 5·50 |
|---|---|---|---|---|---|

## 1d. Red Controls, Wmk. Crown

Controls with a stop after the letter A are from preliminary printings made at Somerset House.

| | | | I. | P. | | | | I. | P. |
|---|---|---|---|---|---|---|---|---|---|
| NC102 | A. 11 | Die 1A .. | 6·00 | 6·00 | NC103 | A. 11 | Die 1B .. | 30 | 30 |
| NC232 | A 11 (w) | Die 1A .. | 50 | 40 | NC234 | A 11 (w) | Die 1B .. | 3·00 | — |
| NC232a | A 11 (c) | Die 1A .. | 3·00 | 12·00 | NC234a | A 11 (c) | Die 1B .. | 20 | 20 |

(c) " close " and (w)  " wide " refer to the space between the figures (1 mm. and 1½ mm. respectively).

Variety N7*a*.  1d. on chalk-surfaced paper, is known with Somerset House control A. 11

| Cat. No. | S.G. No. | Watermark | Die | Shades | Unused | Used |
|---|---|---|---|---|---|---|

**1912 (JUNE AND AUGUST).   1d. SCARLET, TYPE N3**

| | | | | | | |
|---|---|---|---|---|---|---|
| N9 | 332/3 | W.12 | 1B | (1) Scarlet | 1·50 | 1·00 |
| a. | Watermark inverted | .. | 1·50 | 1·25 | (2) Pale scarlet | 2·50 | 1·50 |
| | | | | (3) Bright scarlet | 1·50 | 1·00 |
| | | | | (4) Aniline scarlet | 15·00 | 8·00 |

| | | | | | | |
|---|---|---|---|---|---|---|
| N10 | 336/7 | W.14 | 1B | (1) Scarlet | 50 | 40 |
| a. | No watermark | .. | .. | (2) Pale scarlet | 1·25 | 75 |
| b. | Watermark inverted | .. | 80 | 60 | (3) Bright scarlet | 50 | 40 |
| c. | Watermark reversed | .. | 20·00 | (4) Deep bright scarlet | 3·00 | 2·50 |
| d. | Wmk. inverted and reversed | — | 15·00 | | |
| e. | Bright scarlet in varnish ink | 15·00 | | |
| s. | "Specimen", Type 22 | .. | 3·00 | | |

**Booklet panes of six.   Die 1B, Wmk. Crown**

NB4   1d. Scarlet, watermark            NB4a   1d. Scarlet, watermark
            upright                12·00                      inverted          12·00
NB4b   1d. Aniline scarlet    £100       NB4c   1d. Aniline scarlet,
                                                                    watermark inverted  £100

**Booklet panes of six.   Die 1B, Wmk. Simple Cypher**

NB5   1d. Scarlet (shades),              NB5a   1d. Scarlet (shades),
            watermark upright   4·00                   watermark inverted   4·00

**Controls.**   NONE.   These issues were made for use in booklets only.

**1912 (JANUARY 1).   1d. SCARLET, TYPE N4.   WMK. CROWN**

| | | | | | | |
|---|---|---|---|---|---|---|
| N11 | 341/3 | W.12 | 2 | (1) Scarlet | 8 | 5 |
| a. | Watermark inverted | .. | 5·00 | (2) Bright scarlet | 8 | 5 |
| b. | No cross on Crown .. | .. | 3·50 | 1·75 | (3) Deep bright scarlet | 50 | 25 |
| ba. | Do. wmk. inverted .. | .. | 30·00 | (4) Very deep bright scarlet | 5·00 | 3·00 |
| c. | No cross on Crown and broken | | (5) Aniline scarlet | 15·00 | 10·00 |
| | frame.. | .. | .. | .. | 10·00 | 5·00 | |
| d. | No cross on Crown shade (5) | £100 | | |
| e. | Coloured blot on O of | | |
| | ONE (Pl. 5, R. 20/10) | .. | 6·00 | | |
| s. | "Cancelled", Type 24 | .. | 3·00 | | |
| t. | "Cancelled", Type 25 | .. | | |

Our prices for the aniline scarlet 1d. stamps, listed above, are for specimens in which the
colour is suffused on the surface of the stamp and shows through clearly on the back.
Specimens without these characteristics, but which show " aniline " reactions under the
quartz lamp are relatively common.

**Perforation**

Types 2 or 2A

**Plates.**   18 plates have been identified.

**1912 (AUGUST).   1d. SCARLET, TYPE N4.   WMK. SIMPLE CYPHER**

| | | | | | | |
|---|---|---|---|---|---|---|
| N12 | 345 | W.14 | 2 | (1) Scarlet | 12 | 5 |
| a. | No watermark | .. | 15·00 | (2) Bright scarlet | 15 | 5 |
| b. | Watermark inverted | .. | 1·50 | 1·50 | (3) Deep bright scarlet | 2·00 | 1·25 |
| c. | Watermark reversed | .. | 1·25 | 1·25 | | |
| d. | Watermark inverted and re- | | ed. | Do. watermark inverted and |
| | versed | .. | .. | 1·25 | 1·25 | | reversed | .. | .. | .. | 18·00 |
| e. | No cross on Crown | .. | 8·00 | 2·50 | f. | No cross on Crown and |
| eb. | Do. watermark inverted | .. | 20·00 | | broken frame | .. | .. | 15·00 | 5·00 |
| ec. | Do. watermark reversed | .. | 30·00 | s. | "Cancelled", Type 24 | .. | |

**Perforation**

Types 2 or 2A

**1912 (OCTOBER).   1d. SCARLET, TYPE N4.   WMK. MULTIPLE CYPHER**

| | | | | | | |
|---|---|---|---|---|---|---|
| N13 | 349/50 | W.13 | 2 | (1) Scarlet | 35 | 20 |
| a. | Watermark inverted | .. | 1·00 | (2) Bright scarlet | 45 | 30 |
| b. | Watermark reversed | .. | 1·00 | (3) Deep bright scarlet | 85 | 60 |
| c. | Watermark inverted and re- | | fb. | Do. watermark reversed | .. | 15·00 |
| | versed | .. | .. | 30·00 | 30·00 | fd. | Do. watermark sideways | .. | 75·00 |
| d. | Watermark sideways | .. | 10·00 | 10·00 | g. | No cross on Crown and |
| e. | Imperforate | .. | 8·00 | | broken frame | .. | .. | 15·00 | 7·00 |
| f. | No cross on Crown | .. | 10·00 | 4·00 | h. | Crown missing in watermark |
| fa. | Do. watermark inverted | .. | 15·00 | | |

**Perforation**

Types 2 or 2A

**Die Proofs**

Unadopted die

The third line of shading in the upper right hand ribbon is complete.
Without value, numbered 42A (reversed) in black or red .. .. .. *Each* 75·00
Showing a white patch on the lion's haunches. In varying stages of completion to the shading on the lion's body
In black or stone .. .. .. .. .. .. .. .. .. *Each* 75·00

Approved die

The second line of shading in the upper right hand ribbon is complete. With or without value, and showing varying stages of completion to the shading on the lion's body, in black .. .. .. .. .. .. .. .. .. .. .. .. 75·00

Accepted die

On Crown watermarked paper with gum, in carmine .. .. .. .. .. £175

**Colour Trials**

Modified die. Both second and fourth lines of shading in the upper right hand ribbon are complete
In blue-geranium .. .. .. .. .. .. .. .. .. 40·00
Amended die. Only the second line of shading in the upper right hand ribbon is complete
In issued colour or Royal Scarlet .. .. .. .. .. .. .. *Each* 40·00
Approved die. Similar to the amended die, but showing less shading in the foliage
In yellow. No watermark, Imperf. .. .. .. .. .. .. .. .. 50·00
Wmk. Crown (upright or sidways), Imperf.
In blue .. .. .. .. .. .. .. .. .. .. .. 50·00
In pink, crimson, 3 shades of carmine, 2 shades of vermilion or scarlet .. .. *From* 20·00
Wmk. Crown, Perf. 14
In vermilion, carmine, brownish carmine, Royal scarlet or brilliant scarlet .. *From* 25·00

**Paper Trials.** No watermark. Imperf.

On Austrian enamelled paper

In carmine or pale carmine (F) .. .. .. .. .. .. .. *Each* 18·00

On wove paper

(*a*) In carmine on John Dickinson extra superfine very white paper .. .. 10·00
(*b*) In carmine on John Allen special finish very thin paper .. .. .. 10·00
(*c*) Ditto Plate glazed on face only .. .. .. .. .. .. 10·00
(*d*) Ditto Plate glazed both sides .. .. .. .. .. .. .. 10·00
(*e*) In scarlet, machine finish (face only) .. .. .. .. .. .. 10·00
(*f*) Ditto but thinner paper .. .. .. .. .. .. .. .. 10·00
(*g*) Ditto on gummed paper .. .. .. .. .. .. .. .. 10·00

**1d. Scarlet Controls, Die 2**

Controls with a stop after the letter are from preliminary printings made at Somerset House.

| Wmk. Crown | | I. | P. | Wmk. Simple Cypher | | I. | P. | Wmk. Multiple Cypher | | I. | P. |
|---|---|---|---|---|---|---|---|---|---|---|---|
| *NC104* | B. 11 .. | 1·25 | 1·25 | *NC241* | B 12 (w) | 25 | 25 | *NC105b* | B. 12 .. | £100 | £110 |
| *NC105* | B. 12 .. | 75 | 75 | *NC243* | B 13 .. | 25 | 25 | *NC245* | B 12 (w) | 50 | 75 |
| *NC236* | B 11 .. | 25 | 25 | | | | | *NC245a* | B 12 (w) | | |
| *NC238* | B 12 (c) | 25 | 25 | | | | | | (Wmk. sideways) | 45·00 | † |
| *NC238a* | B 12 (w) | 25 | 25 | | | | | | | | |

(c) " close " and (w) " wide " refer to the space between " B " and the serif of " 1 " 4¼ mm. and 6 mm. respectively).

Watermark varieties. The following controls are known:—

Wmk. inverted .. .. .. NC241, NC245.
Wmk. reversed .. .. .. NC245.
Wmk. inverted and reversed .. NC241, NC245.

## 1912-22. Wmk. Royal Cypher

N5      N6      N7

N8      N9

Printed by Harrison & Sons, except for the 6d. printed at Somerset House by the Stamping Department of the Board of Inland Revenue, who also made printings of other values which can only be distinguished by the stop controls.

### Perforation

Types 2 or 2A throughout the issue.

In addition, the variety Type 2C, is known on the 1½d., 2d., 4d., 6d. and 1s. values and Types 3 and 3A are known on the 2d. and 6d. values.

Imperforate stamps of this issue exist but may be war-time colour trials.

| Cat. No. | S.G. No. | Wmk. | | | Shades | | | Unused | Used |
|---|---|---|---|---|---|---|---|---|---|

**1913 (JANUARY). ½d. GREEN, TYPE N6**

| | | | | | | | | Unused | Used |
|---|---|---|---|---|---|---|---|---|---|
| N14 | | 351/56 | W.14 Simple Cypher | | (1) | Green | | 5 | 5 |
| a. | Doubly printed | | .. | £500 | (2) | Deep green | | 75 | 15 |
| b. | No watermark | | .. | 4·00 | (3) | Pale green | | 50 | 8 |
| c. | Watermark inverted | | .. 15 | 10 | (4) | Very pale green (1919) | | 2·50 | 1·00 |
| d. | Watermark reversed | | .. 1·50 | 1·50 | (5) | Very deep green (1919) | | 6·50 | 4·00 |
| e. | Watermark inverted and re- | | | | (6) | Bright green | | 8 | 5 |
| | versed | | .. 75 | 75 | (7) | Deep bright green | | 75 | 15 |
| f. | "New Moon" flaw | | .. 25·00 | 25·00 | (8) | Yellow-green | | 1·00 | 25 |
| g. | Cracked plate | | .. | 6·00 | (9) | Dull yellow- ("apple") | | | |
| h. | "Ruffled Hair" (Pl. 28, | | | | | green (1915) | | 2·50 | 1·00 |
| | R.20/1) | | .. | 20·00 | (10) | Very yellow- ("Cyprus") | | | |
| j. | Stop after "HALFPENNY" | | | | | green (1914) | | £140 | |
| | (Pl. 16c, R.19/3) | | .. | 7·00 | (11) | Bright yellow-green | | 6·00 | 2·50 |
| s. | "Specimen", Type 23 | | .. | 1·00 | (12) | Olive-green (1916) | | 7·00 | 6·00 |
| t. | "Specimen", Type 26 | | .. | 3·00 | (13) | Pale olive-green (1916) | | 3·00 | 2·50 |
| u. | Do. Imperf. .. | | .. | 4·00 | (14) | Blue-green (1913 & 1918) | | 5·00 | 2·50 |
| v. | "Cancelled", Type 24 | | .. | 1·00 | (15) | Deep blue- ("Myrtle") | | | |
| w. | Do. Imperf... | | .. | 2·00 | | green | | 10·00 | 7·00 |
| x. | "Cancelled", Type 28 | | .. | 3·00 | (16) | Deep myrtle-green | | 20·00 | 15·00 |
| | | | | | (17) | Cobalt-green (1922) .. | | 1·50 | 1·50 |
| | | | | | (18) | Deep cobalt-green (1922) | | 8·00 | 8·00 |

Var. *f.* is found on the 6th stamp of a booklet pane.

Var. *h.* is only found with control I 16. Printings with the J 17 control are from the re-chromed plate.

Var. *j.* is found on late printings with control G 15, and all printings with control H 16.

Six specimens are known of variety *a*, showing partial double prints in the lower portions of the stamp (control G 15).

Shades (12) and (13) are highly fugitive, and used copies are consequently very rare.

N14*f*                    N14*g*

**Plates**
83 plates have been identified.

Normal Head                    Small Head

**Die Proofs of Accepted Head only believed used for ½d. to 7d. and 1s.**
On glazed card or watermarked paper
Uncleared in black, red or green    ..    ..    ..    ..    ..    ..    .. *From* 30·00
**Small unappropriated head only**
Cleared or uncleared, in black..    ..    ..    ..    ..    ..    ..    .. *Each* 75·00
For Die proofs of accepted head used for the 8d., 9d. and 10d. see under 8d. value.

**Die Proofs of ½d.**
Approved die on thick paper in black, green or scarlet    ..    ..    ..    .. *Each* £175

**Booklet panes**
Panes of six (various shades)

| | | | | | |
|---|---|---|---|---|---|
| NB6 | Watermark upright | 60 | NB6a | Watermark inverted | 1·00 |
| *s.* | " Specimen ", Type 23 .. | 5·00 | *as.* | " Specimen ", Type 23 .. | 5·00 |
| *t.* | " Cancelled ", Type 24 .. | 5·00 | *at.* | " Cancelled ", Type 24 .. | 5·00 |
| *u.* | Cancelled " London E.C." .. | 2·00 | *au.* | Cancelled " London E.C." .. | 2·00 |

**Controls**
Printed at Somerset House.    Wmk. Simple Cypher

| | I. | P. | | I. | P. |
|---|---|---|---|---|---|
| A. Type I | | | B. Type II | | |
| *NC109* B. 13 .. | 10 | 12·00 | *NC109a* B. 13 .. | 75 | † |

Printed by Harrison & Sons
**A. Wmk. Simple Cypher, Type I**

| | I. | P. | | I. | P. |
|---|---|---|---|---|---|
| *NC248a* C 13 .. | 10 | 12 | *NC261a* D 14 .. | 1·00 | 1·50 |

**B. Wmk. Simple Cypher, Type II**

| | I. | P. | | I. | P. | | I. | P. |
|---|---|---|---|---|---|---|---|---|
| *NC248* | C 13 .. | 10 | 10 | *NC331a* J 17 .. | 15 | 15 | *NC432a* Q 21 .. | 25 | 60 |
| *NC256* | C 14 .. | 15 | 15 | *NC344a* K 17 .. | — | 2·00 | *NC441a* R 21 .. | — | 8·50 |
| *NC261* | D 14 .. | 10 | 10 | *NC354a* K 18 .. | † | 8·00 | *NC474a* T 22 .. | 2·00 | 3·00 |
| *NC273* | E 14 .. | 10 | 10 | *NC391a* N 19 .. | 1·00 | 75 | *NC486a* U 22 .. | 15 | 15 |
| *NC279* | F 15 .. | 10 | 10 | *NC402a* O 19 .. | 1·50 | 5·50 | *NC493* U 23 .. | 10 | 10 |
| *NC292* | G 15 .. | 10 | 10 | *NC410a* O 20 .. | 15 | 25 | *NC504* V 23 .. | 10 | 10 |
| *NC305* | H 16 .. | 10 | 15 | *NC419a* P 20 .. | — | † | *NC514* W 23 .. | 15 | 15 |
| *NC318* | I 16 .. | 10 | 10 | | | | *NC519* W 24 .. | 1·00 | 1·00 |

C. Wmk. Simple Cypher, Type III

| | | | | | | | | | | |
|---|---|---|---|---|---|---|---|---|---|---|
| NC331 | J 17 .. | 10 | 10 | NC402 | O 19 .. | 10 | 10 | NC462 | S 22 .. | 10 | 10 |
| NC344 | K 17 .. | 10 | 10 | NC410 | O 20 .. | 10 | 10 | NC474 | T 22 .. | 10 | 10 |
| NC354 | K 18 .. | 10 | 10 | NC419 | P 20 .. | 10 | 10 | NC486 | U 22 .. | 10 | 10 |
| NC361 | L 18 .. | 10 | 10 | NC426 | Q 20 .. | 10 | 10 | NC493a | U 23 .. | 15 | 15 |
| NC373 | M 18 .. | 10 | 10 | NC432 | Q 21 .. | 10 | 10 | NC504a | V 23 .. | 1·00 | 1·00 |
| NC384 | M 19 .. | 15 | 15 | NC441 | R 21 .. | 10 | 10 | NC514a | W23 .. | 35 | 25 |
| NC391 | N 19 .. | 10 | 10 | NC450 | S 21 .. | 15 | 15 | | | | |

| Cat. No. | S.G. No. | Wmk. | Shades | Unused | Used |
|---|---|---|---|---|---|
| **1913 (AUGUST).** | | **½d. GREEN, TYPE N6** | | | |
| N 15 | 397 | W.13 Multiple Cypher | (1) Bright green | 6·00 | 5·00 |
| a. | Block of four | .. 75·00 | (2) Green | 6·00 | 5·00 |
| b. | Pair showing coil join | .. 15·00 | | | |
| c. | Watermark inverted | .. 30·00 | | | |
| d. | Crown missing in wmk. | .. 15·00 | | | |

Originally issued in vertical rolls of 480 stamps. Subsequently a sheet or part sheet was found, so that horizontal pairs and blocks are known.

**Control.** Wmk. Multiple Cypher

| | I. | P. |
|---|---|---|
| NC245b | C 13 .. — | — |

**Watermark varieties.** The following controls are known:—

Wmk. inverted .. .. .. NC109, 248, 256, 273, 279, 292, 305, 318, 331, 344, 354, 361, 373, 384, 391, 402, 410, 419, 426, 432, 441, 450, 474, 493, 504, 514, 519.

Wmk. reversed .. .. .. NC109, 248, 256, 279, 292, 305, 331, 344, 361, 384, 419, 450, 474.

Wmk. inverted and reversed .. NC109, 248, 256, 261, 273, 279, 292, 305, 318, 331, 344, 354, 361, 373, 384, 391, 402, 410, 419, 426, 432, 441, 462, 474, 486, 493, 504.

**1912 (OCTOBER).** 1d. RED, TYPE N5

| N 16 | 357/61 | W.14 Simple Cypher | | (1) Bright scarlet | 8 | 5 |
|---|---|---|---|---|---|---|
| a. | No watermark | .. | 4·00 | (2) Deep bright scarlet | 80 | 50 |
| b. | Watermark inverted | .. | 12 | 5 | (3) Scarlet | 8 | 5 |
| c. | Watermark reversed | .. | 75 | 75 | (4) Deep scarlet | 40 | 15 |
| d. | Watermark inverted and re- | | | | (5) Brick-red | 30 | 10 |
| | versed | .. .. | 45 | 15 | (6) Deep brick-red | 1·25 | 45 |
| e. | Tête-bêche (pair) .. | .. | £800 | (7) Vermilion | 30 | 10 |
| f. | Printed on the back* | .. | 75·00 | (8) Pale red | 1·00 | 40 |
| g. | Varnish ink (Control C.13) | | 15·00 | (9) Pale rose-red | 20 | 5 |
| h. | Q for O (Control E 14, | | | (10) Pink | 10·00 | 6·00 |
| | R. 1/4) .. .. .. | | 28·00 | 15·00 | (11) Carmine-red | 1·10 | 35 |
| i. | Q for O (Control T 22, | | | (12) Bright carmine-red | 1.10 | 35 |
| | R. 4/11)† .. .. | | 35·00 | 20·00 | (13) Deep carmine-red | 3·00 | 1·00 |
| j. | Reversed Q for O (Control | | | (14) Scarlet-vermilion | 5·00 | 3·00 |
| | T 22, R. 15/9) .. .. | | 35·00 | 20·00 | (15) Orange-vermilion (1917- |
| k. | Inverted Q for O (R. 20/3) .. | | 50·00 | 19) | 8·00 | 4·75 |
| l. | Broken frame (Pl. 17, | | | 16) Deep orange-vermilion |
| | R. 19/12) .. .. | | 7·00 | (1918) | 15·00 | 8·00 |
| m. | Broken corner (Pl. 43, | | | | | |
| | R. 19/10) .. .. | | 3·50 | | | |
| s. | " Specimen ", Type 23 .. | | 1·00 | | | |
| t. | " Specimen ", Type 26 .. | | 3·00 | | | |
| u. | Do. Imperf.. .. .. | | 4·00 | | | |
| v. | " Specimen ", Type 30 (from | | | | | |
| | trial coils) .. .. | | 3·00 | | | |
| w. | " Cancelled ", Type 24 .. | | 1·00 | | | |
| x. | Do. Imperf.. .. .. | | 2·00 | | | |

*The impression on variety f is set sideways, and is very pale.

N16i

N16i

N16j

N16h

N16k

N16l          N16m

†There are two versions of variety i as illustrated but it is not known if they occur in different positions or whether one is a second state of the other.

**Plates**
120 plates have been identified

## 1d.   Colour Trials, 1912

Colour trials were made in eight different shades of red on paper with Simple Cypher watermark, perforated 15 × 14.

They were made from plates of 240 each with Control $\dfrac{C}{X}\dfrac{8}{12}$ in the bottom margin together with a One Penny stamp of King Edward VII which was left imperforate.

As with the colour essays of the 1911 issue some were marked with the colour makers' reference numbers as shown below. The colours in the second column are as we would describe them.

| Inscribed | shade |
|---|---|
| A M/B Scarlet 25568 | Pale scarlet-vermilion |
| B M/B Scarlet 25569 | Scarlet-vermilion |
| C     — | Deep scarlet-vermilion |
| D     — | Scarlet |
| E M/B Scarlet 25602 | Bright scarlet |
| F S.E. 3181 | Rose-red |
| G     — | Deep rose-red |
| H Blue Geranium | Carmine-lake |

As far as is known only two sheets of each were prepared, one of which is in the Royal Collection.

Prices

In carmine-lake (" Blue
 Geranium ") .. .. 25·00
In the other seven shades
                    *Each* 10·00
Block of twelve as illustrated
            *Each trial from*  £500

## Master Die Proofs

Without value. The dies for the 1d. and 2½d. plates were made from this master die.

Progressive proofs in black or red .. .. .. .. .. .. .. *From* £150
Finished die in red, blue, deep blue or Prussian blue .. .. .. .. *Each* £150

## Die Proofs

Finished die with value, in black, blue or issued colour.. .. .. .. *Each* £175

## Plate Proofs. On thick paper or card

Wmk. Crown (vertical or sideways) in blue or red.. .. .. .. .. *From* 30·00
Without watermark in blue or red .. .. .. .. .. .. *From* 35·00
Wmk. Simple Cypher in the issued colour .. .. .. .. .. .. 35·00

## Booklet panes

Panes of six (various shades)

| | | | | | | |
|---|---|---|---|---|---|---|
| NB7 | Watermark upright | | 50 | NB7a | Watermark inverted | 1·00 |
| *s.* | " Specimen ", Type 23 | .. | 8·00 | *as.* | " Specimen ", Type 23 .. | 8·00 |
| *t.* | " Cancelled ", Type 24 | .. | 8·00 | *at.* | " Cancelled ", Type 24 .. | 8·00 |
| *u.* | Cancelled " London E.C." | .. | 4·00 | *au.* | Cancelled " London E.C." | 4·00 |

## Controls

Printed by Harrison & Son

### A. Wmk. Simple Cypher, Type I

| | | | I. | P. | | | I. | P. |
|---|---|---|---|---|---|---|---|---|
| NC246 | C 12 | . | 10 | 10 | NC248a C 13 .. | | 10 | 15 |

### B. Wmk. Simple Cypher, Type II

| | | I. | P. | | | I. | P. | | | I. | P. |
|---|---|---|---|---|---|---|---|---|---|---|---|
| NC249 | C 13 .. | 10 | 10 | NC332a | J 17 .. | 10 | 10 | NC442a | R 21 .. | 75 | 60 |
| NC257 | C 14 .. | 10 | 10 | NC345a | K 17 .. | 1·00 | 2·00 | NC463a | S 22 .. | — | — |
| NC262 | D 14 .. | 10 | 10 | NC355a | K 18 .. | — | — | NC475a | T 22 .. | † | 60 |
| NC274 | E 14 .. | 10 | 10 | NC392a | N 19 .. | 40 | 40 | NC487a | U 22 .. | 20 | 20 |
| NC280 | F 15 .. | 10 | 10 | NC403a | O 19 .. | 1·00 | 1·00 | NC494 | U 23 .. | 10 | 10 |
| NC293 | G 15 .. | 10 | 10 | NC411a | O 20 .. | 1·25 | 1·25 | NC505 | V 23 .. | 10 | 10 |
| NC306 | H 16 .. | 10 | 10 | NC420a | P 20 .. | — | † | NC515 | W23 .. | 15 | 12 |
| NC319 | I 16 .. | 15 | 15 | NC433a | Q 21 .. | 75 | 75 | NC520 | W24 .. | 1·00 | 1 00 |

### C. Wmk. Simple Cypher Type III

| | | I. | P. | | | I. | P. | | | I. | P. |
|---|---|---|---|---|---|---|---|---|---|---|---|
| NC332 | J 17 .. | 10 | 10 | NC385 | M 19 .. | 15 | 15 | NC451 | S 21 .. | 10 | 10 |
| NC345 | K 17 .. | 10 | 10 | NC392 | N 19 .. | 10 | 10 | NC463 | S 22 .. | 10 | 10 |
| NC355 | K 18 .. | 10 | 10 | NC403 | O 19 .. | 10 | 10 | NC475 | T 22 .. | 10 | 10 |
| NC362 | L 18 .. | 10 | 10 | NC411 | O 20 .. | 10 | 10 | NC487 | U 22 .. | 10 | 10 |
| NC374 | M 18 .. | 15 | 15 | NC420 | P 20 .. | 10 | 10 | NC494a | U 23 .. | 10 | 10 |
| NC374a | " M " | | | NC427 | Q 20 .. | 10 | 10 | NC505a | V 23 .. | 1·50 | 1·50 |
| | only (18 | | | NC433 | Q 21 .. | 10 | 10 | NC515a | W23 .. | 50 | 40 |
| | omitted) | 40·00 | — | NC442 | R 21 .. | 10 | 10 | NC520a | W24 .. | 1·00 | 1·00 |

Watermark Varieties. The following controls are known:—

Wmk. inverted .. .. .. NC246, 248, 262, 274, 280, 293, 319, 332, 345, 355, 362, 388, 392, 411,
420, 427, 433, 442, 451, 463, 475, 494, 505, 515, 520.
Wmk. reversed .. .. .. NC246, 248, 262, 293, 306, 319, 345, 362, 385, 420, 427, 442, 451, 475.
Wmk. inverted and reversed .. NC246, 248, 257, 262, 274, 280, 293, 306, 319, 332, 345, 355, 362, 374,
385, 392, 403, 411, 420, 427, 433, 442, 463, 475, 494, 505, 515, 520.

| Cat No. | S.G. No. | Wmk. | | Shades | | Unused | Used |
|---|---|---|---|---|---|---|---|

## 1913 (AUGUST). 1d. RED, TYPE N5

| | | | | | | | |
|---|---|---|---|---|---|---|---|
| N17 | 398 | W.13 Multiple Cypher | | (1) Scarlet | | 9·00 | 7·00 |
| *a.* | Block of four | .. | 75·00 | (2) Dull scarlet | | 9·00 | 7·00 |
| *b.* | Pair showing coil join | .. | 20·00 | | | | |
| *c.* | Watermark inverted | .. | 30·00 | | | | |
| *d.* | Crown missing in wmk. | .. | 15·00 | | | | |

The note after No. N15 also applies here.

### Control. Wmk. Multiple Cypher

| | | I. | P. |
|---|---|---|---|
| NC245c | C 13 .. | — | † |

| Cat. No | S.G. No. | Wmk. | Shades | Unused | Used |
|---|---|---|---|---|---|

**1912 (OCTOBER). 1½d. RED-BROWN, TYPE N6**

| | | | |
|---|---|---|---|
| N18 | 362/65 | W 14 Simple Cypher | |
| a. | No watermark | .. .. 14·00 | |
| b. | Watermark inverted | .. 50 | 25 |
| c. | Watermark reversed | .. 1·25 | 1·00 |
| d. | Watermark inverted and reversed | .. .. 1·00 | 90 |
| e. | Error PENCF (Pl. 12, R.15/12) .. .. | .. 20·00 | 15·00 |
| f. | Error PENCF (Pl. 29, R.15/12) .. .. | .. 7·00 | 5·00 |
| g. | Corrected error (Pl. 12, R.15/12) .. .. | .. £100 | |
| h. | Corrected error (Pl. 29, R.15/12) .. .. | .. 60·00 | |
| s. | " Specimen ", Type 23 | .. 1·00 | |
| t. | " Specimen ", Type 26 | .. 3·00 | |
| u. | " Cancelled ", Type 24 | .. 1·00 | |

| | Shades | Unused | Used |
|---|---|---|---|
| (1) | Red-brown | 5 | 5 |
| (2) | Pale red-brown | 75 | 50 |
| (3) | Deep red-brown | 12 | 8 |
| (4) | Very deep red-brown (1922) | 12·00 | 5·00 |
| (5) | Chocolate-brown | 12 | 8 |
| (6) | Deep chocolate-brown (1918-19) | 2·50 | 1·00 |
| (7) | Chocolate (1919) | 6·00 | 3·00 |
| (8) | Brown (1918) | 25·00 | 25·00 |
| (9) | Pale brown (1918) | 20·00 | 15·00 |
| (10) | Yellow-brown (1916-18) | 2·00 | 1·25 |
| (11) | Deep yellow-brown (1916) | 3·00 | 2·00 |
| (12) | Bright yellow-brown (1920-21) | 2·50 | 1·25 |
| (13) | Chestnut | 40 | 5 |
| (14) | Bright chestnut (1922-23) | 2·50 | 1·00 |
| (15) | Orange-brown (1919-20) | 45 | 10 |
| (16) | Bright orange-brown (1920) | 5·00 | 2·00 |

N18e      N18f      N18h
Thin rule     Thick rules

Fig. 3

Fig. 4

**Perforation**

Variety Type 2C is known with controls C13 and J17 (*Price £6 each in strip of* 3).

**Plates.** 47 plates have been identified.

**Die Proofs** of the accepted design

| | |
|---|---|
| Finished die in black on white glazed card .. .. .. .. .. .. .. 75·00 |
| Finished die in brown on wove paper .. .. .. .. .. .. .. 40·00 |
| Finished die in red or brown on paper, Wmk. W. 14 .. .. .. .. *Each* 40·00 |

**Colour Essays**

Fig. 3. Various colours on white paper (*See* ½d., 1911 *value*) .. .. .. *From* 25·00
Engraver's Sketch Die, Fig. 4
   In black on thick glazed paper .. .. .. .. .. .. .. 60·00
   On card; in brown, yellow-brown, chocolate-brown, turquoise-green, purple or
     violet .. .. .. .. .. .. .. .. .. *Each* 25·00
   On thin wove paper; in magenta, red-brown or chocolate-brown .. .. *Each* 25·00

**Booklet panes**

Panes of six (various shades)

| | | | | | | |
|---|---|---|---|---|---|---|
| NB8 | Watermark upright | 1·50 | | NB8a | Watermark inverted | 3·50 |
| s. | " Specimen ", Type 23 .. | 7·00 | | as. | " Specimen ", Type 23 .. | 7·00 |
| t. | " Cancelled ", Type 24 .. | 7·00 | | at. | " Cancelled ", Type 24 .. | 7·00 |
| u. | Cancelled " London E.C." .. | 5·00 | | au. | Cancelled " London E.C." .. | 5·00 |

Panes of four with two advertisement labels *se-tenant*.

| | | | | | |
|---|---|---|---|---|---|
| NB9 | Watermark upright | 12·00 | | NB9a | Watermark inverted | 12·00 |

## Controls

Printed at Somerset House
Wmk. Simple Cypher, Type I

|  |  | I. | P. |  |  |  | I. | P. |
|---|---|---|---|---|---|---|---|---|
| *NC106* | A. 12 (w) | 25 | 5·00 | *NC106a* | A. 12 (c) | | 25 | — |

(c) and (w) refer to close and wide spacing (1¾ mm. and 4 mm. between "A" and the serif of " 1 " respectively).

Printed by Harrison & Sons
A. Wmk. Simple Cypher, Type I

| | | | | |
|---|---|---|---|---|
| *NC250a* | C 13 | | 30 | 25 |

B. Wmk. Simple Cypher, Type II

|  |  | I. | P. |  |  | I. | P. |  |  | I. | P. |
|---|---|---|---|---|---|---|---|---|---|---|---|
| *NC250* | C 13 .. | 15 | 15 | *NC356b* | K 18 .. | † | 3·00 | *NC488* | U 22 .. | 15 | 15 |
| *NC263* | D 14 .. | 15 | 15 | *NC363a* | L 18 .. | 4·00 | 2·50 | *NC495* | U 23 .. | 15 | 15 |
| *NC281* | F 15 .. | 45 | 30 | *NC393a* | N 19 .. | 1·00 | 50 | *NC506* | V 23 .. | 15 | 15 |
| *NC294* | G 15 .. | 15 | 15 | *NC404a* | O 19 .. | 4·00 | 3·50 | *NC516* | W23 .. | 20 | 20 |
| *NC307* | H 16 .. | 25 | 20 | *NC412a* | O 20 .. | 25 | 25 | *NC521* | W24 .. | 2·00 | 2·00 |
| *NC333a* | J 17 .. | 75 | 1·00 | *NC434a* | Q 21 .. | — | 1·00 | | | | |

C. Wmk. Simple Cypher, Type III

|  |  | | |  |  | | |  |  | | |
|---|---|---|---|---|---|---|---|---|---|---|---|
| *NC333* | J 17 .. | 50 | 35 | *NC386a* | 19 only | | | *NC434* | Q 21 .. | 20 | 30 |
| *NC356* | K 18 .. | 1·00 | 1·00 | | (M omitted) | | | *NC476* | T 22 .. | 15 | 15 |
| *NC356a* | 18 only | | | *NC393* | N 19 .. | 15 | 15 | *NC488a* | U 22 .. | 25 | 20 |
| | (K omitted) | 18·00 | 22·00 | *NC404* | O 19 .. | 15 | 15 | *NC495a* | U 23 .. | 25 | 20 |
| *NC363* | L 18 .. | 15 | 15 | *NC412* | O 20 .. | 15 | 15 | *NC506a* | V 23 .. | 2·00 | 2·00 |
| *NC375* | M 18 .. | 20 | 20 | *NC428* | Q 20 .. | 30 | 30 | *NC516a* | W23 .. | 30 | 20 |
| *NC386* | M 19 .. | 15 | 15 | | | | | | | | |

Watermark varieties.  The following controls are known:—

| | | |
|---|---|---|
| Wmk. inverted | .. | NC363, 375, 386, 393, 404, 412, 434, 476, 488, 495, 506. |
| Wmk. reversed | .. | NC363, 393, 434, 476, 488, 495. |
| Wmk. inverted and reversed | .. | NC106, 250, 263, 281, 294, 363, 375, 386, 393, 404, 412, 428, 434, 476, 488, 495, 506, 516. |

| Die I | Die II |
|---|---|
| Inner frame line at top and sides close to solid of background. *Four* complete lines of shading between top of head and oval frame-line. White line round " TWOPENCE " thin. | Inner frame-line farther from solid of background. *Three* lines between top of head and oval. White line round " TWO-PENCE " thicker. |

| Cat. No. | S.G. No. | Wmk. | | | Shades | Unused | Used |
|---|---|---|---|---|---|---|---|

### 1912 (AUGUST).   2d. ORANGE, TYPE N7.   DIE I

| Cat. No. | S.G. No. | Wmk. | | | Shades | Unused | Used |
|---|---|---|---|---|---|---|---|
| N19 | 366/69 | W.14 Simple Cypher | | | (1) Orange-yellow (1912) | 50 | 25 |
| a. | No watermark | .. | 10·00 | | (2) Reddish orange (1913) | 25 | 5 |
| b. | Watermark inverted | .. | 1·00 | 75 | (3) Deep reddish orange | | |
| c. | Watermark reversed | .. | 1·30 | 1·00 | (1916) | 5·00 | 3·00 |
| d. | Watermark inverted and reversed | .. | 1·00 | 75 | (4) Pale orange | 12 | 10 |
| e. | Frame line double (1) | .. | 6·00 | | (5) Orange | 8 | 5 |
| f. | Broken frame at left (Pl. 14, R.19/1) | .. | 6·00 | | (6) Brown-orange (1921) | 2·00 | 1·25 |
| | | | | | (7) Bright orange | 25 | 5 |
| s. | " Specimen ", Type 26 | .. | 3·00 | | (8) Deep bright orange | 50 | 20 |
| t. | " Cancelled ", Type 24 | .. | | | (9) Intense bright orange | 25·00 | 10·00 |

Variety *e* occurs between the 6th and 7th stamps in some rows of the sheet.

Shade (9) is a printing in fugitive ink, highly suffused, and showing through to the back of the stamp.

The change of colour from orange-yellow to reddish orange in 1913 was deliberate.

**Perforation**

    Normally Types 2 or 2A, but most control pieces from C.13 show Types 3A or 2C.

**Plates.**  20 plates have been identified.

**Die Proofs** of the accepted design

    In black on white glazed card.  Varying stages of completion  ..    ..    .. *From* 75·00

**Plate Proofs**

    Special plate of four on surfaced paper in black or orange  ..    .. *Per block* £250

**Colour Trials**

    Imperf. on gummed paper

        In cadmium orange, bright green, magenta or the issued colour ..    ..    .. *From*  35·00

    Fig. 5           Fig. 6           Fig. 7

**Colour Essays**

    Fig. 5.  Various colours on white or tinted paper (*See* ½d., 1911 *value*)  .. *From* 25·00

    Engraver's Sketch Die

**Fig. 6 (without value)**

    In Die Proof form in red  ..    ..    ..  ..  ..  ..  ..  .. 80·00

    No watermark, in black or pink  ..    ..    ..  ..  ..  ..  .. 40·00

    Wmk. Crown, in brown  ..    ..  ..  ..  ..  ..  ..  .. 40·00

**Fig. 7 (with value)**

    In Die Proof form in black on white glazed card  ..    ..    .. *From* 60·00

    In black with faulty head  ..    ..    ..  ..  ..  .. 50·00

    In black with correct head  ..    ..    ..  ..  ..  .. 50·00

    In bistre, Wmk. Crown Perf. 15 × 14  ..    ..  ..  ..  .. £250

**Booklet Panes**

Panes of six (Die I)

NB10  Watermark upright   4·00          NB 10a Watermark inverted  8·00

  *s.*  Cancelled " London E.C." ..  6·00        *as.* Cancelled " London E.C." ..  8·00

**Controls**

Printed at Somerset House.  Wmk. Simple Cypher, Type I

                             I.      P.

*NC114*    C. 13 ..    ..    ..    50      50

Printed by Harrison & Sons

**A. Wmk. Simple Cypher, Type I**

*NC247*  NONE (left corner pair)..   3·00     3·00

**B. Wmk. Simple Cypher, Type II**

| | | I. | P. | | | | I. | P. | | | | I. | P. |
|---|---|---|---|---|---|---|---|---|---|---|---|---|---|
| *NC258* | C 14 .. | 25 | 20 | *NC321* | I 16 .. | | 20 | 1·50 | *NC413a* | O 20 .. | | 3·50 | 2·00 |
| *NC264* | D 14 .. | 20 | 20 | *NC334a* | J 17 .. | | | 35 | *NC421a* | P 20 .. | | — | † |
| *NC282* | F 15 .. | 20 | 30 | *NC347a* | K 17 .. | 4·00 | | † | *NC435a* | Q 21 .. | | 25 | 40 |
| *NC295* | G 15 .. | 20 | 20 | *NC394a* | N 19 .. | 1·25 | | † | *NC443a* | R 21 .. | | 75 | 75 |
| *NC308* | H 16 .. | 20 | 18·00 | *NC405a* | O 19 .. | 5·00 | | — | *NC477a* | T 22 .. | | — | — |

**C. Wmk. Simple Cypher, Type III**

| | | I. | P. | | | | I. | P. | | | | I. | P. |
|---|---|---|---|---|---|---|---|---|---|---|---|---|---|
| *NC334* | J 17 .. | 20 | 40 | *NC405* | O 19 .. | | 25 | 6·50 | *NC443* | R 21 .. | | 20 | 20 |
| *NC347* | K 17 .. | 20 | 1·50 | *NC413* | O 20 .. | | 20 | 20 | *NC453* | S 21 .. | | 30 | 30 |
| *NC364* | L 18 .. | 20 | 15 | *NC421* | P 20 .. | | 20 | 20 | *NC465* | S 22 .. | | 30 | 30 |
| *NC387* | M 19 .. | 35 | 75 | *NC429* | Q 20 .. | | 20 | 20 | *NC477* | T 22 .. | | 35 | 35 |
| *NC394* | N 19 .. | 20 | 75 | *NC435* | Q 21 .. | | 20 | 20 | | | | | |

Watermark varieties.  The following controls are known:—

    Wmk. inverted  ..    ..    .. NC247, 308, 321, 347, 387, 394, 413, 421, 429, 435, 453.

    Wmk. reversed  ..    ..    .. NC247, 295, 321, 421.

    Wmk. inverted and reversed  .. NC114, 247, 295, 308, 321, 364, 387, 394, 405, 413, 421, 429, 435, 443,

                                         453, 477.

Cat. No.  S.G. No.                 Wmk.                    Shades              Unused  Used

## 1921 (SEPTEMBER).  2d. ORANGE, TYPE N7.  DIE II

| | | | | | | |
|---|---|---|---|---|---|---|
| N20 | 370 | W.14 Simple Cypher | | (1) Orange | 40 | 15 |
| a. | No watermark .. .. | | | (2) Pale orange | 40 | 15 |
| b. | Watermark inverted .. | 2·00 | 1·50 | (3) Deep orange | 80 | 30 |
| c. | Watermark inverted and reversed .. .. | 3·00 | 3·00 | (4) Bright orange | 80 | 30 |
| s. | " Specimen ", Type 15 .. | | | | | |
| t. | " Specimen ", Type 23 .. | | | | | |

### Plates

6 Plates have been identified.

### Booklet panes

Panes of six (Die II)

| | | | |
|---|---|---|---|
| NB11 Watermark upright | 5·00 | NB11a Watermark inverted | 14·00 |
| s. Cancelled " London E.C." .. | 4·00 | s. Cancelled " London E.C." .. | 8·00 |

### Controls

Printed by Harrison & Sons

A. Wmk. Simple Cypher, Type II

| | | I. | P. | | | I. | P. | | | I. | P. |
|---|---|---|---|---|---|---|---|---|---|---|---|
| NC478a | T 22 .. | 2·00 | 65 | NC496a | U 23 .. | 1·00 | 75 | NC517 | W 23 .. | 60 | 60 |
| NC489 | U 22 .. | 60 | 60 | NC507 | V 23 .. | 60 | 60 | NC522 | W 24 .. | 2·00 | 2·50 |

B. Wmk. Simple Cypher, Type III

| | | I. | P. | | | I. | P. | | | I. | P. |
|---|---|---|---|---|---|---|---|---|---|---|---|
| NC454 | S 21 .. | 60 | 60 | NC489a | U 22 .. | 75 | 75 | NC517a | W 23 .. | 75 | 60 |
| NC466 | S 22 .. | 60 | 60 | NC496 | U 23 .. | 60 | 60 | | | | |
| NC478 | T 22 .. | 60 | 60 | NC507a | V 23 .. | 15·00 | 1·50 | | | | |

Watermark varieties.  The following controls are known:—

> Wmk. inverted .. .. .. NC466, 517, 522.
> Wmk. inverted and reversed .. NC454, 466, 478, 496, 517, 522.

## 1912 (OCTOBER).  2½d. BLUE, TYPE N5

| | | | | | | |
|---|---|---|---|---|---|---|
| N21 | 371/73 | W.14 Simple Cypher | | (1) Cobalt- blue (1912-14) | 20 | 8 |
| a. | No watermark .. .. | 25·00 | | (2) Cobalt-violet-blue (1912) | 3·00 | 2·00 |
| b. | Watermark inverted .. | 2·50 | 1·50 | (3) French blue (1913-16) | 20 | 8 |
| c. | Watermark reversed .. | 1·50 | 1·25 | (4) Bright blue (1914-17) | 10 | 5 |
| d. | Watermark inverted and reversed .. .. .. | 1·50 | 1·75 | (5) Deep bright blue (1916) | 25·00 | |
| s. | " Specimen ", Type 15 .. | | | (6) Milky blue (1917) | 75 | 50 |
| t. | " Specimen ", Type 23 .. | 1·50 | | (7) Pale milky blue (1917) | 18·00 | |
| u. | " Specimen ", Type 26 .. | 3·00 | | (8) Powder blue (1918) | 30 | 25 |
| v. | Imperf. optd. " Cancelled ", Type 24 .. .. .. | 4·00 | | (9) Violet-blue (1918) | 3·00 | 2·00 |
| | | | | (10) Blue | 10 | 8 |
| | | | | (11) Pale blue (1917-19) | 20 | 8 |

Shade (7) is from a worn printing of Plate 1 (Control J 17).  Shades (14), (15), (16) are printed in fugitive ink; used copies in the correct shades are consequently very rare.  Most printings of shade (12) Control P 20 are also fugitive.

Shade (15) was formerly described as indigo-blue and should not be confused with shade (17) which is a duller Prussian blue which is unlike the rare Prussian blue shade of the 2½d. Jubilee issue.

| | | |
|---|---|---|
| (12) Deep blue (1920-22) | 30 | 8 |
| (13) Dull blue (1920) | 15 | 10 |
| (14) Indigo-blue (1920) | 20·00 | 20·00 |
| (15) Deep dull blue (toned paper) (1920) | £100 | £100 |
| (16) Royal blue (1920) | 20·00 | 20·00 |
| (17) Dull Prussian blue (1921) | 50·00 | 50·00 |
| (18) Ultramarine | 20 | 8 |

### Perforation

Variety Type 2C is known with control C14  ..  ..  ..  ..  ..  *Strip of 3* 5·00

**Plates.**  12 Plates have been identified.

**Die Proof** of the accepted design

In blue on thick paper  ..  ..  ..  ..  ..  ..  ..  ..  ..  £175

Fig. 8                    Fig. 9

## Colour Essays

Fig. 8.   Various colours on white paper (*See* ½d., 1911 *value*)   ..   ..   .. *From* 25·00

Engraver's Sketch Die.   Fig. 9 in black on thin card

Four stages, differing in the lettering " TWO PENCE HALFPENNY "   .. *From* 80·00
Fig. 9.  Wmk. Crown Perf. 15 × 14, in indigo-blue   ..   ..   ..   .. £250

## Controls

Printed at Somerset House.   Wmk. Simple Cypher

| | | I. | P. | | | I. | P. |
|---|---|---|---|---|---|---|---|
| A. Type I | | | | B. Type II | | | |
| NC107 | A. 12 .. .. .. | 30 | 25·00 | NC130 | J. 17 .. .. .. | 12·00 | † |

Printed by Harrison & Sons

**A. Wmk. Simple Cypher, Type I**

NC251a   C 13   ..   ..   ..   25     30

**B. Wmk. Simple Cypher, Type II**

| | | I. | P. | | | I. | P. | | | I. | P. |
|---|---|---|---|---|---|---|---|---|---|---|---|
| NC251 | C 13 .. | 25 | 25 | NC309 | H 16 .. | 25 | 25 | NC377a | M 18 .. | — | † |
| NC259 | C 14 .. | 20 | 25 | NC322 | I 16 .. | 25 | 40 | NC414a | O 20 .. | 5·00 | 4·50 |
| NC265 | D 14 .. | 1·25 | 1·25 | NC335a | J 17 .. | 40 | 50 | NC444a | R 21 .. | † | — |
| NC275 | E 14 .. | 25 | 25 | NC348a | K 17 .. | 3·00 | 17·00 | NC497 | U 23 .. | 40 | 30 |
| NC296 | G 15 .. | 25 | 25 | NC365a | L 18 .. | — | † | NC508 | V 23 .. | 25 | 25 |

**C. Wmk. Simple Cypher, Type III**

| | | | | | | | | | | | |
|---|---|---|---|---|---|---|---|---|---|---|---|
| NC335 | J 17 .. | 25 | 30 | NC395 | N 19 .. | 25 | 25 | NC444 | R 21 .. | 25 | 25 |
| NC348 | K 17 .. | 20 | 8·00 | NC406 | O 19 .. | 40 | 40 | NC455 | S 21 .. | 20 | 20 |
| NC365 | L 18 .. | 25 | 25 | NC414 | O 20 .. | 20 | 25 | NC467 | S 22 .. | 20 | 20 |
| NC377 | M 18 .. | 75 | 70 | NC422 | P 20 .. | 25 | 25 | NC479 | T 22 .. | 20 | 20 |
| NC388 | M 19 .. | 80 | 75 | NC436 | Q 21 .. | 25 | 20 | | | | |

Watermark varieties.   The following controls are known:—

Wmk. inverted   ..   ..   ..   NC107, 259, 335a, 365, 395, 406, 414, 436, 444.
Wmk. reversed   ..   ..   ..   NC296.
Wmk. inverted and reversed   ..   NC107, 251, 259, 296, 309, 335, 365, 377, 388, 395, 406, 414, 422, 444, 479.

| Cat. No. | S.G. No. | Wmk. | Shades | Unused | Used |
|---|---|---|---|---|---|

**1912 (OCTOBER).   3d. VIOLET, TYPE N7**

| | | | | | |
|---|---|---|---|---|---|
| N22 | 374/77 | W.14 Simple Cypher | (1) Reddish violet (1912-13) | 1·50 | 50 |
| a. | No watermark .. .. | 16·00 | (2) Dull reddish violet | | |
| b. | Watermark inverted .. | 2·50 | 2·50 | (1912-13) | 1·00 | 25 |
| c. | Watermark reversed .. | 6·00 | 6·00 | (3) Violet | 30 | 5 |
| d. | Watermark inverted and re- | | | (4) Pale violet (1917-18) | 50 | 8 |
| | versed .. .. .. | 2·50 | 2·50 | (5) Very pale violet (1916) | 1·00 | 25 |
| e. | Frame broken (Pl. 4, R.20/2) | | | (6) Bright violet | 30 | 5 |
| s. | " Specimen ", Type 15 .. | | | (7) Bluish violet | 30 | 5 |
| t. | " Specimen ", Type 23 .. | 2·00 | | (8) Lavender-violet | 30 | 5 |
| u. | " Cancelled ", Type 24 .. | 3·50 | | (9) Dull violet (1920) | 35 | 8 |
| v. | " Specimen ", Type 26 .. | 3·00 | | (10) Very deep violet (1922-23) | 2·50 | 1·75 |
| | | | | (11) Heliotrope (1919) | 50 | 10 |
| | | | | (12) Brownish violet (1921) | 30 | 30 |

Shade (11) heliotrope has a decidedly pinkish tone.   The change of colour from reddish to bluish violet was deliberate.

## Plates

13 plates have been identified.

Fig. 10  Fig. 11  Fig. 12  Fig. 13

## Colour Essays

Fig. 10. Solid back to figures in various colours on white or tinted paper .. *From* 25·00

Fig. 11. In various colours on white or vellow paper .. .. .. .. *From* 25·00

Fig. 12. In various colours on white paper, also in purple on yellow paper .. *From* 25·00
In black on white paper Wmk. Crown .. .. .. .. .. .. 50·00

Engraver's Sketch Die. Fig. 13. Lines of shading behind figures

(i) Both upper corners shaded
  (a) White background to head
    In various colours on thick white paper .. .. .. .. .. *From* 35·00
  (b) Shaded background to head with uncleared surround
    In red or black on thick white paper .. .. .. .. *From* 75·00

(ii) Both upper corners solid
    In various colours on thick white paper .. .. .. .. *From* 35·00
    In various colours on paper Wmk. Crown (upright or sideways) .. *From* 35·00
    In yellow, with uncleared surround on paper Wmk. Crown .. .. 75·00

## Controls

Printed at Somerset House
Wmk. Simple Cypher

| | | I. | P. | | | I. | P |
|---|---|---|---|---|---|---|---|
| *NC108* | A. 12 (w) reddish violet.. | 2·50 | 20·00 | *NC115* | C. 13 bluish violet .. | 60 | 3·50 |
| *NC108a* | A. 12 (c) ,, ,, .. | 1·50 | 2·00 | | | | |
| *NC110* | B. 13 ,, ,, .. | 1·00 | 1·25 | | | | |

(c) and (w) refer to close and wide spacing (1¼ mm. and 4 mm. between " A " and " 1 " respectively).

Printed by Harrison & Sons

| A. Wmk. Simple Cypher, Type I | | | | B. Type II | | | |
|---|---|---|---|---|---|---|---|
| *NC252* | C 13 | reddish violet .. | 2·50 | 2·50 | *NC252a* | C 13 reddish violet .. | — — |
| *NC276a* | E 14 | bluish violet .. | — | † | | | |

B. Wmk. Simple Cypher, Type II (Bluish violet shades)

| | | I. | P. | | | I. | P. | | | I. | P. |
|---|---|---|---|---|---|---|---|---|---|---|---|
| *NC253* | C 13 .. | 40 | 40 | *NC310* | H 16 .. | 50 | 75 | *NC445a* | R 21 .. | 75 | 75 |
| *NC266* | D 14 .. | 40 | 40 | *NC323* | I 16 .. | 50 | 50 | *NC490* | U 22 .. | 50 | 50 |
| *NC276* | E 14 .. | 40 | 40 | *NC336a* | J 17 .. | 50 | 80 | *NC498* | U 23 .. | 50 | 50 |
| *NC284* | F 15 .. | 40 | 40 | *NC396a* | N 19 .. | 1·25 | 80 | *NC509* | V 23 .. | 50 | 50 |
| *NC297* | G 15 .. | 1·00 | 40 | *NC415a* | O 20 .. | 1·25 | 1·25 | *NC518* | W 23 .. | 50 | 50 |

C. Wmk. Simple Cypher, Type III

| | | I. | P. | | | I. | P. | | | I. | P. |
|---|---|---|---|---|---|---|---|---|---|---|---|
| *NC336* | J 17 .. | 40 | 50 | *NC423* | P 20 .. | 40 | 40 | *NC480* | T 22 .. | 50 | 50 |
| *NC366* | L 18 .. | 40 | 40 | *NC437* | Q 21 .. | 40 | 40 | *NC490a* | U 22 .. | 70 | 70 |
| *NC378* | M 18 .. | 40 | 50 | *NC445* | R 21 .. | 40 | 40 | *NC498a* | U 23 .. | 60 | 60 |
| *NC396* | N 19 .. | 40 | 40 | *NC456* | S 21 .. | 40 | 40 | *NC509a* | V 23 .. | 1·00 | 1·75 |
| *NC415* | O 20 .. | 40 | 40 | *NC468* | S 22 .. | 40 | 40 | *NC518a* | W 23 .. | 1·00 | 1·00 |

Watermark varieties. The following controls are known:—

Wmk. inverted .. .. .. NC110, 297, 366, 396, 490, 498, 509.
Wmk. reversed .. .. .. NC323, 437.
Wmk. inverted and reversed .. NC110, 253, 276, 284, 297, 323, 336, 366, 396, 415, 437, 445, 468, 490

| Cat. No. | S.G. No. | Wmk. | | Shades | Unused | Used |
|---|---|---|---|---|---|---|

**1913 (JANUARY).  4d. GREY-GREEN, TYPE N7**

| | | | | | | |
|---|---|---|---|---|---|---|
| N23 | 378/80 | W.14 Simple Cypher | | (1) Grey-green | 30 | 8 |
| a. | No watermark | .. | .. 10·00 | (2) Pale grey-green | 75 | 15 |
| b. | Watermark inverted | .. | 1·50    1·50 | (3) Deep grey-green | 2·50 | 80 |
| c. | Watermark reversed | .. | 2·50    2·00 | (4) Slate-green | 30 | 8 |
| d. | Watermark inverted and reversed | .. .. | .. 1·50    1·50 | (5) Pale slate-green | 75 | 15 |
| e. | Break above O of FOUR | | | (6) Deep slate-green | 2·00 | 50 |
| | (Pl. 1, R. 19/2) | .. .. | 2·00    1·00 | (7) Bluish grey-green (1919) | 2·00 | 50 |
| f. | Cracked plate (Pl. 2, R.19/1) | | 5·00    2·50 | | | |
| g. | Breaks in bottom frame (R.10/11) | .. .. | .. | | | |
| s. | " Specimen ", Type 15 | .. | | u.  " Cancelled ", Type 24   .. | 4·00 | |
| t. | " Specimen ", Type 23 | .. | 1·50 | v.  " Specimen ", Type 26   .. | 3·00 | |

N23e            N23f            N23g

**Perforation**

Variety Type 2C is known with control J 17.  ..   ..   ..   ..   .. *Strip of* 3 6·00

**Plates.**  4 plates have been identified.

**Die Proof** of the accepted design

In black on white glazed card   ..   ..   ..   ..   ..   ..   ..   .. 75·00

**Plate Proofs**

In pale ultramarine on thick paper  ..   ..   ..   ..   ..   ..   ..   .. 30·00
In grey-green on thin gummed paper  ..   ..   ..   ..   ..   ..   ..   .. 35·00

Fig. 14        Fig. 15        Fig. 16        Fig. 17
                              ← 23 mm. →      ← 22 mm. →

**Colour Essays**

Fig. 14.  In various colours on white paper (*See* ½d., 1911 *value*)   ..   .. *From* 25·00

**Engraver's Sketch Die.  Fig. 15**

Head on solid background
   Die proof in black   ..   ..   ..   ..   ..   ..   ..   .. 75·00
Head on shaded background
   In black or yellow   ..   ..   ..   ..   ..   ..   .. *From* 35·00
   In orange on paper Wmk. Crown   ..   ..   ..   ..   ..   .. 50·00

**Trials by the " Motley " Process**

(a) Large head as Fig. 16, but the shading at sides extends down to the lower ornaments.
   In light turquoise-blue, Wmk. Crown ..   ..   ..   ..   ..   .. 30·00
(b) Small head Fig. 17.
   Proof in black on white glazed card   ..   ..   ..   ..   ..   .. 20·00
   Reversed Die proof with (M/S) approval   ..   ..   ..   ..   .. £100
   15 different colour trials on white paper   ..   ..   ..   .. *From* 30·00
   In blue on pink, brown on pink or purple on blue ..   ..   .. *Each* 40·00
(c) Large head as Fig. 16, shading as in (a).
   Plate proof in black on white glazed card   ..   ..   ..   ..   .. 20·00
   In various colours on white paper   ..   ..   ..   ..   .. *Each* 35·00
(d) Large head as Fig. 16.  Shading stops halfway down the sides
   Die proof in black or brown   ..   ..   ..   ..   ..   .. *Each* 75·00
   In pale blue, Wmk. Simple Cypher (sideways)   ..   ..   ..   .. ..

## Controls

Printed at Somerset House.  Wmk. Simple Cypher, Type I

|        |        | I.    | P.   |
|--------|--------|-------|------|
| *NC111* | B. 13 .. | 2·00 | 7·00 |

Printed by Harrison & Sons

**A. Wmk. Simple Cypher, Type I**

|        |        | I.  | P.  |
|--------|--------|-----|-----|
| *NC254a* | C 13 .. | 40 | 80 |

**B. Wmk. Simple Cypher, Type II**

|          |         | I.   | P.   |          |        | I.   | P.  |          |         | I.   | P.   |
|----------|---------|------|------|----------|--------|------|-----|----------|---------|------|------|
| *NC254*  | C 13 .. | 40   | 40   | *NC324*  | I 16 ..| 40   | 75  | *NC446a* | R 21 .. | 45   | 40   |
| *NC267*  | D 14 .. | 40   | 40   | *NC337a* | J 17 ..| 50   | 40  | *NC491*  | U 22 .. | 1·25 | 1·50 |
| *NC285*  | F 15 .. | 40   | 40   | *NC350a* | K 17 ..| 1·50 | †   | *NC499*  | U 23 .. | 2·00 | 40   |
| *NC298*  | G 15 .. | 40   | 40   | *NC357a* | K 18 ..| †    | —   | *NC510*  | V 23 .. | 40   | 40   |
| *NC311*  | H 16 .. | 50   | 5·00 | *NC416a* | O 20 ..| 40   | 40  |          |         |      |      |

**C. Wmk. Single Cypher, Type III**

|         |         | I.  | P.   |         |         | I.  | P.  |          |         | I.   | P.   |
|---------|---------|-----|------|---------|---------|-----|-----|----------|---------|------|------|
| *NC337* | J 17 .. | 40  | 40   | *NC397* | N 19 .. | 40  | 40  | *NC457*  | S 21 .. | 2·00 | 80   |
| *NC350* | K 17 .. | 40  | 8·00 | *NC416* | O 20 .. | 40  | 40  | *NC469*  | S 22 .. | 40   | 1·00 |
| *NC357* | K 18 .. | 40  | 40   | *NC438* | Q 21 .. | 80  | 80  | *NC481*  | T 22 .. | 40   | 40   |
| *NC379* | M 18 .. | 40  | 40   | *NC446* | R 21 .. | 40  | 40  | *NC499a* | U 23 .. | 2·50 | 1·25 |

**Watermark varieties.**  The following controls are known:—

| Wmk. inverted .. | .. | .. | NC111, 298, 350, 357, 379. |
| Wmk. reversed .. | .. | .. | NC254, 337, 509 |
| Wmk. inverted and reversed | .. | NC111, 254, 298, 324, 337, 350, 379, 446, 491. |

| Cat. No. | S.G. No. | Wmk. | Shades | Unused | Used |

## 1913 (JUNE).  5d. BROWN, TYPE N8

| N25 | 381/83 | W.14 Simple Cypher | | | |
|-----|--------|--------------------|--|--|--|

*a.*  No watermark  .. .. 35·00
*b.*  Watermark inverted  .. 10·00  7·00
*c.*  Watermark inverted and reversed  .. .. 6·00  6·00
*d.*  Varnish ink .. .. .. 75·00
*s.*  "Specimen", Type 15
*t.*  "Specimen", Type 26  .. 3·00

Shades:

| (1) Brown | 50 | 25 |
| (2) Reddish brown | 50 | 25 |
| (3) Yellow-brown | 75 | 25 |
| (4) Ochre-brown (1916) | 3·50 | 3·00 |
| (5) Ginger-brown (1917) | 2·00 | 1·00 |
| (6) Bistre-brown | 2·25 | 1·10 |

## Plates

3 plates have been identified.

**Die Proofs** of the accepted design

| Without value in black | .. .. .. .. .. .. .. .. .. | £100 |
| In black on white glazed card.. | .. .. .. .. .. .. .. | 75·00 |

## Plate Proofs

| In black on paper Wmk. Simple Cypher (sideways) | .. .. .. .. | 75·00 |
| In ochre on paper Wmk. Simple Cypher (upright) | .. .. .. .. | 50·00 |

Fig. 18

Fig. 19

## Colour Essays

Fig. 18  In various colours on white paper (*See ½d.*, 1911 *value*) .. .. .. *From* 25·00

Fig. 19
Proofs in black on card, or in blue on white paper.. .. .. .. .. *From* 35·00
Colour Trials in various colours on white paper .. .. .. .. .. *From* 35·00
In light blue on paper Wmk. Crown .. .. .. .. .. .. .. 40·00
Mackennal head as before, but with "Pillar" frame as in Fig. 29. Without
values, in black on glazed card .. .. .. .. .. .. .. 40·00
On paper Wmk. Simple Cypher (sideways) .. .. .. .. .. ..

### Trials by the "Motley" Process

Profile head in "wreath" frame similar to Fig. 17.
In black with even shading or with graduated shading to background    .. *From* 25·00

### Controls

Printed at Somerset House.   Wmk. Simple Cypher

| | | | | | | |
|---|---|---|---|---|---|---|
| A. Type I | I. | P. | B. Type II | I. | P. | |
| *NC112a* B.13 .. | 15·00 | † | *NC112* B. 13 .. | 60 | 75 | |

Printed by Harrison & Sons

### A.   Wmk. Simple Cypher, Type II

| | | I. | P. | | | I. | P. | | | I. | P. |
|---|---|---|---|---|---|---|---|---|---|---|---|
| *NC260* | C 14 .. | 65 | 65 | *NC325* | I 16 .. | 65 | 65 | *NC439* | Q 21 .. | 65 | 80 |
| *NC268* | D 14 .. | 65 | 65 | *NC351a* | K 17 .. | 1·50 | 2·50 | *NC447* | R 21 .. | 65 | 65 |
| *NC286* | F 15 .. | 65 | 65 | *NC398a* | N 19 .. | 1·25 | 2·50 | *NC500* | U 23 .. | 65 | 65 |
| *NC299* | G 15 .. | 65 | 80 | *NC406b* | O 19 .. | 6·50 | 7·00 | *NC511* | V 23 .. | 65 | 65 |
| *NC312* | H 16 .. | 65 | 65 | | | | | | | | |

### B.   Wmk. Simple Cypher, Type III

| | | I. | P. | | | I. | P. | | | I. | P. |
|---|---|---|---|---|---|---|---|---|---|---|---|
| *NC338* | J 17 .. | 75 | 75 | *NC406a* | O 19 .. | 75 | 75 | *NC470* | S 22 .. | 1·00 | 8·00 |
| *NC351* | K 17 .. | 75 | 80 | *NC439a* | Q 21 .. | — | — | *NC482* | T 22 .. | 75 | 60 |
| *NC368* | L 18 .. | 75 | 75 | *NC458* | S 21 .. | 75 | 75 | *NC500a* | U 23 .. | 1·25 | — |
| *NC398* | N 19 .. | 75 | 75 | | | | | | | | |

Watermark varieties.   The following controls are known:—

Wmk. inverted    ..       ..       .. NC312, 368, 398.
Wmk. inverted and reversed    .. NC268, 398.

| Cat. No. | S.G. No. | Wmk. | Shades | Unused | Used |
|---|---|---|---|---|---|

**1913 (AUGUST).   6d. PURPLE, TYPE N8.   CHALK-SURFACED PAPER**

| | | | | | |
|---|---|---|---|---|---|
| N26 | 384/86 | W.14 Simple Cypher | (1) Dull purple (1913) | 2·00 | 1·00 |
| *a.* | No watermark .. | .. 18·00 | (2) Slate-purple (1913) | 3·00 | 1·50 |
| *b.* | Watermark inverted | .. 1·50    1·50 | (3) Reddish purple | 40 | 10 |
| *c.* | Watermark reversed | .. 22·00 | (4) Pale reddish purple | 40 | 10 |
| *d.* | Watermark inverted and re- | | (5) Deep reddish purple | 75 | 60 |
| | versed   ..     ..     . | 2·00    2·00 | (6) Purple | 75 | 10 |
| *e.* | Perforation 14    .. | .. 6·00    2·50 | (7) Rosy mauve | 75 | 10 |
| *s.* | "Specimen", Type 15 | .. | (8) Plum | 1·00 | 20 |
| *t.* | "Specimen", Type 23 | .. 1·50 | | | |
| *u.* | "Specimen", Type 26 | .. 2·00 | | | |
| *v.* | "Cancelled", Type 28 | .. | | | |

### Die Proof of the accepted design

In black on white glazed card..    ..    ..    ..    ..    ..    ..    ..    .. 75·00

### Perforation

Normally Types 2 or 2A but the following are also known:

| | | | Strip of 3 |
|---|---|---|---|
| Type 3 | C.13 Dull purple    ..    ..    ..    ..    ..    .. | 9·00 |
| | C.13 Reddish purple ..    ..    ..    ..    ..    .. | 2·50 |
| Type 3A | C.13 Dull purple    ..    ..    ..    ..    ..    .. | 12·00 |
| Type 2C | C.13 Reddish purple ..    ..    ..    ..    ..    .. | 9·00 |
| | W.23    ..     ..    ..    ..    ..    ..    ..    .. | |
| | A.24 Plum    ..    ..    ..    ..    ..    ..    .. | 3·00 |
| | B.24 Plum    ..  ..    ..    ..    ..    ..    .. | 4·00 |

Fig. 20

### Plates.   18 plates have been identified.

### Colour Essays

Fig. 20   In various colours on white paper (*see* ½d., 1911 *value*)    ..    .. *From* 25·00

## Controls

Printed at Somerset House

### A. Wmk. Simple Cypher, Type II

|  |  |  | I. | P. |  |  |  |  | I. | P. |
|---|---|---|---|---|---|---|---|---|---|---|
| NC116 | C. 13 | dull purple | 2·00 | 2·00 | NC117 | C. 13 | reddish purple | | 60 | 60 |

|  |  | I. | P. |  |  | I. | P. |  |  | I. | P. |
|---|---|---|---|---|---|---|---|---|---|---|---|
| NC122 | D. 14 .. | 65 | † | NC129 | J. 17 .. | 65 | † | NC138a | Q. 20 | | |
| NC123 | E. 14 .. | 65 | 65 | NC135a | O. 19 .. | 1·25 | † | | (14) .. | 4·50 | † |
| NC124 | F. 15 .. | 1·25 | 25·00 | NC136a | P. 20 .. | 85 | † | NC141a | S. 21.. | 75 | — |
| NC126 | G. 15 .. | 65 | † | NC137a | Q. 20 | | | NC144a | V. 23.. | 1·50 | † |
| NC127 | H. 16 .. | 65 | † | | (15 × 14) | 2·50 | † | NC145 | W. 23.. | 85 | † |
| NC128 | I. 16 .. | 65 | † | | | | | NC146 | A. 24.. | 85 | † |
| | | | | | | | | NC147 | B. 24.. | 1·75 | † |

### B. Wmk. Simple Cypher, Type III

|  |  | I. | P. |  |  | I. | P. |  |  | I. | P. |
|---|---|---|---|---|---|---|---|---|---|---|---|
| NC129a | J. 17 .. | 1·50 | † | NC136 | P. 20 .. | 65 | † | NC140 | R. 21 | | |
| NC131 | K. 17.. | 65 | † | NC137 | Q. 20 | | | | (15 × 14) | 85 | † |
| NC132 | L. 18.. | 65 | 3·50 | | (15 × 14) | 70 | † | NC141 | S. 21 .. | 75 | 4·00 |
| NC132a | L. 18 | | | NC138 | Q. 20 | | | NC142 | T. 22 .. | 75 | 6·00 |
| | (no stop) | 75 | † | | (14) .. | 2·00 | † | NC143 | U. 22 .. | 75 | † |
| NC133 | M. 18.. | 65 | 40·00 | NC139 | R. 21 | | | NC144 | V. 23 .. | 80 | † |
| NC134 | N. 19.. | 65 | 4·00 | | (14) .. | 2·50 | † | NC146a | A. 24 .. | — | † |
| NC135 | O. 19.. | 65 | † | | | | | NC147a | B. 24 .. | — | † |

**Watermark varieties.** The following controls are known:—

| Wmk. inverted | .. | .. | .. | NC117, 123, 127, 132, 133, 134, 135, 136, 137, 140, 141, 144, 145, 146 |
|---|---|---|---|---|
| Wmk. reversed | .. | .. | .. | NC122, 135. |
| Wmk. inverted and reversed | .. | NC122, 123, 131, 134, 135, 136, 140, 142, 143. |

## 1913 (AUGUST). 7d. OLIVE, TYPE N8

| Cat. No. | S.G. No. | Wmk. | | | Shades | Unused | Used |
|---|---|---|---|---|---|---|---|
| N27 | 387/89 | W.14 Simple Cypher | | | (1) Olive | 1·50 | 60 |
| a. | No watermark | .. | .. | 25·00 | (2) Olive-grey | 1·50 | 60 |
| b. | Watermark inverted | .. | 3·00 | 3·00 | (3) Bronze-green (1915) | 3·00 | 1·00 |
| s. | "Specimen", Type 26 | .. | 4·00 | | (4) Sage-green (1917) | 2·00 | 75 |

## Perforation

Variety Type 2C is known with control J 17.

## Plates

2 plates have been identified.

## Die Proof of the accepted design

| In black on white glazed card.. | .. | .. | .. | .. | .. | .. | .. | 75·00 |
|---|---|---|---|---|---|---|---|---|

Fig. 21

Fig. 22

Fig. 23

## Colour Essays

| Fig. 21 | In various colours on white or on coloured papers | .. | .. | .. | From 25·00 |
|---|---|---|---|---|---|
| Fig. 22 | In various colours on white paper .. | .. | .. | .. | .. | From 25·00 |
| | Die proof in red dated "Nov 1910" | .. | .. | .. | .. | 60·00 |
| | Die proof in sage-green, double impression | .. | .. | .. | 50·00 |
| Fig. 23 | In various colours on white paper | .. | .. | .. | .. | From 25·00 |
| | In red or black paper Wmk. Crown | .. | .. | .. | .. | From 40·00 |

Fig. 24                    Fig. 25

## Trials by the " Motley " Process

Fig. 24 on gummed paper or thin card.
In bistre-brown, greenish grey, purple-brown, red-brown, vermilion or yellow-
green   .. .. .. .. .. .. .. .. .. .. *From* 35·00
In black on glazed card   .. .. .. .. .. .. .. .. 35·00
As Fig. 24 but shading behind head, solid at top left, and lined at lower right.
In bright yellow-green   .. .. .. .. .. .. .. .. 35·00
In black on glazed card   .. .. .. .. .. .. .. .. 35·00
As Fig. 24 but lines of shading all round the head.
In black on glazed card.  Special Plate of four ..   .. .. .. .. £150
Fig. 25 on gummed paper.
In bistre-brown, turquoise or magenta   .. .. .. .. .. *From* 35·00
In black on glazed card.  Special Plate of four ..   .. .. .. .. £125
Fig. 25 optd. " ESSAY ".
In magenta or bistre-brown   .. .. .. .. .. .. *From* 20·00

## Controls

Printed at Somerset House.  Wmk. Simple Cypher.

| | I. | P. | | | I. | P. |
|---|---|---|---|---|---|---|
| A. Type I | | | B. Type II | | | |
| NC118a   C. 13   .. .. | 18·00 | † | NC118   C. 13   .. .. | | 2·50 | † |

Printed by Harrison & Sons
A. Wmk. Simple Cypher, Type II

| | I. | P. | | I. | P. | | I. | P. |
|---|---|---|---|---|---|---|---|---|
| NC255  C 13 .. | 2·50 | 2·50 | NC287  F 15 .. | 2·50 | 2 50 | NC313  H 16 .. | 2·50 | 2·50 |
| NC269  D 14 .. | 2·50 | 2·50 | NC300  G 15 .. | 2·50 | 2·50 | NC339a  J 17 .. | 5·00 | — |

B. Wmk. Simple Cypher, Type III
NC339   J 17 ..   3·00   3·00 | NC370   L 18 ..   3·00   8·00 |
Watermark varieties.  The following controls are known:—
Wmk. inverted   .. .. NC339, 370.

| Cat. No. | S.G. No. | Wmk. | Shades | Unused | Used |
|---|---|---|---|---|---|

## 1913 (AUGUST).  8d. BLACK ON YELLOW, TYPE N8

N28    390/91  W.14 Simple Cypher         Yellow Paper
 a.  No watermark   .. .. 25·00     (1) Black              2·00  1·00
 b.  Watermark inverted   .. 4·00   4·00
 c.  Watermark reversed   .. 6·00       Yellow-buff Paper (Granite)
 d.  Watermark inverted and re-
 versed   .. .. .. 90·00         (2) Black (1917-18)    2·50  1·00
 e.  Frame broken lower right
 side (R.20/10)   .. .. 6·00   6·00
 f.  Frame broken (R.1-10?/12) 12·00  5·00   s.  " Specimen ", Type 26   .. 6·00

Paper.  Granite paper was of poorer quality and shows hairs and other particles in the
texture.

**Plate**
Only one plate was used.

**Die Proofs** of the accepted design
In black on white glazed card ..   .. .. .. .. .. .. 75·00

N28f                    Fig. 26

Fig. 27          Fig. 28          Fig. 29          Fig. 30

## Colour Essays
Engraver's Sketch Die Fig. 26

Die proof in black on card .. .. .. .. .. .. .. .. 75·00
In blue on paper Wmk. Crown .. .. .. .. .. .. 40·00
Fig. 27  In various colours on white paper (*See ½d., 1911 value*) .. .. *From* 25·00
In black on various green papers .. .. .. .. *From* 25·00
With shading around the head removed.
In various colours on white paper .. .. .. .. *From* 25·00

## Trials by the " Motley " Process
(*a*) Design similar to Fig. 28 but with shaded background, the " V " of " REVENUE "
is horizontal, and there are no stops after " POSTAGE " and before " REVENUE ".
Die proofs in black or brown .. .. .. .. .. *From* 60·00
(*b*) Fig. 28 (Solid background)
Proof in black .. .. .. .. .. .. .. .. 20·00
Colour trials.  Wmk. Simple Cypher.
In brown, red-brown, agate or magenta .. .. .. *From* 35·00
(*c*) Fig. 29 (Background shaded at right)
Proof in black .. .. .. .. .. .. .. .. 30·00
Colour trials.  Wmk. Simple Cypher.
In pale red-brown, agate or orange-brown .. .. .. .. *From* 35·00
*d*) Background shading deep at top, shallow at base.
Proof in black .. .. .. .. .. .. .. .. 20·00
Colour trial in agate, Wmk. Simple Cypher .. .. .. .. 35·00
Colour trials on unwmkd. paper optd. " ESSAY ".
In various colours .. .. .. .. .. .. *From* 20·00
(*e*) Background evenly shaded.
Proof in black .. .. .. .. .. .. .. .. 20·00
(*f*) Fig. 30 Smaller profile.
Proof in black .. .. .. .. .. .. .. .. 30·00
In red-purple or greenish grey .. .. .. .. .. *From* 35·00
In black on orange-buff .. .. .. .. .. .. 35·00
Colour trials optd. " ESSAY ".
In various colours on white paper .. .. .. .. *From* 20·00
In various colours on coloured papers .. .. .. .. *From* 20·00

## Controls
Printed at Somerset House.   Wmk. Simple Cypher, Type II
　　　　　　　I.　　P.
*NC119*   C. 13 ..   2·50   †
Printed by Harrison & Sons
A. Wmk. Simple Cypher, Type II

| | I. | P. | | | I. | P. | | | I. | P. |
|---|---|---|---|---|---|---|---|---|---|---|
| *NC270* | D 14 .. | 2·50 | 2·50 | *NC301* G 15 .. | 2·50 | 2·50 | *NC327* I 16 .. | 2·50 | 2·50 |
| *NC288* | F 15 .. | 2·50 | 2·50 | *NC314* H 16 .. | 2·50 | 2·50 | *NC340* J 17 .. | 3·50 | 3·50 |

B. Wmk. Simple Cypher, Type III (granite paper)
*NC340a* J 17 ..   2·75   2·75 | *NC358* K 18 ..   15·00   2·75 |
Watermark varieties.   The following controls are known:—
Wmk. inverted .. .. .. NC288
Wmk. reversed .. .. .. NC301, 314.
Wmk. inverted and reversed .. NC270.

| Cat. No. | S.G. No. | Wmk. | Shades | Unused | Used |
|---|---|---|---|---|---|

**1913 (JUNE).   9d. AGATE, TYPE N9**

N29   392/93   W.14 Simple Cypher
*a.* No watermark .. .. 25·00
*b.* Watermark inverted .. 4·00   4·00
*c.* Watermark inverted and reversed .. .. .. 4·00   4·00
*d.* Frame broken at left (each
side of O of POSTAGE)
(R. 3/1) .. .. .. 6·00   3·00

(1) Agate　　　　　　　1·25　50
(2) Pale agate　　　　　1·25　50
(3) Deep agate　　　　　1·50　50
(4) Very deep agate　　2·50　1·00

*s.* " Specimen ", Type 26 .. 3·00

**Plates**

3 plates have been identified.

**Die Proof** of the accepted design

In black on white glazed card.. .. .. .. .. .. .. .. .. 75·00

**Plate Proofs**

In black on gummed paper Wmk. Simple Cypher (sideways) .. .. .. .. 75·00
Plate Proof in black on poor quality buff paper .. .. .. .. .. .. 8·00

Fig. 31

**Colour Essays**

Fig. 31   In various colours on white paper (*see ½d.*, 1911 *value*) .. .. .. *From* 25·00
In black on various coloured papers .. .. .. .. .. *From* 25·00
With shading around head removed, in red on white paper .. .. .. 35·00

**Controls**

Printed at Somerset House.   Wmk. Simple Cypher, Type II

|  | I. | P. |
|---|---|---|
| *NC113*   B. 13 .. | 1·50 | † |

Printed by Harrison & Sons

A. Wmk. Simple Cypher, Type II

|  | I. | P. |  | I. | P. |  | I. | P. |
|---|---|---|---|---|---|---|---|---|
| *NC277*   E 14 .. | † | 1·50 | *NC315*   H 16 .. | 1·75 | 1·50 | *NC417a*   O 20 .. | 2·00 | 1·75 |
| *NC289*   F 15 .. | 2·00 | 5·00 | *NC328*   I 16 .. | 1·50 | 5·00 | *NC448a*   R 21 .. | 2·75 | — |
| *NC302*   G 15 .. | 1·50 | 1·50 | *NC341a*   J 17 .. | 1·75 | 1·75 |  |  |  |

B. Wmk. Simple Cypher, Type III

|  | I. | P. |  | I. | P. |  | I. | P. |
|---|---|---|---|---|---|---|---|---|
| *NC341*   J 17 .. | 1·50 | 1·50 | *NC399*   N 19 .. | 1·50 | 1·50 | *NC430*   Q 20 .. | 1·50 | 1·50 |
| *NC352*   K 17 .. | 1·50 | 1·50 | *NC407*   O 19 .. | 1·50 | 1·50 | *NC448*   R 21 .. | 1·50 | 1·50 |
| *NC359*   K 18 .. | 1·50 | 1·50 | *NC417*   O 20 .. | 1·50 | 1·50 | *NC459*   S 21 .. | 1·50 | 1·50 |
| *NC371*   L 18 .. | 1·50 | 1·50 | *NC424*   P 20 .. | 1·50 | 1·50 | *NC471*   S 22 .. | 2·25 | 1·50 |

Watermark varieties.   The following controls are known:—

Wmk. inverted .. .. .. NC113, 289, 371, 407, 424, 430.
Wmk. inverted and reversed .. NC302, 341, 407, 424, 430, 459, 471.

| Cat. No. | S.G. No. |  | Wmk. | | Shades | Unused | Used |
|---|---|---|---|---|---|---|---|
| **1922 (SEPTEMBER).** | | **9d. OLIVE-GREEN, TYPE N9** | | | | | |
| N30 | 393a/b | W.14 Simple Cypher | | | (1) Olive-green | 11·00 | 1·50 |
| *a.* Watermark inverted | | .. | 30·00 | 30·00 | (2) Pale olive-green | 12·00 | 1·50 |
| *b.* Watermark inverted and re- | | | | | (3) Deep olive-green | 12·00 | 1·50 |
| versed .. .. | | .. | 25·00 | 25·00 | | | |
| *s.* " Specimen ", Type 15 | | .. | 15·00 | | | | |
| *t.* " Specimen ", Type 23 | | .. | 15·00 | | | | |

**Controls**

Printed by Harrison & Sons

A. Wmk. Simple Cypher, Type II

|  | I. | P. |  |  | I. | P. |
|---|---|---|---|---|---|---|
| *NC501*   U 23 .. | .. 12·00 | 12·00 | *NC512*   V 23 .. | .. | 12·00 | 12·00 |

B. Wmk. Simple Cypher, Type III

|  | I. | P. |  |  | I. | P. |
|---|---|---|---|---|---|---|
| *NC483*   T 22 .. | .. 12·00 | 12·00 | *NC501a*   U 23 .. | .. | — | 20·00 |

Watermark varieties.   The following controls are known:—

Wmk. inverted .. .. .. NC501.
Wmk. inverted and reversed .. NC501.

| Cat. No. | S.G. No. | Wmk. | Shades | Unused | Used |
|---|---|---|---|---|---|

**1913 (AUGUST). 10d. TURQUOISE-BLUE, TYPE N9**

N31  394  W.14 Simple Cypher

a. Watermark inverted .. 15·00 12·00
b. Watermark inverted and reversed .. .. .. 12·00 10·00
c. Frame broken by E of POSTAGE .. .. .. 8·00
s. "Specimen", Type 15 .. 10·00
t. "Specimen", Type 23 .. 10·00
u. "Cancelled", Type 24 .. 5·00
v. "Specimen", Type 26 .. 5·00

(1) Bright turquoise-blue — 1·50 — 75
(2) Turquoise-blue — 1·50 — 75
(3) Deep turquoise-blue — 1·60 — 1·10
(4) Greenish blue — 1·50 — 75
(5) Pale greenish blue — 1·50 — 75

**Plates**

2 plates have been identified.

**Die Proof** of the accepted design
In black on white glazed card .. .. .. .. .. .. .. .. 75·00

Fig. 32

**Colour Essays**

Fig. 32 In various colours on white paper (*see* ½d., 1911 *value*) .. .. *From* 25·00
In black on various coloured papers .. .. .. .. .. *From* 25·00

**Controls**

Printed at Somerset House. Wmk. Simple Cypher, Type II

|  |  | I. | P. |
|---|---|---|---|
| NC120 | C.13 .. | 1·75 | 40·00 |

Printed by Harrison & Sons
A. Wmk. Single Cypher, Type I

NC290a F 15 .. — —

B. Wmk. Single Cypher, Type II

| | | I. | P. | | | I. | P. | | | I. | P. |
|---|---|---|---|---|---|---|---|---|---|---|---|
| NC271 | D 14 .. | 1·75 | 1·75 | NC316 | H 16 .. | 1·75 | 3·50 | NC360a | K 18 .. | † | — |
| NC290 | F 15 .. | 2·00 | 2·25 | NC320 | I 16 .. | 1·75 | 2·00 | NC502 | U 23 .. | 1·75 | 1·75 |
| NC303 | G 15 .. | 2·50 | 3·50 | NC342a | J 17 .. | 6·00 | 2·25 | | | | |

C. Wmk. Single Cypher, Type III

| | | I. | P. | | | I. | P. | | | I. | P. |
|---|---|---|---|---|---|---|---|---|---|---|---|
| NC342 | J 17 .. | 2·50 | 1·75 | NC408 | O 19 .. | 1·75 | 1·75 | NC472 | S 22 .. | 5·00 | 1·75 |
| NC360 | K 18 .. | 5·00 | 1·75 | NC440 | Q 21 .. | 1·75 | 1·75 | NC484 | T 22 .. | 2·00 | 1·75 |
| NC389 | M 19 .. | 1·75 | 1·75 | NC460 | S 21 .. | 1·75 | 1·75 | | | | |

**Watermark varieties.** The following controls are known:—
Wmk. inverted .. .. .. NC316, 389.
Wmk. inverted and reversed .. NC120, 408, 440.

| Cat. No. | S.G. No. | Wmk. | | Shades | Unused | Used |
|---|---|---|---|---|---|---|

**1913 (AUGUST).   1s. BISTRE-BROWN, TYPE N9**

| | | | | | | |
|---|---|---|---|---|---|---|
| N32 | 395/96 | W.14 Simple Cypher | | (1) Bistre-brown | 1·00 | 15 |
| a. | No watermark | .. .. 35·00 | | (2) Pale bistre-brown | 1·00 | 15 |
| b. | Watermark inverted | .. 5·00 | 4·00 | (3) Deep bistre-brown | 1·25 | 15 |
| c. | Watermark inverted and reversed | .. .. 4·00 | 3·00 | (4) Buff-brown | 1·25 | 15 |
| | | | | (5) Pale buff-brown | 1·75 | 20 |
| d. | Varnish ink .. .. .. 40·00 | | | (6) Fawn-brown (1916-17) | 3·00 | 1·00 |
| s. | "Specimen", Type 15 | .. 10·00 | | (7) Olive-bistre | 1·25 | 15 |
| t. | "Specimen", Type 23 | .. 10·00 | | (8) Pale olive-bistre | 1·25 | 20 |
| u. | "Cancelled", Type 24 | .. 5·00 | | (9) Olive-brown (1920) | 2·00 | 75 |
| v. | "Specimen", Type 26 | .. 4·00 | | (10) Deep bronze-brown | | |
| w. | "Specimen", Type 31 | .. 10·00 | | (1920) | 50·00 | |

Shade (10) is from a part sheet and stamps should therefore match up to the perforation centring which is low and to the right.

**Perforation**

Variety Type 2C is known with control J 17    ..    ..    ..    .. *Strip of* 3 7·00

**Plates.**   6 plates have been identified.

**Die Proof** of the accepted design

In black on white glazed card   ..   ..   ..   ..   ..   ..   ..   .. 75·00

Fig. 33

**Colour Essays**

| Fig. 33 | In various colours on white paper (*see* ½d., 1911 *value*) | .. | .. *From* 25·00 |
|---|---|---|---|
| | In black on various coloured papers | .. .. .. .. | .. *From* 25·00 |

**Controls**

Printed at Somerset House.   Wmk. Simple Cypher, Type II

|  | I. | P. |
|---|---|---|
| NC121 C. 13 .. | 1·50 | 4·00 |

Printed by Harrison & Sons

**A.   Wmk. Simple Cypher, Type II**

| | I. | P. | | | I. | P. | | | I. | P. |
|---|---|---|---|---|---|---|---|---|---|---|
| NC272 | D 14 .. | 1·25 | 1·25 | NC330 | I 16 .. | 1·25 | 2·25 | NC449a | R 21 .. | 2·00 | 2·00 |
| NC278 | E 14 .. | 35·00 | 35·00 | NC343a | J 17 .. | 1·50 | 2·75 | NC492 | U 22 .. | 1·25 | 1·25 |
| NC291 | F 15 .. | 1·25 | 1·25 | NC353a | K 17 .. | — | † | NC503 | U 23 .. | 1·35 | 1·25 |
| NC304 | G 15 .. | 1·25 | 1·25 | NC418a | O 20 .. | 2·25 | 2·25 | NC513 | V 23 .. | 1·25 | 1·25 |
| NC317 | H 16 .. | 1·25 | 2·00 | | | | | | | | |

**B.   Wmk. Single Cypher, Type III**

| | | I. | P. | | | I. | P. | | | I. | P. |
|---|---|---|---|---|---|---|---|---|---|---|---|
| NC343 | J 17 .. | 1·25 | 1·75 | NC409 | O 19 .. | 1·25 | 1·25 | NC461 | S 21 .. | 1·25 | 1·25 |
| NC353 | K 17 .. | 1·25 | 6·00 | NC418 | O 20 .. | 1·50 | 1·25 | NC473 | S 22 .. | 1·25 | 1·25 |
| NC372 | L 18 .. | 1·25 | 1·25 | NC425 | P 20 .. | 1·25 | 1·25 | NC485 | T 22 .. | 1·25 | 1·25 |
| NC390 | M 19 .. | 2·25 | 1·25 | NC431 | Q 20 .. | 1·25 | 1·25 | NC503a | U 23 .. | 2·00 | 2·00 |
| NC401 | N 19 .. | 1·25 | 1·25 | NC449 | R 21 .. | 1·25 | 1·25 | | | | |

**Watermark varieties.**   The following controls are known:—

Wmk. inverted .. .. .. NC343, 353, 409, 425, 431, 449, 461.
Wmk. inverted and reversed .. NC272, 291, 304, 330, 372, 401, 409, 425, 431, 461, 492.

## 1924-26. Wmk. Block Cypher

All stamps are watermarked Block Cypher, Type **W.15** except for the 1d. and 1½d. on experimental paper Wmk. Type **W.16** listed as varieties.

### Perforation
Normally Type 2, but see list of other Types on page 88.

Cat. No.   S.G. No.

**1924 (APRIL).   ½d. GREEN, TYPE N6**

|  |  |  |  | Shades | Unused | Used |
|---|---|---|---|---|---|---|
| N33 |  | 418 |  | (1) Green | 5 | 5 |
| a. | Watermark inverted | .. | 8    5 | (2) Pale green | 5 | 5 |
| b. | Watermark sideways Crown pointing to left | .. | 60    30 | (3) Deep green | 10 | 5 |
|  |  |  |  | (4) Bright green | 5 | 5 |
| c. | Ditto Crown pointing to right | .. | 60    30 | (5) Deep bright green | 15 | 10 |
| d. | Doubly printed | .. .. | £300 | (6) Yellow-green | 2·00 | 75 |
| e. | Imperf. between right side and margin .. | .. .. |  |  |  |  |
| s. | " Specimen ", Type 15 | .. | 2·00 | w. " Cancelled ", Type 28 .. | 1·00 |  |
| t. | " Specimen ", Type 23 | .. | 1·00 | wa. " Cancelled ", Type 28P .. |  |  |
| u. | " Specimen ", Type 30 | .. | 1·00 | x. " Cancelled ", Type 33P .. | 1·00 |  |
| ua. | " Specimen ", Type 32 | .. | 3·00 | y. " Cancelled ", Type 33 .. | 2·00 |  |
| v. | " Cancelled ", Type 24 | .. | 3·00 | z. " Specimen ", Type 32 and " Cancelled ", Type 34 .. |  |  |

An example of a double print, each varies slightly

N33d

### Plates
53 plates have been identified, 5 of which had been at press with the previous printer.

### Booklet panes
Panes of six

| NB12   Watermark upright | 50 | | NB12a   Watermark inverted | 70 |
|---|---|---|---|---|
| s. " Specimen ", Type 23 .. | 7·00 | | as. " Specimen ", Type 23 .. | 7·00 |
| t. " Specimen ", Type 30 .. | 7·00 | | at. " Specimen ", Type 30 .. | 7·00 |
| u. " Cancelled ", Type 28 .. | 7·00 | | au. " Cancelled ", Type 28 .. | 7·00 |
| ua. " Cancelled ", Type 28P .. | | | av. " Cancelled ", Type 33P .. | 7·00 |
| ub. Cancelled, " London EC " .. | | | | |
| v. " Cancelled ", Type 33P .. | 7·00 | | | |

### Controls
Printed by Waterlow & Sons

| | I. | P. | | I. | P. | | I. | P. |
|---|---|---|---|---|---|---|---|---|
| NC523   A 24 .. | 10 | 50 | NC574   G 27 .. | 10 | 3·00 | NC653   N 30 .. | 10 | † |
| a. Wmk. inv. | 2·00 | 6·00 | a. Wmk. inv. | 3·00 | † | a. Wmk. inv. | 2·50 | † |
| NC531   B 24 .. | 10 | 3·00 | NC584   H 27 .. | 10 | 3 50 | NC664   O 31 .. | 10 | — |
| a. Wmk. inv. | 2·00 | † | a. Wmk. inv. | 3·00 | † | a. Wmk. inv. | 2·50 | † |
| NC539   C 25 .. | 10 | 4·00 | NC591   I 28 .. | 10 | † | NC675   P 31 .. | 10 | † |
| a. Wmk. inv. | 2·00 | † | a. Wmk. inv. | 3·00 | † | NC686   Q 32 .. | 10 | † |
| NC548   D 25 .. | 10 | † | NC601   J 28 .. | 10 | † | NC697   R 32 .. | 10 | † |
| a. Wmk. inv. | 2·00 | † | a. Wmk. inv. | 3·00 | † | a. Wmk. inv. | 3·00 | † |
| NC556   E 26 .. | 10 | 18·00 | NC612   K 29 .. | 10 | † | NC708   S 33 .. | 10 | † |
| a. Wmk. inv. | 2·00 | † | a. Wmk. inv. | 4·00 | † | NC719   T 33 .. | 10 | † |
| NC563   F 26 .. | 10 | 5·00 | NC631   L 29 .. | 10 | 3·50 | a. Wmk. inv. | 3·50 | † |
| a. Wmk. inv. | 2·00 | † | a. Wmk. inv. | 4·00 | † | NC730c   U 34 .. | — | † |
|  |  |  | NC642   M 30 .. | 10 | † |  |  |  |
|  |  |  | a. Wmk. inv. | 4·00 | † |  |  |  |

Printed by Harrison & Sons

|  | I. | P. |
|---|---|---|
| *NC730*  U 34 .. | 30 | † |
| a. Wmk. inv. | — | † |
| b. Doubly ptd. | — | † |

| Streaky Gum | | |
|---|---|---|
|  | I. | P. |
| *NC737*  U 34 .. | 55 | † |

| Streaky Gum | | |
|---|---|---|
|  | I. | P. |
| *NC745*  V 34 .. | 10 | 1·75 |
| a. Wmk. inv. | 4·00 | † |

| Cat. No. | S.G. No. | | Shades | Unused | Used |
|---|---|---|---|---|---|

**1924 (APRIL).  1d. RED, TYPE N5**

N34     419
a. Experimental paper,
   Watermark Type W.16  ..  4·00
b. Watermark inverted   ..   10   5
c. Watermark sideways   ..   1·00   1·00
d. Inverted Q for O in ONE
   (R.20/3)  ..  ..  ..  25·00
e. Damaged top.  No Cross on
   Crown  ..  ..  ..
s. " Specimen ", Type 15  ..
t. " Specimen ", Type 23  ..   1·00
u. Imperf. optd. " Specimen ",
   Type 23  ..  ..  ..  3·00
v. " Specimen ", Type 30  ..  1·00

(1) Scarlet   5   5
(2) Pale scarlet   5   5
(3) Scarlet-vermilion   5   5
(4) Deep scarlet-vermilion   60   25

w. Imperf. " Cancelled ", Type 24   4·00
wa. " Cancelled ", Type 24   ..   3·00
x. " Cancelled ", Type 28   ..   1·00
xa. " Cancelled ", Type 28P   ..
xb. Cancelled, " London EC "   ..
y. " Cancelled ", Type 33P   ..   1·00
z. " Cancelled ", Type 33   ..
za. " Specimen ", Type 32 and
    " Cancelled ", Type 34   ..

N34*e*

**Plates**

25 plates have been identified, 6 of which had been at press with the previous printer.

**Booklet panes**

Panes of six

| NB13  Watermark upright | 50 |
|---|---|
| s. " Specimen ", Type 23  .. | 7·00 |
| t. " Specimen ", Type 30  .. | 7·00 |
| u. " Cancelled ", Type 28  .. | 7·00 |
| v. " Cancelled ", Type 33P  .. | 7·00 |

| NB13a  Watermark inverted | 65 |
|---|---|
| as. " Specimen ", Type 23  .. | 7·00 |
| at. " Specimen ", Type 30  .. | 7·00 |
| au. " Cancelled ", Type 28  .. | 7·00 |
| av. " Cancelled ", Type 33P  .. | 7·00 |

**Controls**

Printed by Waterlow & Sons

|  | I. | P. |  | I. | P. |  | I. | P. |
|---|---|---|---|---|---|---|---|---|
| *NC524*  A 24 .. | 15 | 3·00 | *NC575*  G 27 .. | 10 | † | *NC643*  M 30 .. | 10 | † |
| a. Wmk. inv. | 4·00 | † | a. Wmk. inv. | 4·00 | † | a. Wmk. inv. | 4·00 | † |
| *NC532*  B 24 .. | 10 | 4·00 | *NC585*  H 27 .. | 10 | † | *NC654*  N 30 .. | 50 | † |
| b. Wmk. inv. | 4·00 | † | a. Wmk. inv. | 4·00 | † | *NC665*  O 31 .. | 10 | — |
| *NC540*  C 25 .. | 10 | 1·50 | *NC592*  I 28 .. | 10 | † | a. Wmk. inv. | 4·00 | † |
| a. Wmk. inv. | 4·00 | † | a. Wmk. inv. | 5·00 | † | *NC676*  P 31 .. | 10 | † |
| *NC549*  D 25 .. | 10 | † | *NC602*  J 28 .. | 10 | † | *NC687*  Q 32 .. | 10 | † |
| a. Wmk. inv. | 4·00 | † | a. Wmk. inv. | 4·00 | † | a. Wmk. inv. | — | † |
| *NC557*  E 26 .. | 10 | † | *NC613*  K 29 .. | 10 | † | *NC698*  R 32 .. | 50 | † |
| a. Wmk. inv. | 4·00 | † | a. Wmk. inv. | 4·50 | † | *NC709*  S 33 .. | 10 | † |
| *NC564*  F 26 .. | 10 | † | *NC632*  L 29 .. | 10 | 9·00 | *NC720*  T 33 .. | 10 | † |
| a. Wmk. inv. | 4·00 | † | a. Wmk. inv. | 4·50 | † | a. Wmk. inv. | — | † |
|  |  |  |  |  |  | *NC731b*  U 34 .. | — | † |

Experimental paper.  Wmk. **W.16**

*NC532a*  B 24 ..   6·00   †

Printed by Harrison & Sons

| *NC731*  U 34 .. | 40 | † |
|---|---|---|
| a. Wmk. inv. | 7·00 | † |

| Streaky Gum | | |
|---|---|---|
| *NC738*  U 34 .. | 75 | † |

| Streaky Gum | | |
|---|---|---|
| *NC746*  V 34 .. | 20 | 2·50 |

## 1924 (APRIL). 1½d. RED-BROWN, TYPE N6

| Cat. No. | S.G. No. | | | |
|---|---|---|---|---|
| N35 | 420 | | | |
| a. | Tête-bêche (pair) .. | .. | 30·00 | 30·00 |
| aa. | Do. with gutter margin | .. | 32·00 | 32·00 |
| b. | Experimental paper, Watermark Type W.16 | .. | 5·00 | |
| c. | Watermark inverted | .. | 15 | 10 |
| d. | Watermark sideways | .. | 70 | 25 |
| e. | Printed on the gum | .. | 25·00 | |
| f. | Imperf. between right side and margin .. | .. | 20·00 | |
| g. | Imperf. between left side and margin | .. | 20·00 | |
| h. | Frame broken at left | .. | 8·00 | |
| i. | Blob on King's nose | | | |
| s. | " Specimen ", Type 15 | .. | | |
| t. | " Specimen ", Type 23 | .. | 1·00 | |
| u. | " Specimen ", Type 30 | .. | 1·00 | |
| ua. | " Specimen ", Type 32 | .. | | |
| v. | " Cancelled ", Type 24 | .. | | |
| w. | " Cancelled ", Type 28 | .. | 1·00 | |

| | Shades | Unused | Used |
|---|---|---|---|
| (1) | Red-brown | 10 | 5 |
| (2) | Deep red-brown | 12 | 5 |
| (3) | Pale red-brown | 50 | 15 |
| (4) | Chestnut (1924) | 10 | 5 |
| (5) | Bright chestnut (1926-7) | 25 | 8 |
| (6) | Orange-brown (1925) | 10 | 5 |
| (7) | Chocolate-brown (1924) | 25 | 10 |
| (8) | Yellow-brown (1932-34) | 8 | 5 |
| (9) | Deep yellow-brown (1934) | 25 | 5 |
| (10) | Bright yellow-brown (1934) | 30 | 8 |

| | | | |
|---|---|---|---|
| wa. | " Cancelled ", Type 28P | .. | |
| x. | " Cancelled ", Type 33P | .. | 1·00 |
| y. | " Cancelled ", Type 33 | .. | |
| z. | " Specimen ", Type 32 and " Cancelled ", Type 34 | .. | |

Variety *e.*  One sheet known to exist from Control U34

Variety *i* comes from the Waterlow printings made into continuous coils (Wmk. sideways) on every thirteenth stamp and is rare.

N35*h*

## Plates

56 plates have been identified, 2 of which had been at press with the previous printer.

## Booklet panes

Panes of six

| NB14 | Watermark upright | 60 |
|---|---|---|
| s. | " Specimen ", Type 23 .. | 6·00 |
| t. | " Specimen ", Type 30 .. | 6·00 |
| u. | " Cancelled ", Type 28 .. | 6·00 |
| ua. | " Cancelled ", Type 28P .. | |
| ub. | Cancelled, " London E.C." | |
| v. | " Cancelled ", Type 33P .. | 6·00 |

| NB14a | Watermark inverted | 75 |
|---|---|---|
| as. | " Specimen ", Type 23 .. | 6·00 |
| at. | " Specimen ", Type 30 .. | 6·00 |
| au. | " Cancelled ", Type 28 .. | 6·00 |
| aua. | " Cancelled ", Type 28P .. | |
| aub. | Cancelled, " London E.C." | |
| av. | " Cancelled ", Type 33P .. | 6·00 |

Panes of four with two advertisement labels *se-tenant*

| NB15 | Watermark upright | 6·00 |
|---|---|---|
| s. | " Specimen ", Type 23 .. | 10·00 |
| t. | " Specimen ", Type 30 .. | 10·00 |
| u. | " Cancelled ", Type 28 .. | 10·00 |
| v. | " Cancelled ", Type 33P .. | 10·00 |

| NB15a | Watermark inverted | 6·00 |
|---|---|---|
| as. | " Specimen ", Type 23 .. | 10·00 |
| at. | " Specimen ", Type 30 .. | 10·00 |
| au. | " Cancelled ", Type 28 .. | 10·00 |
| av. | " Cancelled ", Type 33P .. | 10·00 |
| NB15b | Watermark sideways | 75·00 |

## Controls

Printed at Somerset House

| | I. | P. |
|---|---|---|
| NC152 | E.26 .. 35·00 | † |

## Printed by Waterlow & Sons

| | I. | P. | | I. | P. | | I. | P. |
|---|---|---|---|---|---|---|---|---|
| NC525  A 24 .. | 15 | 50 | NC576  G 27 .. | 15 | † | NC644  M 30 .. | 15 | † |
| b. Wmk. inv. | 2·50 | † | a. Wmk. inv. | 2·00 | † | a. Wmk. inv. | 4·50 | † |
| NC533  B 24 .. | 15 | 10·00 | NC586  H 27 .. | 15 | 5·00 | NC655  N 30 .. | 15 | — |
| b. Wmk. inv. | 2·50 | † | a. Wmk. inv. | 2·50 | † | a. Wmk. inv. | 4·00 | † |
| NC541  C 25 .. | 15 | — | NC593  I 28 .. | 15 | 10·00 | NC666  O 31 .. | 15 | † |
| a. Wmk. inv. | 2·50 | † | a. Wmk. inv. | 2·50 | † | a. Wmk. inv. | 2·00 | † |
| NC550  D 25 .. | 15 | † | NC603  J 28 .. | 15 | † | NC677  P 31 .. | 15 | † |
| b. Wmk. inv. | 2·50 | † | a. Wmk. inv. | 2·75 | † | NC688  Q 32 .. | 15 | † |
| NC558  E 26 .. | 15 | † | NC614  K 29 .. | 15 | 10·00 | NC699  R 32 .. | 15 | † |
| a. Wmk. inv. | 2·50 | † | a. Wmk. inv. | 3·50 | † | NC710  S 33 .. | 15 | † |
| NC565  F 26 .. | 15 | 4·50 | NC633  L 29 .. | 15 | † | NC721  T 33 .. | 15 | † |
| a. Wmk. inv. | 2·50 | † | | | | NC732a  U 34 .. | — | † |

### Experimental paper.   Wmk. W.16

| | | | | | | | |
|---|---|---|---|---|---|---|---|
| NC525a A 24 .. | 7·00 | † | NC533a  B 24 .. | 9·00 | † | NC550a  D 25 .. | 8·00 | † |

| Printed by Harrison & Sons | | | Streaky Gum | | | Streaky Gum | | |
|---|---|---|---|---|---|---|---|---|
| NC732  U 34 .. | 25 | † | NC739  U 34 .. | 50 | | NC747  V 34 .. | 20 | — |
| | | | a. printed on the gum.. | — | † | | | |

| Cat. No. | S.G. No. | Shades | Unused | Used |
|---|---|---|---|---|

## 1924 (APRIL).   2d. ORANGE, TYPE N7, DIE II

| N36 | 421 | | | | Shades | Unused | Used |
|---|---|---|---|---|---|---|---|
| a. | No watermark | .. .. | 15·00 | | (1) Orange | 25 | 5 |
| b. | Watermark inverted | .. | 1·50 | 1·25 | (2) Deep orange | 30 | 5 |
| c. | Watermark sideways | .. | 5·00 | 3·00 | (3) Yellow-orange | 25 | 5 |
| s. | " Specimen ", Type 23 | .. | 1·50 | | (4) Deep yellow-orange | 75 | 10 |
| t. | " Specimen ", Type 32 | .. | | | (5) Pale yellow-orange | 30 | 5 |
| u. | " Specimen ", Type 32 and | | | | | | |
| | " Cancelled ", Type 34 | .. | | | | | |

Variety a, One sheet known to exist from Control C 25

### Plates

18 plates have been identified, 4 of which had been at press with the previous printer.

### Controls

Printed by Waterlow & Sons

| | I. | P. | | I. | P. | | I. | P. |
|---|---|---|---|---|---|---|---|---|
| NC526  A 24 .. | 30 | † | NC566  F 26 .. | 35 | † | NC634  L 29 .. | 30 | † |
| a. Wmk. inv. | 4·00 | † | a. Wmk. inv. | 4·00 | † | NC645  M 30 .. | 30 | † |
| NC534  B 24 .. | 30 | 7·00 | NC577  G 27 .. | 35 | † | a. Wmk. inv. | 4·50 | † |
| a. Wmk. inv. | 4·00 | † | a. Wmk. inv. | 4·00 | † | NC656  N 30 .. | 30 | † |
| NC542  C 25 .. | 30 | † | NC587  H 27 .. | 35 | † | NC667  O 31 .. | 30 | † |
| a. No wmk. | — | † | a. Wmk. inv. | 5·00 | † | NC678  P 31 .. | 30 | † |
| b. Wmk. inv. | 5·00 | † | NC594  I 28 .. | 35 | 10·00 | a. Wmk. inv. | 5·00 | † |
| NC551  D 25 .. | 15 | † | a. Wmk. inv. | 5·00 | † | NC689  Q 32 .. | 30 | † |
| a. Wmk. inv. | 4·50 | † | NC604  J 28 .. | 35 | † | NC700  R 32 .. | 30 | 15·00 |
| NC559  E 26 .. | 30 | † | a. Wmk. inv. | 4·50 | † | a. Wmk. inv. | 5·00 | † |
| a. Wmk. inv. | 3·50 | † | NC615  K 29 .. | 35 | † | NC711  S 33 .. | 30 | † |
| | | | a. Wmk. inv. | 5·00 | † | NC722  T 33 .. | 30 | † |

| Printed by Harrison & Sons | | | Streaky Gum | | | Streaky Gum | | |
|---|---|---|---|---|---|---|---|---|
| NC733  U 34 .. | 70 | † | NC740  U 34 .. | 80 | † | NC748  V 34 .. | 20 | — |

## 1924 (APRIL).   2½d. BLUE, TYPE N5

| N37 | 422 | | | | | Unused | Used |
|---|---|---|---|---|---|---|---|
| a. | No watermark | .. .. | 15·00 | | (1) Blue | 30 | 5 |
| b. | Watermark inverted | .. | 1·50 | 1·50 | (2) Pale blue (1924) | 30 | 5 |
| s. | " Specimen ", Type 23 | .. | | | (3) Bright blue | 30 | 5 |
| t. | " Specimen ", Type 32 | .. | | | (4) Ultramarine | 40 | 8 |
| u. | " Specimen ", Type 32 and | | | | | | |
| | " Cancelled ", Type 34 | .. | | | | | |

Variety a.   One sheet known to exist from Control B 24.

### Plates

15 plates have been identified, 3 of which had been at press with the previous printer.

## Controls

### Printed by Waterlow & Sons

| | | I. | P. | | | I. | P. | | | I. | P. |
|---|---|---|---|---|---|---|---|---|---|---|---|
| NC535 | B 24 .. | 35 | † | NC560 | E 26 .. | 35 | † | NC646 | M 30 .. | 35 | † |
| a. No wmk. | | — | † | a. Wmk. inv. | | 5·50 | † | a. Wmk. inv. | | 6·00 | † |
| b. Wmk. inv. | | 5·00 | † | NC578 | G 27 .. | 35 | 18·00 | NC657 | N 30 .. | 35 | † |
| NC543 | C 25 .. | 35 | † | a. Wmk. inv. | | 6·00 | † | NC668 | O 31 .. | 36·00 | † |
| a. Wmk. inv. | | 5·00 | † | NC588 | H 27 .. | 70 | † | NC690 | Q 32 .. | 35 | † |
| NC552 | D 25 .. | 35 | † | NC595 | I 28 .. | 35 | † | NC701 | R 32 .. | 40 | † |
| a. Wmk. inv. | | 5·00 | † | a. Wmk. inv. | | 6·00 | † | NC712 | S 33 .. | 75 | † |
| | | | | NC616 | K 29 .. | 35 | † | NC723 | T 33 .. | 40 | † |

### Printed by Harrison & Sons

| | | I. | P. | | | | | |
|---|---|---|---|---|---|---|---|---|
| NC749 | V 34 | 2·00 | † | NC756 | W 35 | 75 | 2·00 | |
| a. Wmk. inv. | | 12·00 | † | | | | | |

| Cat. No. S.G. No. | Shades | Unused | Used |
|---|---|---|---|

## 1924 (APRIL). 3d. VIOLET, TYPE N7

| N38 | 423 | | | | (1) Violet | 35 | 5 |
|---|---|---|---|---|---|---|---|
| a. | Watermark inverted | .. | 1·50 | 1·25 | (2) Pale violet (1924-25) | 45 | 5 |
| s. | " Specimen ", Type 23 | .. | | | (3) Pale dull reddish violet | | |
| t. | " Specimen ", Type 32 | .. | | | (1924-25) | 60 | 10 |
| u. | " Specimen ", Type 32 and | | | | (4) Deep violet | 65 | 10 |
| | " Cancelled ", Type 34 | .. | | | (5) Bright violet | 50 | 10 |
| | | | | | (6) Deep brownish violet | 75 | 20 |

### Plates

8 plates have been identified, 2 of which had been at press with the previous printer.

### Controls

### Printed by Waterlow & Sons

| | | I. | P. | | | I. | P. | | | I. | P. |
|---|---|---|---|---|---|---|---|---|---|---|---|
| NC536 | B 24 .. | 40 | † | NC561 | E 26 .. | 40 | † | NC647 | M 30 .. | 40 | † |
| a. Wmk. inv. | | 5·00 | † | a. Wmk. inv. | | 5·00 | † | NC658 | N 30 .. | 40 | † |
| NC544 | C 25 .. | 40 | † | NC579 | G 27 .. | 40 | 9·00 | NC680 | P 31 .. | 50 | † |
| a. Wmk. inv. | | 5·50 | † | a. Wmk. inv. | | 6·00 | † | NC702 | R 32 .. | 40 | † |
| NC553 | D 25 .. | 70 | † | NC596 | I 28 .. | 45 | † | NC713 | S 33 .. | 60 | † |
| a. Wmk. inv. | | 5·50 | † | a. Wmk. inv. | | 5·00 | † | NC724 | T 33 .. | 40 | † |
| | | | | NC617 | K 29 .. | 45 | † | | | | |

### Printed by Harrison & Sons
NC750 V 34 .. 50 †

## 1924 (APRIL). 4d. GREY-GREEN, TYPE N7

| N39 | 424 | | | | (1) Deep grey-green | 65 | 8 |
|---|---|---|---|---|---|---|---|
| a. | Watermark inverted | .. | 1·50 | 1·50 | (2) Grey-green | 65 | 8 |
| b. | Printed on the gum | .. | £175 | † | (3) Very deep grey-green | | |
| s. | " Specimen ", Type 23 | .. | | | (1934-35) | 1·25 | 10 |
| t. | " Specimen ", Type 32 | .. | | | | | |
| u. | " Cancelled ", Type 28 | .. | | | | | |
| v. | " Specimen ", Type 32 and | | | | | | |
| | " Cancelled ", Type 34 | .. | | | | | |

### Plates

8 plates have been identified, 2 of which had been at press with the previous printer.

### Controls

### Printed by Waterlow & Sons

| | | I. | P. | | | I. | P. | | | I. | P. |
|---|---|---|---|---|---|---|---|---|---|---|---|
| NC537 | B 24 .. | 75 | † | NC580 | G 27 .. | 75 | † | NC648 | M 30 .. | 75 | † |
| a. Wmk. inv. | | 5·00 | † | a. Wmk. inv. | | 6·00 | † | a. Wmk. inv. | | 6·00 | † |
| NC545 | C 25 .. | 75 | † | NC597 | I 28 .. | 75 | † | NC670 | O 31 .. | 75 | † |
| a. Wmk. inv. | | 5·00 | † | a. Wmk. inv. | | 6·00 | † | NC692 | Q 32 .. | 75 | † |
| NC562 | E 26 .. | 75 | † | NC618 | K 29 .. | 75 | † | NC703 | R 32 .. | 75 | † |
| a. Wmk. inv. | | 5·00 | † | | | | | NC725 | T 33 .. | 75 | † |

### Printed by Harrison & Sons

| | | | | | | | | | | |
|---|---|---|---|---|---|---|---|---|---|---|
| NC751 | V 34 .. | 75 | † | NC756a | W 35 .. | 1·25 | † | NC759a | X 35 .. | 60 | — |

## 1924 (APRIL). 5d. BROWN, TYPE N8

| N40 | 425 | | | | (1) Brown | 1·00 | 12 |
|---|---|---|---|---|---|---|---|
| a. | Watermark inverted | .. | 2·00 | 2·00 | (2) Deep brown | 1·00 | 12 |
| s. | " Specimen ", Type 23 | .. | 1·30 | | (3) Reddish brown (1927-28) | 1·25 | 15 |
| t. | " Specimen ", Type 32 | .. | | | (4) Bright ochre-brown | 1·00 | 12 |
| u. | " Specimen ", Type 32 and | | | | (5) Deep bright ochre-brown | | |
| | " Cancelled ", Type 34 | .. | | | (1934) | 1·50 | 20 |

**Plates**

2 plates have been identified, one of which had been at press with the previous printer.

**Controls**

Printed by Waterlow & Sons

| | I. | P. | | | I. | P. | | | I. | P. |
|---|---|---|---|---|---|---|---|---|---|---|
| *NC527* | A 24 .. | 1·50 | 1·50 | *NC589* | H 27 .. | 1·50 | † | *NC671* | O 31 .. | 1·75 | † |
| a. Wmk. inv. | | 8·00 | † | *NC598* | I 28 .. | 1·50 | † | *NC693* | Q 32 .. | 2·50 | † |
| *NC546* | C 25 .. | 1·50 | † | a. Wmk. inv. | | 8·00 | † | *NC715* | S 33 .. | 1·75 | † |
| a. Wmk. inv. | | 8·00 | † | *NC619* | K 29 .. | 1·50 | † | *NC726* | T 33 .. | 23·00 | † |
| *NC570* | F 26 .. | 1·50 | † | *NC638* | L 29 .. | 1·50 | † | *NC734a* | U 34 .. | — | † |
| a. Wmk. inv. | | 8·00 | † | *NC649* | M 30 .. | 2·00 | † | | | | |

Printed by Harrison & Sons

| | | I. | P. | | | I. | P. | | | I. | P. |
|---|---|---|---|---|---|---|---|---|---|---|---|
| *NC734* | U 34 .. | 1·50 | † | *NC752* | V 34 .. | 1·50 | † | *NC759b* | X 35 .. | 1·50 | |

| Cat. No. | S.G. No. | Shades | Unused | Used |
|---|---|---|---|---|

## 1924 (APRIL).   6d. PURPLE, TYPE N8.   CHALK-SURFACED PAPER

| | | | | | Shades | Unused | Used |
|---|---|---|---|---|---|---|---|
| N41 | 426 | | | | Somerset House Printing (1924/5) | | |
| a. | Watermark inverted | | .. | 2·00 | (1) Plum | 2·00 | 70 |
| b. | Watermark inverted and re- | | | | (2) Rosy mauve | 1·50 | 35 |
| | versed | .. | .. | 4·50 | | | |
| | | | | | Harrison Printing (1936) | | |
| | | | | | (3) Reddish purple | 1·50 | 35 |
| | | | | | (4) Deep reddish purple | 1·75 | 45 |

**Plates**

2 plates have been identified, previously used with the Simple Cypher watermark, and 2 other plates were used by Harrison & Sons in 1936.

**Controls**

Printed at Somerset House

| | | I. | P. | | | I. | P | | | I. | P. |
|---|---|---|---|---|---|---|---|---|---|---|---|
| *NC148* | B. 24 .. | 2·50 | † | *NC149* | C. 25 .. | 2·25 | † | *NC150* | D. 25 .. | 2·25 | † |
| a. Wmk. inv. | | 6·00 | † | a. Wmk. inv. | | 6·00 | † | a. Wmk. inv. | | 6·00 | † |
| b. Wmk. inv. | | | | b. Wmk. inv. | | | | | | | |
| and rev. .. | | 10·00 | † | and rev. .. | | 10·00 | † | | | | |

Printed by Harrison & Sons

| | | I. | P. | | | I. | P. |
|---|---|---|---|---|---|---|---|
| *NC759g* | Y 36 .. | 12·00 | † | *NC759i* | Z 36 .. | 2·25 | † |
| | | | | ia. Wmk. inv. | | 7·50 | † |

## 1926.   6d. PURPLE, TYPE N8.   ORDINARY PAPER

| | | | | | | Unused | Used |
|---|---|---|---|---|---|---|---|
| N42 | 426a | | | | (1) Rosy mauve | 75 | 8 |
| a. | Watermark inverted | | .. | 2·50 | 2·50 | (2) Pale rosy mauve (1927-28) | 90 | 10 |
| s. | " Specimen ", Type 32 | .. | | | (3) Reddish purple (1932-33) | 85 | 10 |
| t. | " Specimen ", Type 26 and | | | | (4) Deep reddish purple | | |
| | " Cancelled ", Type 34 | .. | | | | (1934-36) | 1·00 | 10 |
| u. | " Cancelled ", Type 34 | .. | | | (5) Purple (1935-38) | 75 | 8 |
| | | | | | (6) Deep purple (1935-38) | 1·25 | 20 |

**Plates**

11 plates have been identified at press with Somerset House. Harrison & Sons used 7 plates, one of which had been used at Somerset House.

**Controls**

Printed at Somerset House

| | | I. | P | | | I. | P. | | | I. | P. |
|---|---|---|---|---|---|---|---|---|---|---|---|
| *NC151* | D. 25 .. | 4·50 | † | *NC157* | I. 28 .. | 1·00 | 1·50 | *NC162* | N. 30 .. | 90 | † |
| *NC153* | E. 26 .. | 90 | 14·00 | a. Wmk. inv. | | 4·50 | † | a. Wmk. inv. | | 4·50 | † |
| a. Wmk. inv. | | 4·00 | † | *NC158* | J. 28 .. | 90 | 2·00 | *NC163* | O. 31 .. | 90 | † |
| *NC154* | F. 26 .. | 90 | † | a. Wmk. inv. | | 5·00 | † | *NC164* | P. 31 .. | 90 | † |
| a. Wmk. inv. | | 4·00 | † | *NC159* | K. 29 .. | 90 | † | *NC165* | Q. 32 .. | 90 | † |
| *NC155* | G. 27 .. | 90 | † | a. Wmk. inv. | | 4·00 | † | *NC166* | R. 32 .. | 90 | † |
| a. Wmk. inv. | | 4·00 | † | *NC160* | L. 29 .. | 90 | † | *NC167* | S. 33 .. | 1·00 | † |
| *NC156* | H. 27 .. | 90 | † | a. Wmk. inv. | | 4·00 | † | *NC168* | T. 33 .. | 90 | † |
| a. Wmk. inv. | | 4·00 | † | *NC161* | M. 30 .. | 90 | 28·00 | | | | |

Printed by Harrison & Sons

| | | I. | P. | | | I. | P. | | | I. | P. |
|---|---|---|---|---|---|---|---|---|---|---|---|
| *NC753* | V 34 .. | 1·00 | † | *NC759f* | Y 36 .. | 1·00 | † | *NC759k* | B 37 .. | 1·00 | — |
| a. Wmk. inv. | | 6·00 | † | fa. Wmk. inv. | | 6·50 | † | ka. Wmk. inv. | | 6·50 | † |
| *NC757* | W 35 .. | 1·50 | 1·25 | *NC759h* | Z 36 .. | 1·00 | † | *NC759l* | C 38 .. | 1·00 | † |
| a. Wmk. inv. | | 6·50 | † | ha. Wmk. inv. | | 6·50 | † | la. Wmk. inv. | | 6·50 | † |
| *NC759c* | X 35 .. | 1·00 | 1·25 | *NC759i* | A 37 .. | 1·00 | † | *NC759m* | D 38 .. | 1·00 | 1·00 |
| ca. Wmk. inv. | | 6·00 | † | ja. Wmk. inv. | | 6·00 | † | ma. Wmk. inv. | | 7·00 | † |

| Cat. No. | S.G. No. | | | Shades | Unused | Used |
|---|---|---|---|---|---|---|

## 1924 (APRIL). 9d. OLIVE-GREEN, TYPE N9

| | | | | | | |
|---|---|---|---|---|---|---|
| N43 | 427 | | | (1) Olive-green | 2·50 | 25 |
| *a.* | Watermark inverted | .. 4·00 | 2·50 | (2) Pale olive-green | 5·00 | 40 |
| *s.* | " Specimen ", Type 23 | .. 2·50 | | (3) Deep olive-green | 4·00 | 40 |
| *t.* | " Specimen ", Type 32 | .. | | (4) Olive-yellow-green (1933) | 7·00 | 3·00 |
| *u.* | " Specimen ", Type 32 and | | | | | |
| | " Cancelled ", Type 34 | .. | | | | |

### Plates
5 plates have been identified.

### Controls
Printed by Waterlow & Sons

| | I. | P. | | | I. | P. | | | I. | P. |
|---|---|---|---|---|---|---|---|---|---|---|
| *NC528* A 24 .. | 3·00 | 2·50 | *NC599* I 28 .. | 3·00 | † | *NC661* N 30 .. | 3·00 | † |
| a. Wmk. inv. | 6·00 | † | a. Wmk. inv. | 7·50 | † | *NC683* P 31 .. | 3·00 | † |
| *NC547* C 25 .. | 3·00 | † | *NC609* J 28 .. | 3·00 | † | a. Wmk. inv. | 7·50 | † |
| a. Wmk. inv. | 6·50 | † | a. Wmk. inv. | 7·50 | † | *NC705* R 32 .. | 3·00 | † |
| *NC571* F 26 .. | 3·50 | † | *NC639* L 29 .. | 3·00 | † | *NC727* T 33 .. | 4·50 | † |
| a. Wmk. inv. | 7·00 | † | | | | | | |

Printed by Harrison & Sons

*NC754* V 34 .. 3·00 † | *NC758* W 35 .. 3·50 † | *NC759d* X 35 .. 3·00 3·50

## 1924 (APRIL). 10d. TURQUOISE, TYPE N9

| | | | | | | |
|---|---|---|---|---|---|---|
| N44 | 428 | | | (1) Turquoise-blue | 2·50 | 75 |
| *a.* | Watermark inverted | .. 10·00 | | (2) Deep greenish blue | 4·00 | 1·00 |
| *s.* | " Specimen ", Type 23 | .. | | (3) Dull greenish blue | 2·50 | 75 |
| *t.* | Do. Imperf... | .. 3·00 | | (4) Deep dull greenish blue | | |
| *u.* | " Specimen ", Type 32 | .. | | (1935) | 4·00 | 1·00 |
| *v.* | " Specimen ", Type 32 and | | | | | |
| | " Cancelled ", Type 34 | .. .. | | | | |

### Plates
3 plates have been identified, 2 of which had been at press with the previous printer.

### Controls
Printed by Waterlow & Sons

| | I. | P. | | | I. | P. | | | I. | P. |
|---|---|---|---|---|---|---|---|---|---|---|
| *NC529* A 24 .. | 8·00 | 4·00 | *NC583* G 27 .. | 4·00 | † | *NC695* Q 32 .. | 9·00 | † |
| *NC554* D 25 .. | 4·00 | † | *NC610* J 28 .. | 4·00 | † | *NC717* S 33 .. | 4·50 | † |
| a. Wmk. inv. | 15·00 | † | *NC640* L 29 .. | 5·00 | † | *NC735a* U 34 .. | — | † |
| *NC572* F 26 .. | 4·00 | † | *NC673* O 31 .. | 5·50 | † | | | |
| a. Wmk. inv. | 15·00 | | | | | | | |

Printed by Harrison & Sons

*NC735* U 34 .. 8·00 † | *NC754a* V 34 .. 6·00 † | *NC758a* W 35 .. 4·00 †

## 1924 (APRIL). 1s. BISTRE-BROWN, TYPE N9

| | | | | | |
|---|---|---|---|---|---|
| N45 | 429 | | (1) Bistre-brown | 2·25 | 15 |
| *a.* | Watermark inverted | .. 5·00 | (2) Buff-brown | 2·25 | 15 |
| *s.* | " Specimen ", Type 23 | .. | (3) Pale buff-brown (1924-25) | 3·00 | 20 |
| *t.* | Do. Imperf... | .. 3·50 | (4) Fawn-brown | 2·25 | 15 |
| *u.* | " Specimen ", Type 32 | .. | (5) Deep fawn-brown (1935) | 5·00 | 30 |
| *v.* | " Specimen ", Type 32 and | | | | |
| | " Cancelled ", Type 34 | .. | | | |

### Plates
5 plates have been identified, 2 of which had been at press with the previous printer.

## Controls

Printed by Waterlow & Sons

| | | I. | P. | | | I. | P. | | | I. | P. |
|---|---|---|---|---|---|---|---|---|---|---|---|
| NC530 | A 24 .. | 2·50 | 5·00 | NC590 | H 27 .. | 2·50 | † | NC641 | L 29 .. | 2·50 | † |
| a. Wmk. inv. | | 8·00 | † | NC600 | I 28 .. | 2·50 | † | a. Wmk. inv. | | 9·00 | † |
| NC538 | B 24 .. | 2·50 | † | a. Wmk. inv. | | 9·00 | † | NC663 | N 30 .. | 2·50 | † |
| NC555 | D 25 .. | 2·50 | † | NC611 | J 28 .. | 2·50 | † | NC685 | P 31 | 2·50 | † |
| a. Wmk. inv. | | 8·00 | † | a. Wmk. inv. | | 9·00 | † | NC707 | R 32 .. | 4·00 | † |
| NC573 | F 26 .. | 2·50 | † | NC622 | K 29 .. | 3·00 | † | NC718 | S 33 .. | 3·50 | † |
| a. Wmk. inv. | | 8·00 | † | | | | | NC736a | U 34 .. | — | † |

Printed by Harrison & Sons

| | | I. | P. | | | I. | P. | | | I. | P. |
|---|---|---|---|---|---|---|---|---|---|---|---|
| NC736 | U 34 .. | 3·00 | † | NC755 | V 34 .. | 3·00 | 10·00 | NC759 | W 35 .. | 3·00 | † |
| NC759e | X 35 .. | 3·00 | † | | | | | | | | |

## Perforation of ½d. to 1s.

Nos. N33/45 are normally Type 2 but the following may be found:

Type 2A
- ½d. A 24, C 25, E 26
- 1d. C 25
- 1½d. F 26, I 28
- 2d. B 24, I 28
- 3d. G 27
- 6d. W 35, X 35, B 37, D 38
- 9d. X 35
- 1s V 34

Variety Type 2C
- ½d. E 26, H 27
- 1d. E 26
- 1½d. B 24, E 26
- 2d. B 24
- 3d. B 24
- 4d. B 24, E 26
- 6d. B. 24, C. 25

Type 3A
- ½d. A 24, E 26, F 26, G 27, H 27, L 29, V 34
- 1d. A 24, L 29, V 34
- 1½d. A 24, H 27
- 2d. B 24
- 5d. A 24
- 6d. E. 26, I. 28, J. 28, M. 30
- 9d. A 24
- 10d. A 24
- 1s. A 24

Type 4
- ½d. U 34, V34
- 1d. U 34, V 34
- 1½d. V 34
- 2d. V 34
- 2½d. V 34
- 3d. V 34
- 4d. V 34
- 5d. V 34
- 6d. B 34, W 35
- 9d. V 34
- 1s. V 34

# King George V

## Photogravure Issues, 1934-36

### General Notes on Photogravure Issues

The following is a brief description of the terms used in connection with the photogravure process. For further information on this and other forms of stamp printing, see *Postage Stamps in the Making* by John Easton.

**MULTIPOSITIVE.** The prepared design is photographed in such a manner as to give a positive image on the plate. This positive is then used to make the multipositive plate. This plate contains 480 images, the equivalent of two post office sheets. The images on the plate will appear as negatives.

A photograph of the multipositive is now reproduced on to a carbon tissue. This has been prepared with a screen of fine lines which are insoluble, and result in the break-up of the design with numerous tiny dots.

**THE CYLINDER.** The carbon (with a positive impression) is now wrapped round the copper cylinder and treated with an acid resistant. The lighter portions and therefore smaller dots of the design will leave smaller recesses on the cylinder. Several cylinders may be made from a single multipositive, and constant flaws existing on two or more cylinders are called multipositive flaws.

**PRINTING.** The cylinder is inked by means of an inking roller, and then scraped with the doctor knife. This leaves the cylinder clean but for the ink left in the recesses. The cylinder now meets the paper on the impression roller and the printing is thus accomplished.

Each revolution of the cylinder prints two panes of 240 stamps and these revolutions are continuous until the whole of the reel of paper has been printed. This is known as " web " printing.

In some cases one of the panes must have been faulty as cylinder blocks are known from only one side of the cylinder (e.g. the 4d. 1934 cyl. 3). Some cylinder numbers are unique, or perhaps only two or three copies are known. They are probably registration sheets that were put into circulation, and provide the collector of modern issues the same excitement of discovery as a Victorian " abnormal ". These numbers are shown in the cylinder listings with an asterisk. Single pane cylinders have been used, however, first in the reign of King George VI and note is simply made of these in our listing.

Occasionally the paper breaks and is simply joined by overlapping and sticking together the two ends. This gives rise to the joined paper varieties, where stamps are printed on paper of double thickness.

**CYLINDER MARKS.** Various marginal markings were etched on the cylinders, such as perforation register squares, and small lines and crosses used as guide marks. The punched holes are to facilitate accurate perforation. They fit on to lugs at the sides of the perforating machine.

**CYLINDER NUMBERS.** These are records of every cylinder made, whether or not they were put to press. They were etched twice on each cylinder. The left-hand pane had the number without a full stop, and the right-hand pane had a full stop after the number. When the cylinder number was followed by the letter " R ", it signified that the cylinder had to be worked in the reverse direction. This only applied in the early days, when Harrison & Sons were using German machines that only printed one sheet at a time. From these early printings came the varieties " printed on the gum " and inverted watermarks on the stamps with large format.

**CONTROLS.** The control was now no longer screwed into the plate, but etched on the cylinder in the margin. When it became necessary to change the control, the old control had to be filled in, and a new one etched in its place. Traces of the old control are sometimes visible. On the lesser used values where new cylinders were rarely needed, the practice was to add a line under the control to show the new period. Subsequently another line was added at the left and so on until the whole control was " boxed in ". (*See illustration.*)

**VARIETIES.** To produce a perfect cylinder by the methods described must be difficult, and probably many cylinders were spoiled and not used. The gaps in the numbering of the cylinders known to philatelists point to that conclusion. Even with the cylinders that are used, most show a small number of minor flaws inherent in the process. Larger and more obvious flaws are collectable items, more especially when attempts at retouching have been made after the cylinder has been put to press. Retouches can be made to the multipositive, or to the cylinder, and most of the retouches known are in the latter category. Some of these repairs are well executed, and others can be detected with the naked eye.

**PERFORATION.** For notes on perforators see Appendix I.

### PHOTOGRAVURE CONTROL PRICES.

The fractional controls are best collected in blocks, to show the control, cylinder number and both left and bottom margins.

Our prices are for blocks of six except for Nos. NC767, 768, 768a, 768b and 769 which are for blocks of four. Where strips, pairs or singles are in stock, they will be supplied at the prices quoted, less an allowance for the reduced number of stamps.

In our list " P." now refers to items where BOTH side and bottom margins are perforated. " I." is where one or both margins are imperf.

Boxed Control
These are listed
in small type.

Fractional Control.   Perf.

All stamps in this Section were printed by Harrison & Sons with watermark Type **W.15** and perforated 15 × 14 in sheets of 240 (20 rows of 12). Detailed lists of cylinder numbers are given in Appendix N and booklet panes with cylinder numbers are given in Appendix M.

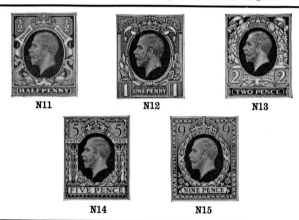

N11          N12          N13

N14          N15

| Cat. No. | S.G. No. | Type | Date | Description | | Unused | Used |
|----------|----------|------|------|-------------|---|--------|------|
| **LARGE FORMAT.** | | **Designs measure approx. 18½ × 22½ mm.** | | | | | |
| N46 | — | **N12** | 24.9.34 | 1d. (1) Scarlet | | 10 | 10 |
| a. | Watermark inverted | | .. 4·50 | (2) Bright scarlet | | 10 | 10 |
| b. | Printed on the gum | | .. 30·00 | | | | |
| c. | Imperf. between (pair) | | .. | | | | |
| N47 | — | **N11** | 20.8.34 | 1½d. (1) Red-brown | | 10 | 10 |
| a. | Watermark inverted | | .. 15·00 | (2) Bright-red-brown | | 10 | 10 |

The designs were reduced in size to facilitate more accurate perforation.

#### Controls

(a) Control below second stamp bottom row

| | | | | I. | P. |
|--|--|--|--|----|----|
| NC764 | U 34 | 1½d. | .. | 3·00 | 3·50 |
| NC765 | V 34 | 1½d. | .. | 1·50 | 1·50 |

(b) " Fractional " control (letter above numeral) in left margin opposite the 19th row

| | | | | | |
|--|--|--|--|--|--|
| NC768 | V 34 | 1d. | .. | 50 | 50 |
| NC769 | V 34 | 1½d. | .. | 60 | 60 |

| Cat. No. | S.G. No. | Type | Date | Description | Unused | Used |
|---|---|---|---|---|---|---|

**INTERMEDIATE FORMAT. Designs measure approx. 18¼ × 22 mm.***

N48 — **N11** 19.11.34 ½d. (1) Green 10 5
- *a.* Watermark inverted .. 1·75 1·00 (2) Bluish green 10 5
- *b.* Imperf three sides† ..
- *s.* " Specimen ", Type 32 ..
- *t.* " Cancelled ", Type 28P ..

N49 — **N12** 1934 1d. (1) Scarlet 35 8
- *a.* Watermark inverted .. 1·75 1·00 (2) Bright scarlet 35 8
- *s.* " Specimen ", Type 32 .. (3) Pale scarlet 35 8
- *t.* " Cancelled ", Type 28P ..

N50 — **N11** 1934 1½d. Red-brown 50 8
- *a.* Watermark inverted .. 1·75 1·00
- *b.* Imperf. (pair) .. .. 45·00
- *c.* Imperf. 3 sides (pair) .. 50·00
- *t.* " Cancelled ", Type 28P ..

N51 — **N13** 21.1.35 2d. (1) Orange 35 35
- *a.* Broken tablet (Cyl. 5, (2) Bright orange 35 35
  R.20/9) .. .. .. 10·00
- *b.* Ditto retouched .. 3·00

*The specific sizes of the stamps are: ½d., 18.3 × 22·2; 1d., 18·4 × 22·1; 1½d., 18·2 × 22·2; 2d., 18·4 × 22·2 mm.

These designs were again reduced in size.

†This is known in a block of four in which the bottom pair is imperf. at top and sides. It is believed that these came from a sheet, not a booklet.

N51*a*

N52*d*

**Booklet panes of six**

NB20 ½d. Wmk. upright 4·00
- *c.* Cylinder No. .. .. 5·00
- *t.* " Cancelled ", Type 28P ..

NB21 1d. Wmk. upright 4·00
- *c.* Cylinder No. .. .. 5·00
- *t.* " Cancelled ", Type 28P ..

NB22 1½d. Wmk. upright 4·00
- *c.* Cylinder No. .. .. 5·00
- *t.* " Cancelled ", Type 28P ..

NB20a ½d. Wmk. inverted 12·00
- *at.* " Cancelled ", Type 28P ..

NB21a 1d. Wmk. inverted 12·00
- *at.* " Cancelled ", Type 28P ..

NB22a 1½d. Wmk. inverted 12·00
- *at.* " Cancelled ", Type 28P ..

**Booklet pane of four, with two advertisement labels**

The advertisements are printed in red-brown (for complete list, see appendix L)

NB23 1½d. Wmk. upright 15·00
- *c.* Cylinder No. .. .. 20·00
- *t.* " Cancelled ", Type 28P ..

NB23a 1½d. Wmk. inverted 15·00
- *at.* " Cancelled ", Type 28P ..

**CONTROLS**

(a) Control in left margin opposite the 19th row

| | | | | I. | P. |
|---|---|---|---|---|---|
| NC767 | V 34 | ½d. | .. | 25 | 60 |
| NC768a | V 34 | 1d. | .. | 1·50 | 1·50 |
| NC768b | V 34 | 1½d. | .. | 2·00 | 2·00 |

(b) Control in left margin opposite the 18th row

| | | | | I. | P. |
|---|---|---|---|---|---|
| NC769a | V 34 | 1½d. | .. | 12·00 | — |
| NC770 | V 34 | 2d. | .. | 2·50 | 6·50 |
| NC771a | W 35 | ½d. | .. | 60 | 6·00 |
| NC772a | W 35 | 1d. | .. | 10·00 | † |
| NC774 | W 35 | 2d. | .. | 2·00 | 11·00 |

**SMALL FORMAT. Designs measure approx. 18 × 21½ mm.***

N52 439 **N11** 1935 ½d. (1) Green 5 5
- *a.* Watermark inverted .. 50 20 (2) Bluish green 5 5
- *b.* Watermark sideways Crown
  pointing to left .. 40 40 *s.* " Cancelled ", Type 28P .. 1·25
- *c.* Ditto Crown pointing to right — 3·50 *t.* " Cancelled ", Type 33P .. 60
- *d.* Horn variety (Cyl. 36, R.1/12) 6·00 *u.* " Cancelled ", Type 33 .. 2·00

**91**

| Cat. No. | S.G. No. | Type | Date | | Description | | Unused | Used |
|---|---|---|---|---|---|---|---|---|
| N53 | 440 | **N12** | 1935 | | 1d. | (1) Scarlet | 5 | 5 |
| a. | Watermark inverted | | 50 | 15 | | (2) Bright scarlet | 5 | 5 |
| b. | Watermark sideways Crown | | | | | | | |
| | pointing to left .. | .. | 50 | 40 | f. | Double impression .. | .. | £200 |
| c. | Ditto Crown pointing to right | | 5·00 | | s. | " Cancelled ", Type 28P | .. | 1·00 |
| d. | Imperf. (pair) | .. | £180 | | t. | " Cancelled ", Type 33P | .. | 75 |
| e. | Imperf. 3 sides (pair) | .. | | | u. | " Cancelled ", Type 33 | .. | 2·00 |
| N54 | 441 | **N11** | 1935 | | 1½d. | (1) Red-brown | 5 | 5 |
| a. | Watermark inverted | .. | 25 | 5 | | (2) Bright red-brown | 5 | 5 |
| b. | Watermark sideways | .. | 75 | 40 | | | | |
| c. | Flaw in N.E. corner (Cyls. | | | | | | | |
| | 116, 119, R.19/1) .. | .. | 2·00 | | s. | " Cancelled ", Type 28P | .. | 1·00 |
| d. | Ditto retouched (Cyl. 116, | | | | t. | " Cancelled ", Type 33P | .. | 75 |
| | R.19/1) .. | .. | 2·00 | | u. | " Cancelled ", Type 33 | .. | 2·00 |
| N55 | 442 | **N13** | 1935 | | 2d. | (1) Orange | 15 | 5 |
| a. | Watermark sideways | .. | 6·00 | 4·50 | | (2) Bright orange | 15 | 5 |
| b. | Imperf. (pair) | .. | £200 | | d. | Broken value tablet (Cyl. 8, | | |
| c. | Retouched leaves (Cyl. 13., | | | | | R.20/1) .. .. | .. | 3·25 |
| | Control A 37, R.18/1) | .. | 3·00 | | s. | " Specimen ", Type 30 | .. | |
| N56 | 443 | **N12** | 18.3.35 | | 2½d. | (1) Bright blue | 30 | 5 |
| a. | Retouched panel (Cyl. 8, | | | | | (2) Ultramarine | 30 | 5 |
| | R.18/1) .. .. | .. | 1·50 | 1·00 | | | | |
| b. | Retouched panel (Cyl. 8., | | | | s. | " Specimen ", Type 23 | | |
| | R.18/1) .. .. | .. | 1·50 | 1·00 | 3d. | (1) Reddish violet | 30 | 5 |
| N57 | 444 | **N13** | 18.3.35 | | | (2) Violet | 40 | 5 |
| s. | " Specimen ", Type 30 | .. | | | 4d. | (1) Deep grey-green | 40 | 8 |
| N58 | 445 | **N13** | 2.12.35 | | | (2) Blackish green | 45 | 8 |
| s. | " Specimen ", Type 23 | .. | | | 5d. | (1) Yellow-brown | 80 | 12 |
| N59 | 446 | **N14** | 17.2.36 | | | (2) Deep yellow-brown | 90 | 15 |
| s. | " Specimen ", Type 23 | .. | | | 9d. | Deep olive-green | 1·75 | 20 |
| N60 | 447 | **N15** | 2.12.35 | | | | | |
| s. | " Specimen ", Type 23 | .. | | | 10d. | Turquoise-blue | 2·25 | 25 |
| N61 | 448 | **N15** | 24.2.36 | | | | | |
| s. | " Specimen ", Type 32 | .. | | | 1s. | Bistre-brown | 2·00 | 10 |
| N62 | 449 | **N15** | 24.2.36 | | t. | " Specimen ", Type 23 .. | | |
| a. | Double impression .. | .. | £300 | | | | | |
| s. | " Specimen ", Type 32 | .. | 3·00 | | | | | |

*The specific sizes of the stamps are ½d., 17·9 × 21·6; 1d., 18·1 × 21·7; 1½d., 17·9 × 21·8;
2d., 18 × 21·8 mm. The other values vary but none was issued in more than one size.

N53f

N62a

N54c

N55c          N55d          N56a     N56b

### Booklet panes of six

| | | | | |
|---|---|---|---|---|
| NB24 | ½d. Wmk. upright | 1·00 | | |
| c. | Cylinder No. | .. | .. | 1·50 |
| t. | " Cancelled ", Type 33P | .. | 4·00 | |
| u. | " Cancelled ", Type 33 | .. | 14·00 | |
| v. | " Cancelled ", Type 28P | .. | 4·00 | |
| NB25 | 1d. Wmk. upright | 1·00 | | |
| c. | Cylinder No. | .. | .. | 1·50 |
| t. | " Cancelled ", Type 33P | . | 5·00 | |
| u. | " Cancelled ", Type 33 | .. | 14·00 | |
| v. | " Cancelled ", Type 28P | .. | 5·00 | |
| NB26 | 1½d. Wmk. upright | 60 | | |
| c. | Cylinder No. | .. | .. | 1·25 |
| t. | " Cancelled ", Type 33P | .. | 5·00 | |
| u. | " Cancelled ", Type 33 | .. | 14·00 | |
| v. | " Cancelled ", Type 28P | .. | 5·00 | |

| | | | | |
|---|---|---|---|---|
| NB24a | ½d. Wmk. inverted | 3·50 | | |
| ac. | Cylinder No. | .. | .. | |
| at. | " Cancelled ", Type 33P | .. | 4·00 | |
| au. | " Cancelled ", Type 33 | .. | 14·00 | |
| av. | " Cancelled ", Type 28P | .. | 4·00 | |
| NB25a | 1d. Wmk. inverted | 3·50 | | |
| | | | | |
| at. | " Cancelled ", Type 33P | .. | 5·00 | |
| au. | " Cancelled ", Type 33 | .. | 14·00 | |
| av. | " Cancelled ", Type 28P | .. | 5·00 | |
| NB26a | 1½d. Wmk. inverted | 1·75 | | |
| | | | | |
| at. | " Cancelled ", Type 33P | .. | 5·00 | |
| au. | " Cancelled ", Type 33 | .. | 14·00 | |
| av. | " Cancelled ", Type 28P | .. | 5·00 | |

### Booklet panes of four with two advertisement labels

The advertisements are printed in black (for complete list see Appendix L).

| | | | | |
|---|---|---|---|---|
| NB27 | 1½d. Wmk. upright | 2·50 | | |
| c. | Cylinder No. | .. | .. | 4·50 |
| t. | " Cancelled ", Type 33P | .. | 10·00 | |
| u. | " Cancelled ", Type 33 | .. | 25·00 | |

| | | | | |
|---|---|---|---|---|
| NB27a | 1½d. Wmk. inverted | 2·50 | | |
| ac. | Cylinder No. | .. | .. | 20·00 |
| at. | " Cancelled ", Type 33P | .. | 10·00 | |
| au. | " Cancelled ", Type 33 | .. | 25·00 | |

### Controls

Control in left margin opposite the 18th row

| | | | | I. | P. | | | | | I. | P. |
|---|---|---|---|---|---|---|---|---|---|---|---|
| NC771 | W 35 | ½d. | .. | 30 | 1·50 | NC792 | Y 36 | 5d. | .. | 3·00 | 10·00 |
| NC772 | W 35 | 1d. | .. | 9·00 | † | NC795 | Y 36 | 10d. | .. | 7·00 | † |
| NC773 | W 35 | 1½d. | .. | 55 | 90 | a. Bar | — | .. | .. | 7·50 | † |
| NC775 | W 35 | 2½d. | .. | 1·40 | 4·50 | b. Bars | ⌐ | .. | .. | 7·50 | † |
| NC776 | W 35 | 3d. | .. | 1·50 | 1·50 | c. Bars | ⌐ | .. | .. | 7·50 | † |
| NC777 | W 35 | 4d. | .. | — | 2·00 | d. Bars | ☐ | .. | .. | 9·00 | † |
| NC778 | X 35 | ½d. | .. | 30 | 2·25 | NC796 | Y 36 | 1s. | .. | 7·00 | † |
| NC779 | X 35 | 1d. | .. | 35 | 2·50 | NC797 | Z 36 | ½d. | .. | 40 | † |
| NC780 | X 35 | 1½d. | .. | 55 | 4·50 | NC798 | Z 36 | 1½d. | .. | 55 | 4·50 |
| NC781 | X 35 | 2d. | .. | 90 | † | NC799 | Z 36 | 2d. | .. | 90 | 5·50 |
| NC782 | X 35 | 3d. | .. | 1·50 | † | NC800 | Z 36 | 3d. | .. | 1·50 | 5·50 |
| NC783 | X 35 | 4d. | .. | 2·25 | 7·50 | a. Bar | — | .. | .. | 1·50 | † |
| NC783a | X 35 | 5d. | .. | 30·00 | † | b. Bars | ⌐ | .. | .. | 1·50 | † |
| NC784 | X 35 | 9d. | .. | 5·50 | † | NC801 | Z 36 | 5d. | .. | 3·25 | † |
| a. Bar | — | .. | .. | 5·00 | † | a. Bar | — | .. | .. | 3·25 | 10·00 |
| b. Bars | ⌐ | .. | .. | 6·00 | † | b. Bars | ⌐ | .. | .. | 3·50 | † |
| c. Bars | ⌐ | .. | .. | 6·00 | † | c. Bars | ⌐ | .. | .. | 3·50 | † |
| d. Bars | ☐ | .. | .. | 7·00 | † | d. Bars | ☐ | .. | .. | 3·50 | † |
| NC785 | Y 36 | ½d. | .. | 12 | 7·50 | NC802 | Z 36 | 1s. | .. | 7·50 | † |
| NC786 | Y 36 | 1d. | .. | 35 | 2·25 | a. Bar | — | .. | .. | 7·50 | † |
| NC787 | Y 36 | 1½d. | .. | 55 | 2·50 | b. Bars | ⌐ | .. | .. | 9·00 | † |
| NC788 | Y 36 | 2d. | .. | 90 | † | c. Bars | ⌐ | .. | .. | 9·00 | † |
| NC789 | Y 36 | 2½d. | .. | 2·25 | 7·50 | d. Bars | ☐ | .. | .. | 10·00 | † |
| NC790 | Y 36 | 3d. | .. | 1·50 | 5·50 | NC803 | A 37 | 2d. | .. | 90 | † |
| NC791 | Y 36 | 4d. | .. | 2·00 | † | | | | | | |
| a. Bar | — | .. | .. | 2·00 | † | | | | | | |
| b. Bars | ⌐ | .. | .. | 2·00 | † | | | | | | |
| c. Bars | ⌐ | .. | .. | 2·00 | † | | | | | | |
| d. Bars | ☐ | .. | .. | 2·00 | † | | | | | | |

**Essay.** Imperf. on paper Wmk. Type **W.15.** Similar to issue design, but with large head

| | | | | | | | | | | |
|---|---|---|---|---|---|---|---|---|---|---|
| 1d. scarlet | .. | .. | .. | .. | .. | .. | .. | .. | .. | 5·00 |

**Colour trials.** Imperf. on paper Wmk. Type **W.15**

1½d. in the large format
| | | | | | | | |
|---|---|---|---|---|---|---|---|
| Ultramarine, deep grey-green or scarlet | .. | .. | .. | .. | *From* | 10·00 |
| Red-brown | .. | .. | .. | .. | .. | .. | 10·00 |

Care should be taken not to confuse the red-brown colour trial with the issued Imperf. The colour trial exhibits all the traits of a finished proof. The highlights are noticeable when compared with the rather flat impression of the issued stamps and the paper is of better quality.

### Mourning Essay

Printed by Harrison in black on chalk-surfaced paper Wmk. Type **W.16,** Perf. 15 × 14 or Imperf. for King George's Jubilee Trust.

It was proposed that the stamp should be sold for 3d., the premium being devoted to the Trust.

Only eight of these " in memory " stamps were proofed, and after consideration the project was abandoned.

# SECTION N 3

# King George V

## Engraved Issues, 1913-1934

---

## General Notes

**INTRODUCTION.** The high values, 2s. 6d., 5s., 10s. and £1 were designed by Bertram Mackennal, and separate dies for each value were engraved by J. A. C. Harrison. The original printers, Waterlow Bros. & Layton, relinquished the contract to De la Rue & Co. in 1915, who were in turn replaced by Bradbury, Wilkinson & Co. in 1918. The £1 value, which passed from currency in 1915, was only printed by Waterlow. When, in 1934, the contract passed back to Waterlow & Sons, the re-engraved dies were used.

**HOW TO DISTINGUISH BETWEEN THE PRINTINGS.** The vertical measurement of the Waterlow and De la Rue stamps was exactly 22 mm. A good deal of the De la Rue work was from the previously used Waterlow plates, and printings from worn plates are attributable to them. In the De la Rue printings, the gum is usually patchy and yellowish, and the colour of the stamp, particularly the 5s., tends to show through the back. The holes of the perforation are smaller than those of the other two printers.

Bradbury Wilkinson used rotary plates, and the height of the stamps is now 22¾ or 23 mm. On most of the 22¾ mm. high stamps, a minute coloured dot appears in the margin just above the middle of the upper frame line. This dot was on the transfer roller and assisted the craftsman in the laying down of the plate. If the roller was not rocked to its full extent then the dot would not appear.

In 1927, Bradbury Wilkinson made a new set of plates, none of which showed the guide dots. The printed stamps are now 23 mm. high, and the difference in height is explained by the method of printing. The earlier plates were used with dampened paper which shrunk on drying, and in consequence the printed stamps were smaller in size. For this reason, we are not listing the sizes in the catalogue.

The Waterlow printings in 1934 were from re-engraved dies, the most noticeable difference being the crosshatch shading in the medallion.

**MARGINAL MARKINGS ON THE PLATES.** Each sheet contained 40 stamps arranged in 10 rows of 4, and showed hand engraved marginal markings. On each Waterlow and De la Rue plate, marginal crosses appear centrally on the four sides of each sheet. Plate numbers were also engraved in the top margin, although they were so far above the stamps that they rarely appear on the issued sheets.

On the Bradbury Wilkinson plates, lines were engraved on either side of the crosses—horizontally in the top and bottom margins, and vertically in the side margins. As these lines and crosses were engraved by hand, slight differences in the lengths are apparent, and are an aid in plating.

The study of these plates is still in hand, and for the moment, we are not attempting a catalogue listing.

**PAPER.** The paper was stout wove until 1926, when printings were made on undamped paper. From this date until 1934, the paper was softer and more porous. In 1921 a kind of " laid " paper was used for an experimental period. When held up to the light, faint horizontal lines are noticeable in the texture.

Early Stage                    Later Stage

## Die Proofs without Value

The first die proofs were heraldically incorrect. There were lines of shading in the St. Andrew's Cross, and the Cross of the St. George was missing.

Die proofs on card in various stages of completion (Aug. and Sept, 1912)

| | |
|---|---|
| In brown (early stage) white head to horse  ..  ..  ..  ..  ..  ..  .. | £550 |
| In blue-black, sepia, deep blue, chestnut, deep green or carmine  ..  ..  .. | *From* £350 |

Die proof on paper with flag erased from the shield, and replaced with zig-zag line

| | |
|---|---|
| In deep-grey-blue  ..  ..  ..  ..  ..  ..  ..  ..  .. | £500 |
| Ditto but with blue wash on and around design  ..  ..  ..  ..  ..  .. | £500 |

Colour trials from the heraldically incorrect die. Taken in January, 1913, and endorsed " From Master Plate—Waterlows Ink " in manuscript

| | |
|---|---|
| In brown, carmine, indigo, ultramarine or green  ..  ..  ..  ..  .. | *Each* £500 |

## Die Proofs with Value from the correct Die

These exist in varying stages.

(a) Before the ornaments in the top frame had been completed, and before the guide lines had been removed.
(b) The finished die after guide lines had been removed.

They are listed under their respective values.

All stamps in this Section are Type **N10**, watermarked Single Cypher, Type **W.17** and the word " POSTAGE " in each of the four margins and perforated 11 × 12. Printed in sheets of 40 arranged in 10 rows of 4.

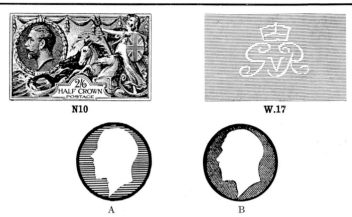

N10                              W.17

A                                B

Type A.   Background around portrait consists of horizontal lines
Type B.   Background around portrait consists of horizontal and diagonal lines

## Background Type A

Cat. No.  S.G. No.      Date

**1913-18.  2s. 6d. BROWN**

**(a) Waterlow printings**

| | | | | | Shades | Unused | Used |
|---|---|---|---|---|---|---|---|
| N63 | 399/400 | 2.7.13 | | | (1) Deep sepia-brown | 15·00 | 5·00 |
| *a.* | Re-entry (R.2/1) | .. | .. £100 | 75·00 | (2) Sepia-brown | 10·00 | 3·50 |
| *s.* | " Specimen ", Type 26 | .. | 7·00 | | | | |
| *t.* | " Specimen ", Type 29 | .. | 10·00 | | *v.* " Cancelled ", Type 27 .. | 8·00 | |
| *u.* | " Cancelled ", Type 24 | .. | 7·00 | | *w.* " Cancelled ", Type 27 Imperf. | 18·00 | |

**Die Proofs**

| | | | | | | | | |
|---|---|---|---|---|---|---|---|---|
| State (a) Blue-green on card.. | .. | .. | .. | .. | .. | | .. | £250 |
| State (b) Deep green on card | | .. | .. | .. | .. | | .. | £200 |
| Vermilion on India paper .. | | .. | .. | .. | .. | | .. | £250 |
| Brown on India paper | | .. | .. | .. | .. | | .. | £250 |

**Plate Proofs**

| | | | | | | | |
|---|---|---|---|---|---|---|---|
| Blue-green on wove paper | .. | .. | .. | .. | .. | .. | 60·00 |
| Black on thin gummed paper. Wmk. James Weigley—219 | | | | .. | .. | £100 |
| On plate-glazed paper: Red, blue, green, brown or black | | | | .. | *From* 60·00 |
| In green on thin card (after plate had been cleaned) | | | .. | .. | .. | £200 |

**Colour Trials**

Imperf. on ungummed " Weigley " paper, 19 different colours ..   *From* 40·00

**(b) De la Rue printings**

| | | | | | Shades | Unused | Used |
|---|---|---|---|---|---|---|---|
| N64 | 405/408 | 12.15 | | | (1) Deep yellow-brown | 8·00 | 5·00 |
| *a.* | Re-entry (R.2/1) | .. | .. £100 | 80·00 | (2) Yellow-brown | 7·00 | 3·50 |
| *b.* | Re-entry (R.10/4) | .. | .. £200 | | (3) Pale yellow-brown | 8·00 | 5·00 |
| *c.* | No watermark | .. | .. 60·00 | | (4) Bright yellow-brown | 8·00 | 5·00 |
| *d.* | Wmk. " POSTAGE " inverted. Strip of 3 | .. | .. 75·00 | | (5) Cinnamon-brown | 35·00 | 25·00 |
| | | | | | (6) Grey-brown | 6·00 | 3·50 |
| *e.* | Wmk. " POSTAGE " reversed. Strip of 3 .. | | .. 75·00 | | (7) Pale brown | 6·00 | 3·50 |
| *f.* | Wmk. inverted:— | | | | (8) Pale brown (worn plate) | 5·00 | 3·50 |
| | Shade (1) | .. | .. 25·00 | | (9) Very deep brown | 35·00 | 35·00 |
| | ,, (2) | .. | .. 25·00 | | (10) Seal-brown | 6·00 | 6·00 |
| | ,, (8) | .. | .. 20·00 | | (11) Blackish brown | 9·00 | 9·00 |
| | ,, (9) | .. | .. 35·00 | | | | |
| | ,, (10) | .. | .. 25·00 | | | | |
| *g.* | Wmk. reversed:— | | | | | | |
| | Shade (2) | .. | .. 15·00 | | | | |
| | ,, (8) | .. | .. 20·00 | | | | |
| | ,, (10) | .. | .. 20·00 | | | | |

Shades (10) and (11) are often found with dark brown gum.  Shade (9) only issued with watermark inverted.

*s.* " Cancelled ", Type 24   ..   7·00

No. N64a is from the Waterlow plate, and the re-entry marks, although identical, are usually much fainter.  It only exists with watermark inverted.

No. N64b is from a worn plate, and the re-entered lines are very clear.  This re-entry was probably made after the plate had been put to press.

### Colour Trials

The issued shades (1), (2) and (3) Imperf. on gummed paper. Wmk.
Type **W.17** .. .. .. .. .. .. .. .. *From* 60·00
Perf. 11 × 12 on gummed paper.  Wmk. Type **W.17**
Ultramarine, indigo, green, purple, grey or brown .. .. .. .. *Each* £150
Perf. 11 × 12 on ungummed paper.  No wmk.
Bright brown, bright blue, magenta, sepia, carmine, indigo or green .. *Each* £150

### 2s. 6d. Re-entries

N63/4a        N64b        N65c

N65a

N65b

| Cat. No. | S.G. No. | Date | | | Shades | Unused | Used |
|---|---|---|---|---|---|---|---|

**(c) Bradbury, Wilkinson printings**

| | | | | | | | |
|---|---|---|---|---|---|---|---|
| N65 | 413a/415a | 12.18 | | | (1) Olive-brown | 4·25 | 90 |
| a. | Re-entry (R.1/2) | .. | .. £120 | 75·00 | (2) Chocolate-brown | 3·75 | 90 |
| b. | Re-entry (R.1/3) | .. | .. 45·00 | 30·00 | (3) Reddish brown | 10·00 | 3·00 |
| c. | Re-entry (R.1/4) | .. | .. 35·00 | 15·00 | (4) Pale brown | 8·00 | 2·50 |
| d. | Laid paper .. | .. | .. 9·00 | 3·50 | | | |
| s. | " Specimen ", Type 15 | .. | | | w. " Cancelled ", Type 24 | .. 5·00 | |
| t. | " Specimen ", Type 23 | .. | | | x. " Cancelled ", Type 28 | .. 7·00 | |
| u. | " Specimen ", Type 26 | .. | | | y. " Cancelled ", Type 33 | .. 4·00 | |
| v. | " Specimen ", Type 31 | .. | | | z. " Specimen ", Type 23 and | | |
| va. | " Specimen ", Type 32 | .. | | | " Cancelled ", Type 34 | .. | |

**Plate Proofs**

| | | | | | |
|---|---|---|---|---|---|
| Grey-green on glazed card | .. | .. | .. | .. | 15·00 |
| Rough proofs, on buff paper in brown, carmine or indigo | .. | *Each* | 8·00 |

**Experimental printing** on paper watermarked Type **W.14** (sideways), perf.
11 × 12 and overprinted " Cancelled ", Type 24    ..    ..    ..    10·00

## 1913-18    5s.    CARMINE

**(a) Waterlow printings**

| | | | | | | | |
|---|---|---|---|---|---|---|---|
| N66 | 401 | 7.13 | | | (1) Rose-carmine | 18·00 | 6·00 |
| s. | " Specimen ", Type 26 | .. | 7·00 | | (2) Pale rose-carmine | 18·00 | 6·00 |
| t. | " Cancelled ", Type 24 | .. | 6·00 | | (3) Carmine-red | 18·00 | 6·00 |
| u. | " Cancelled ", Type 27 | .. | 8·00 | | | | |
| v. | " Cancelled ", Type 27 | | | | | | |
| | Imperf... | .. | .. | 12·00 | | | |

**Die Proofs**

| | | |
|---|---|---|
| State (a) on card in sepia-brown .. | .. .. .. .. .. | £400 |
| State (b) on card | | |
| Sepia, indigo-blue or blue-green | .. .. .. | *Each from* £350 |
| on India paper | | |
| Blue, brown, carmine or green | .. .. .. .. | *From* £250 |
| on thin paper | | |
| Red-brown, dark brown, chestnut-brown, deep blue, carmine, green or blue-green | .. .. .. .. | *From* £250 |
| on esparto paper | | |
| Indigo-blue .. | .. .. .. .. .. | £300 |

**(b) De la Rue printings**

| | | | | | | | |
|---|---|---|---|---|---|---|---|
| N67 | 409/410 | 12.15 | | | (1) Bright carmine | 18·00 | 6·00 |
| a. | No watermark | | 90·00 | | (2) Carmine | 25·00 | 7·00 |
| b. | Watermark inverted | .. | 90·00 | | (3) Pale carmine (worn plate) | 18·00 | 6·00 |
| c. | Watermark reversed | .. | £100 | | | | |
| d. | Watermark inverted and reversed | .. .. | £175 | | On shade (2) the colour shows through to | | |
| s. | " Cancelled ", Type 24 | .. | 8·00 | | the back of the stamp. | | |

**(c) Bradbury, Wilkinson printings**

| | | | | | | | |
|---|---|---|---|---|---|---|---|
| N68 | 416 | 12.18 | | | (1) Rose-carmine | 8·00 | 1·25 |
| a. | Laid paper .. | .. | .. 18·00 | 10·00 | (2) Rose-red | 8·00 | 1·25 |
| s. | " Specimen ", Type 15 | .. | | | | | |
| t. | " Specimen ", Type 26 | .. | | | w. " Cancelled ", Type 28 | .. 12·00 | |
| u. | " Specimen ", Type 31 | .. | | | x. " Specimen ", Type 23 and | | |
| v. | " Specimen ", Type 32 | .. | | | " Cancelled ", Type 34 | .. | |

**Rough plate proof** on buff in carmine    ..    ..    ..    ..    8·00

**Experimental printing** on paper watermarked Type **W.14** (sideways),
perf. 11 × 12 and overprinted " Cancelled " Type 24 ..    ..    ..    10·00

## 1913-18    10s.    BLUE

**(a) Waterlow printings**

| | | | | | | | |
|---|---|---|---|---|---|---|---|
| N69 | 402 | 7.13 | | | (1) Indigo-blue | 75·00 | 30·00 |
| s. | " Specimen ", Type 23 | .. | 12·00 | | (2) Indigo | 85·00 | 35·00 |
| t. | " Specimen ", Type 26 | .. | 15·00 | | | | |
| u. | " Specimen ", Type 29 | .. | 12·00 | | w. " Cancelled ", Type 27 | .. 30·00 | |
| v. | " Cancelled ", Type 24 | .. | 8·00 | | x. " Cancelled ", Type 28 | .. | |

**Die Proofs**

| | | |
|---|---|---|
| State (a) on card in blue-green .. | .. .. .. .. .. | £500 |
| State (b) on card in deep green marked " 2 " .. | .. .. .. | £500 |

**Colour Trial**

On paper watermarked Type **W.17**, gummed, in near to issued colour    ..    ..    ..

| Cat. No. | S.G. No. | Date | | Shades | Unused | Used |
|---|---|---|---|---|---|---|

**(b) De la Rue printings**

| N70 | 411/413 | 12.15 | | (1) Blue | 90·00 | 12·00 |
| s. | "Specimen", Type 26 | .. | | (2) Deep blue | £130 | 20·00 |
| t. | "Cancelled", Type 24 | .. 25·00 | | (3) Deep blue (worn plate) | £150 | 30·00 |
| | | | | (4) Deep (intense) bright blue | £250 | 75·00 |
| | | | | (5) Bright (" Cambridge ") | | |
| | | | | blue | £250 | 75·00 |
| | | | | (6) Pale blue | 90·00 | 12·00 |

**(c) Bradbury, Wilkinson printings**

| N71 | 417 | 12.18 | | (1) Dull blue | 25·00 | 2·50 |
| a. | Re-entry (R.1/1) | .. 60·00 | 30·00 | (2) Dull grey-blue | 25·00 | 2·50 |
| b. | Re-entry (R.6/1) | .. £250 | £150 | | | |
| s. | "Specimen", Type 15 | .. | | w. "Cancelled ", Type 24 | .. | |
| t. | "Specimen", Type 26 | .. | | x. "Cancelled ", Type 28 | .. 25·00 | |
| u. | "Specimen", Type 31 | .. | | y. "Specimen ", Type 23 and | | |
| v. | "Specimen", Type 32 | .. | | "Cancelled ", Type 34 | .. | |

On some plates, every stamp shows a broken " S " in " POSTAGE ". No. N71a is from one of these plates. The re-entry marks on No. N71b are similar but more pronounced, and the letter " S " in " POSTAGE " is perfect.

N71a

N71b

**1913  £1 GREEN.**  Printed by Waterlow

| N72 | 403/404 | 7.13 | | (1) Green | £140 | 60·00 |
| s. | "Specimen", Type 23 | .. 55·00 | | (2) Deep green | £180 | £100 |
| t. | "Specimen", Type 26 | .. 50·00 | | (3) Dull blue-green | £130 | 60·00 |
| u. | "Cancelled ", Type 24 | .. 50·00 | | | | |
| v. | "Cancelled ", Type 27 | .. 70·00 | | | | |

**Die Proofs**

State (a) on card in blue-green .. .. .. .. .. .. £500
State (b) on card in dark green, marked " 4 ".. .. .. .. £500

**Colour Trial**

On paper, watermarked Type **W.17**, in near to issued colour (yellowish) .. .. .. £175

## Background Type B.  The re-engraved Die

The background to the portrait consists of horizontal and diagonal lines. There are numerous other minor differences between this and the original die.

Printed in sheets of 40, in 10 rows of 4. The sheet was marked with horizontal and vertical lines in all four corners. There were also short vertical lines in the perforation gutter between the second and third stamps in the top and bottom rows.

**1934 (OCTOBER).**  Printed by Waterlow

| N73 | 450 | 10.34 | | 2s. 6d. (1) Chocolate-brown | 8·00 | 75 |
| s. | "Specimen", Type 30 | .. | | (2) Reddish brown | 12·00 | 1·50 |
| N74 | 451 | 10.34 | | 5s. Bright rose-red | 15·00 | 1·50 |
| s. | "Specimen", Type 30 | .. | | | | |
| N75 | 452 | 10.34 | | 10s. Indigo | 25·00 | 2·00 |
| s. | "Specimen", Type 30 | .. | | | | |

# SECTION N4

# King George V

## Commemorative Issues, 1924-1935

All stamps in this section are watermarked Multiple Block G v R and Crown Type **W.15**, except No. NCom9.

**N16**

**N17**

(Des. Harold Nelson)

## 1924 and 1925 BRITISH EMPIRE EXHIBITION

Recess-printed by Waterlow & Sons from dies and plates of their own manufacture and printed in sheets of 120 stamps in two panes of 60, the panes being separated before issue into post office sheets of 10 rows of 6. There were no Controls. Many constant plate flaws exist.

The perforation was at first by a line machine which had very small holes. Later this was changed for a comb machine with larger holes.

The 1924 1d. value was also available from stamp vending machines at the exhibition from rolls of 1200 stamps made up from sheets joined at every tenth stamp.

The 1924 1½d. value is known printed on both sides, the one on the back being partly sideways; we do not list this as a variety, being more in the nature of a freak.

### 1924 (APRIL 23). TYPE N16, DATED " 1924 "

| Cat. No. | S.G. No. | Perforation | | Description | | | Unused | Used |
|---|---|---|---|---|---|---|---|---|
| NCom1 | 430 | Line 14 | | 1d. Scarlet | | | 90 | 1·00 |
| *a.* | Bottom margin imperf. | .. 75·00 | 75·00 | | | | | |
| *b.* | Tail to N of EXHIBITION | | | | | | | |
| | (R1/5) | .. .. .. 4·00 | 4·00 | | | | | |
| *c.* | Comb perf. 14 | .. .. 1·00 | 1·00 | *t.* "Specimen", Type 30 | .. | 9·00 | | |
| *s.* | "Specimen", Type 15 | .. | | *u.* "Cancelled", Type 28 | .. | 9·00 | | |
| NCom2 | 431 | Line 14 | | 1½d. Brown | .. | .. | 1·60 | 1·75 |
| *a.* | Comb perf. 14 | .. .. 1·75 | 2·00 | | | | | |
| *b.* | Left side margin imperf. | .. 75·00 | | *t.* "Cancelled", Type 24 | .. | 9·00 | | |
| *s.* | "Specimen", Type 15 | .. | | *u.* "Cancelled", Type 28 | .. | 9·00 | | |
| NCom1/2 | First Day Cover | .. .. .. .. .. .. | | | | | † | 20·00 |

Imperforate 1d. and 1½d. affixed to cards signed by the designer in pencil "Harold Nelson" exists.

NCom1*b*

### 1925 (MAY 9), TYPE N17, DATED " 1925 "

| | | | | | | | | |
|---|---|---|---|---|---|---|---|---|
| NCom3 | 432 | Comb 14 | | 1d. Scarlet | .. | .. | 4·00 | 3·50 |
| NCom4 | 433 | Comb 14 | | 1½d. Brown | .. | .. | 6·00 | 6·00 |
| NCom3/4 | First Day Cover | .. .. .. .. .. .. .. | | | | | † | 60·00 |

### Essays

Various designs by Harold Nelson .. .. .. .. .. *From* 75·00

Essays were also submitted by Eric Gill, N. Rooke, J. D. Batten and E. W. Tristan.

### Die Proofs

1924 1½d. unfinished die in issued colour, on card .. .. .. ..

1924 1½d. finished die in black, on card .. .. .. .. ..

Proofs from the 1d. and 1½d. dies are also known in black on white wove paper. All are very rare and some unique.

**N18**

(Des. J. Farleigh)

**N19**

(Des. E. Linzell)

**N20**

(Des. J. Farleigh)

## 1929 (MAY 10) POSTAL UNION CONGRESS

### A. Typographed Issues

Typographed by Waterlow & Sons from plates made at the Royal Mint. The layout and perforation is the same as for the concurrent typographed set.

| Cat. No | S.G. No. | Type | Perforation | | | Description | Unused | Used |
|---|---|---|---|---|---|---|---|---|
| NCom5 | 434 | **N18** | 15 × 14 | | | ½d. Green | 35 | 8 |
| a. | Watermark inverted | | .. | 3·00 | 3·00 | | | |
| b. | Watermark sideways | | .. | 7·00 | 5·00 | | | |
| s. | Imperf. optd. " Specimen ", Type 30 | | | | | t. " Cancelled ", Type 33 .. | 5·00 | |
| NCom6 | 435 | **N19** | 15 × 14 | | | 1d. Scarlet | 75 | 20 |
| a. | Watermark inverted | | .. | 3·00 | 3·00 | s. Imperf. Optd. " Specimen ", | | |
| b. | Watermark sideways | | .. | 7·00 | 5·00 | Type 30 .. .. .. | | |
| c. | Varnish ink .. | | .. | 12·00 | | t. " Cancelled ", Type 33 .. | 5·00 | |
| NCom7 | 436 | **N19** | 15 × 14 | | | 1½d. Purple-brown | 35 | 8 |
| a. | Watermark inverted | | .. | 2·00 | 2·00 | s. Imperf. optd. " Specimen ", | | |
| b. | Watermark sideways | | .. | 6·00 | 7·50 | Type 30 .. .. .. | | |
| c. | 1829 for 1929 (R.2/5) | | .. | | | t. " Cancelled ", Type 33 .. | 4·00 | |
| NCom8 | 437 | **N20** | 15 × 14 | | | 2½d. (1) Blue | 2·00 | 1·50 |
| a. | Watermark inverted | | | | | (2) Pale blue | 3·00 | 2·00 |
| | Shade (1) .. | | .. | 35·00 | 20·00 | | | |
| | Shade (2) .. | | .. | 25·00 | 20·00 | | | |
| s. | Imperf. optd. " Specimen ", Type 30 .. .. .. | | | | | t. " Specimen ", Type 32 . | 15·00 | |
| NCom5/8 | First Day Cover | | .. | .. | .. | .. .. .. .. .. | † | 7·50 |

### Booklet panes of six

| | | | | | | |
|---|---|---|---|---|---|---|
| NComB1 | ½d. Watermark upright | 3·00 | | NComB1a | ½d. Watermark inverted | 20·00 |
| t. | " Cancelled ", Type 33 .. | 30·00 | | at. | " Cancelled ", Type 33 .. | 30·00 |
| u. | " Cancelled ", Type 33P .. | | | au. | " Cancelled ", Type 33P .. | |
| NComB2 | 1d. Watermark upright | 5·50 | | NComB2a | 1d. Watermark inverted | 20·00 |
| t. | " Cancelled ", Type 33 .. | 30·00 | | at. | " Cancelled ", Type 33 .. | 30·00 |
| u. | " Cancelled ", Type 33P .. | | | au. | " Cancelled ", Type 33P .. | |
| NComB3 | 1½d. Watermark upright | 2·50 | | NComB3a | 1½d. Watermark inverted | 14·00 |
| b. | Q for O in UNION (R.2/1) | 35·00 | | ab | Q for O in UNION (R.2/1) | 40·00 |
| t. | " Cancelled ", Type 33 .. | 28·00 | | at. | " Cancelled ", Type 33 .. | 30·00 |
| u. | " Cancelled ", Type 33P .. | | | au. | " Cancelled ", Type 33P .. | |

### Booklet panes of four, with two advertisement labels

The advertisements are printed in black. (For complete list, see appendix L.)

| | | | | | | |
|---|---|---|---|---|---|---|
| NComB4 | 1½d. Watermark upright | 15·00 | | NComB4a | 1½d. Watermark inverted | 15·00 |
| t. | " Cancelled ", Type 33 .. | 25·00 | | at. | " Cancelled ", Type 33 .. | 25·00 |

### Controls

| | | | | I. | P. | | | | | | I. | P. |
|---|---|---|---|---|---|---|---|---|---|---|---|---|
| NComC623 | K 29 | ½d. | .. | 70 | † | | NComC627 | L 29 | ½d. | .. | 2·00 | † |
| a. | Wmk. inverted | | .. | — | † | | a. | Wmk. inverted | | .. | — | † |
| NComC624 | K 29 | 1d. | .. | 1·00 | † | | NComC628 | L 29 | 1d. | .. | 3·00 | † |
| a. | Wmk. inverted | | .. | — | † | | NComC629 | L 29 | 1½d. | .. | 3·00 | † |
| NComC625 | K 29 | 1½d. | .. | 90 | † | | NComC630 | L 29 | 2½d. | .. | 5·00 | † |
| a. | Wmk. inverted | | .. | — | † | | a. | Wmk. inverted | | .. | — | † |
| NComC626 | K 29 | 2½d. | .. | 4·00 | † | | | | | | | |
| a. | Wmk. inverted | | .. | — | † | | | | | | | |

## Die Proofs

All values are known in black on glazed card.

Progressive proofs from the master-die of Linzell's design (without value) are known in black.

On wove paper

    1d. and 1½d. in black.

    1d. in red or red-brown; 1½d. in purple-brown.

    All are extremely rare and some unique.

## Proofs

From specially prepared miniature sheets of four stamps.

Imperf. on thin white glazed paper.   ½d., 1d., 1½d. and 2½d.       .. *Each* £250

## Plates

See introduction to Appendix J

Prices are for the control piece (cheapest control).   Positional blocks from the top left corners are four to six times these prices.

| Plate No. | Description | Controls | | | Unused From |
|---|---|---|---|---|---|
| **½d. Green** | | | | | |
| 1 | ½ dot (base) under 1st | K 29 | L 29 | .. | 1·00 |
| 2 | ½ dot (base) under 2nd | K 29 | L 29 | .. | 1·00 |
| 3 | ½ dot (top) under 3rd | K 29 | L 29 | .. | 1·50 |
| 4 | Dot 20th left side 7 mm. | K 29 | L 29 | .. | 1·00 |
| 5 | Dot 19th left side 7 mm. | K 29 | L 29 | .. | 2·00 |
| 6 | Dot (inner) 19th left side 20 mm. | K 29 | L 29 | .. | 2·00 |
| 7 | No marking | K 29 | L 29 | .. | 6·00 |
| 8 | Large dot (breaking top) under 4th | K 29 | L 29 | .. | 2·50 |
| **1d. Scarlet** | | | | | |
| 1 | Dot 1st left side; scoop 19th right side; dot 20th right side | K 29 | L 29 | .. | 1·50 |
| 2 | Dot 2nd left side; minute dot 20th right side 10 mm. | K 29 | L 29 | .. | 1·50 |
| 3 | Dot 3rd left side; vertical crack 19th left side | K 29 | L 29 | .. | 3·00 |
| 4 | Dot 4th left side; tiny dot 2nd left side.   (The rules 19th and 20th right side are thicker than those of plate 3) | K 29 | L 29 | .. | 3·00 |
| **1½d. Purple-brown** | | | | | |
| 1 | Dot 1st left side | K 29 | L 29 | .. | 1·00 |
| 2 | Dot 2nd left side; ½ cut top at right of 3rd | K 29 | L 29 | .. | 1·50 |
| 3 | Dot 3rd left side; internal score 20th left side | K 29 | L 29 | .. | 1·50 |
| 4 | Dot 4th left side; base of 3rd slightly ragged | K 29 | | .. | 1·50 |
| 5 | Large dot above 1st top row; ½ cut (base) at right of 2nd | K 29 | L 29 | .. | 1·00 |
| **2½d. Blue** | | | | | |
| 1 | ½ dot (inner) 20th left side | K 29 | L 29 | .. | 4·00 |
| 2a | No marking | K 29 | | .. | 25·00 |
| 2b | Added ½ dot (outer) 19th left side | K 29 | L 29 | .. | 8·00 |

**Quantities Sold** ½d. 677,500,000; 1d. 341,000,000; 1½d. 751,250,000; 2½d. 26,750,000

**N21**

(Des. Harold Nelson)

**W.18**

| Cat. No. | S.G. No. | Type | Perforation | Description | Unused | Used |
|---|---|---|---|---|---|---|

**B. Recess-printed Issue**

Recess-printed by Bradbury, Wilkinson & Co. from a die and plate of their own manuacture in sheets of twenty (five rows of four). Watermark Type **W.18**

| | | | | | | |
|---|---|---|---|---|---|---|
| NCom9 | 438 | **N21** | Line 12 | £1 Black | 75·00 | 65·00 |
| s. | "Specimen", Type 32 in red | .. .. .. .. | 60·00 | | | |
| NCom9 | First Day Cover | .. .. .. .. .. .. .. | | | † | £150 |
| NCom5/9 | First Day Cover | .. .. .. .. .. .. .. | | | † | £160 |

Most of the stamps in the sheet show traces of guide (hair) lines used when laying down the plate.

**Essays**

Artists drawings by Harold Nelson .. .. .. .. *From* £100

**Proof**

From a specially prepared miniature sheet of four stamps. Imperf. on thin white card .. .. .. .. .. .. *Each stamp* £500

**Quantity Sold** 61,000

N22

N23

(Des. Barnett Freedman)

## 1935 (**MAY 7**) SILVER JUBILEE

Printed in photogravure by Harrison & Sons in sheets of 120 stamps (20 rows of 6). For the ½d., 1d. and 1½d. values, three different multipositives were used. Type I was used for sheets, Type II (inverted wmk.) and Type III were used for the booklet printings.

Differences between the types:—

| | | |
|---|---|---|
| ½d. | Type I | "FPE" of "HALFPENNY" solid shading. |
| | Type II | "FPE" of "HALFPENNY" solid at top, shaded below. |
| | Type III | "FPE" as Type II, frame lines below "HALFPENNY" thinner. |
| 1d. | Type I | Wide shading between "NN" of "PENNY". |
| | Type II | Narrow shading between "NN" of "PENNY". |
| | Type III | Wide shading between "NN" of "PENNY". |
| | | The depth of shading in the fleur-de-lis and surround is deeper than in Types I and II. |
| 1½d. | Type I | Top frame lines thick. |
| | Type II | Top frame lines thin. |
| | Type III | Top frame line shows thickening over "JU". |

| | | | | | | |
|---|---|---|---|---|---|---|
| NCom10 | 453 | **N22** | 15 × 14 | ½d. green (Type I) | 5 | 5 |
| a. | Type II (inv. wmk.) | | 60 | 35 | | |
| b. | Type III | .. .. | 60 | 60 | | |
| t. | "Cancelled", Type 28P | .. | | u. "Cancelled", Type 33P .. | 2·00 | |
| NCom11 | 454 | **N22** | 15 × 14 | 1d. Scarlet (Type I) | 20 | 8 |
| a. | Type II (inv. wmk.) | .. | 60 | 35 | | |
| b. | Type III | .. .. | 60 | 60 | | |
| s. | "Specimen", Type 23 | | | | | |
| t. | "Cancelled", Type 28P | .. | | u. "Cancelled", Type 33P .. | 2·00 | |
| NCom12 | 455 | **N23** | 15 × 14 | 1½d. Red-brown (Type I) | 8 | 5 |
| a. | Type II (inv. wmk.) | .. | 25 | 12 | | |
| b. | Type III | .. .. | 35 | 25 | | |
| s. | "Specimen", Type 23 | | | u. "Cancelled", Type 28P .. | | |
| t. | "Cancelled", Type 28 | .. | | v. "Cancelled", Type 33P .. | 1·50 | |
| NCom13 | 456 | **N23** | 15 × 14 | 2½d. Blue | 90 | 75 |
| a. | Retouch to left panel and top of 2½ (Cyl. 34, R.17/1).. | 3·00 | 2·50 | | | |
| NCom14 | 456a | **N23** | 15 × 14 | 2½d. Prussian blue | £325 | £250 |
| NCom10/13 | First Day Cover | .. .. | .. .. .. .. .. | | † | 7·50 |

In No. NCom13a the panel on the left containing " 19 " and " Post " has been considerably deepened.  The retouching has extended downwards into the top of the figures " 2 " and " ½ ".

No. NCom14 is a colour trial of which three sheets were perforated and accidentally issued at a Post Office in Edmonton.

## Controls

| | | | I. | P. | | | | | I. | P. |
|---|---|---|---|---|---|---|---|---|---|---|
| NComC760 | ½d. | W 35 | .. 60 | † | NComC761 | 1d. | W 35 | .. | 1·75 | † |
| NComC762 | 1½d. | W 35 | .. 1·10 | † | NComC763 | 2½d. | W 35 | .. | 4·50 | † |

## Cylinder Numbers

Descriptions of the perforation types will be found in Appendix I.
Type 5A is Type 5 with the extension hole missing in the left margin.

Prices are for blocks of six.

| Value | Cyl. No. | | | Perf. Type | | Cyl. No. | | | | | Perf. Type | |
|---|---|---|---|---|---|---|---|---|---|---|---|---|
| | | | 5 | 6 | 5A | | | | | | 5 | 6B |
| ½d. | 18 .. | .. | 65 | 55 | 60 | 18. | .. | .. | .. | .. | 65 | 55 |
| | *20 .. | .. | — | † | † | 20. | .. | .. | .. | .. | † | † |
| | 47 .. | .. | † | 2·25 | † | 47. | .. | .. | .. | .. | † | 2·25 |
| | 55 .. | .. | 55 | 60 | 70 | 55. | .. | .. | .. | .. | 55 | 60 |
| | 60 .. | .. | 60 | 55 | 5·00 | 60. | .. | .. | .. | .. | 60 | 55 |
| | 61 .. | .. | 80 | 65 | 3·50 | 61. | .. | .. | .. | .. | 80 | 65 |
| | 62 .. | .. | 3·50 | † | 4·25 | 62. | .. | .. | .. | .. | 3·25 | † |
| 1d. | 14 .. | .. | 1·50 | 1·50 | 1·50 | 14. | .. | .. | .. | .. | 1·50 | 1·50 |
| | 22 .. | .. | 1·75 | 1·75 | 3·00 | 22. | .. | .. | .. | .. | 1·75 | 1·75 |
| 1½d. | * 2 .. | .. | † | † | — | 2. | .. | .. | .. | .. | † | † |
| | 7 .. | .. | 1·10 | 90 | 4·00 | 7. | .. | .. | .. | .. | 1·10 | 90 |
| | 21 .. | .. | 1·10 | 90 | 90 | 21. | .. | .. | .. | .. | 90 | 90 |
| | 27 .. | .. | — | 3·50 | — | 27. | .. | .. | .. | .. | — | 3·25 |
| | 48 .. | .. | 90 | 90 | 90 | 48. | .. | .. | .. | .. | 90 | 90 |
| 2½d. | 34 .. | .. | 6·00 | † | 5·00 | 34. | .. | .. | .. | .. | 5·00 | † |

* = "Abnormal". (See under "Printing" on page 89.)

## Booklet panes of four

| Type III | | Type II | |
|---|---|---|---|
| NComB5  ½d. Watermark | | NComB5a  ½d. Watermark | |
| upright | 3·50 | inverted | 3·50 |
| c.  Cylinder number .. .. | 8·00 | | |
| s.  "Cancelled ", Type 33P .. | 7·00 | as.  " Cancelled ", Type 33P .. | 7·00 |
| NComB6  1d. Watermark | | NComB6a  1d. Watermark | |
| upright | 3·50 | inverted | 3·50 |
| c.  Cylinder number .. .. | 8·00 | | |
| s.  "Cancelled ", Type 33P .. | 7·00 | as.  " Cancelled ", Type 33P .. | 7·00 |
| NComB7  1½d. Watermark | | NComB7a  1½d. Watermark | |
| upright | 1·75 | inverted | 1·75 |
| c.  Cylinder number .. .. | 5·00 | | |
| s.  "Cancelled ", Type 33P .. | 4·50 | as.  " Cancelled ", Type 33P .. | 4·50 |

## Booklet panes of four with cylinder numbers

| Value | Cyl. No. | | | | | Value | Cyl. No. | | | | |
|---|---|---|---|---|---|---|---|---|---|---|---|
| ½d. | 33 | .. | .. | .. | 8·00 | 1½d. | 30 | .. | .. | .. | 5·00 |
| ½d. | 35 | .. | .. | .. | 8·00 | | 41 | .. | .. | .. | 5·00 |
| 1d, | 26 | .. | .. | .. | — | | 58 | .. | .. | .. | — |
| 1d. | 37 | .. | .. | .. | 8·00 | | 59 | .. | .. | .. | 5·00 |
| | | | | | | | 66 | .. | .. | .. | 5·00 |

## Essays

Unadopted Essays for the 1d. and 1½d. values were submitted by Harrisons in October 1934.  The 1½d. is similar to the issued design of King Edward VIII.  These are in the N.P.M.

## Quantities Sold (including those in booklets)

½d. 353,400,000; 1d. 150,400,000; 1½d. 490,000,000; 2½d. 14,200,000

# SECTION P
# King Edward VIII Issue, 1936

**W.19**          **P1**

Printed in photogravure by Harrison & Sons in sheets of 240 (20 rows of 12)

## 1936 (SEPTEMBER). TYPE P1. WMK. TYPE W.19, PERF. 15 × 14

| Cat. No. | S.G. No. | Date | Description | Unused | Used |
|---|---|---|---|---|---|
| P1 | 457 | 1.9.36 | ½d. Green | 5 | 5 |
| a. | Watermark inverted .. | 12 | 5 | | |
| b. | Pearl beside crown (Cyl. 7., | | | s. "Specimen", Type 30 .. | | |
| | 10. or 12., R.20/2) | 60 | 30 | t. "Cancelled", Type 33P .. | 50 | |
| | | | | u. "Cancelled", Type 33 .. | 1·75 | |
| P2 | 458 | 14.9.36 | 1d. Scarlet | 5 | 5 |
| a. | Watermark inverted .. | 12 | 8 | | |
| s. | "Specimen", Type 30 .. | | | u. "Cancelled", Type 33P .. | 50 | |
| t. | "Specimen", Type 32 .. | | | v. "Cancelled", Type 33 .. | 1·75 | |
| P3 | 459 | 1.9.36 | 1½d. Red-brown | 5 | 5 |
| a. | Watermark inverted .. | 10 | 5 | | |
| b. | Coiff flaw (Cyl. 2, R.18/1).. | 2·00 | 1·50 | s. "Specimen", Type 30 .. | | |
| | (later states only) | | | t. "Cancelled", Type 33P .. | 50 | |
| c. | Ditto, retouched .. .. | 3·50 | 2·00 | u. "Cancelled", Type 33 .. | 1·75 | |
| P4 | 460 | 1.9.36 | 2½d. Bright blue | 8 | 10 |

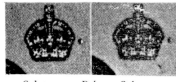

Cyl. 7., 10.   P1b   Cyl. 12.                    P3b

Later states of No. P1b from re-chromed cylinders show the flaw very faintly

### Booklet panes of six

| | | | | | | |
|---|---|---|---|---|---|---|
| PB1 | ½d. Watermark upright | 30 | | PB1a | ½d. Watermark inverted | 75 |
| c. | Cylinder No. .. .. | 60 | | | | |
| s. | "Cancelled", Type 33P .. | 3·00 | | as. | "Cancelled", Type 33P .. | 3·00 |
| u. | "Cancelled", Type 33 .. | 11·00 | | au. | "Cancelled", Type 33 .. | 11·00 |
| PB2 | 1d. Watermark upright | 30 | | PB2 | 1d. Watermark inverted | 75 |
| c. | Cylinder No. .. .. | 60 | | | | |
| s. | "Cancelled", Type 33P .. | 3·00 | | as. | "Cancelled", Type 33P .. | 3·00 |
| u. | "Cancelled", Type 33 .. | 11·00 | | au. | "Cancelled", Type 33 .. | 11·00 |
| PB3 | 1½d. Watermark upright | 30 | | PB3 | 1½d. Watermark inverted | 60 |
| c. | Cylinder No. .. .. | 60 | | | | |
| s. | "Cancelled", Type 33P .. | 3·00 | | as. | "Cancelled", Type 33P .. | 3·00 |
| u. | "Cancelled", Type 33 .. | 11·00 | | au. | "Cancelled", Type 33 .. | 11·00 |

### Booklet panes of four, with two advertisement labels
(For complete list see appendix L)

| | | | | | | |
|---|---|---|---|---|---|---|
| PB4 | 1½d. Watermark upright | 1·50 | | PB4a | 1½d. Watermark inverted | 5·00 |
| c. | Cylinder No. .. .. | 2·00 | | | | |
| s. | "Cancelled", Type 33P .. | 3·00 | | as. | "Cancelled", Type 33P .. | 6·00 |
| u. | "Cancelled", Type 33 .. | 10·00 | | au. | "Cancelled", Type 33 .. | 12·00 |

### Booklet panes of two

| | | | | | | |
|---|---|---|---|---|---|---|
| PB5 | 1½d. Watermark upright | 45 | | PB5a | 1½d. Watermark inverted | 1·50 |

### Controls

| | | | | | I. | P. | | | | | | | I. | P. |
|---|---|---|---|---|---|---|---|---|---|---|---|---|---|---|
| PC804 | A 36 | ½d. | .. | .. | 10 | 2·25 | | PC808 | A 37 | ½d. | .. | .. | 10 | † |
| PC805 | A 36 | 1d. | .. | .. | 20 | 10·00 | | PC809 | A 37 | 1d. | .. | .. | 30 | † |
| PC806 | A 36 | 1½d. | .. | .. | 25 | 2·50 | | PC810 | A 37 | 1½d. | .. | .. | 20 | † |
| PC807 | A 36 | 2½d. | .. | .. | 40 | † | | | | | | | | |
| a. | Bar — | .. | .. | .. | 50 | † | | | | | | | | |

(For list of cylinder numbers see Appendix N and for booklet cylinder Nos. see Appendix M.)

# SECTION Q 1

# King George VI

## Photogravure Issues, 1937-1951

All stamps in this Section are watermarked Multiple Block GvIR and Crown, Type **W.20** and perforated 15 × 14 and were printed in photogravure by Harrison & Sons in sheets of 240 (20 rows of 12). Detailed lists of cylinder numbers are given in Appendix N and booklet panes with cylinder numbers are listed in Appendix M and with advertisements in Appendix L.

All Controls in this Section have imperf. margins except the ½d. QC812a, 1d. QC817a and 1½d. QC828a and QC837a.

**W.20**

**Q1**

**Q2**

**Q3**

(Des. E. Dulac (head) and
Eric Gill (frames))

(Des. E. Dulac)

---

## 1937 (MAY 10). ½d. GREEN, TYPE Q1

| Cat. No. | S.G. No. | | | | Shades | | Unused | Used |
|----------|----------|---|---|---|--------|---|--------|------|
| Q1 | 462 | | | | Green | | 5 | 5 |
| a. | Watermark inverted | .. | 40 | 35 | s. | " Cancelled ", Type 33 | .. | 1·00 | |
| b. | Watermark sideways | .. | 25 | 12 | t. | "Cancelled ", Type 33P | .. | 50 | |
| c. | Broken circle to value (Cyl. 18, R.19/2) .. | .. | .. | 1·00 | | | | |

### Booklet panes

Panes of six

| QB1 | Watermark upright | 35 | | QB1a | Watermark inverted | 2·40 |
|-----|-------------------|----|---|------|--------------------|----|
| c. | With cylinder No. .. | .. | 50 | ac. | With cylinder No. .. | .. | 6·00 |
| s. | " Cancelled ", Type 33P | .. | 3·00 | as. | " Cancelled ", Type 33P | .. | 3·00 |

Panes of four

| QB2 | Watermark sideways. Binding edge at top | 2·00 | 1·50 | QB2a | Watermark sideways. Binding edge at bottom | 2·00 | 1·50 |
|-----|------------------------------------------|------|------|------|---------------------------------------------|------|------|
| c. | With cylinder No. .. | .. | 3·00 | | | | |

Panes of two

| QB3 | Watermark upright | 75 | | QB3a | Watermark inverted | 80 |
|-----|-------------------|----|---|------|--------------------|----|
| c. | With cylinder No. .. | .. | 1·50 | | | | |

### ½d. Green Controls

| | | | | | | | | | | | | | |
|---|---|---|---|---|---|---|---|---|---|---|---|---|---|
| QC812 | A 37 | .. | .. | 12 | QC821 | C 38 | .. | .. | 12 | QC849 | F 39 | .. | .. | 12 |
| a. | Perf. | .. | .. | 4·00 | QC826 | D 38 | .. | .. | 12 | QC855 | G 40 | .. | .. | 15 |
| QC816 | B 37 | .. | .. | 12 | QC835 | E 39 | .. | .. | 12 | QC889 | I 41 | .. | .. | 12 |

| Cat. No. | S.G. No. | | Shades | Unused | Used |
|---|---|---|---|---|---|

### 1941 (SEPTEMBER 1). ½d. PALE GREEN, TYPE Q1

| | | | | | |
|---|---|---|---|---|---|
| Q2 | 485 | | Pale green | 5 | 5 |

| | | | |
|---|---|---|---|
| a. | Tête-bêche (horizontal pair) | £180 | |
| b. | Watermark inverted .. | 25 | 15 |
| c. | Imperf. (pair) .. .. | £200 | |
| d. | Spur to R of REVENUE | | |
| | (Cyl. 153., R.1/5) .. .. | 1·25 | |

| | | | |
|---|---|---|---|
| e. | Closed final E of REVENUE | | |
| | (Cyl. 153, R.3/1) .. .. | 5·00 | |
| t. | " Cancelled ", Type 24 .. | | |
| u. | " Cancelled ", Type 33 .. | | |

Q2/3d

Q2/3e

## Booklet panes

### Panes of six

| | | | | | |
|---|---|---|---|---|---|
| QB4 | Watermark upright | 35 | QB4a | Watermark inverted | 1· 50 |
| c. | With cylinder No. .. .. | 50 | | | |

### Panes of four

| | | |
|---|---|---|
| QB5 | Watermark upright. Binding edge at top | QB5a | Watermark upright. Binding edge at bottom |

### Panes of two

| | | |
|---|---|---|
| QB6 | Watermark upright | 12 |
| | With cylinder No. .. .. | 20 |

### ½d. Pale Green Controls

| | | | | | | | | | |
|---|---|---|---|---|---|---|---|---|---|
| QC903 | J 41 .. | .. | 8 | QC 959 N 43 .. | .. | 8 | QC1015 | R 45 .. | .. | 8 |
| QC917 | K 42 .. | .. | 8 | QC 973 O 44 .. | .. | 8 | QC1029 | S 46 .. | .. | 8 |
| QC931 | L 42 .. | .. | 10 | QC 987 P 44 .. | .. | 8 | QC1045 | T 46 .. | .. | 8 |
| QC945 | M 43 .. | .. | 10 | QC1001 Q 45 .. | .. | 8 | QC1059 | U 47 .. | .. | 8 |

### 1951 (MAY 3). ½d. ORANGE, TYPE Q1

| | | | | | |
|---|---|---|---|---|---|
| Q3 | 503 | | Pale orange | 5 | 5 |

| | | | |
|---|---|---|---|
| a. | Tête-bêche (horizontal pair) | £1000 | |
| b. | Watermark inverted .. | 15 | 10 |
| c. | Imperf. (pair) | | |
| d. | Spur to R of REVENUE | | |
| | (Cyl. 153., R.1/5) .. .. | 1·00 | |

| | | | |
|---|---|---|---|
| e | Closed final E of REVENUE | | |
| | (Cyl. 153, R.3/1) .. .. | 3·00 | |

## Booklet panes

### Panes of six

| | | | | | |
|---|---|---|---|---|---|
| QB7 | Watermark upright | 35 | QB7a | Watermark inverted | 90 |
| c. | With cylinder No. .. .. | 45 | | | |

### Panes of four

| | | | |
|---|---|---|---|
| QB8 | Watermark upright. Binding edge at top | 25 | QB8a | Watermark inverted. Binding edge at top | 75 |
| b. | Binding edge at bottom .. | 25 | | | |

### Panes of two

| | | |
|---|---|---|
| QB9 | Watermark upright | 12 |
| c. | With cylinder No. .. .. | 20 |

| Cat. No. | S.G. No. | | | Shades | | Unused | Used |
|---|---|---|---|---|---|---|---|

### 1937 (MAY 10).  1d. SCARLET, TYPE Q1

| | | | | | | | |
|---|---|---|---|---|---|---|---|
| Q4 | 463 | | | Scarlet | | 5 | 5 |
| a. | Watermark inverted | .. | 2·50 | 1·00 | s. | "Cancelled", Type 33  .. | 1·00 |
| b. | Watermark sideways | .. | 1·50 | 50 | t. | "Cancelled", Type 33P .. | 50 |

**Booklet panes**

Panes of six

| | | | | | |
|---|---|---|---|---|---|
| QB10 | Watermark upright | 75 | QB10a | Watermark inverted | 15·00 |
| c. | With cylinder No. .. .. | 1·00 | as. | "Cancelled", Type 33P .. | 3·00 |
| s. | "Cancelled", Type 33P .. | 3·00 | | | |

Panes of four

| | | | | | |
|---|---|---|---|---|---|
| QB11 | Watermark sideways. | | QB11a | Watermark sideways. | |
| | Binding edge at top | 6·50 | 4·00 | Binding edge at bottom | 6·50 | 4·00 |
| | | | ac. | With cylinder No. .. .. | 9·00 |

Panes of two

| | | | | | |
|---|---|---|---|---|---|
| QB12 | Watermark upright | 75 | QB12a | Watermark inverted | 6·00 |
| c. | With cylinder No. .. .. | 1·50 | | | |

### 1d. Scarlet Controls

| | | | | | | | | | | |
|---|---|---|---|---|---|---|---|---|---|---|
| QC813 | A 37 .. | .. | 2·00 | QC827 | D 38 .. | .. | 20 | QC856 | G 40 .. .. | 20 |
| QC817 | B 37 .. | .. | 2·00 | QC836 | E 39 .. | .. | 20 | QC876 | H 40 .. .. | 20 |
| a. | Perf. .. | .. | 9·00 | QC850 | F 39 .. | .. | 20 | QC890 | I 41 .. .. | 20 |
| QC822 | C 38 .. | .. | 2·00 | | | | | | | |

### 1941 (AUGUST 11).  1d. PALE SCARLET, TYPE Q1

| | | | | | | |
|---|---|---|---|---|---|---|
| Q5 | 486 | | | Pale scarlet (Type I) | 5 | 5 |
| a. | Watermark sideways | .. | 20 | 20 | | |
| ba. | Ditto, thick paper | .. | 50 | 50 | | |
| c. | Imperf. (pair) | .. .. | £225 | | | |
| d. | Imperf. three sides (pair) .. | £130 | | | | |
| e. | Imperf. between (vert. pair) | | | g. | Type II .. .. | 12 | 10 |
| f. | Flaw on cheek bone | | | h. | Thick paper, Type II .. | 60 | 30 |
| | (Cyl. 149, R.3/4) .. | .. | 12·00 | t. | "Cancelled", Type 24 .. | |
| | | | | u. | "Cancelled", Type 33 .. | |

Type II was used on all cylinders from 174 onwards, and shows retouching to the multi-positive, especially to the white spot in front of the ear, and the strand of hair behind the ear.

Type I          Type II          Q5f

**Booklet panes**

Panes of four (Type I)

| | |
|---|---|
| QB13  Watermark upright. | QB13a  Watermark upright. |
| Binding edge at top | Binding edge at bottom |

Panes of two

| | | |
|---|---|---|
| Type I | | Type II |
| QB14  Watermark upright | 12 | QB14a  Watermark upright | 30 |
| c.  With cylinder No. .. .. | 20 | ac.  With cylinder No. .. .. | 40 |

### 1d. Pale Scarlet Controls

| | | | | | | | | | | |
|---|---|---|---|---|---|---|---|---|---|---|
| QC904 | J 41 .. | .. | 15 | QC960 | N 43 .. | .. | 12 | QC1016 | R 45 .. | .. | 12 |
| QC918 | K 42 .. | .. | 12 | QC974 | O 44 .. | .. | 12 | QC1030 | S 46 .. | .. | 12 |
| QC932 | L 42 .. | .. | 12 | QC988 | P 44 .. | .. | 12 | QC1046 | T 46 .. | .. | 12 |
| QC946 | M 43 .. | .. | 12 | QC1002 | Q 45 .. | .. | 12 | QC1060 | U 47 .. | .. | 12 |

## 1951 (MAY 3). 1d. ULTRAMARINE, TYPE Q1

| Cat. No. | S.G. No. | | | | Shades | Unused | Used |
|---|---|---|---|---|---|---|---|
| Q6 | 504 | | | | Light ultramarine (Type II) | 5 | 5 |

*a.* Watermark inverted
  (Type II) .. .. .. 15  15
*b.* Watermark sideways
  (Type I) .. .. .. 10  5
*c.* Imperf. (pair) .. .. £180
*d.* Imperf. three sides (pair) .. 75·00

*e.* " Keyhole " flaw (Cyl. 192.,
  R.6/12) .. .. .. 7·00
*f.* Retouched nose and forehead
  Wmk. sideways .. .. 1·00
*g.* Partial tête-bêche pane .. £1000

Q6e

## Booklet panes (Type II)

Panes of six

QB15 Watermark upright 30
*c.* With cylinder No. .. .. 50

QB15a Watermark inverted 90

Panes of four

QB16 Watermark upright.
  Binding edge at top 25
*b.* Binding edge at bottom .. 25

QB16a Watermark inverted.
  Binding edge at top 65

Panes of two

QB17 Watermark upright 12
*c.* With cylinder No. .. .. 20

**109**

Booklet panes of three with three printed labels:—

Minimum Inland Printed Paper Rate 1½d.  17 mm. high

QB18  Watermark upright      30        QB18a  Watermark inverted    90
  *c.*  With cylinder No.  ..    50

Minimum Inland Printed Paper Rate 1½d.  15 mm. high

QB19  Watermark upright     1·75        QB19a  Watermark inverted    1·75
  *c.*  With cylinder No.  ..  4·50

Shorthand in one week

QB20  Watermark upright     1·25        QB20a  Watermark inverted    1·25
  *c.*  With cylinder No.  ..  3·50

## Proofs

On plain paper.  Booklet page with "Shorthand in one week" labels only

Imperforate  ..  ..  ..  ..  ..  ..  ..  ..  ..  15·00

On paper watermarked " Harrison and Sons London ".  " Shorthand in one week " labels only

Perf. 15 × 14  ..  ..  ..  ..  ..  ..  ..  ..  ..  20·00

## 1937 (JULY 30).  1½d. RED-BROWN, TYPE Q1

| Cat. No. | S.G. No. | | | Shades | Unused | Used |
|---|---|---|---|---|---|---|
| Q7 | 464 | | | Red-Brown | 5 | 5 |
| *a.* | Watermark inverted | .. | 1·00 | 50 | | |
| *b.* | Watermark sideways | .. | 50 | 15 | | |
| *c.* | Imperf. three sides (pair) | .. | | | | |
| *d.* | Crown flaw (Cyl. 145., 150., | | | *s.* | " Cancelled ", Type 33 | .. | 1·00 |
| | R.19/7) | .. | .. | 2·00 | *t.* | " Cancelled ", Type 33P | .. | 40 |

Q7*d*

## Booklet panes

### Panes of six

QB21  Watermark upright      45        QB21a  Watermark inverted   6·00
  *c.*  With cylinder No. ..  ..   65      *as.* " Cancelled ", Type 33P ..  2·40
  *s.*  " Cancelled ", Type 33P ..  2·40

### Panes of four, with two advertisement labels

QB22  Watermark upright     1·50        QB22a  Watermark inverted   4·00
  *c.*  With cylinder No. ..  ..  2·00      *ac.* With cylinder No. ..  ..  4·50
  *s.*  " Cancelled ", Type 33P ..  2·50      *as.* " Cancelled ", Type 33P ..  2·50

### Panes of two

QB23  Watermark upright      35        QB23a  Watermark inverted   2·50
  *b.*  With cylinder No. ..  ..  1·50

## 1½d. Red-Brown Controls

| | | | | | | | | | | | |
|---|---|---|---|---|---|---|---|---|---|---|---|
| *QC814* | A 37 | .. | .. | 35 | *QC828* | D 38 | .. | .. | 30 | *QC851* | F 39 | .. | .. | 30 |
| *QC818* | B 37 | .. | .. | 25 | *a.* | Perf. | .. | .. | 6·00 | *QC857* | G 40 | .. | .. | 50 |
| *QC823* | C 38 | .. | .. | 30 | *QC837* | E 39 | .. | .. | 30 | | | | | |
| | | | | | *a.* | Perf. | .. | .. | 20·00 | | | | | |

Cat. No.  S.G. No.                                      Shades               Unused  Used

## 1942 (SEPTEMBER 28).  1½d. PALE RED-BROWN, TYPE Q1

Q8       487                              Pale red-brown              10       5
  *d.*  Spot in daffodil leaf (Cyl. 192.,
     R.10/10)  ..      ..      ..   1·50
  *e.*  Extended serif to 1 of ½                *t.*  " Cancelled ", Type 28   ..
     (Cyl. 192., R7/11) ..      ..   1·50    *u.*  " Cancelled ", Type 33   ..

Q8/9*d*

Q8/9*e*

### Booklet panes

Panes of four

QB24  Watermark upright.                   QB24a  Watermark upright.
      Binding edge at top                          Binding edge at bottom

Panes of two

QB25  Watermark upright        25
  *c.*  With cylinder No. ..     ..     45

### 1½d. Pale Red-brown Controls

| | | | | | | | |
|---|---|---|---|---|---|---|---|
| *QC933* L 42 .. | .. | 20 | *QC 989* P 44 .. | .. | 20 | *QC1031* S 46 .. | .. | 20 |
| *QC961* N 43 .. | .. | 20 | *QC1003* Q 45 .. | .. | 20 | *QC1061* U 47 .. | .. | 20 |
| *QC975* O 44 .. | .. | 20 | *QC1017* R 45 .. | .. | 20 | | | |

## 1951 (MAY 3).  1½d. GREEN, TYPE Q1

Q9       505                              Pale green                  5       5
  *a.*  Watermark inverted      ..     15     15    *d.*  Spot in daffodil leaf (Cyls.
  *b.*  Watermark sideways      ..     10      5         192., 195., 196., R.10/10)   1·00
  *c.*  Retouched  forehead  (Cyl.             *e.*  Extended serif to 1 of ½
     192, R.19/1)  ..     ..   3·50         (Cyls. 192., 195., R.7/11)   1·00

### Booklet panes

Panes of six

QB26  Watermark upright        35
  *c.*  With cylinder No. ..     ..     45    QB26a  Watermark inverted  1·00

Panes of four

QB27  Watermark upright        25          QB27a  Watermark inverted  75

Panes of two

QB28  Watermark upright        13
  *c.*  With cylinder No. ..     ..     20

## 1938 (JANUARY 31).  2d. ORANGE, TYPE Q1

Q10      465                              Orange                     25       5
  *a.*  Bisect (on cover)  ..     ..    †      5·00
  *b.*  Watermark inverted      ..   3·50   2·00    *s.*  " Cancelled ", Type 33   ..
  *c.*  Watermark sideways      ..   2·50   1·00    *t.*  " Cancelled ", Type 33P ..   1·00

*Bisects:* On December 24th 1940, authority was given by Post Office notice, that pre-
payment of penny postage could be effected by using half a British 2d. stamp, diagonally
bisected.  Such stamps were used in Guernsey during the German occupation.  Earliest
known date 27th December 1940.

### Booklet panes of six

QB29  Watermark upright       1·75          QB29a  Watermark inverted 22·00
  *c.*  With cylinder No. ..     ..   2·50
  *s.*  " Cancelled ", Type 33P ..   6·00          *as.* " Cancelled ", Type 33P ..   6·00

### 2d. Orange Controls

| | | | | | | | |
|---|---|---|---|---|---|---|---|
| *QC819* B 37 .. | .. | 1·25 | *QC838* E 39 .. | .. | 1·25 | *QC878* H 40 .. | .. | 1·25 |
| *QC824* C 38 .. | .. | 4·00 | *QC852* F 39 .. | .. | 1·25 | *QC892* I 41 .. | .. | 1·25 |
| *QC829* D 38 .. | .. | 1·25 | *QC858* G 40 .. | .. | 1·25 | | | |

Cat. No.   S.G. No.                                   Shades              Unused  Used

### 1941 (OCTOBER 6).   2d. PALE ORANGE, TYPE Q1

Q11        488                            Pale orange                     10      5
  *a.* Watermark inverted      ..    1·00     75
  *b.* Watermark sideways      ..     60      60   *d.* Imperf. (pair)    ..    ..  £600
  *c.* Tête-bêche (horizontal pair)  £400        *t.* " Cancelled ", Type 33  ..

### Booklet panes of six

QB30  Watermark upright          65          QB30a  Watermark inverted  6·00
  *c.* With cylinder No. 4.  ..     80

### 2d. Pale Orange Controls

| | | | | | | | |
|---|---|---|---|---|---|---|---|
| *QC906* | J 41 .. .. | 20 | *QC 962* | N 43 .. | .. | 20 | *QC1018* R 45 .. | .. | 20 |
| *QC920* | K 42 .. .. | 20 | *QC 976* | O 44 .. | .. | 20 | *QC1032* S 46 .. | .. | 20 |
| *QC934* | L 42 .. .. | 20 | *QC 990* | P 44 .. | .. | 20 | *QC1048* T 46 .. | .. | 20 |
| *QC948* | M 43 .. .. | 20 | *QC1004* | Q 45 .. | .. | 20 | *QC1062* U 47 .. | .. | 20 |

### 1951 (MAY 3).   2d. RED-BROWN, TYPE Q1

Q12        506                            (1) Pale red-brown              12      5
  *a.* Watermark inverted      ..    50      50   (2) Bright red-brown            30     30
  *b.* Watermark sideways
    Shade (1)    ..    ..    20      10
    Shade (2)    ..    ..    50      50
  *c.* Tête-bêche (horiz. pair)  ..  £850
  *d.* Imperf. three sides (pair) ..  £100   Retouches to Rose, Thistle
  *e.* " Swan head " to 2 (wmk.              and Cross on Crown (Cyl. 75,
    sideways)  ..    ..    ..   3·00   3·00   R.1/3 & 4) ..    ..    ..   3·00
  *f.* Ditto retouched
    Shade (1)    ..    ..    50      50
    Shade (2)    ..    ..    60      60

Q12*g* (R.1/3)                          Q12*e*

### Booklet panes of six

QB31  Watermark upright          75          QB31a  Watermark inverted  3·00
  *c.* With cylinder No. ..    ..    1·00

### 1937 (MAY 10).   2½d. ULTRAMARINE, TYPE Q1

Q13        466                            Ultramarine                     15      5
  *a.* Watermark inverted      ..    3·50     1·00
  *b.* Watermark sideways      ..    2·00     1·50   *s.* " Cancelled ", Type 33   ..
  *c.* Tête-bêche (horizontal pair)               *t.* " Cancelled ", Type 33P            80

### Booklet panes of six

QB32  Watermark upright          2·50         QB32a  Watermark inverted  22·00
  *c.* With cylinder No. ..    ..    4·00
  *s.* " Cancelled ", Type 33P  ..  5·00        *as.* " Cancelled ", Type 33P  ..  5·00

### 2½d. Ultramarine Controls

| | | | | | | | |
|---|---|---|---|---|---|---|---|
| *QC815* | A 37 .. .. | 65 | *QC839* | E 39 .. | .. | 65 | *QC879* H 40 .. | .. | 65 |
| *QC820* | B 37 .. .. | 65 | *QC859* | G 40 .. | .. | 75 | *QC893* I 41 .. | .. | 65 |
| *QC830* | D 38 .. .. | 65 | | | | | | |

| Cat. No. | S.G. No. | | Shades | Unused | Used |
|---|---|---|---|---|---|

### 1941 (JULY 21). 2½d. LIGHT ULTRAMARINE, TYPE Q1

| | | | | | |
|---|---|---|---|---|---|
| Q14 | 489 | | Light ultramarine | 8 | 5 |
| *a.* | Watermark inverted .. | 50 | 20 | *e.* b for d in value (Cyl. 239., | |
| *b.* | Watermark sideways .. | 35 | 20 | R.18/3) .. .. .. 4·00 | |
| *c.* | Tête-bêche (horizontal pair) | £400 | | *t.* " Cancelled ", Type 28 .. | |
| *d.* | Imperf. (pair) .. .. | £225 | | *u.* " Cancelled ", Type 33 | |

Q14e          Q15cb

### Booklet panes of six

| QB33 Watermark upright | 50 | QB33a Watermark inverted | 3·00 |
|---|---|---|---|
| *c.* With cylinder No. .. .. | 75 | | |

### 2½d. Light Ultramarine Controls

| | | | | | | | |
|---|---|---|---|---|---|---|---|
| QC907 J 41 .. .. | 20 | QC 963 N 43 .. .. | 20 | QC1019 R 45 .. .. | 20 |
| QC921 K 42 .. .. | 20 | QC 977 O 44 .. .. | 20 | QC1033 S 46 .. .. | 20 |
| QC935 L 42 .. .. | 20 | QC 991 P 44 .. .. | 20 | QC1049 T 46 .. .. | 20 |
| QC949 M 43 .. .. | 20 | QC1005 Q 45 .. .. | 20 | QC1063 U 47 .. .. | 20 |

### 1951 (MAY 3). 2½d. SCARLET, TYPE Q1

| | | | | | |
|---|---|---|---|---|---|
| Q15 | 507 | | Pale scarlet | 10 | 5 |
| *a.* | Watermark inverted .. | 30 | 25 | *cb.* Damaged S in POSTAGE .. 90 | |
| *b.* | Watermark sideways .. | 35 | 15 | *d.* Tête-bêche (horizontal pair) | |

### Booklet panes of six

| QB34 Watermark upright | 65 | QB34a Watermark inverted | 2·00 |
|---|---|---|---|
| *c.* With cylinder No. .. .. | 80 | | |

### 1938 (JANUARY 31). 3d. VIOLET, TYPE Q1

| Q16 | 467 | Violet | 50 | 5 |
|---|---|---|---|---|

### 3d. Violet Controls

| | | | | | |
|---|---|---|---|---|---|
| QC825 C 38 .. .. | 2·00 | QC840 E 39 .. .. | 2·25 | QC880 H 40 .. .. | 2·25 |
| QC831 D 38 .. .. | 2·25 | QC860 G 40 .. .. | 2·25 | | |

### 1941 (NOVEMBER 3). 3d. PALE VIOLET, TYPE Q1

| | | | | |
|---|---|---|---|---|
| Q17 | 490 | | Pale violet | 20 | 5 |
| *a.* | Damaged hair (Cyl. 34., | | *c.* Broken circle to value (Cyl. | |
| | R.9/10) .. .. .. 5·00 | | 27, R.18/2) .. .. .. 2·00 | |
| *b.* | Ditto, retouched .. 4·50 | | *t.* " Cancelled ", Type 33 | |

On cylinder 27 the dividing arrow was incorrectly engraved between stamps 7 and 8 in the upper and lower margins. This was erased by lines and re-engraved in the correct position between stamps 6 and 7.

Q17b

## 3d. Pale Violet Controls

| | | | | | | | | |
|---|---|---|---|---|---|---|---|---|
| QC908 | J 41 | .. | .. | 30 | QC950 | M 43 | .. | .. | 30 | QC 992 | P 44 | .. | .. | 30 |
| QC922 | K 42 | .. | .. | 30 | QC964 | N 43 | .. | .. | 30 | QC1006 | Q 45 | .. | .. | 30 |
| QC936 | L 42 | .. | .. | 30 | QC978 | O 44 | .. | .. | 30 | QC1020 | R 45 | .. | .. | 30 |

Cat. No.   S.G. No.                                                  Shades                          Unused   Used

## 1938 (NOVEMBER 21).   4d. GREY-GREEN, TYPE Q2

Q19    468                                         Grey-green                         25      8
  a.  Imperf. (pair)   ..   ..   £225
  b.  Imperf. three sides (pair) ..                s.  " Cancelled ", Type 33   ..

### 4d. Grey-green Controls

| QC832 | D 38 | .. | .. | 1·00 | QC923 | K 42 | .. | .. | 1·00 | QC979 | O 44 | .. | .. | 1·00 |
|---|---|---|---|---|---|---|---|---|---|---|---|---|---|---|
| QC841 | E 39 | .. | .. | 1·00 | a. | Bar | — | .. | 1·00 | a. | Bar | — | .. | 1·00 |
| QC861 | G 40 | .. | .. | 1·00 | b. | Bars | ⌐ | .. | 1·00 | b. | Bars | ⌐ | .. | 1·00 |
| QC895 | I 41 | .. | .. | 1·00 | | | | | | c. | Bars | ⌐ | .. | 1·00 |

## 1950 (OCTOBER 2).   4d. ULTRAMARINE, TYPE Q2

Q20    508                                         Light ultramarine                         12      5
  a.  Retouched background to POS (Cyl. 13, R.9/2)   ..   1·50

## 1938 (NOVEMBER 21).   5d. BROWN, TYPE Q2

Q21    469                                         Brown                         25      8
  a.  Imperf. (pair)   ..   ..   £225      b.  Imperf. three sides (pair) ..   £150

### 5d. Brown Controls

| QC833 | D 38 | .. | .. | 75 | QC924 | K 42 | .. | 85 | QC938c. | Bars | ⌐ | .. | 75 |
|---|---|---|---|---|---|---|---|---|---|---|---|---|---|
| QC842 | E 39 | .. | .. | 75 | QC938 | L 42 | .. | 18·00 | d. | Bars | □ | .. | 75 |
| QC862 | G 40 | .. | .. | 75 | a. | Bar | — | 85 | e. | Bars | ⊔ | .. | 75 |
| QC896 | I 41 | .. | .. | 75 | b. | Bars | ⌐ | 75 | | | | |

## 1939 (JANUARY 30).   6d. PURPLE, TYPE Q2

Q22    470                                         Purple                         30      5
  s.  " Cancelled ", Type 33   ..

### 6d. Purple Controls (Typographed in black)

| QC834 | D 38 | .. | .. | 1·00 | QC911 | J 41 | .. | .. | 75 | QC 981 | O 44 | .. | .. | 75 |
|---|---|---|---|---|---|---|---|---|---|---|---|---|---|---|
| QC843 | E 39 | .. | .. | 75 | QC925 | K 42 | .. | .. | 75 | QC1009 | Q 45 | .. | .. | 75 |
| QC853 | F 39 | .. | .. | 90 | QC939 | L 42 | .. | .. | 75 | QC1053 | T 46 | .. | .. | 75 |
| QC863 | G 40 | .. | .. | 90 | QC953 | M 43 | .. | .. | 75 | QC1067 | U 47 | .. | .. | 75 |
| QC883 | H 40 | .. | .. | 1·00 | QC967 | N 43 | .. | .. | 75 | | | | |

## 1939 (FEBRUARY 27).   7d. EMERALD-GREEN, TYPE Q3

Q23    471                                         Emerald-green                         35      8
  a.  Imperf. three sides (pair) ..   £175
  b.  Cracked cylinder (Cyl. 10., R.20/12)   ..   ..                s.  " Cancelled ", Type 33   ..

### 7d. Emerald-green Controls

| QC844 | E 39.. | .. | 1·00 | QC844c. | Bars | ⌐ | .. | 1·00 | QC844f. | Bars | □ | .. | 1·00 |
|---|---|---|---|---|---|---|---|---|---|---|---|---|
| a. | Bar — | .. | 1·00 | d. | Bars | □ | .. | 1·00 | QC1038 | S 46 | .. | .. | 1·00 |
| b. | Bars ⌐ | .. | 1·00 | e. | Bars | □ | .. | 1·00 | | | | |

## 1939 (FEBRUARY 27).   8d. CARMINE, TYPE Q3

Q24    472                                         Bright carmine                         35      10
  s.  " Cancelled ", Type 33   ..

### 8d. Carmine Controls

| QC845 | E 39.. | .. | 1·25 | QC845c. | Bars | ⊔ | .. | 1·25 | QC 983 | O 44.. | .. | 1·25 |
|---|---|---|---|---|---|---|---|---|---|---|---|
| a. | Bar — | .. | 1·25 | d. | Bars | □ | .. | 1·25 | a. | Bar — | .. | 1·50 |
| b. | Bars ⌐ | .. | 1·25 | e. | Bars | □ | .. | 1·25 | QC1039 | S 46.. | .. | 1·25 |
| | | | | | | | | | a. | Bar — | .. | 1·25 |

| Cat. No. | S.G. No. | | Shades | Unused | Used |
|---|---|---|---|---|---|

### 1939 (MAY 1).   9d. OLIVE-GREEN, TYPE Q3

Q25   473   Deep olive-green   45   10
*s.*  " Cancelled ", Type 33   ..

### 9d. Olive-green Controls (Typographed in black)

| | | | | | | | | | |
|---|---|---|---|---|---|---|---|---|---|
| QC846 E 39 | .. | .. | 1·10 | QC928 K 42 | .. | .. | 1·10 | QC 984 O 44 .. | .. | 1·10 |
| QC866 G 40 | .. | .. | 1·10 | QC942 L 42 | .. | .. | 1·10 | QC 998 P 44 .. | .. | 1·10 |
| QC886 H 40 | .. | .. | 1·10 | QC070 N 43 | .. | .. | 1·10 | QC1026 R 45 .. | .. | 1·10 |
| QC900 I 41 | .. | .. | 1·10 | | | | | | |

### 1939 (MAY 1).   10d. TURQUOISE-BLUE, TYPE Q3

Q26   474   Turquoise-blue   50   12
*a.*  Imperf. (pair)   ..   ..
*b.*  Broken Fleur-de-lis (Cyl. 7,
   R.20/7)   ..   ..   ..   2·00   *t.*  " Cancelled ", Type 33   ..

Q26*b*

### 10d. Turquoise-blue Controls (Typographed in black)

| | | | | | | | | | |
|---|---|---|---|---|---|---|---|---|---|
| QC847 E 39 | .. | .. | 1·50 | QC929 K 42 | .. | .. | 1·50 | QC 985 O 44 .. | .. | 1·50 |
| QC854 F 39 | .. | .. | 1·50 | QC943 L 42 | .. | .. | 1·50 | QC1013 Q 45 .. | .. | 1·50 |
| QC887 H 40 | .. | .. | 1·50 | QC957 M 43 | .. | .. | 1·50 | QC1057 T 46 .. | .. | 1·50 |
| QC901 I 41 | .. | .. | 1·50 | QC971 N 43 | .. | .. | 1·50 | QC1071 U 47 .. | .. | 1·50 |
| QC915 J 41 | .. | .. | 1·50 | | | | | | |

### 1947 (DECEMBER 29).   11d. PLUM, TYPE Q3

Q27   474*a*   Plum   75   30

### 1939 (MAY 1).   1s. BISTRE-BROWN, TYPE Q3

Q28   475   Bistre-brown   50   5
*a.*  Broken Crown (Cyl. 16.,
   S 46, R.18/2)   ..   ..   8·00
*s.*  " Specimen ", Type 23   ..   1·50   *t.*  " Cancelled", Type 33   ..

Q28*a*

### 1s. Bistre-brown Controls

Photogravure in bistre-brown
QC848 E 39   ..   ..   1·60 | QC868   G 40 ..   ..   1·60

Typographed in black

| | | | | | | | | | |
|---|---|---|---|---|---|---|---|---|---|
| QC888 H 40 | .. | .. | 1·60 | QC 958 M 43 .. | .. | 1·60 | QC1042 S 46 .. | .. | 1·60 |
| QC916 J 41 | .. | .. | 1·60 | QC 986 O 44 .. | .. | 1·60 | QC1072 U 47 .. | .. | 1·60 |
| QC930 K 42 | .. | .. | 1·60 | QC1014 Q 45 .. | .. | 1·60 | | | |

# SECTION Q 2
## King George VI
### Recess-printed Issues, 1939-1951

All stamps in this section are watermarked Block GviR and Crown, Type **W.21** and were recess-printed by Waterlow & Sons. It is known that more than one plate was used for these issues which accounts for the listed varieties not existing on all sheets.

**W.21**

**Q4**

(Des. E. Dulac)

**Q5**

(Des. Hon. George R. Bellew, M.V.O.)

**1939-48.** Printed in sheets of 40, arranged in 5 rows of 8

Cat. No.  S.G. No.  Perf.                                                    Shades         Unused   Used

### 1939 (SEPTEMBER 4).  2s. 6d. BROWN, TYPE Q4

Q29      476      14                                  Brown                         3·00     75
a. Mark in Shield (R. 1/7)   ..  25·00  12·00      c. Gashed Crown (R.5/5)   ..  15·00   5·00
b. Gashed Crown (R. 2/7)    ..  15·00   5·00      s. " Specimen ", Type 23   ..   5·00

### 1942 (MARCH 9).  2s. 6d. YELLOW-GREEN, TYPE Q4

Q30      476a     14                                  Yellow-green                  1·25     12
a. Major re-entry (R. 5/2)  ..  40·00  20·00      c. Minor re-entries  ..  From  4·00   2·00
b. Re-entry in shield and left                     s. " Specimen ", Type 23   ..   5·00
   frame (R. 1/7)    ..    ..  30·00  10·00      t. " Cancelled ", Type 24   ..

### 1939 (AUGUST 21).  5s. RED, TYPE Q4

Q31      477      14                                  Red                           3·50     35
a. Major re-entry (R. 4/2)  ..  35·00  25·00      d. Guide mark in hair (T or ⊥)  5·00   3·00
b. Re-entry in harp, etc. (R. 2/1) 18·00  12·00  s. " Specimen ", Type 23   ..   8·00
c. Minor re-entries   .. From  4·25   2·25      t. " Cancelled ", Type 24   ..

### 1939 (OCTOBER 3).  10s. DARK BLUE, TYPE Q5

Q32      478      14                                  (1) Dark blue                15·00   2·25
a. Major re-entry (R. 3/7)  ..  25·00  10·00      (2) Steel blue-black         18·00   3·25
b. Minor re-entries   .. From  18·00   4·00
c. Retouched medallion (R. 4/1) 25·00   8·00      e. Retouch to lower lip (R. 2/7) 20·00   5·00
d. Dot on scroll (R. 2/5)   ..  20·00   5·00      s. " Specimen ", Type 23   ..  10·00

### 1942 (NOVEMBER 30).  10s. ULTRAMARINE, TYPE Q5

Q33      478a     14                                  Ultramarine                   3·25     50
s. " Specimen ", Type 23   ..   5·00               t. " Cancelled ", Type 24   ..

### 1948 (OCTOBER 1).  £1, BROWN, TYPE Q5

Q34      478b     14                                  Brown                         4·25    2·00
s. " Specimen ", Type 30   ..

Varieties

Q29b

Q29a

Q29c

Q30a

Q30b

Q31a

Q32a

Q32c

Q32d

Q32e

**Q6.**  H.M.S. *Victory*

**Q7.**  White Cliffs of Dover

(Des. Mary Adshead)

**Q8.**   St George and the Dragon

**Q9.**   Royal Coat-of-Arms

(Des. Percy Metcalfe, c.v.o.)

**1951.**  Printed in sheets of 40, arranged in 10 rows of 4

| Cat. No. | S.G. No. | Perf. | Shades | Unused | Used |
|---|---|---|---|---|---|
| **1951 (MAY 3).** | **2s. 6d. YELLOW-GREEN, TYPE Q6** | | | | |
| Q35 | 509 | 11 × 12 | Yellow-green | 1·25 | 15 |
| **1951 (MAY 3).** | **5s. RED, TYPE Q7** | | | | |
| Q36 | 510 | 11 × 12 | Red | 2·00 | 45 |
| **1951 (MAY 3).** | **10s. ULTRAMARINE, TYPE Q8** | | | | |
| Q37 | 511 | 11 × 12 | Ultramarine | 2·75 | 75 |
| **1951 (MAY 3).** | **£1, BROWN, TYPE Q9** | | | | |
| Q38 | 512 | 11 × 12 | Brown | 6·00 | 1·50 |
| a. | Re-entry in DIEU (R. 5/1 and R. 5/4) .. .. .. | | 10·00 | 5·00 | |

Q38a

**Die Proofs**

In black on small sheet.

| | | | | | | | | |
|---|---|---|---|---|---|---|---|---|
| Head and crown for 2s. 6d. and 5s. | .. | .. | .. | .. | .. | .. | .. | 75·00 |
| St. George and dragon for 10s. .. | .. | .. | .. | .. | .. | .. | .. | 50·00 |
| Head only for 10s. and £1 | .. | .. | .. | .. | .. | .. | .. | 50·00 |

# SECTION Q3
# King George VI
## Commemorative Issues, 1937-1951

All stamps in this section are watermarked Multiple Block GVIR and Crown, Type **W.20** and were printed in photogravure by Harrison & Sons. Printed in sheets of 120 arranged in 20 rows of 6, with the exception of the 1940 Stamp Centenary issue and the £1 Silver Wedding stamp.

**Q10.** King George VI and Queen Elizabeth
(Des. E. Dulac)

## 1937 (MAY 13). CORONATION OF KING GEORGE VI

| Cat. No. | S.G. No. | Type No. | Perf. | | Description | | | Unused | Used |
|---|---|---|---|---|---|---|---|---|---|
| QCom1 | 461 | **Q10** | 15 × 14 | | 1½d. Maroon | | | 8 | 5 |
| a. | Ray flaw | .. | .. | .. | 35 | i. | Pearl in Orb.. | .. | .. | 35 |
| b. | Ray flaw corrected | | .. | 75 | j. | Crack in Orb | | .. | 1·50 |
| c. | Colon flaw | .. | .. | 90 | k. | Short foot to 2 | | .. | 3·00 |
| d. | "Comet" flaw | .. | .. | 5·00 | l. | Patch in oval | | .. | 1·00 |
| e. | Spur to A in MAY | .. | 50 | m. | Long tail to S | .. | .. | 1·00 |
| f. | Extra decoration | .. | .. | 5·00 | n. | Extended bar to E | | .. | 1·00 |
| g. | Pearl behind tiara | .. | 3·00 | o. | Inner line in 1 | | .. | 1·30 |
| h. | Spot in lacing by Orb | .. | 1·75 | p. | "Beetle" on monogram | .. | 5·00 |

QCom1    First Day Cover    ..    ..    ..    ..    ..    ..    ..    †    1·00

### Varieties

a. Ray flaw. This was a multipositive flaw (R. 19/1) in which the right arm of the ornament in upper left corner is almost solid. It was issued on cylinders 4, 6, 7, 8, 10, 12, 16, 17, 19 and 24, all without dot.

b. Ray flaw corrected. This was corrected before issue on cylinders 2, 3, 18, 20, 23, 27 and 30 and cylinders 4, 7, 10, 16 and 19 were also reissued with the correction. Naturally there is some variation in the skill of the correction from cylinder to cylinder so it is not practical to give an illustration of this. Every stamp in position R.19/1 either has the flaw or it has been corrected.

c. Colon flaw. Two white dots between 12 and MAY (Cyl. 7, R.10/1). Later retouched.

d. "Comet" flaw between MAY and 1937 (Cyl. 6., R. 16/6).

e. Spur to A in MAY (R.18/4 on cyls. 2, 3, 4, 6, 7 all no dot).

f. Extra decoration on King's uniform in the shape of a white cross (Cyl. 7, R. 1/5).

g. Pearl behind Queen's tiara (Cyl. 7, R. 6/6). Later corrected.

h. Spot in lacing to right of Cross of Orb (R. 6/6). This is a multipositive variety which was issued on cyls. 4 and 6 dot but was not quite successfully corrected on cylinders 7 and 8 but completely touched out on cylinders 10 onwards. This stamp also contains another variety, a small white dot above left arm of Y in MAY but it only occurs on cylinder 6.

i. Pearl in Orb. A faint white spot on lower part of Orb which is visible on all dot cylinders in position R.18/1.

j. Crack in Orb. Very marked variety which is constant but its position is not known.

k. Short foot in 2 of date (Cyl. 2., R.15/5).

l. Large patch in oval at bottom right. Constant but position unknown.

m. Long tail to bottom of S of POSTAGE. Constant, position unknown.

n. Extended middle bar to first E of REVENUE (Cyl. 23., R.9/2).

o. Inner line to large figure 1 of value at left. Constant, position unknown.

p. "Beetle" on "E" of monogram. Constant, position unknown.

The above varieties are shown in the composite illustration on the next page.
There are many other flaws on this stamp which are fully described in *Great Britain. The Coronation Stamp, 1937* by L. Birch.

### Control
QComC811  A 37  ..  50

### Cylinder Numbers
An R shows the existence of the Ray flaw, and RC denotes Ray flaw corrected.
Perforation Type 5

| Cyl. No. | | Cyl. No. | | Cyl. No. | | Cyl. No. | | Cyl. No. | | Cyl. No. | |
|---|---|---|---|---|---|---|---|---|---|---|---|
| 2 | 40 | 2. | 40 | 10R | 50 | 10. | 40 | 19R | 50 | 19. | 40 |
| 3 | 40 | 3. | 40 | 10RC | 6·00 | | | 19RC | 1·75 | | |
| 4R | 50 | 4. | 40 | 12R | 50 | 12. | 40 | 20 | 40 | 20. | 40 |
| 4RC | 18·00 | | | 16R | 75 | 16. | 50 | 23 | 40 | 23. | 40 |
| 6R | 50 | 6. | 40 | 16RC | 1·75 | | | 24R | 2·00 | 24. | 2·00 |
| 7R | 50 | 7. | 40 | 17R | 65 | 17. | 50 | 27 | 1·00 | 27. | 1·00 |
| 7RC | 1·00 | | | 18 | 40 | 18. | 40 | 30 | 40 | 30. | 40 |
| 8R | 65 | 8. | 50 | | | | | | | | |

**Quantity Sold** 388,731,000

Coronation Varieties

**Q11.** Queen Victoria and King George VI
(Des. H. L. Palmer)

## 1940 (MAY 6). CENTENARY OF FIRST ADHESIVE POSTAGE STAMPS
Printed in sheets of 160 arranged in 20 rows of 8.

| Cat. No. | S.G. No. | Type No. | Perf. | Description | Unused | Used |
|---|---|---|---|---|---|---|
| QCom2 | 479 | **Q11** | $14\frac{1}{2} \times 14$ | $\frac{1}{2}$d. Green | 5 | 5 |
| QCom3 | 480 | **Q11** | $14\frac{1}{2} \times 14$ | 1d. Scarlet | 10 | 5 |
| QCom4 | 481 | **Q11** | $14\frac{1}{2} \times 14$ | $1\frac{1}{2}$d. Red-brown | 15 | 15 |
| QCom5 | 482 | **Q11** | $14\frac{1}{2} \times 14$ | 2d. Orange | 15 | 12 |
| *a* | Bisect (on cover)* | | † | 1·75 | | |
| QCom6 | 483 | **Q11** | $14\frac{1}{2} \times 14$ | $2\frac{1}{2}$d. Ultramarine | 25 | 5 |
| *a.* | Retouched neck (Cyl. 2., R. 20/2) | | 5·00 | 3·50 | | |
| *b.* | Retouch to King's face and hair (Cyl. 5, R.20/1) | | 2·50 | 1·50 | *c.* Loop to Crown (position?) | 3·00 | 2·00 |
| QCom7 | 484 | **Q11** | $14\frac{1}{2} \times 14$ | 3d. Violet | 50 | 50 |
| QCom2/7 | First Day Cover | | .. | .. | .. | † | 1·50 |

*See note after No. Q10 *re* use in the Channel Islands.

QCom6a

QCom6c

QCom6b

### Controls

| | | | | | | | | |
|---|---|---|---|---|---|---|---|---|
| QComC869 | G 40 | $\frac{1}{2}$d. | .. | 30 | QComC872 | G 40 | 2d. | .. | 1·50 |
| QComC870 | G 40 | 1d. | .. | 75 | QComC873 | G 40 | $2\frac{1}{2}$d. | .. | 2·00 |
| QComC871 | G 40 | $1\frac{1}{2}$d. | .. | 1·40 | QComC874 | G 40 | 3d. | .. | 3·50 |

### Cylinder Numbers

| | Cyl. No. | | | | Cyl. No. | | | | Cyl. No. | | | | Cyl. No. | | |
|---|---|---|---|---|---|---|---|---|---|---|---|---|---|---|---|
| $\frac{1}{2}$d. | 1 | .. | 65 | | 1. | .. | 65 | 2d. | 1 | .. | 1·25 | | 1. | .. | 1·25 |
| | 3 | .. | 30 | | 3. | .. | 30 | | 2 | .. | 1·25 | | 2. | .. | 1·25 |
| | 6 | .. | 35 | | 6. | .. | 35 | | 3 | .. | 1·60 | | 3. | .. | 1·60 |
| 1d. | 1 | .. | 75 | | 1. | .. | 75 | $2\frac{1}{2}$d. | 2 | .. | 1·75 | | 2. | .. | 5·00 |
| | 2 | .. | 1·50 | | 2. | .. | 1·50 | | 3 | .. | 1·75 | | 3. | .. | 1·75 |
| | 3 | .. | 75 | | 3. | .. | 75 | | 4 | .. | † | | 4. | .. | 5·00 |
| | 5 | .. | 75 | | 5. | .. | 75 | | 5 | .. | 2·50 | | 5. | .. | 1·75 |
| $1\frac{1}{2}$d. | 2 | .. | 1·40 | | 2. | .. | 1·40 | | 7 | .. | 2·00 | | 7. | .. | 2·00 |
| | 3 | .. | 1·25 | | 3. | .. | 1·25 | 3d. | 5 | .. | 3·50 | | 5. | .. | 3·50 |

### Quantities Sold
$\frac{1}{2}$d. 82,896,960; 1d. 232,903,680; $1\frac{1}{2}$d. 40,412,800; 2d. 121,065,120; $2\frac{1}{2}$d. 312,957,440; 3d. 22,128,000

**Q12**

**Q13**

Symbols of Peace and Reconstruction

(Des. H. L. Palmer)                    (Des. Reynolds Stone)

---

## 1946 (JUNE 11).   VICTORY ISSUE

| Cat. No. | S.G. No. | Type No. | Perf. | | Description | Unused | Used |
|---|---|---|---|---|---|---|---|
| QCom8 | 491 | **Q12** | 15 × 14 | | 2½d. Ultramarine | 5 | 5 |

   *a.* Extra port-hole abaft
     (Cyl. 11, R.16/1) .. ..    4·00   2·50      *s.* "Cancelled", Type 28  ..
   *b.* Extra port-hole at fore
     (Cyl. 8., R.5/6)    .. ..    6·00   3·50

| QCom9 | 492 | **Q13** | 15 × 14 | | 3d. Violet | 10 | 5 |

   *a.* Shiny ink .. .. ..    15    5      *s.* "Cancelled", Type 28  ..
   *b.* Seven berries (Cyl. 4, R.12/5)   1·00   75
   *c.* Gash on temple (Cyls. 2., 4.,
     5., R.9/6) .. .. ..    1·00   75

QCom8/9   First Day Cover    ••   ••    ..    ..    ..    ..    ..    †   1·00

QCom8*a*                    QCom9*b*                    QCom8*b*

### Controls

*QComC1043*  S 46  2½d.         ..      30 | *QComC1044* S 46  3d.    ••    ..      40

### Cylinder Numbers

2½d. Ultramarine.   Perforation Type 5

| Cyl. No. | | | Cyl. No. | | | Cyl. No. | | | Cyl. No. | | |
|---|---|---|---|---|---|---|---|---|---|---|---|
| 3 | .. | 20 | 3. | .. | 20 | 11 | .. | 20 | 11. | .. | 20 |
| 4 | .. | 20 | 4. | .. | 20 | 12 | .. | 20 | 12. | .. | 20 |
| 6 | .. | † | 6. | .. | — | 13 | .. | 30 | 13. | .. | 30 |
| 7 | .. | 20 | 7. | .. | 20 | 15 | .. | 25 | 15. | .. | 25 |
| 8 | .. | 20 | 8. | .. | 20 | 17 | .. | 20 | 17. | .. | 20 |
| 9 | .. | 50 | 9. | .. | 50 | | | | | | |
| 10 | .. | 20 | 10. | .. | 20 | | | | | | |

2½d. Ultramarine.   Perforation Type 6

| 9 | .. | 45 | 9. | .. | 45 |
|---|---|---|---|---|---|

3d. Violet.   Perforation Type 5

| 2 | .. | 5·00 | 2. | .. | — | 5 | .. | 50 | 5. | .. | 50 |
|---|---|---|---|---|---|---|---|---|---|---|---|
| 4 | .. | 5·00 | 4. | .. | — | | | | | | |

Cylinder 5 was printed in shiny ink.

3d. Violet.   Perforation Type 6 (no dot) and 6B (dot)

| 2 | .. | 25 | 2. | .. | 25 | 4 | .. | 25 | 4. | .. | 25 |
|---|---|---|---|---|---|---|---|---|---|---|---|

Cylinder 4 has a vertical line in the margin under the first stamp in the bottom row. Early printings without this line 50p each.

**Quantities Sold** 2½d. 307,832,500; 3d. 43,085,700

Stamps of this issue were overprinted for use in Tangier.   In the case of the 3d. value, the overprint was applied to the stop panes of Cyls. 2. and 4., Perforation Type 5.

**Q14.**   King George VI and Queen Elizabeth   **Q15**
(Des. G. T. Knipe and Joan Hassall from
photographs by Dorothy Wilding)

## 1948 (APRIL 26).   ROYAL SILVER WEDDING

£1 printed in sheets of 20, arranged in 4 rows of 5.

| Cat. No. | S.G. No. | Type No. | Perf. | Description | Unused | Used |
|---|---|---|---|---|---|---|
| QCom10 | 493 | **Q14** | 15 × 14 | 2½d. Ultramarine | 5 | 5 |
| a. Spot on shoulder (Cyl. 5, R.15/1) | .. | .. | 1·75 | 1·00 | | |
| QCom11 | 494 | **Q15** | 14 × 15 | £1 Blue | 6·00 | 5·00 |
| s. "Cancelled", Type 24P .. | | | | | | |
| QCom10/11 First Day Cover | .. | .. | .. | .. | .. | † | 15·00 |

QCom10a

### Cylinder Numbers

2½d.   Perforation Type 5

| Cyl. No. | | | Cyl. No. | | | Cyl. No. | | | Cyl. No. | | |
|---|---|---|---|---|---|---|---|---|---|---|---|
| 1 | .. | 25 | 1. | .. | 25 | 5 | .. | 20 | 5. | .. | 20 |
| 4 | .. | 20 | 4. | .. | 20 | 6 | .. | 2·50 | 6. | .. | 2·50 |

£1   *Prices for blocks of four*

| Cyl. No. | | | Cyl. No. | | |
|---|---|---|---|---|---|
| 1 | .. | 24·00 | 1. | .. | 24·00 |

**Quantities Sold**   2½d. 147,500,000; £1  419,628

**Q16.**   Gathering Vraic          **Q17.**   Islanders gathering Vraic
(Des. J. R. R. Stobie)          (From drawing by E. Blampied)

| Cat. No. | S.G. No. | Type No. | Perf. | Description | Unused | Used |
|---|---|---|---|---|---|---|

**1948 (MAY 10).   CHANNEL ISLANDS LIBERATION**

Issued to commemorate the third anniversary of the liberation, these stamps were issued primarily for use in the Channel Islands.   They were also available at eight Head Post Offices in Great Britain.

| QCom12 | C 1 | **Q16** | 15 × 14 | | 1d. Scarlet | | 10 | 10 |
|---|---|---|---|---|---|---|---|---|
| QCom13 | C 2 | **Q17** | 15 × 14 | | 2½d. Ultramarine | | 15 | 15 |
| a. | Wheel flaw (R.20/5) | .. | 1·25 | 1·25 | b. Crown flaw (R.1/1) | .. | 1·00 | 75 |
| QCom12/13 First Day Cover | | .. | .. | .. | .. | .. | .. | † | 50 |

QCom13*a*                         QCom13*b*

**Cylinder Numbers**

Perforation Type 6

| | Cyl. No. | | | | Cyl. No. | |
|---|---|---|---|---|---|---|
| 1d. | 2 | .. | 75 | 2½d. | 4 | .. | 1·10 |

Perforation Type 6B

| 1d. | | .. | 90 | 2½d. | 4 | .. | 1·25 |
|---|---|---|---|---|---|---|---|

**Quantities Sold** 1d. 5,934,000; 2½d. 5,398,000

**Q18.**   Globe and Laurel Wreath
(Des. Percy Metcalfe, c.v.o.)

**Q19.**   " Speed "
(Des. Abram Games)

**Q20.**   Olympic Symbol
(Des. Stanley D. Scott)

**Q21.**   Winged Victory
(Des. Edmund Dulac)

**1948 (JULY 29).   OLYMPIC GAMES**

| QCom14 | 495 | **Q18** | 15 × 14 | | 2½d. Ultramarine | 5 | 5 |
|---|---|---|---|---|---|---|---|
| QCom15 | 496 | **Q19** | 15 × 14 | | 3d. Violet | 5 | 5 |
| a. | Crown flaw (Cyl. 1, R.20/2) | | 1·00 | 1·00 | | | |
| b. | Crown flaw retouch (Cyl. 1, R.20/2) | .. | .. | 3·75 | 3·75 | | |
| QCom16 | 497 | **Q20** | 15 × 14 | | 6d. Bright purple | 12 | 10 |
| a. | Initials H.L.P. (Strip of 3) .. | | 30·00 | | | | |
| b. | Ditto, retouched (Strip 3) | | 1·75 | | | | |
| QCom17 | 498 | **Q21** | 15 × 14 | | 1s. Brown | 15 | 12 |
| QCom14/17 First Day Cover | | .. | .. | .. | .. | .. | † | 1·50 |

In the 6d. value the initials H, L and P (H. L. Palmer) were engraved on the 4th, 5th and 6th rules respectively, on the bottom row of Cylinder 9.   They were soon erased by retouching which show as darker patches of colour.

QCom15a

**Cylinder Numbers**

Perforation Type 5

| | Cyl. No | | | | Cyl. No. | | | | | Cyl. No. | | | | Cyl. No. | |
|---|---|---|---|---|---|---|---|---|---|---|---|---|---|---|---|
| 2½d. | 2 | .. | 30 | 2. | .. | 30 | 6d. | 9 | .. | 75 | 9. | .. | 75 |
| | 3 | .. | 30 | 3. | .. | 30 | 1s. | 3 | .. | 95 | 3. | .. | 95 |
| 3d. | 1 | .. | 1·10 | 1. | .. | 30 | | | | | | | |

**Quantities Sold**

2½d. 155,350,000; 3d. 32,554,000; 6d. 24,397,000; 1s. 32,187,000

**Q22.** Two Hemispheres
(Des. Mary Adshead)

**Q23.** U.P.U. Monument, Berne
(Des. Percy Metcalfe, c.v.o.)

**Q24.** Goddess Concordia, Globe and
Points of Compass
(Des. H. Fleury)

**Q25.** Posthorn and Globe

(Des. George R. Bellew, m.v.o.)

## 1949 (OCTOBER 10). UNIVERSAL POSTAL UNION

Commemorating the 75th Anniversary

| Cat. No. | S.G. No. | Type No. | Perf. | | Description | Unused | Used |
|---|---|---|---|---|---|---|---|
| QCom18 | 499 | **Q22** | 15 × 14 | | 2½d. Ultramarine | 5 | 5 |
| a. | Major retouch (Cyl. 5, R.18/2) | .. | .. 4·50 | 3·00 | b. Lake in Asia (Cyl. 3., R. 14/1) | 2·50 | 1·50 |
| | | | | | c. Lake in India (Cyl. 2, R.8/2) | 2·00 | |
| QCom19 | 500 | **Q23** | 15 × 14 | | 3d. Violet | 12 | 10 |
| QCom20 | 501 | **Q24** | 15 × 14 | | 6d. Bright purple | 20 | 20 |
| QCom21 | 502 | **Q25** | 15 × 14 | | 1s. Brown | 30 | 30 |
| a. | Retouched background to 1/- (R.8/5) | .. | .. 1·75 | 1·75 | | | |
| QCom18/21 First Day Cover | | .. | .. .. | .. .. | .. .. | † | 1·50 |

Many retouches are known on the 2½d. value.

QCom18a

QCom18b

**Cylinder Numbers**

Perforation Type 5

|  | Cyl. No. |  |  | Cyl. No. |  |  | Cyl. No. |  |  | Cyl. No. |  |  |
|---|---|---|---|---|---|---|---|---|---|---|---|---|
| 2½d. | 2 | .. | 30 | 2. | .. | 30 |  | 5 | .. | 4·00 | 5. | .. | 35 |
|  | 3 | .. | 35 | 3. | .. | 35 |  |  |  |  |  |  |

Single Pane cylinders
Perforation Type 6

| 3d. | 2 | .. | .. | 90 | 6d. | 2 | .. | .. | 1·40 | 1s. | 2 | .. | .. | 2·10 |

Perforation Type 6B

| 3d. | 2 | .. | .. | 4·50 | 6d. | 2 | .. | .. | 1·50 | 1s. | 2 | .. | .. | 2·10 |

**Quantities Sold**    2½d. 135,150,000; 3d. 16,450,000; 6d. 11,450,000; 1s. 11,400,000

**Q26.**   " Commerce and Prosperity "
(Des. Edmund Dulac)

**Q27.**   Festival Symbol
(Des. Abram Games)

| Cat. No. | S.G. No. | Type No. | Perf. | Description | Unused | Used |
|---|---|---|---|---|---|---|
| **1951 (MAY 3).   FESTIVAL OF BRITAIN** |  |  |  |  |  |  |
| QCom22 | 513 | **Q26** | 15 × 14 | 2½d. Scarlet | 5 | 5 |
| QCom23 | 514 | **Q27** | 15 × 14 | 4d. Ultramarine | 15 | 15 |
| QCom22/3 | First Day Cover | .. | .. | .. .. .. .. .. .. | † | 75 |

**Cylinder Numbers**

Perforation Type 5

|  | Cyl. No. |  |  | Cyl. No. |  |
|---|---|---|---|---|---|
| 2½d. | 5 | .. | 25 | 2½d. | 5. | .. | 25 |

Single Pane cylinders
Perforation Type 5

|  | Cyl. No. |  |  | Cyl. No. |  |
|---|---|---|---|---|---|
| 2½d. | 3 | .. | 45 | 4d. | 1 | .. | 60 |

**Quantities Sold**   2½d. 260,142,000; 4d. 22,197,000

# SECTION R
# Postage Due Stamps
## King George V, 1914-31

In the Post Office circular No. 5 (April 14, 1914) the announcement was made of the introduction of Postage Due labels of the values ½d., 1d., 2d. and 5d. Other values were issued later.

Typographed in sheets of 240 stamps, arranged in 12 rows of 20. The watermarks are always sideways, and are normally found with Crown pointing to the left of the stamp. In cases where the sheets were fed into the press the wrong way round, the watermark appears as sideways with Crown pointing to the right. *These descriptions are based on the watermark as seen from the front of the stamp.*

All stamps in this Section are perf. 14 × 15.

R1

R2

### 1914-23. TYPE R1. WMK. SIMPLE CYPHER, TYPE W.14

The 1s. value was printed exclusively by Somerset House, who also made small preliminary printings of the ½d., 1d., 2d. and 5d. values. These can only be distinguished with certainty when they have attached control. The preliminary printings almost always show the watermark with Crown pointing to the right of the stamp.

The remaining values were printed by Harrison & Sons. These, with the exception of the 1½d. and 4d., are normally found with the watermark with Crown pointing to the left of the stamp.

| Cat. No. | S.G. No. | Date | | | Description | | Unused | Used |
|---|---|---|---|---|---|---|---|---|
| R1 | D1 | 1914 | | | ½d. Emerald | | 8 | 8 |
| a. | Wmk. Crown to right | .. | 30 | 30 | c. | Wmk. reversed Crown to right | | |
| b. | Wmk. reversed Crown to left | | | | s. | " Specimen ", Type 23 .. | 1·50 | |
| R2 | D2/2a | 1914 | | | (1) 1d. Carmine | | 10 | 5 |
| a. | Wmk. Crown to right | .. | 25 | 25 | (2) 1d. Pale carmine | | 15 | 5 |
| b. | Wmk. reversed, Crown to right .. | .. | .. | 1·50 | | s. | " Specimen ", Type 23 .. | 1·50 |
| R3 | D3 | 1923 | | | 1½d. Chestnut | | 4·00 | 2·50 |
| a. | Wmk. Crown to right | .. | 6·00 | 3·50 | | | | |
| s. | " Specimen ", Type 23 | .. | 2·00 | | | | | |
| R4 | D4 | 1914 | | | 2d. Agate | | 15 | 5 |
| a. | Wmk. Crown to right | .. | 50 | 50 | | | | |
| b. | Wmk. reversed, Crown to right .. | .. | .. | 1·00 | s. | " Specimen ", Type 23 .. | 1·00 | |
| | | | | | t. | " Specimen ", Type 26 .. | 1·00 | |
| R5 | D5/5a | 1918 | | | (1) 3d. Violet | | 35 | 8 |
| a. | Wmk. Crown to right | .. | 75 | 25 | (2) 3d. Bluish violet | | 45 | 8 |
| s. | " Specimen ", Type 23 | .. | 1·00 | | | | | |
| t. | " Specimen ", Type 26 | .. | 3·00 | | | | | |
| R6 | D6 | 1921 | | | 4d. Dull grey-green | | 40 | 12 |
| s. | " Specimen ", Type 23 | .. | 1·00 | | | | | |
| R7 | D7 | 1914 | | | 5d. Bistre-brown | | 35 | 5 |
| a. | Wmk. Crown to right | .. | 1·25 | 1·25 | | | | |
| s. | " Specimen ", Type 23 | .. | 1·00 | | | | | |
| R8 | D8/8a | 1915 | | | (1) 1s. Bright blue | | 1·50 | 12 |
| a. | Wmk. Crown to right | .. | 1·75 | 50 | (2) 1s. Deep bright blue | | 1·50 | 12 |
| s. | " Specimen ", Type 23 | .. | | | | | | |
| t. | " Specimen ", Type 26 | .. | | | | | | |

The 1d. is known bisected and used to make up 1½d. rate on understamped letters from Ceylon (1921).

## Die Proofs

In black on white glazed card ½d., 1d., 2d., 5d. .. .. .. *Each* 30·00

## Plate Proof

1s. value. Imperf. Wmk. Type **W.14,** overprinted " Cancelled ",
Type 28 .. .. .. .. .. .. .. .. .. 8·00

## Colour Trials

Wmk. Simple Cypher (Crown to right). Type **W.14,** Perf. 14 × 15

2d. value in various colours (18 different) .. .. .. .. *Each* 2·25
As above but overprinted " Specimen ", Type 23 .. .. .. *Each* 4·00

The above were described as faunce green, green No. 10, green No. 19, scarlet, carmine, orange, royal blue, azure blue, blue, violet, bronze-green, mauve, magenta, claret, fawn, bartilizzi brown, red-brown, amber.

## Controls

Printed at Somerset House

Wmk. Simple Cypher, Type I, Crown to right

| | | | | I. | P. | | | | | I. | P. |
|---|---|---|---|---|---|---|---|---|---|---|---|
| RCD1 | D. 14 | ½d. | .. | † | 1·00 | RCD3 | D. 14 | 2d. | .. | † | 1·50 |
| RCD2 | D. 14 | 1d. | .. | † | 1·00 | RCD4 | D. 14 | 5d. | .. | † | 1·60 |

Wmk. Simple Cypher, Type II, Crown to right

| | | | | I. | P. |
|---|---|---|---|---|---|
| RCD5 | F. 15 | 1s. | .. | † | 2·00 |

Wmk. Simple Cypher, Type III, Crown to right

| | | | | I. | P. | | | | | | |
|---|---|---|---|---|---|---|---|---|---|---|---|
| RCD6 | O. 19 | 1s. | .. | † | 4·00 | RCD7 | S. 21 | 1s. | .. | | 4·00 |

Wmk. Simple Cypher, Type III, Crown to left

| | | | | | | |
|---|---|---|---|---|---|---|
| RCD8 | V. 23 | 1s. | .. | 3·00 | † | |

Printed by Harrison & Sons

Wmk. Simple Cypher, Type II

| | | | | | | | | | | | |
|---|---|---|---|---|---|---|---|---|---|---|---|
| RCD21 | D 14 | ½d. | .. | 20 | 20 | RCD30 | I 16 | 2d. | .. | 40 | 1·00 |
| RCD22 | D 14 | 1d. | .. | 35 | 35 | RCD40a | P 20 | 2d. | .. | 75 | — |
| RCD23 | D 14 | 2d. | .. | 50 | 40 | RCD51a | T 22 | 1d. | .. | — | — |
| RCD24 | D 14 | 5d. | .. | 1·00 | 15·00 | RCD52a | T 22 | 3d. | .. | 75 | 45 |
| RCD25 | E 14 | 1d. | .. | 30 | 20 | RCD55 | U 23 | 1d. | .. | 20 | 20 |
| RCD26 | G 15 | 1d. | .. | 25 | 2·00 | RCD60 | V 23 | 1½d. | .. | 4·75 | 3·00 |
| RCD27 | H 16 | 2d. | .. | 30 | 30 | RCD61a | V 23 | 3d. | .. | 35 | 35 |
| RCD28 | I 16 | ½d. | .. | 35 | 35 | RCD62 | W 23 | ½d. | .. | 1·00 | 1·50 |
| RCD29 | I 16 | 1d. | .. | 20 | 40 | RCD63 | W 23 | 3d. | .. | 70 | 2·00 |

Wmk. Simple Cypher, Type III

| | | | | | | | | | | | |
|---|---|---|---|---|---|---|---|---|---|---|---|
| RCD31 | K 17 | 1d. | .. | 25 | 25 | RCD45 | R 21 | 1d. | .. | 25 | 50 |
| RCD32 | K 17 | 2d. | .. | 1·25 | 25 | RCD46 | R 21 | 2d. | .. | 30 | 1·00 |
| RCD33 | L 18 | 3d. | .. | 50 | 1·00 | RCD47 | S 21 | 1d. | .. | 30 | 25 |
| RCD34 | N 19 | ½d. | .. | 25 | 40 | RCD48 | S 22 | ½d. | .. | † | 25 |
| RCD35 | N 19 | 1d. | .. | 40 | 25 | RCD49 | S 22 | 1d. | .. | 30 | 30 |
| RCD37 | O 19 | 2d. | .. | 50 | 50 | RCD51 | T 22 | 1d. | .. | 35 | 35 |
| RCD38 | O 20 | 3d. | .. | 40 | 50 | RCD52 | T 22 | 3d. | .. | 60 | 40 |
| RCD39 | P 20 | 1d. | .. | 25 | † | RCD53 | U 22 | ½d. | .. | 25 | 1·50 |
| RCD40 | P 20 | 2d. | .. | 25 | 75 | RCD54 | U 22 | 1½d. | .. | 5·00 | † |
| RCD41 | Q 20 | 1d. | .. | 1·00 | † | RCD55a | U 23 | 1d. | .. | 30 | 30 |
| RCD42 | Q 20 | 4d. | .. | 1·50 | 60 | RCD56 | U 23 | 1½d. | .. | 5·00 | † |
| RCD43 | Q 21 | 1d. | .. | 1·00 | 2·00 | RCD57 | U 23 | 2d. | .. | 2·50 | 25 |
| RCD44 | R 21 | ½d. | .. | 25 | 75 | RCD61 | V 23 | 3d. | .. | 60 | 60 |

Watermarks are normally with Crown to left, but the following numbers are usually found with watermarks showing Crown to right: RCD 42, 44, 45, 46, 47, 49, 51, 52, 53, 54, 55, 56, 57, 61a, 62, 63.

## 1924. TYPE R1. THICK CHALK-SURFACED PAPER. WMK. SIMPLE CYPHER, TYPE W.14.

Printed by Waterlow & Sons

| Cat. No. | S.G. No. | | Description | | Unused | Used |
|---|---|---|---|---|---|---|
| R9 | D9 | | 1d. Carmine | | 60 | 50 |

## Controls

| | | | | I. | P. | | | | | I. | P. |
|---|---|---|---|---|---|---|---|---|---|---|---|
| RCD64 | B 24 | 1d. | .. | 1·50 | † | RCD65 | C 25 | 1d. | .. | 1·00 | † |

## 1924-31. TYPES R1 AND R2 (2s. 6d.). WMK. BLOCK CYPHER, TYPE W.15

Printed by Waterlow & Sons, and later (from 1934) by Harrison & Sons

| Cat. No. | S.G. No. | Date | | | | Description | Unused | Used |
|---|---|---|---|---|---|---|---|---|
| R10 | D10 | 1924 | | | | ½d. Emerald | 5 | 8 |
| a. | Wmk. Crown to right | | .. | 50 | 50 | | | |
| s. | " Specimen ", Type 23 | | .. | | | t.  " Specimen ", Type 30 | .. | |
| R11 | D11 | 1924 | | | | 1d. Carmine | 5 | 5 |
| a. | Wmk. Crown to right | | .. | | | | | |
| s. | " Specimen ", Type 23 | | | | | t.  " Specimen ", Type 30 | .. | |
| R12 | D12 | 1924 | | | | 1½d. Chestnut | 3·50 | 3·50 |
| s. | " Specimen ", Type 23 | | .. | | | | | |
| R13 | D13 | 1924 | | | | 2d. Agate | 8 | 5 |
| s. | " Specimen ", Type 23 | | .. | | | | | |
| t. | " Specimen ", Type 30 | | .. | | | | | |
| R14 | D14 | 1924 | | | | 3d. Dull violet | 25 | 8 |
| a. | Wmk. Crown to right | | .. | 1·00 | | | | |
| b. | Experimental paper, | | | | | c.  Printed on the gum | .. 20·00 | † |
| | Wmk. W.16 .. | .. | .. | 12·00 | 9·00 | s.  " Specimen ", Type 23 | .. | |
| R15 | D15 | 1924 | | | | 4d. Dull grey-green | 30 | 20 |
| a. | Wmk.  Crown to right | | .. | | | | | |
| s. | " Specimen ", Type 23 | | .. | | | | | |
| R16 | D16 | 1931 | | | | 5d. Bistre-brown | 1·75 | 75 |
| R17 | D17 | 1924 | | | | 1s. Deep blue | 45 | 20 |
| a. | Wmk.  Crown to right | | .. | | | s.  " Specimen ", Type 23 | .. | |
| R18 | D18 | 1924 | | | | 2s. 6d. Purple/*yellow* | 1·50 | 30 |
| a. | Wmk.  Crown to right | | .. | | | | | |
| s. | " Specimen ", Type 23 | | .. | 1·00 | | t.  " Specimen ", Type 30 | .. | |

The Harrison printings can only be distinguished when they have attached control.

### Colour Trial

½d. purple on yellow  ..   ..   ..   ..   ..   ..   ..   ..   7·00

### Controls

Printed by Waterlow & Sons

| Cat. No. | | | | I. | P. | | Cat. No. | | | | I. | P. |
|---|---|---|---|---|---|---|---|---|---|---|---|---|
| RCD 66 | A 24 | 2d. | .. | 40 | † | | RCD109 | L 29 | 1d. | .. | 25 | † |
| RCD 67 | A 24 | 4d. | .. | 3·50 | † | | RCD110 | L 29 | 2d. | .. | 25 | † |
| RCD 68 | A 24 | 1s. | .. | 50·00 | † | | RCD111 | L 29 | 3d. | .. | 50 | † |
| RCD 68a | B 24 | ½d. | .. | † | 25 | | RCD112 | L 29 | 4d. | .. | 60 | † |
| RCD 69 | B 24 | 1d. | .. | 1·25 | † | | RCD114 | L 29 | 2s. 6d. | .. | 3·50 | † |
| RCD 70 | B 24 | 1½d. | .. | 6·00 | † | | RCD115 | M 30 | ½d. | .. | 25 | † |
| RCD 71 | B 24 | 3d. | .. | 40 | † | | RCD117 | M 30 | 2d. | .. | 25 | † |
| RCD 72 | B 24 | 4d. | .. | 60 | † | | RCD120 | M 30 | 1s. | .. | 2·00 | † |
| RCD 73 | B 24 | 1s. | .. | 2·00 | † | | RCD123 | N 30 | 1d. | .. | 25 | † |
| RCD 74 | B 24 | 2s. 6d. | .. | 3·00 | † | | RCD125 | N 30 | 3d. | .. | 40 | † |
| RCD 76 | C 25 | 2d. | .. | 30 | † | | RCD126 | N 30 | 4d. | .. | 50 | † |
| RCD 77 | C 25 | 1s. | .. | 2·00 | † | | RCD127 | N 30 | 5d. | .. | 1·00 | † |
| RCD 78 | D 25 | 3d. | .. | 75 | † | | RCD128 | N 30 | 2s. 6d. | .. | 5·00 | † |
| a. | Wmk. W.16 | .. | .. | — | † | | RCD129 | O 31 | ½d. | .. | 40 | † |
| RCD 79 | E 26 | 2d. | .. | 40 | † | | RCD130 | O 31 | 1d. | .. | 40 | † |
| RCD 80 | E 26 | 3d. | .. | 25 | † | | RCD131 | O 31 | 2d. | .. | 40 | † |
| RCD 81 | E 26 | 4d. | .. | 1·00 | † | | RCD132 | O 31 | 3d. | .. | 40 | † |
| RCD 82 | E 26 | 1s. | .. | — | 2·00 | | RCD133 | O 31 | 5d. | .. | 75 | † |
| RCD 83 | F 26 | ½d. | .. | 20 | † | | RCD134 | O 31 | 1s. | .. | 2·00 | † |
| RCD 84 | F 26 | 1d. | .. | 25 | 75 | | RCD135 | O 31 | 2s. 6d. | .. | 4·00 | † |
| RCD 85 | F 26 | 2d. | .. | 30 | † | | RCD136 | P 31 | ½d. | .. | 25 | † |
| RCD 86 | F 26 | 3d. | .. | 40 | † | | RCD137 | P 31 | 2d. | .. | 25 | † |
| RCD 87 | F 26 | 4d. | .. | 75 | † | | RCD138 | Q 32 | ½d. | .. | 25 | † |
| RCD 88 | F 26 | 1s. | .. | 1·00 | † | | RCD139 | Q 32 | 1d. | .. | 25 | † |
| RCD 89 | G 27 | 3d. | .. | 40 | † | | RCD140 | Q 32 | 2d. | .. | 40 | † |
| RCD 90 | G 27 | 1s. | .. | 1·00 | † | | RCD141 | Q 32 | 3d. | .. | 40 | † |
| RCD 91 | H 27 | 2d. | .. | 3·50 | † | | RCD142 | Q 32 | 4d. | .. | 60 | † |
| RCD 92 | H 27 | 3d. | .. | † | 2·00 | | RCD143 | Q 32 | 5d. | .. | 1·00 | † |
| RCD 93 | H 27 | 2s. 6d. | .. | 3·50 | † | | RCD144 | Q 32 | 1s. | .. | 75 | † |
| RCD 94 | I 28 | ½d. | .. | 20 | † | | RCD145 | Q 32 | 2s. 6d. | .. | 2·50 | † |
| RCD 95 | I 28 | 1d. | .. | 20 | † | | RCD146 | R 32 | 2d. | .. | 50 | † |
| RCD 96 | I 28 | 2d. | .. | 20 | † | | RCD147 | R 32 | 3d. | .. | 50 | † |
| RCD 97 | I 28 | 3d. | .. | 50 | † | | RCD148 | R 32 | 4d. | .. | 60 | † |
| RCD 98 | I 28 | 4d. | .. | † | 2·00 | | RCD149 | R 32 | 1s. | .. | 60 | † |
| RCD 99 | I 28 | 1s. | .. | 1·00 | † | | RCD150 | R 32 | 2s. 6d. | .. | 2·50 | † |
| RCD100 | I 28 | 2s. 6d. | .. | 3·00 | † | | RCD151 | S 33 | ½d. | .. | 20 | † |
| RCD101 | K 29 | ½d. | .. | † | 25 | | RCD152 | S 33 | 1d. | .. | 20 | 3·50 |
| RCD102 | K 29 | 1d. | .. | 20 | 3·50 | | RCD154 | S 33 | 5d. | .. | 20 | † |
| RCD103 | K 29 | 2d. | .. | 25 | † | | RCD155 | S 33 | 1s. | .. | 1·75 | † |
| RCD104 | K 29 | 3d. | .. | 35 | † | | RCD156 | S 33 | 2s. 6d. | .. | 3·50 | † |
| RCD105 | K 29 | 4d. | .. | 60 | † | | RCD157 | T 33 | 2d. | .. | 4·00 | † |
| RCD106 | K 29 | 1s. | .. | 75 | † | | RCD158 | T 33 | 3d. | .. | 40 | † |
| RCD107 | K 29 | 2s. 6d. | .. | 3·50 | — | | RCD159 | T 33 | 4d. | .. | 15·00 | † |
| RCD108 | L 29 | ½d. | .. | 20 | † | | | | | | | |

Printed by Harrison & Sons

| | | | | I. | P. | | | | | I. | P. |
|---|---|---|---|---|---|---|---|---|---|---|---|
| *RCD160* | U 34 | ½d. | .. | 2·00 | † | *RCD170a* | W 35 | 5d. | .. | 1·00 | † |
| *a.* Streaky gum .. | | .. | .. | 50 | | *RCD171* | W 35 | 1s. | .. | 3·50 | † |
| *RCD161* | U 34 | 1d. | .. | 4·00 | 4·00 | *RCD171a* | X 35 | 2d. | .. | 40 | † |
| *RCD162* | U 34 | 5d. | .. | 3·00 | † | *RCD171b* | X 35 | 4d. | .. | 2·50 | † |
| *RCD163* | U 34 | 1s. | .. | 2·50 | † | *RCD172* | X 35 | 1s. | .. | 4·00 | † |
| *RCD164* | U 34 | 2s. 6d. | .. | 7·00 | † | *RCD173* | X 35 | 2s. 6d. | .. | 6·00 | † |
| *RCD166* | V 34 | 2d. | .. | 4·00 | † | *RCD174* | Y 36 | ½d. | .. | 25 | † |
| *RCD167* | V 34 | 4d. | .. | 3·50 | † | *RCD175* | Y 36 | 1d. | .. | 40 | ·— |
| *RCD167a* | V 34 | 2s. 6d. | .. | 7·00 | † | *RCD176* | Y 36 | 2d. | .. | 45 | † |
| *RCD168* | W 35 | ½d. | .. | 50 | † | *RCD177* | Y 36 | 3d. | .. | 75 | 1·25 |
| *RCD169* | W 35 | 1d. | .. | 2·00 | † | *RCD178* | Z 36 | 2s. 6d. | .. | 4·00 | † |
| *RCD170* | W 35 | 3d. | .. | 2·00 | † | | | | | | |

Nos. RCD160 and RCD161/4 are on smooth gummed paper. Later controls and No. RCD160a are on paper with streaky gum.

## King Edward VIII, 1936-37

| Cat. No. | S.G. No. | Date | Description | Unused | Used |
|---|---|---|---|---|---|

**1936-37. TYPES R1 AND R2 (2s. 6d.). WMK. " E 8 R ", TYPE W.19**

Printed by Harrison & Sons

| | | | | | |
|---|---|---|---|---|---|
| R19 | D19 | June 1937 | ½d. Emerald | 10 | 10 |
| R20 | D20 | May 1937 | 1d. Carmine | 15 | 15 |
| R21 | D21 | May 1937 | 2d. Agate | 35 | 30 |
| R22 | D22 | Mar. 1937 | 3d. Dull violet | 25 | 20 |
| *s.* " Specimen ", Type 30 .. | | | | | |
| R23 | D23 | Dec. 1936 | 4d. Dull grey-green | 50 | 75 |
| *s.* " Specimen ", Type 30 .. | | | | | |
| R24 | D24/a | Nov. 1936 | 5d. (1) Bistre-brown | 60 | 75 |
| | | | (2) Yellow-brown ('37) | 3·00 | 2·00 |
| *s.* " Specimen ", Type 30 .. | | | | | |
| R25 | D25 | Dec. 1936 | 1s. Deep blue | 50 | 50 |
| *s.* " Specimen ", Type 30 .. | | | | | |
| R26 | D26 | May 1937 | 2s. 6d. Purple/*yellow* | 2·00 | 1·00 |

**Controls**

| | | | | I. | P. | | | | | I. | P. |
|---|---|---|---|---|---|---|---|---|---|---|---|
| *RCD179* | A 36 | 4d. | .. | 90 | † | *RCD184* | A 37 | 2d. | .. | 70 | † |
| *RCD180* | A 36 | 5d. | .. | 1·25 | † | *RCD185* | A 37 | 3d. | .. | 60 | † |
| *RCD181* | A 36 | 1s. | .. | 1·25 | † | *RCD186* | A 37 | 5d. | .. | 1·25 | † |
| *RCD182* | A 37 | ½d. | .. | 20 | † | *RCD187* | A 37 | 2s. 6d. | .. | 4·00 | † |
| *RCD183* | A 37 | 1d. | .. | 20 | † | *RCD188* | C 38 | 2s. 6d. | .. | 3·00 | † |

## King George VI, 1937-52

**1937-38. TYPES R1 AND R2 (2s. 6d.). WMK. " G<sub>VI</sub>R ", TYPE W.20**

Printed by Harrison & Sons

| | | | | | | | | |
|---|---|---|---|---|---|---|---|---|
| R27 | D27 | 1938 | | | ½d. Emerald | | 10 | 8 |
| *a.* Broken " 2 " in " ½ " (R. 3/14) .. .. | | | .. | 7·00 | | | | |
| R28 | D28 | 1938 | | | 1d. Carmine | | 15 | 12 |
| *t.* " Cancelled ", Type 33 | | | .. | | | | | |
| R29 | D29 | 1938 | | | 2d. Agate | | 10 | 5 |
| *a.* Wmk. Crown to right | | | .. | 2·50 | *t.* " Cancelled ", Type 33 | .. | | |
| R30 | D30 | 1938 | | | 3d. Violet | | 15 | 5 |
| *a.* Wmk. Crown to right | | | .. | 3·00 | *t.* " Cancelled ", Type 33 | .. | | |
| R31 | D31 | 1937 | | | 4d. Dull grey-green | | 35 | 10 |
| *t.* " Cancelled ", Type 33 | | | .. | | | | | |
| R32 | D32 | 1938 | | | 5d. Yellow-brown | | 20 | 8 |
| *a.* Wmk. Crown to right | | | .. | 2·50 | *t.* " Cancelled ", Type 33 | .. | | |
| R33 | D33 | 1937 | | | 1s. Deep blue | | 80 | 20 |
| *a.* Wmk. Crown to right | | | .. | — | 5·00 | *t.* " Cancelled ", Type 33 | .. | |
| R34 | D34 | 1938 | | | 2s. 6d. Purple/*yellow* | | 1·40 | 30 |
| *t.* " Cancelled ", Type 33 | | | .. | | | | | |

The " Cancelled " are from Control Q45.

The 2d. is known bisected (Harpenden, 30 October 1954).

## Controls

| | | | | I. | P. | | | | | I. | P. |
|---|---|---|---|---|---|---|---|---|---|---|---|
| RCD189 | B 37 | 3d. | .. | 50 | † | RCD259 | K 42 | 3d. | .. | 8·00 | — |
| RCD190 | B 37 | 4d. | .. | 60 | † | RCD260 | K 42 | 4d. | .. | † | 60 |
| RCD191 | B 37 | 1s. | .. | 1·50 | † | RCD262 | K 42 | 1s. | .. | 1·50 | † |
| RCD192 | C 38 | ½d. | .. | 35 | † | RCD263 | K 42 | 2s. 6d. | .. | 20·00 | — |
| RCD193 | C 38 | 1d. | .. | 40 | † | RCD271 | L 42 | 2s. 6d. | .. | 15·00 | † |
| RCD194 | C 38 | 2d. | .. | 60 | † | RCD273 | M 43 | 1d. | .. | 30 | † |
| RCD195 | C 38 | 3d. | .. | 50 | † | RCD274 | M 43 | 2d. | .. | 40 | † |
| RCD196 | C 38 | 4d. | .. | 1·00 | † | RCD275 | M 43 | 3d. | .. | 50 | † |
| RCD197 | C 38 | 5d. | .. | 75 | † | RCD276 | M 43 | 4d. | .. | 60 | † |
| RCD198 | C 38 | 1s. | .. | 1·50 | † | RCD277 | M 43 | 5d. | .. | 1·00 | † |
| RCD199 | C 38 | 2s. 6d. | .. | 2·50 | † | RCD278 | M 43 | 1s. | .. | 1·50 | † |
| RCD203 | D 38 | 3d. | .. | 60 | † | RCD281 | O 44 | 1d. | .. | 90 | † |
| RCD207 | D 38 | 2s. 6d. | .. | 2·50 | 4·50 | RCD282 | O 44 | 2d. | .. | 9·00 | † |
| RCD208 | E 39 | ½d. | .. | 20 | † | RCD283 | O 44 | 3d. | .. | 90 | † |
| RCD209 | E 39 | 1d. | .. | 30 | † | RCD284 | O 44 | 4d. | .. | — | † |
| RCD210 | E 39 | 2d. | .. | 75 | † | RCD285 | O 44 | 5d. | .. | 1·00 | † |
| RCD212 | E 39 | 4d. | .. | 50 | † | RCD286 | O 44 | 1s. | .. | 1·50 | † |
| RCD213 | E 39 | 5d. | .. | 40 | † | RCD287 | O 44 | 2s. 6d. | .. | 2·50 | † |
| RCD214 | E 39 | 1s. | .. | 2·50 | † | RCD292 | P 44 | 4d. | .. | 60 | † |
| RCD215 | E 39 | 2s. 6d. | .. | 3·00 | † | RCD293 | P 44 | 5d. | .. | 75 | † |
| RCD219 | F 39 | 3d. | .. | † | 9·00 | RCD294 | P 44 | 1s. | .. | 1·50 | † |
| RCD224 | G 40 | ½d. | .. | 8·00 | 14·00 | RCD295 | P 44 | 2s. 6d. | .. | 2·50 | — |
| RCD225 | G 40 | 1d. | .. | 60 | — | RCD297 | Q 44 | 1d. | .. | — | † |
| RCD226 | G 40 | 2d. | .. | — | 75 | RCD298 | Q 44 | 2d. | .. | † | — |
| RCD228 | G 40 | 4d. | .. | † | — | RCD305 | Q 45 | 1d. | .. | 12·00 | † |
| RCD229 | G 40 | 5d. | .. | 75 | † | RCD306 | Q 45 | 2d. | .. | 40 | † |
| RCD230 | G 40 | 1s. | .. | 1·50 | † | RCD311 | Q 45 | 2s. 6d. | .. | — | † |
| RCD236 | H 40 | 4d. | .. | 12·00 | † | RCD315 | R 45 | 3d. | .. | 60 | † |
| RCD241 | I 41 | 1d. | .. | 30 | 30 | RCD318 | R 45 | 1s. | .. | 1·50 | † |
| RCD242 | I 41 | 2d. | .. | — | 8·00 | RCD326 | S 46 | 1s. | .. | 1·75 | † |
| RCD243 | I 41 | 3d. | .. | † | 50 | RCD327 | S 46 | 2s. 6d. | .. | — | † |
| RCD244 | I 41 | 4d. | .. | † | 70 | RCD332 | T 46 | 4d. | .. | 60 | † |
| RCD245 | I 41 | 5d. | .. | † | 75 | RCD333 | T 46 | 5d. | .. | 85 | † |
| RCD247 | I 41 | 2s. 6d. | .. | 15·00 | — | RCD335 | U 47 | 1d. | .. | 60 | † |
| RCD254 | J 41 | 1s. | .. | 1·50 | † | RCD336 | U 47 | 2d. | .. | 40 | † |
| RCD257 | K 42 | 1d. | .. | † | 30 | RCD337 | U 47 | 3d. | .. | 50 | — |
| RCD258 | K 42 | 2d. | .. | — | 35 | RCD341 | U 47 | 2s. 6d. | .. | — | † |

## 1951-52. COLOURS CHANGED AND NEW VALUE. TYPE R1. WMK. " GVIR ", TYPE W.20

Printed by Harrison & Sons

| Cat. No. | S.G. No. | Date | | Description | Unused | Used |
|---|---|---|---|---|---|---|
| R35 | D35 | 18.9.51 | | ½d. Orange | 12 | 10 |
| a. | Broken " 2 " in " ½ " (R.3/14) | .. | .. | | | |
| R36 | D36 | 6.6.51 | | 1d. Violet-blue | 15 | 15 |
| R37 | D37 | 11.2.52 | | 1½d. Green | 20 | 15 |
| a. | Wmk. Crown to right | .. | 50 | | | |
| b. | Stop after THREE.. | .. | | | | |
| R38 | D38 | 14.8.51 | | 4d. Blue | 50 | 40 |
| R39 | D39 | 6.12.51 | | 1s. Bistre-brown | 60 | 35 |

The dates of issue given above are those on which the stamps were first issued by the Supplies Department to postmasters.

The 1d. is known bisected (Camberley, 6th April, 1954).

On 7th June 1952, the post office at Bury St. Edmunds ran out of 1d. Postage Due stamps. Two unofficial handstamps were made on the instructions of the postmaster, and the overprint applied to the current 1d. postage stamp. About a hundred were said to have been used on that day. *Price on piece £50*

# King George V Simple Cypher Watermark Varieties

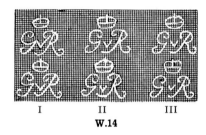

I      II      III
**W.14**

See notes under Watermarks on page 52. The prices quoted are for the cheapest shade in each value except where specific shades are quoted.

**Watermark Upright**

| Cat. No. | Description | Type I Unused | Used | Type II Unused | Used | Type III Unused | Used |
|---|---|---|---|---|---|---|---|
| W 1 | ½d. Green .. .. .. | 10 | 10 | 5 | 5 | 5 | 5 |
| W 2 | 1d. Scarlet .. .. | 10 | 10 | 5 | 5 | 5 | 5 |
| W 3 | 1½d. Red-brown .. .. | 15 | 5 | 5 | 5 | 5 | 5 |
| W 4 | 2d. Orange-yellow .. | 50 | 30 | † | | † | |
| W 5 | 2d. Reddish orange .. | 50 | 30 | † | | † | |
| W 6 | 2d. Orange (Die I) .. | † | | 8 | 5 | 8 | 5 |
| W 7 | 2d. Orange (Die II) .. | † | | 35 | 15 | 35 | 15 |
| W 8 | 2½d. Blue .. .. .. | 40 | 20 | 10 | 5 | 10 | 5 |
| W 9 | 3d. Reddish violet .. | 1·00 | 50 | 1·00 | 50 | † | |
| W10 | 3d. Violet .. .. | 60 | 50 | † | | † | |
| W11 | 3d. Bluish violet .. | 5·00 | — | 30 | 5 | 30 | 5 |
| W12 | 4d. Grey-green .. | 60 | 40 | 30 | 8 | 30 | 8 |
| W13 | 5d. Brown .. .. | 15·00 | 9·00 | 50 | 25 | 50 | 25 |
| W14 | 6d. Reddish purple .. | † | | 40 | 10 | 40 | 10 |
| W15 | 7d. Olive .. .. | 12·00 | 10·00 | 1·50 | 60 | 1·50 | 60 |
| W16 | 8d. Black on yellow .. | † | | 2·00 | 1·00 | 2·00 | 1·00 |
| W17 | 9d. Agate .. .. | † | | 1·25 | 50 | 1·25 | 50 |
| W18 | 9d. Olive-green .. | † | | 11·00 | 1·50 | 11·00 | 1·50 |
| W19 | 10d. Turquoise-blue .. | 25·00 | — | 1·50 | 75 | 1·50 | 75 |
| W20 | 1s. Bistre-brown .. .. | † | | 1·00 | 15 | 1·00 | 15 |

**Watermark Inverted**

| Cat. No. | Description | Type I Unused | Used | Type II Unused | Used | Type III Unused | Used |
|---|---|---|---|---|---|---|---|
| W21 | ½d. Green .. .. .. | 25 | 20 | 15 | 10 | 15 | 10 |
| W22 | 1d. Scarlet .. .. | 25 | 20 | 12 | 5 | 12 | 5 |
| W23 | 1½d. Red-brown .. .. | † | | 75 | 40 | 50 | 25 |
| W24 | 2d. Orange-yellow .. | 1·00 | 75 | † | | † | |
| W25 | 2d. Reddish orange .. | † | | † | | † | |
| W26 | 2d. Orange (Die I) .. | † | | 1·00 | 75 | 1·00 | 75 |
| W27 | 2d. Orange (Die II) .. | † | | 4·00 | 3·00 | 2·00 | 1·50 |
| W28 | 2½d. Blue .. .. .. | 2·50 | 1·50 | 3·00 | 1·50 | 2·50 | 1·50 |
| W29 | 3d. Reddish violet .. | † | | — | — | † | |
| W30 | 3d. Violet .. .. | — | — | † | | † | |
| W31 | 3d. Bluish violet .. | † | | 3·00 | 3·00 | 2·50 | 2·50 |
| W32 | 4d. Grey-green .. | 2·50 | 2·50 | 1·50 | 1·50 | 1·50 | 1·50 |
| W33 | 5d. Brown .. .. | † | | 14·00 | 12·00 | 10·00 | 7·00 |
| W34 | 6d. Reddish purple .. | † | | 1·50 | 1·50 | 1·50 | 1·50 |
| W35 | 7d. Olive .. .. | † | | † | | 2·00 | 3·00 |
| W36 | 8d. Black on yellow .. | † | | 4·00 | 4·00 | † | |
| W37 | 9d. Agate .. .. | † | | 5·00 | 5·00 | 4·00 | 4·00 |
| W38 | 9d. Olive-green .. | † | | 30·00 | 30·00 | † | |
| W39 | 10d. Turquoise-blue .. | † | | 12·00 | 12·00 | 15·00 | — |
| W40 | 1s. Bistre-brown .. | † | | † | | 5·00 | 4·00 |

## Watermark Reversed

| Cat. No. | Description | Type I Unused | Type I Used | Type II Unused | Type II Used | Type III Unused | Type III Used |
|---|---|---|---|---|---|---|---|
| W41 | ½d. Green .. | 2·00 | 2·00 | 1·50 | 1·50 | 1·50 | 1·50 |
| W42 | 1d. Scarlet | 75 | 75 | 75 | 75 | 75 | 75 |
| W43 | 1½d. Red-brown .. | † | | 1·25 | 1·00 | 1·25 | 1·00 |
| W44 | 2d. Orange-yellow | 2·00 | 1·50 | † | | † | |
| W45 | 2d. Orange (Die I) | † | | 1·30 | 1·00 | † | |
| W46 | 2½d. Blue | † | | 1·50 | 1·25 | — | — |
| W47 | 3d. Bluish violet .. | † | | 6·00 | 6·00 | — | — |
| W48 | 4d. Grey-green .. | † | | 1·50 | 1·50 | † | |
| W49 | 6d. Reddish purple | † | | 22·00 | — | † | |
| W50 | 8d. Black on yellow | † | | 6·00 | — | † | |

## Watermark Inverted and Reversed

| Cat. No. | Description | Type I Unused | Type I Used | Type II Unused | Type II Used | Type III Unused | Type III Used |
|---|---|---|---|---|---|---|---|
| W51 | ½d. Green .. | 1·00 | 1·00 | 75 | 75 | 75 | 75 |
| W52 | 1d. Scarlet | 70 | 60 | 45 | 15 | 45 | 15 |
| W53 | 1½d. Red-brown .. | 1·50 | 1·50 | 1·00 | 90 | 1·00 | 90 |
| W54 | 2d. Orange-yellow | 1·00 | 75 | † | | † | |
| W55 | 2d. Reddish orange | 1·00 | 75 | † | | † | |
| W56 | 2d. (Die I) | † | | 1·00 | 75 | 1·00 | 75 |
| W57 | 2d. Orange (Die II) | † | | 4·50 | 5·00 | 3·00 | 3·00 |
| W58 | 2½d. Blue .. | 1·50 | 1·75 | 1·50 | 1·75 | 1·50 | 1·75 |
| W59 | 3d. Bluish violet .. | † | | 1·50 | 1·75 | 3·00 | 3·00 |
| W60 | 4d. Grey-green .. | 2·50 | 2·50 | 2·50 | 2·00 | 3·00 | 3·00 |
| W61 | 5d. Brown | † | | 6·00 | 6·00 | 7·00 | 8·00 |
| W62 | 6d. Reddish purple | † | | 2·00 | 2·00 | 2·00 | 2·00 |
| W63 | 8d. Black on yellow | † | | 95·00 | † | † | |
| W64 | 9d. Agate .. | † | | 4·00 | 4·00 | 4·00 | 4·00 |
| W65 | 9d. Olive-green .. | † | | 25·00 | — | † | |
| W66 | 10d. Turquoise-blue | † | | 12·00 | 10·00 | 12·00 | 10·00 |
| W67 | 1s. Bistre-brown | † | | 4·50 | 3·50 | 4·00 | 3·00 |

## Misplaced Watermarks

A Single stamp showing letters from POSTAGE

B Vertical strip sufficient to show complete POSTAGE watermark

The watermark "POSTAGE" appears in the margins on both sides of each pane, as in the K.E.VII issues. Occasionally sheets were incorrectly fed into the printing press, resulting in the word "POSTAGE" appearing on five stamps of the first or the twelfth vertical rows. The remaining five stamps were without watermark, these being listed in Section N1.

## Broken Dandy Roll Varieties

C Missing Crow  
D Missing G  
E Missing v  
F Missing R  

G Missing Gv  
H Missing vR  
I Missing Crown vR  
J Missing Crown GvR  

K Missing left side of R  
L Missing tail to R (GvP)  
M Long tail to G  

Except for column B the prices are for unused single stamps in the cheapest shade and with watermark upright.

| Cat. No. | Value | A | B | C | D | E | F | G | H | I | J | K | L | M |
|---|---|---|---|---|---|---|---|---|---|---|---|---|---|---|
| W68 | ½d. | 1·50 | 8·00 | 75 | 3·00 | 1·50 | 4·50 | 2·50 | 4·00 | 4·50 | + | 3·00 | 1·25 | 4·50 |
| W69 | 1d. | 1·50 | 8·00 | 75 | 3·00 | 1·50 | 3·00 | + | 3·00 | 4·50 | + | + | 1·25 | 4·50 |
| W70 | 1½d. | 3·00 | 15·00 | 1·50 | 3·00 | 2·50 | 3·00 | 3·00 | 4·50 | 4·50 | + | + | 1·50 | 8·00 |
| W71 | 2d. Die I | 3·00 | 15·00 | 1·75 | 4·00 | 2·75 | 4·00 | 3·50 | 7·00 | 6·00 | 22·00 | + | 2·50 | 6·00 |
| W72 | 2d. Die II | 7·00 | 35·00 | 3·00 | + | 4·00 | + | + | + | + | + | + | + | + |
| W73 | 2½d. | 4·50 | 23·00 | 2·50 | 5·00 | 2·50 | 5·00 | 5·00 | 6·00 | 7·00 | + | + | 2·50 | 9·00 |
| W74 | 3d. | 4·50 | 23·00 | 2·00 | 6·00 | 3·50 | + | + | 6·00 | 6·50 | + | 5·50 | 2·50 | 8·00 |
| W75 | 4d. | 3·00 | 15·00 | 2·50 | 6·00 | 3·50 | — | 7·00 | 9·00 | 7·00 | + | 5·50 | 3·50 | 8·00 |
| W76 | 5d. | 10·00 | 50·00 | 3·00 | 9·00 | 4·00 | — | + | 9·00 | 9·00 | + | 7·00 | 3·50 | 9·00 |
| W77 | 6d. | 10·00 | 50·00 | 3·00 | + | 4·00 | 6·00 | + | 9·00 | 9·00 | + | + | + | + |
| W78 | 6d. Perf. 14 | + | + | 10·00 | + | + | — | + | + | + | + | + | 9·00 | + |
| W79 | 7d. | 8·00 | 40·00 | 10·00 | + | 10·00 | + | + | + | + | + | + | + | + |
| W80 | 8d. | 8·00 | 40·00 | + | 12·00 | 9·00 | + | + | + | + | 35·00 | 12·00 | 8·00 | + |
| W81 | 9d. Agate | + | + | 9·00 | + | 9·00 | + | + | + | + | + | + | + | + |
| W82 | 9d. Green | + | + | + | + | 15·00 | + | + | + | + | + | + | 12·00 | + |
| W83 | 10d. | + | + | 7·00 | + | 12·00 | + | + | 12·00 | + | + | + | 12·00 | + |
| W84 | 1s. | 10·00 | 50·00 | 5·00 | + | 10·00 | 10·00 | + | + | + | + | + | 7·00 | 12·00 |

## " Specimen " Overprints

| SPECIMEN | SPECIMEN | *S*P*E*C*I*M*E*N* | CANCELLED | CANCELLED |
|---|---|---|---|---|
| 15 | 16 | 17 | 18 | 19 |
| $14\frac{1}{2}\times2-2\frac{1}{4}$ | $15\frac{1}{2}\times2\frac{1}{2}$ | $16\times2\frac{3}{4}$ | $14\frac{1}{4}\times1\frac{1}{2}$ | $14\times1\frac{1}{2}$ |

| CANCELLED | CANCELLED. | SPECIMEN | SPECIMEN | CANCELLED |
|---|---|---|---|---|
| 20 | 21 | 22 | 23 | 24 |
| $12\frac{1}{4}\times1\frac{1}{2}$ | $24\times2\frac{1}{2}$ | $14\frac{3}{4}\times2$ | $9\frac{3}{4}-10\times1\frac{3}{4}$ | $15\times2$ |

| CANCELLED | SPECIMEN | CANCELLED | CANCELLED | SPECIMEN |
|---|---|---|---|---|
| 25 | 26 | 27 | 28 | 29 |
| $12\frac{3}{4}\times1\frac{1}{4}$ | $12\frac{1}{2}\times2$ | $27\times2\frac{3}{4}$ | $11\frac{3}{4}\times1\frac{1}{2}$ | $11\frac{1}{4}\times1\frac{1}{4}$ |

| SPECIMEN | SPECIMEN | SPECIMEN | CANCELLED | CANCELLED |
|---|---|---|---|---|
| 30 | 31 | 32 | 33 | 34 |
| $13\times1\frac{3}{4}$ | $12\frac{1}{4}\times1\frac{3}{4}$ | $10\frac{1}{2}\times2$ | $11-12\times1\frac{3}{4}-2$ <br>(3 Types) | $14\frac{1}{2}\times1\frac{3}{4}$ |

P

Types of Overprints referred to in the Lists
Sizes given in millimetres

The dimensions of handstamped overprints may differ slightly from the measurements given owing to variation in the manufacture of the handstamps.

Type **P** was a handpunch used on booklet panes already overprinted " CANCELLED ". They come from voucher booklets sent to the advertisers.

# Perforators

## King Edward VII

The gauge of the perforators continued to be 14 × 14, until September 1911 when it was altered to 15 × 14 for some of the later printings made by Harrison & Sons. This was done to facilitate easier and equal separation.

### Horizontal Comb Machines

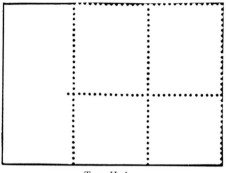

Type H1A

Type H1    With a single extension pin at each end.  Bottom feed.
Type H1A   As above, but top feed.

Set to perforate the sheet either from bottom to top or from top to bottom giving sheet margins as follows:

Bottom feed—    Bottom margin        Imperforate.
                Top margins          Perforated through.
                Side margins         A single extension hole at each side.
Top feed—       Bottom margin        Perforated through.
                Top margin           Imperforate.
                Side margins         A single extension hole.

This machine was used solely by De la Rue and perforated all values with bottom feed. The ½d., 1d., 5d. and 6d. are also known with top feed.

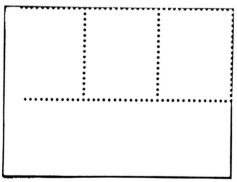

Type H2(c)

Type H2(a)    With a nine pin extension spur at the left and a single extension pin at the right.  Bottom feed.
Type H2A(b)   As (a) but with ten pin extension spur.  Top feed.
Type H2(c)    As (a) but with eleven pin extension spur.  Bottom feed.
Type H2A(c)   As above but top feed.

Type H2(d)   As (a) but with twelve pin extension spur.  Bottom feed.
Type H2A(d)  As above but top feed.
Type H2(e)   As (a) but with fourteen pin extension spur.  Bottom feed.
Type H2A(e)  As above but top feed.
Type H2(f)   As (a) but extension spur of seventeen pins at left.
Type H2(g)   As above but extension spur of thirteen pins at right.

Set to perforate the sheet either from bottom to top or from top to bottom giving sheet margins as follows:

| | | |
|---|---|---|
| Bottom feed— | Bottom margin | Imperforate. |
| | Top margin | Perforated through. |
| | Left margin | Perforated through with eleven pins. |
| | Right margin | A single extension hole. |
| Top feed— | Bottom margin | Perforated through. |
| | Top margin | Imperforate. |
| | Left margin | A single extension hole. |
| | Right margin | Perforated through with eleven pins. |

This machine was used by Harrison and Sons for the perf. 14 printings of the ½d., 1d., 3d. and 4d. values, and also by Somerset House for the £1 value only.

### Vertical Comb Machines

Type V1    With seventeen pin extension spur in top margin.  Bottom margin one extension hole.  Left feed.
Type V1A   As above but right feed.

Set to perforate the sheet from side to side and gave sheet margins as follows:

| | | |
|---|---|---|
| Left feed— | Bottom margin | A single extension hole. |
| | Top margin | Perforated through with seventeen pins. |
| | Left margin | Imperforate. |
| | Right margin | Perforated through. |
| Right feed— | Bottom margin | Perforated through with seventeen pins. |
| | Top margin | A single extension hole. |
| | Left margin | Perforated through. |
| | Right margin | Imperforate. |

This machine was used by all three contractors.

Type V2    With thirteen pin extension spur in bottom margin.  Top margins one extension hole.  Left feed.
Type V2A   As above but right feed.

Set to perforate the sheet from side to side and gave sheet margins as follows:

| | | |
|---|---|---|
| Left feed— | Bottom margin | Perforated through with thirteen pins. |
| | Top margin | A single extension hole. |
| | Left margin | Imperforate. |
| | Right margin | Perforated through. |
| Right feed— | Bottom margin | A single extension hole. |
| | Top margin | Perforated through with thirteen pins. |
| | Left margin | Perforated through. |
| | Right margin | Imperforate. |

This machine was only used by De la Rue for ½d. and 1d. values (both feeds) on Controls C to J 10.  The 4d. value, green and brown on coated paper is also recorded.

## Typographed Booklet Panes

Type B1   Set to perforate the sheets from top to bottom.  The booklet panes always show an extension hole in the margin. Used for the K.E.VII issues and all K.G.V issues until 1918.
Type B2   The above machine, as adapted for the Silver Jubilee issue.
Type B3   This was the Type 2 sheet perforator and it perforated the sheets from left to right or from right to left.  Booklet panes have the margin either imperf. or perforated through.  Used on the K.G.V 1911 issue (watermark Crown) and all the typographed issues from 1918 to 1934.

## King George V
### 1911-24.  Typographed.  ½d. to 1s.

The gauge of perforation was 14¾ or 15 horizontally by 14 vertically, the exception being the Die 1A ½d. and 1d. which have been found perf. 14, and the 6d. perf. 14 issued in 1920–21 when the 15 × 14 machine was out of action.

Type 1   As for Types H2(a) and H2(d) of King Edward VII.  Also a new machine with extension spur of fifteen pins.

Type 1A  As above, but top feed.

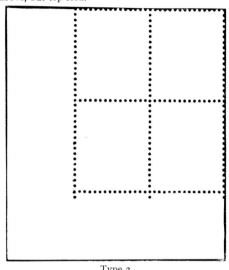

Type 2

Type 2A

Type 2   In general use throughout the period.  Extension spur of fourteen pins at left.
 Left feed—  Bottom margin  A single extension hole.
        Top margin    Perforated through.
        Left margin    Imperforate.
        Right margin   Perforated through.

Type 2A
 Right feed—  Bottom margin  Perforated through.
        Top margin    A single extension hole.
        Left margin    Perforated through.
        Right margin   Imperforate.

Type 2(c) (left feed).  Variety with single extension hole missing in the bottom margin.

Type 2 was a vertical comb perforator perforating a sheet from left to right or right to left as the case may be.  The comb spurs each contain 14 pins and therefore give the perforation 15 × 14.  At least two comb-

heads are known.   In one of them, the pins are set so that the 14 pins perforate a distance one-half milli-
meter in excess of the other comb-head.   Stamps from this comb-head can be recognized by the fact that
the outer top corner perforation is thinner than normal and the gauge is something like 14¾.

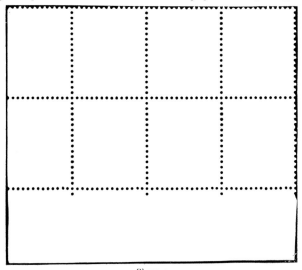

Type 3

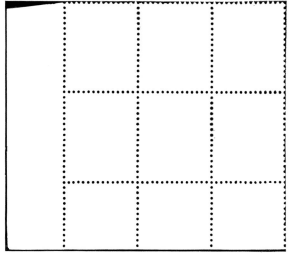

Type 3A

Type 3   Extension spur at right.
      Right feed—     Bottom margin        A single extension hole.
                      Top margin            Perforated through.
                      Left margin            Perforated through.
                      Right margin       Imperforate.
Type 3A
      Left feed—      Bottom margin         Perforated through.
                      Top margin            A single extension hole.
                      Left margin            Imperforate.
                      Right margin       Perforated through.

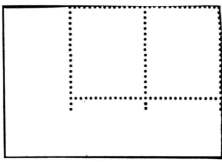

Type 4

Type 4   As for Type 2, but the bottom margin shows two extension holes with left feed.

## 1913-30.   Engraved.   2s. 6d. to £1

The gauge was 11 horizontally by 12 vertically and two machines were in operation:—

(a) Used exclusively by Waterlow and Layton, gave the marginal perforation similar to Type 1 (top feed).

(b) Used by the other two contractors, gave marginal perforations similar to Type 5 (bottom feed).   Bradbury, Wilkinson also used the top feed which gave marginal perforations similar to Type 6B.

## Photogravure

The perforating was done on a separate machine.   The photogravure stamps issued prior to the Silver Jubilee issue were generally perforated on the machines in use at the end of the typographed period—Type 2.   Occasionally Type 4 and rarely Type 3 were also used.

Later, the general perforator in use was a new type of single comb head set to perforate the undivided web from top to bottom.   At each end of the comb head on both dot and no dot panes was a single extension pin (Type 5).

Type 5 perforator was adapted for the Silver Jubilee issued by the removal of alternate sets of vertical pins.

Later still a supplementary perforator in use was as Type 6.   This is a continuous web perforator with a triple comb head enabling three rows of stamps to be perforated at a time.   The outer ends of the comb heads were without extension pins, and the pins crossed the interpane margins.

The machine was soon modified by the removal of the pins in the interpane margin, leaving only single extension pins.   Cylinder blocks from the no dot pane show no alteration.

Type 5.   Cylinder blocks from dot and no dot panes.

| | |
|---|---|
| Left margin | A single extension hole. |
| Bottom margin | Imperforate. |

Type 6.   Cylinder blocks from the no dot pane.

| | |
|---|---|
| Left margin | Imperforate. |
| Bottom margin | Perforated through. |

Type 6A.   Cylinder blocks from the dot pane.

| | |
|---|---|
| Left margin | Perforated through. |
| Bottom margin | Perforated through. |

Type 6B.   Cylinder blocks from the dot pane.

| | |
|---|---|
| Left margin | A single extension hole. |
| Bottom margin | Perforated through. |

## Booklet panes

A new machine was introduced for the booklets containing the stamps printed in photogravure, although occasional use was made of the B3 perforator of the typographed issue.   Booklet panes with cylinder numbers may be found with the following perforations:

| Type | Cyl. No. Pane | Perforation |
|---|---|---|
| B 4 | No dot | Imperf. margin. |
| B 4A | Dot | Perf. margin. |
| B 3 | No dot | Extension hole in the margin. |
| B 3A | Dot | Imperf. margin. |
| B 4B | Dot | Extension hole in the margin. |
| B 5 | Dot | Perforations at bottom only extend across margin. |
| B 6 | Dot | As for B5 except that the two perforation pins next to the stamp margin have been removed. |

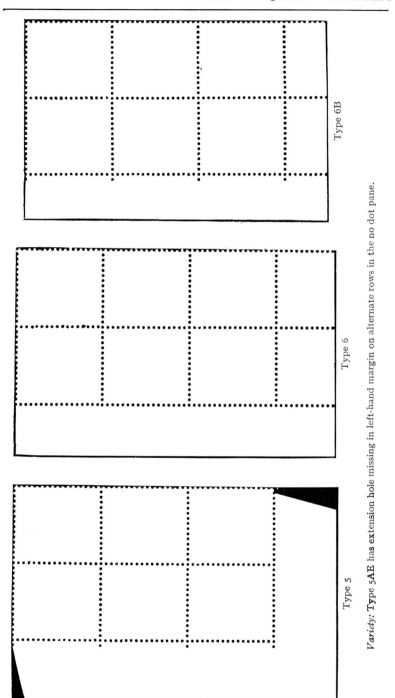

Type 6B

Type 6

Type 5

*Variety:* **Type 5AE** has extension hole missing in left-hand margin on alternate rows in the no dot pane.

# Identification of the Plates

## INTRODUCTION

The plate markings are best collected in bottom row strips of 12 or larger. These pieces are extremely scarce, and fortunately most of the plates may be distinguished from control strips of 3. For further details see pages 17/18.

**PRICES.** Our prices are for the minimum size positional piece necessary for a collection of plate markings. Larger pieces, when in stock, will be supplied at proportionate prices. The price given is for the cheapest control with each plate.

**CUTS.** The cuts in the bottom marginal rule are given positions relative to the letters of wording in the value tablet, followed by the position of the stamp in the bottom row. Cuts in the vertical rules are given a position in millimetres from the bottom of the rule. For example: " Cut 19th right 7 mm." To avoid ambiguity, letters " O " and " N " are shown with the companion letter in brackets. For example " E(N) " signifies the " E " in " PENNY ".

The plates with co-extensive marginal rules nearly always have cuts under the 6th and 7th stamps. These are not plate markings and are not described. On the ½d. Plates 25, 26 and 27 these cuts are filled in, and a single cut made between the two stamps. This is known as the 6-7 rule variety.

New plates are still being discovered, and these have been included and may account for the plate numbers not being consecutive.

**TABULATIONS.** The tabulations which follow for the Edward VII ½d. and 1d. and the George V ½d. to 5d. have been specially devised by the Great Britain Philatelic Society to facilitate the easier allocation of plate markings to their respective plate numbers.

These tabulators must not be used to replace the detailed descriptions. It is suggested that collectors wishing to ascertain the plate number of a positional piece should first refer to the tabulators for quick reference, and then check with the more detailed description shown under the respective plate numbers in the list.

## LEGEND

| | | | | |
|---|---|---|---|---|
| o | = Dot | V | = | V cut |
| ½o | = ½ dot | X | = | X cut |
| 2 | = 2 cuts | > or < | = | Slanting cut |
| 1 | = Single cut | ∧ | = | Indent or nick |
| ¾ | = ¾ cut | ∪ | = | Scoop |
| ½ | = ½ cut | ═══ | = | Break in marginal rule |
| | | ─── | = | Damage to marginal rule |

The position of the markings is indicated by reference to the letters of the value below which they occur; in the rules at the side of the pane we give the measurement in millimetres from the base of the rule to the centre of the cut or dot.

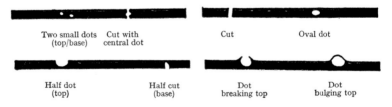

| Two small dots (top/base) | Cut with central dot | Cut | Oval dot |
|---|---|---|---|
| Half dot (top) | Half cut (base) | Dot breaking top | Dot bulging top |

## King Edward VII

### KING EDWARD VII. ½d., TYPE M1. Plate Markings with Continuous Rule

| Plate | Marking | Plate | Marking |
|---|---|---|---|
| 1a | 2 cuts under LFP of 3rd, damaged 12th rule | 6 | No marking, but damage under 12th extending to right of 20th row |
| 1b | Added cut under PE of 2nd, added cut under FP of 6th, added cut under EN of 7th, damage to 12th rule extends | 7 | No marking but break between 11/12 |
| 2 | 2 large cuts under LFPE of 4th | 8 | Cut under PE of 1st, wide and fine cuts under PEN of 8th |
| 3 | Cut under PE of 8th | 9a | Cut under P of 3rd, large cut under ENN of 8th |
| 4 | Cut under HA of 12th, fine break between 10/11 later | 9b | Added cut under P of 1st, and cut under LF of 2nd |
| 5 | Cut under P of 4th, bottom rule damaged at right corner | 9c | Added cut under FP of 4th, and 2 cuts under NY of 7th |

## KING EDWARD VII. ½d., TYPE M1.    Plate Markings with Continuous Rule

| Plate | Marking |
|---|---|
| 10a | Cut under PE of 1st |
| 10b | Added cut under FP of 2nd |
| 11 | Fine cut under P of 2nd |
| 12 | 1½ cuts under P of 7th |
| 13 | Wide break between 11/12, joined break under 11th |
| 14 | Cut between 10/11, break (top) under HA of 11th |
| 16 | Cut under EN of 2nd |
| 18a | Cut under F of 4th |
| 18b | Added cut under P of 7th, dropped rule bottom and right of 12th, break in rule right of row 20, and between 11/12 |

### Plate Markings with Co-extensive Rule

| Plate | Marking |
|---|---|
| 15 | Cut under PE of 1st (wider than on Plate 26b) |
| 20 | Cut under PE of 3rd |
| 25a | Large cut under AL of 1st |
| 25b | Added large cut under P of 8th |
| 26a | Cut under FP of 2nd |
| 26b | Added cut under PE of 1st (finer than Plate 15), cut under LF of 11th |
| 27 | 2 sloping cuts under ALF of 6th |
| 28 | Fine cut under P of 1st |
| 29 | Cut under P of 2nd. With control E 6 the right of rule under 1st damaged |
| 30a | Thin sloping cut under P of 3rd (unlike boat shape of Plate 50). Indent (base) under 9th |
| 30b | Added cut under FP of 4th. Rule right and left of row 20 tapered |
| 32 | Cut under FP of 4th |
| 33 | 1½ cuts under PE of 5th |
| 34 | Cut under N(N) of 7th |
| 35a | Cut under AL of 6th |
| 35b | Added ½ cut under L of 4th |
| 36 | Slanting cut (right to left) under PE of 8th |
| 37a | Cut under PE of 10th |
| 37b | Added ½ cut under P of 3rd |
| 38a | Cut under NN of 9th |
| 38b | Added cut under FP of 4th |
| 38c | Added wide ¾ cut (base) under PE of 3rd |
| 39 | Slanting cut (left to right) under PE of 8th |
| 40a | Nick right end of 1st, cut under and to left of P of 2nd |
| 40b | Added cut under EN of 8th, cut 20th right (3 mm.) |
| 41a | No markings except minute dot under H of 2nd. (See plates 42 and 43) |
| 41b | Added ½ cut (base) under HA of 2nd |
| 42 | No marking. Break under 7th wide |
| 43 | No marking. Break under 7th narrow |
| 44 | Slanting ¾ cut (base, left to right) under HA of 1st. (The similar cut in Plate 47 is vertical) |
| 45a | Cut under FP of 11th |
| 45b | Added cut under PE of 5th |
| 45c | Added 1½ cuts under PE of 1st |
| 46a | Cut under P of 12th |
| 46b | Added cut under PE of 8th |
| 46c | Added 1½ cuts under F of 3rd |

| Plate | Marking |
|---|---|
| 19 | Cut under N(N) of 8th, break between 11/12 |
| 21 | Cut under FP of 1st, cut under PE of 2nd |
| 22a | Cut under NN of 2nd, cut under FP of 3rd |
| 22b | Added cut under LF of 1st |
| 23 | Slanting cut under FP of 4th, 2 cuts under FPE of 5th |
| 24a | 2 cuts under ALF of 4th, 2 ¾ cuts (base) under LF of 6th, 1½ cuts under P of 7th, rule below 12th dropped |
| 24b | Added cut under FP of 3rd |
| 65 | 3 cuts under LF, N(N), NY of 7th |
| 66 | Cuts under PE of 3rd |

| Plate | Marking |
|---|---|
| 46d | Added cut under FP of 1st |
| 47a | ¾ vertical cut (base) under HA of 1st. Indent (base) under 9th. (The ¾ cut of Plate 44 is slanting) |
| 47b | Added large cut under P of 5th. |
| 48 | Large ragged cut under P of 3rd |
| 49a | Cut under P of 4th |
| 49b | Added cut under P of 3rd |
| 50 | ¾ cut (base) under P of 3rd. (Wide and boat shaped, unlike fine and sloping full cut of Plate 30) |
| 51 | Large cut under FP of 3rd |
| 52a | Large semi-circular cut under PEN of 3rd |
| 52b | Added ¾ cut (top) under PE of 8th |
| 52c | Added cut under E of 7th |
| 53a | Irregular cut under HAL of 6th |
| 53b | Added irregular cut under PE of 5th |
| 54 | Cut under PE of 1st. (Unlike the lozenge cut of Plate 62) |
| 55 | Cut under EN of 4th |
| 56a | Large cut under NN of 7th |
| 56b | Added irregular cut under FP of 3rd |
| 57a | Slanting cut under FP of 8th |
| 57b | Added cut right side of 19th row |
| 58a | 1½ cuts under HA of 1st. Faint flaw under FP of 11th |
| 58b | Cut under HA of 4th. Cut 18th right side (8 mm.) |
| 59a | Cut under H of 2nd |
| 59b | Added cut 17th right side (7¾ mm.) |
| 60a | 2 cuts under EN of 3rd |
| 60b | Added cut 18th right side (11 mm.) |
| 61 | Cut under P of 5th. 2 Cuts 19th right side |
| 62 | Lozenge cut (originally double) under PE of 1st |
| 63a | Cut under HA of 6th |
| 63b | Added cut 19th right side (10½ mm.) |
| 64a | Fine cut under (N)N of 7th. (A very spotty plate) |
| 64b | Added cut 20th right side (10½ mm.). The left frame lines of the 10th stamps in rows 18, 19 and 20 received damage. Later a coloured line developed right of the left corner " bit " and the control A 11 was damaged |

### ½d. CONTROL SCHEDULE

| Control | Plate with which it was used |
|---|---|
| A .. .. | 1a, 2, 3, 4, 5, 6, 7, 8, 9a, 11, 65, 66 |
| B .. .. | 1a, 1b, 4, 6, 7, 9a, 10a, 11, 12, 13, 14, 20 |
| C .. .. | 1b, 9b, 10a, 11, 15, 16, 18a, 19, 20 |
| C 4 .. | 1b, 9b, 10b, 16, 18a, 19, 20, 21, 22a, 22b, 23, 24a, 24b, 25a, 26a, 26b, 27 |
| D 4 blue-grn. | 1b, 9c, 15, 18a, 18b, 19, 20, 21, 22b, 23, 24a, 24b, 25a, 25b, 27, 28, 29, 30a, 33 |
| D 4 yell.-grn. | 9c, 15, 18b, 21, 24b, 27, 28, 29, 30a, 32, 33, 34, 35a, 36 |
| D 5 .. | 15, 28, 29, 30a, 32, 33, 34, 35a, 36, 37a |
| E 5 .. | 20, 28, 29, 30a, 30b, 32, 33, 34, 36, 37b, 38a |
| E 6 .. | 28, 29, 32, 33, 34, 37b, 38a, 39 |
| F 6 .. | 27, 28, 29, 32, 33, 34, 35b, 37b, 38a, 39, 40a, 40b, 41a, 42 |

| Control | Plate with which it was used |
|---|---|
| F 7 .. | 28, 33, 34, 35b, 37b, 38a, 39, 40b, 41a, 42 |
| G 7 .. | 28, 33, 34, 35b, 37b, 38a, 39, 41a, 42, 43, 44 |
| G 8 .. | 28, 37b, 38a, 41a, 42, 43, 44 |
| H 8 .. | 37b, 38a, 38b, 38c, 41a, 41b, 42, 43, 44, 45a, 45b, 46a, 46b, 47a, 48, 49a, 50 |
| H 9 .. | 38c, 41b, 43, 45b, 46b, 47a, 48, 49a, 50, 51, 52a, 53a |
| I 9 .. | 37b, 41b, 43, 45c, 46b, 46c, 47a, 48, 49b, 51, 52b, 52c, 53a, 53b, 54, 55, 56a, 56b, 57a |
| I 10 .. | 41b, 45c, 46d, 47a, 49b, 51, 53b, 55, 56b, 57a, 58a, 59a |
| J 10 .. | 41b, 47b, 48, 49b, 51, 53b, 54, 55, 56b, 57a, 58a, 59a, 60a, 61, 62, 63a, 64a |
| A 11 (14) .. | 54, 57b, 58b, 59b, 60b, 63b, 64b |
| A 11 (15 × 14) | 57b, 58b, 59b, 63b, 64b |

**143**

# KING EDWARD VII. ½d., TYPE M1.  Continuous Rule (Plates 1a to 16)

| Plate | 1 | 2 | 3 | 4 | 5 | 6 | 7 | 8 | 9 | 10 | 11 | 12 | 17 | 18 | 19 | 20 | Controls | Prices from |
|---|---|---|---|---|---|---|---|---|---|---|---|---|---|---|---|---|---|---|
| | | | | | | Bottom row, Stamp No. | | | | | | | 12th stamp, Row No. | | | | | Positional piece |
| 1a | | | | | | | | | | | | · | | | | | A, B | 1·50 |
| 1b | | 1 PE | 2 LFP | | | 1 FP | 1 EN | | | | | ∣ | | | | | B, C, C4, D4 | 1·25 |
| 2 | | | | 2 LFPE | | | | | | | | | | | | | A | 2·50 |
| 3 | | | | | | | | 1 PE | | | | | | | | | A | 4·50 |
| 4 | | | | 1 P | | | | | | | ‖ | 1 HA | | | | | A, B | 1·50 |
| 5 | | | | | | | | | | | | ∣ | | | | ∣ | A | 4·50 |
| 6 | | | | | | | | | | | | ∣ | | | | | A, B | 1·50 |
| 7 | | | | | | | | | | | ‖ | | | | | | A, B | 2·00 |
| 8 | 1 PE | | | | | | | 2 PEN | | | | | | | | | A | 4·50 |
| 9a | | | 1 P | | | | | 1 ENN | | | | | | | | | A, B | 3·00 |
| 9b | 1 P | 1 LF | 1 P | | | | | 1 ENN | | | | | | | | | C, C4 | 1·25 |
| 9c | 1 P | 1 LF | 1 P | 1 FP | | | 2 NY | 1 ENN | | | | | | | | | D4 | 1·50 |
| 10a | 1 PE | | | | | | | | | | | | | | | | B, C | 1·30 |
| 10b | 1 PE | 1 FP | | | | | | | | | | | | | | | C4 | 1·25 |
| 11 | | 1 P | | | | | 1½ P | | | | | | | | | | A, B, C | 1·25 |
| 12 | | | | | | | | | | | | | | | | | B | 3·00 |
| 13 | | | | | | | | | | | | | | | | | B | 2·00 |
| 14 | | | | | | | | | | 1 HA | | | | | | | B | 2·00 |
| 16 | | 1 EN | | | | | | | | | | | | | | | C, C4 | 1·25 |

# KING EDWARD VII. ½d., TYPE M1. Continuous Rule (Plates 18a to 66)

|       | Bottom row, Stamp No. | | | | | | | | | | | | 12th Stamp, Row No. | | | | | Positional piece |
| Plate | 1 | 2 | 3 | 4 | 5 | 6 | 7 | 8 | 9 | 10 | 11 | 12 | 17 | 18 | 19 | 20 | Controls | Prices from |
|---|---|---|---|---|---|---|---|---|---|---|---|---|---|---|---|---|---|---|
| 18a |  |  |  | 1 F |  |  |  |  |  |  |  |  |  |  |  |  | C, C 4, D 4 | 1·50 |
| 18b |  |  |  |  |  |  | 1 P |  |  |  |  |  |  |  |  |  | D 4 | 10·00 |
| 19  |  |  |  | 1 F |  |  |  | 1 N(N) |  |  |  |  |  |  |  |  | C, C 4, D 4 | 2·00 |
| 21  | 1 FP | 1 PE |  |  |  |  |  |  |  |  |  |  |  |  |  |  | C 4, D 4 | 1·25 |
| 22a |  | 1 NN | 1 FP |  |  |  |  |  |  |  |  |  |  |  |  |  | C 4 | 1·75 |
| 22b | 1 LF | 1 NN | 1 FP |  |  |  |  |  |  |  |  |  |  |  |  |  | C 4, D 4 | 1·25 |
| 23  |  |  |  | > FP | 2 FPE | ¾,¾ LF |  |  |  |  |  |  |  |  |  |  | C 4, D 4 | 4·50 |
| 24a |  |  |  | 2 ALF |  | ¾,¾ LF | 1¼ P |  |  |  |  |  |  |  |  |  | C 4, D 4 | 2·00 |
| 24b |  |  | 1 FP | 2 ALF |  | ¾,¾ LF | 1⅛ P |  |  |  |  |  |  |  |  |  | D 4 | 2·50 |
| 65  |  |  |  |  |  | 3 LF N(N), NY |  |  |  |  |  |  |  |  |  |  | A | 5·00 |
| 66  |  |  | 1 PE |  |  |  |  |  |  |  |  |  |  |  |  |  | A | 2·50 |

## Co-extensive Rule (Plates 15-25a)

| Plate | 1 | 2 | 3 | 4 | Controls | Prices from |
|---|---|---|---|---|---|---|
| 15  | 1 PE |  |  |  | C, D 4, D 5, | 1·25 |
| 20  |  |  | 1 PE |  | B, C, C 4, D 4, E 5 | 1·25 |
| 25a | 1 AL |  |  |  | C 4, D 4 | 1·25 |

Positional piece Prices from

12th stamp, Row No.

Bottom row, Stamp No.

| Plate | 1 | 2 | 3 | 4 | 5 | 6 | 7 | 8 | 9 | 10 | 11 | 12 | 17 | 18 | 19 | 20 | Controls | Prices from |
|---|---|---|---|---|---|---|---|---|---|---|---|---|---|---|---|---|---|---|
| 25b | I AL | | | | | | | I P | | | | | | | | | D 4 | 2·50 |
| 26a | | I FP | | | | | | | | | | | | | | | C 4 | 1·25 |
| 26b | I PE | I FP | | | | | | | | | | | | | | | C 4 | 1·25 |
| 27 | | | | | | 2< ALF | | | | | I LF | | | | | | C 4, D 4, F 6 | 2·50 |
| 28 | I P | | | | | | | | | | | | | | | | D 4, D 5, E 5, E 6, F 6, F 7, G 7, G 8 | 1·25 |
| 29 | | I P | I P | | | | | | | | | | | | | | D 4, D 5, E 5, E 6, F 6 | 1·25 |
| 30a | | | I P | | | | | | < | | | | | | | | D 4, D 5, E 5 | 1·25 |
| 30b | | | | I FP | | | | | < | | | | | | | | E 5 | 1·50 |
| 32 | | | | I FP | 1½ PE | | | | | | | | | | | | D 4, D 5, E 5, E 6, F 6 | 1·50 |
| 33 | | | | | | | | | | | | ↓ | | | | | D 4, D 5, E 5, E 6, F 6, F 7, G 7 | 1·75 |
| 34 | | | | | | | I N(N) | | | | | | | | | | D 4, D 5, E 5, E 6, F 6, F 7, G 7 | 2·00 |
| 35a | | | | ½ L | | I AL | | | | | | | | | | | D 4, D 5 | 2·00 |
| 35b | | | | | | I AL | | | | | | | | | | | F 6, F 7, G 7 | 2·00 |
| 36 | | | | | | | | V PE | | | | | | | | | D 4, D 5, E 5 | 2·50 |
| 37a | | | | | | | | | | I PE | | | | | | | D 5 | 4·00 |
| 37b | | | ½ P | | | | | | I NN | I PE | | | | | | | E 5, E 6, F 6, F 7, G 7, G 8, H 8, I 9 | 1·25 |
| 38a | | | | | | | | | I NN | | | | | | | | E 5, E 6, F 6, F 7, G 7, G 8, H 8 | 4·50 |
| 38b | | | ¾ PE | I FP | | | | | I NN | | | | | | | | H 8 | 5·50 |
| 38c | | | | I FP | | | | | | | | | | | | | H 8, H 9 | 2·50 |

## KING EDWARD VII. ½d, TYPE M1. Co-extensive Rule (Plates 39 to 49a)

| Plate | \multicolumn{12}{Bottom row, Stamp No.} | | | | | | | | | | | | 12th stamp, Row No. | | | | Controls | Prices from |
|---|---|---|---|---|---|---|---|---|---|---|---|---|---|---|---|---|---|---|

| Plate | 1 | 2 | 3 | 4 | 5 | 6 | 7 | 8 | 9 | 10 | 11 | 12 | 17 | 18 | 19 | 20 | Controls | Prices from |
|---|---|---|---|---|---|---|---|---|---|---|---|---|---|---|---|---|---|---|
| 39 | | | | | | | | ∨ PE | | | | | | | | | E 6, F 6, F 7, G 7 | 2·00 |
| 40a | < | I P | | | | | | | | | | | | | | | F 6 | 1·25 |
| 40b | < | I P | | | | | | I EN | | | | | | | | I 3 mm. | F 6, F 7 | 2·50 |
| 41a | | o H | | | | | | | | | | | | | | | F 6, F 7, G 7, G 8, H 8 | 1·25 |
| 41b | | oï HA | | | | | | | | | | | | | | | H 8, H 9, I 9, I 10, J 10 | 1·25 |
| 42 | | | | | | | Wide | | | | | | | | | | F 6, F 7, G 7, G 8, H 8 | 2·50 |
| 43 | | | | | | | Narrow | | | | | | | | | | G 7, G 8, H 8, H 9, I 9 | 2·50 |
| 44 | ¾∨ HA | | | | | | | | | | | | | | | | G 7, G 8, H 8 | 1·25 |
| 45a | | | | | | | | | | | I FP | | | | | | H 8 | 3·00 |
| 45b | | | | | I PE | | | | | | I FP | | | | | | H 8, H 9 | 2·50 |
| 45c | I¼ PE | | | | I PE | | | | | | I FP | | | | | | I 9, I 10 | 1·25 |
| 46a | | | | | | | | | | | | I PE | | | | | H 8 | 3·50 |
| 46b | | | | | | | | I PE | | | | I PE | | | | | H 8, H 9, I 9 | 2·50 |
| 46c | | | I¼ F | | | | | I PE | | | | I PE | | | | | I 9 | 1·25 |
| 46d | I FP | | I¼ F | | | | | I PE | | | | I PE | | | | | I 10 | 1·25 |
| 47a | ¾ HA | | | | | | | | < | | | | | | | | H 8, H 9, I 9, I 10, J 10 | 1·25 |
| 47b | ¾ HA | | | | I P | | | | < | | | | | | | | J 10 | 2·25 |
| 48 | | I P | I P | | | | | | | | | | | | | | H 8, H 9, I 9, J 10 | 1·25 |
| 49a | | | | I P | | | | | | | | | | | | | H 8, H 9 | 1·50 |

# KING EDWARD VII. ½d, TYPE M1. Co-extensive Rule (Plates 49b to 60a)

| Plate | Bottom row, Stamp No. | | | | | | | | | | | | 12th stamp, Row No. | | | | Controls | Positional piece Prices from |
| --- | --- | --- | --- | --- | --- | --- | --- | --- | --- | --- | --- | --- | --- | --- | --- | --- | --- | --- |
| | 1 | 2 | 3 | 4 | 5 | 6 | 7 | 8 | 9 | 10 | 11 | 12 | 17 | 18 | 19 | 20 | | |
| 49b | | | I P | I P | | | | | | | | | | | | | I 9, I 10, J 10 | 1·50 |
| 50 | | | ¾ P | | | | | | | | | | | | | | H 8, H 9 | 1·50 |
| 51 | | | I FP | | | | | | | | | | | | | | H 9, I 9, I 10, J 10 | 1·25 |
| 52a | | | I PEN | | | | | | | | | | | | | | H 9 | 2·50 |
| 52b | | | I PEN | | | | | ¾ PE | | | | | | | | | I 9 | 2·50 |
| 52c | | | I PEN | | | | I E | ¾ PE | | | | | | | | | I 9 | 2·50 |
| 53a | | | | | | I HAL | | | | | | | | | | | H 9, I 9 | 2·50 |
| 53b | | | | | I PE | I HAL | | | | | | | | | | | I 9, I 10, J 10 | 2·50 |
| 54 | I PE | | | | | | | | | | | | | | | | I 9, J 10, A 11 (14) | 1·25 |
| 55 | | | | I EN | | | | | | | | | | | | | I 9, I 10, J 10 | 1·50 |
| 56a | | | | | | | I NN | | | | | | | | | | I 9 | 3·50 |
| 56b | | | I FP | | | | I NN | | | | | | | | | | I 9, I 10, J 10 | 2·50 |
| 57a | | | | | | | | V FP | | | | | | | | | I 9, I 10, J 10 | 2·50 |
| 57b | | | | | | | | V FP | | | | | | | I | | A 11 (14), A 11 (15×14) | 2·50 |
| 58a | I⅛ HA | | | | | | | | | | flaw FP | | | | | | I 10, J 10 | 2·50 |
| 58b | I⅛ HA | | | I HA | | | | | | | flaw FP | | | I 8 mm. | | | A 11 (14), A 11 (15×14) | 2·50 |
| 59a | | I H | | | | | | | | | | | | | | | I 10, J 10 | 1·25 |
| 59b | | I H | | | | | | | | | | | I 7½ mm. | | | | A 11 (14), A 11 (15×14) | 1·25 |
| 60a | | | ² EN | | | | | | | | | | | | | | J 10 | 2·00 |

# KING EDWARD VII ½d., TYPE M1.   Co-extensive Rule (Plates 60b to 64b)

| Plate | Bottom row, Stamp No. | | | | | | | | | | | | 12th Stamp, Row No. | | | | Controls | Positional piece Prices from |
| | 1 | 2 | 3 | 4 | 5 | 6 | 7 | 8 | 9 | 10 | 11 | 12 | 17 | 18 | 19 | 20 | | |
| --- | --- | --- | --- | --- | --- | --- | --- | --- | --- | --- | --- | --- | --- | --- | --- | --- | --- | --- |
| 60b | | | 2 EN | | | | | | | | | | | 1 11 mm. | | | A 11 (14) | 1·25 |
| 61 | | | | | 1 P | | | | | | | | | | 2 12½ mm. | | J 10 | 2·00 |
| 62 | 2 PE | | | | | | | | | | | | | | | | J 10 | 2·00 |
| 63a | | | | | | 1 HA | | | | | | | | | | | J 10 | 2·50 |
| 63b | | | | | | 1 HA | | | | | | | | | 1 10½ mm. | | A 11 (14), A 11 (15×14) | 1·50 |
| 64a | | | | | | | 1 (N)N | | | | | | | | | | J 10 | 1·75 |
| 64b | | | | | | | 1 (N)N | | | | | | | | | 1 10½ mm. | A 11 (14), A-11 (15×14) | 1·50 |

## KING EDWARD VII. 1d., TYPE M1. Plate Markings with Continuous Rule

| Plate | Marking |
|---|---|
| 1a | Cut under PE of 8th |
| 1b | Added cut under (P)E of 4th, wide cut under PE of 10th, break between 2nd and 3rd |
| 1c | Break between 11th and 12th |
| 1d | Break between 10th and 11th |
| 2 | Cut under PE of 7th |
| 3 | Slanting cut under PE of 10th |
| 4a | ¾ cut (base) under PE of 10th |
| 4b | Break between 10th and 11th |
| 5 | Cut under NE of 11th |
| 6a | Cut under EP of 12th |
| 6b | Breaks between 10/11 and 11/12 |
| 7 | Cut under P of 12th |
| 8 | ½ cut (top) under PE of 7th<br>½ cut (base) under (P)E of 9th |
| 10 | 2 cuts under 1st, cut under 5th, 2 cuts under 6th |
| 11 | Cut under P of 2nd, cut under PE of 5th, cut under EP of 11th, breaks between 9/10 and 10/11 |
| 12 | No cuts, but irregular breaks between 9/10 and 10/11 |
| 13 | Sloping cut under (P)E of 4th |
| 14 | ¾ cut (base) under (N)N of 10th |
| 16a | Cut under EN of 7th |
| 16b | Added cut under PE of 8th |
| 17a | Cut under EP of 5th |
| 17b | Added cut under (E)P of 4th |
| 18 | Cut under NE of 6th, cut under P of 9th |
| 19 | Cut under (P)E of 2nd, cut under PE of 8th, cut under N(Y) of 10th, breaks between 8/9 and 10/11 |
| 20 | Cut under PE of 2nd, cut under PE of 3rd |
| 29 | Slanting cut under NE of 11th |
| 32 | Fine cut under EN of 10th |
| 68 | Cut under P of 6th |
| 69 | Cut under E(N) of 7th |
| 70 | Cut under (P)E of 6th |
| 72 | Cut under PE of 9th |

## KING EDWARD VII. 1d., TYPE M1. Plate Markings with Co-extensive Rule

| Plate | Marking |
|---|---|
| 9a | ¾ flat topped cut (base) under PE of 1st (Plate 49 cut has a pointed top) |
| 9b | Break under P of 2nd |
| 15 | Cut under P of 2nd |
| 21a | Cut under (P)E of 3rd |
| 21b | Added cut under (P)E of 2nd |
| 22a | ¾ cut (base) under PE of 4th |
| 22b | Added diamond shaped cut under PE of 2nd |
| 23a | Sloping cut under E(N) of 4th |
| 23b | Added cut under P of 3rd |
| 24a | Cut under PE of 5th |
| 24b | Added wide ½ cut under NN of 2nd |
| 25a | Cut under (N)E of 6th, widening to two cuts |
| 25b | Added ¾ cut (base) under PE of 12th |
| 26a | Cut under (O)N of 6th, thin and regular |
| 26b | Added cut under P of 11th |
| 26c | Added ½ cut (base) under NE of 2nd |
| 27 | Cut under N(N) of 7th |
| 28a | Full and ½ cut (base) under P of 8th |
| 28b | Added diamond shaped cut under PE of 1st |
| 30 | Slanting crack under NE of 12th |
| 31 | 1½ cuts under NE of 2nd |
| 33a | Two thick cuts under NE of 6th |
| 33b | Added ½ cut (base) under P of 10th, and short rule left of 11th |
| 34a | ½ cut (top) under NE of 11th |
| 34b | Added fine cut and dot under PEN of 9th |
| 34c | Added cut 20th right side (5 mm.) |
| 34d | Added cut 19th right side (8½ mm.) |
| 35 | ½ cut (base) under EP of 2nd |
| 36 | Minute dot under Y of 6th, cut under (P)E of 8th. Small scoop base of 9th |
| 37 | ¾ cut (top) under PE of 10th |
| 38a | Cut under PE of 2nd |
| 38b | Added two double cuts under NN of 7th |
| 39a | Dot under EP of 1st |
| 39b | Added two irregular cuts under PEN of 4th |
| 40a | Curved semi double cut under PE of 2nd |
| 40b | Added two cuts under EPE of 5th |
| 41a | Thin " V " cut under (P)E of 5th |
| 41b | Added ¾ cut under (P)E of 4th |
| 42 | Wide cut under (O)N of 6th |
| 43a | ½ cut (base) under Y of 7th |
| 43b | Added cut under P of 1st |
| 44 | Cut under P of 5th |
| 45a | Two fine cuts under ON of 6th |
| 45b | Right end of 10th cut away |
| 46a | Two ragged cuts under NE of 6th, scoops under 4th and 9th |
| 46b | Added ½ cut (base), a full cut and a ½ cut (base), all under NEP of 5th |
| 47a | Cut under NY of 7th |
| 47b | Added cut under P of 5th |
| 47c | 10th rule broken under Y and dropped |
| 48a | 1½ cuts under P of 8th |
| 48b | Added 1½ cuts under (E)N of 7th, and ½ cut (top) under NY of 10th |
| 49 | ½ cut with pointed top (base) under PE of 1st (Plate 9a had a flat topped cut) |
| 50a | Cut and a minute ½ cut under EP of 1st |
| 50b | Added cut under EP of 4th |
| 51a | ½ cut (base) under PE of 2nd |
| 51b | Added ½ cut (base) under EP of 1st |
| 52a | Ragged cut under PE of 3rd |
| 52b | Added ½ cut (base), under (N)E of 1st |
| 53a | Irregular cut under (P)E of 4th |
| 53b | Added sloping cut under EN of 3rd and ¾ cut (base) under (O)N of 6th |
| 54a | Irregular cut under (P)E of 5th |
| 54b | Added cut under PE of 4th and two ½ cuts (top) under (P)E of 8th |
| 55 | Thin diagonal cut under EP of 12th |
| 56 | Irregular cut under N(N) of 5th |
| 57a | Two very close cuts under N(E) of 6th and dot at left end of 12th rule |
| 57b | Added two cuts under PEN of 5th and cut under EP of 8th |
| 58a | ½ cut (top) under NY of 7th |
| 58b | Added ½ cut (base) under N(N) of 1st and two cuts under EPE of 8th. Several flaw varieties |
| 59 | Two thick sloping cuts under ON of 6th |
| 60 | Small ½ cut (base) under PE of 2nd |
| 61a | ½ cut (base) under EP of 4th |
| 61b | Added large cut under NN of 9th and cut 17th right side (8½ mm.) |
| 62a | Very fine cut (top) under EP of 5th |
| 62b | Added big cut under PE of 11th, cut 19th right (12 mm.) |
| 62c | Added cut 18th right side (11 mm.) |
| 63a | ½ cut (base) under NE of 3rd, cut 17th right (12½ mm.) |
| 63b | Added cut 20th right (9½ mm.) |
| 64 | Fine cut under EN of 7th and ½ nick (top) under NY of 10th |
| 65 | ¾ cut (base) under EN of 7th |
| 66a | ½ cut (base) under P of 8th (ragged) |
| 66b | Added cut under EP of 10th (coarse) and cut 18th right side (10½ mm.) |
| 67 | Fine sloping cut under PE of 11th |
| 71 | Cut under 6th filled in |

## 1d. CONTROL SCHEDULE

| Control | Plate with which it was used |
|---|---|
| A .. | .. 1a, 1b, 2, 3, 4a, 4b, 5, 6a, 6b, 7, 8, 68, 69, 70, 72 |
| B .. | .. 1b, 1c, 1d, 2, 3, 7, 10, 11, 12 |
| C .. | .. 1d, 3, 9a, 13, 14, 15, 16a, 17a, 18, 19 |
| C 4 .. | .. 3, 7, 9a, 11, 14, 15, 16a, 16b, 17a, 18, 19, 71 |
| D 4 .. | .. 3, 7, 9a, 11, 15, 17b, 18, 20, 21a, 22a, 22b, 23a, 24a, 25a, 26a, 27, 28a, 29, 30, 31, 32 |
| D 5 .. | .. 7, 9a, 12, 21a, 23a, 24a, 25a, 27, 28a, 30, 33a, 34a |
| E 5 .. | .. 9a, 9b, 21a, 23a, 24a, 25b, 26b, 27, 28a, 30, 33a, 34a, 35, 36, 37 |
| E 6 .. | .. 9b, 21a, 23a, 24a, 27, 28b, 34a, 36, 38a |
| F 6 .. | .. 9b, 21a, 23a, 24a, 24b, 27, 36, 38a, 38b, 39a, 40a, 41a, 42, 43a |
| F 7 .. | .. 21a, 23a, 31, 36, 38b, 39a, 40a 41a, 42, 43a |

| Control | Plate with which it was used |
|---|---|
| G 7 .. | .. 21a, 23a, 31, 35, 36, 38b, 39a, 40a 40b, 41a, 43a, 44, 45a |
| G 8 .. | .. 23b, 25b, 26b, 31, 33a, 34a, 35, 36, 39a, 41b, 42, 44, 45b, 46a |
| H 8 .. | .. 21b, 23b, 25b, 26b, 26c, 31, 33a, 34a, 35, 39a, 39b, 41b, 43b, 46a, 47a, 48a, 49, 50a, 50b, 51a, 52a, 53a, 53b, 54a, 55 |
| H 9 .. | .. 46a, 47b, 48a, 49, 50b, 51a, 52a, 54a |
| I 9 .. | .. 34a, 44, 46b, 47b, 47c, 48a, 49, 50b, 51a, 52a, 56, 57a, 58a, 59 |
| I 10 .. | .. 34a, 50b, 51a, 52a, 57b, 58a, 60, 61a, 62a |
| J 10 .. | .. 25b, 33b, 34a, 34b, 48b, 51b, 52a, 52b, 54b, 56, 58a, 59, 60, 61a, 62a 63a, 64, 65, 66a, 67 |
| A 11 (14) (c) | 61b, 62b |
| A 11 (14) (w) | 34b, 34c, 62b, 63a, 63b, 66b |
| A 11 (15 × 14) | 34d, 58b, 61b, 62b, 63b |

KING EDWARD VII. 1d., TYPE M1.  Continuous Rule (Plates 1a to 16a)

| | Bottom row, Stamp No. | | | | | | | | | | | | 12th stamp, Row No. | | | | | Positional piece |
| Plate | 1 | 2 | 3 | 4 | 5 | 6 | 7 | 8 | 9 | 10 | 11 | 12 | 17 | 18 | 19 | 20 | Controls | Prices from |
|---|---|---|---|---|---|---|---|---|---|---|---|---|---|---|---|---|---|---|
| 1a | | | | | | | | | | | | | | | | | A | 2·00 |
| 1b | | | | I/(P)E | | | | I/PE | | I/PE | | | | | | | A, B | 1·75 |
| 1c | | | ‖ | I/(P)E | | | | I/PE | | I/PE | | ‖ | | | | | B | 2·00 |
| 1d | | | | I/(P)E | | | I/PE | I/PE | | I/PE | ‖ | | | | | | B, C | 4·50 |
| 2 | | | | | | | | | | ∨/PE | | | | | | | A, B | 3·00 |
| 3 | | | | | | | | | | ¾ PE | | | | | | | A, B, C, C4, D4 | 1·25 |
| 4a | | | | | | | | | | ¾ PE | | | | | | | A | 1·50 |
| 4b | | | | | | | | | | ¾ PE | | | | | | | A | 1·25 |
| 5 | | | | | | | | | | | I/NE | | | | | | A | 1·50 |
| 6a | | | | | | | | | | | | I/EP | | | | | A | 1·75 |
| 6b | | | | | | | | | | | ‖ | I/EP | | | | | A | 1·25 |
| 7 | | | | | | | | | ½ (P)E | | | I/P | | | | | A, B, C4, D4, D5 | 1·00 |
| 8 | 2 | | | | | | ½ PE | | | | | | | | | | A | 4·50 |
| 10 | 2 | I/P | | | I | 2 | | | | | | | | | | | B | 4·50 |
| 11 | | | | | I/PE | | | | | ‖ | I/EP | | | | | | B, C4, D4 | 1·25 |
| 12 | | | | | | | | | ‖ | ‖ | I/EP | | | | | | B, D5 | 1·50 |
| 13 | | | | ∨/(P)E | | | | | | | | | | | | | C | 3·00 |
| 14 | | | | | | | I/EN | | | ¾ (N)N | | | | | | | C, C4 | 1·25 |
| 16a | | | | | | | | | | | | | | | | | C, C4 | 4·50 |

# KING EDWARD VII. [1d., TYPE M1. Continuous Rule_(Plates 16b to 72)

|  | Bottom row, Stamp No. | | | | | | | | | | | | 12th stamp, Row No. | | | | | Positional piece |
| Plate | 1 | 2 | 3 | 4 | 5 | 6 | 7 | 8 | 9 | 10 | 11 | 12 | 17 | 18 | 19 | 20 | Controls | Prices from |
|---|---|---|---|---|---|---|---|---|---|---|---|---|---|---|---|---|---|---|
| 16b |  |  |  |  |  |  |  |  |  |  |  |  |  |  |  |  | C 4 | 2·50 |
| 17a |  |  |  |  | I EP |  | I EN | I PE |  |  |  |  |  |  |  |  | C, C 4 | 2·50 |
| 17b |  |  |  | (E)P | I EP |  |  |  |  |  |  |  |  |  |  |  | D 4 | 2·50 |
| 18 |  | I (P)E |  |  |  | I NE |  |  | I P |  |  |  |  |  |  |  | C, C 4, D 4 | 1·25 |
| 19 |  | I PE | I PE |  |  |  |  | I PE | I PE | I N(Y) |  |  |  |  |  |  | C, C 4 | 1·25 |
| 20 |  |  |  |  |  |  |  |  |  |  |  |  |  |  |  |  | D 4 | 3·00 |
| 29 |  |  |  |  |  |  |  |  |  |  | V NE |  |  |  |  |  | D 4 | 2·00 |
| 32 |  |  |  |  |  |  |  |  |  | I EN |  |  |  |  |  |  | D 4 | 2·00 |
| 68 |  |  |  |  |  | I P |  |  |  |  |  |  |  |  |  |  | A | 4·50 |
| 69 |  |  |  |  |  |  | I E(N) |  |  |  |  |  |  |  |  |  | A | 4·50 |
| 70 |  |  |  |  |  | (P)E |  |  |  |  |  |  |  |  |  |  | A | 4·50 |
| 72 |  |  |  |  |  |  |  |  | I PE |  |  |  |  |  |  |  | A |  |

# Co-extensive Rule (Plates 9a to 21b)

| Plate | 1 | 2 | 3 | 4 | 5 | 6 | 7 | 8 | 9 | 10 | 11 | 12 | 17 | 18 | 19 | 20 | Controls | Prices from |
|---|---|---|---|---|---|---|---|---|---|---|---|---|---|---|---|---|---|---|
| 9a |  | ¾ PE |  |  |  |  |  |  |  |  |  |  |  |  |  |  | C, C 4, D 4, D 5, E 5 | 2·00 |
| 9b |  | ¾ PE |  |  |  | I P |  |  |  |  |  |  |  |  |  |  | E 5, E 6, F 6 | 2·00 |
| 15 |  |  |  |  |  | I P |  |  |  |  |  |  |  |  |  |  | C, C 4, D 4 | 2·00 |
| 21a |  |  | I (P)E |  |  |  |  |  |  |  |  |  |  |  |  |  | D 4, D 5, E 5, E 6, F 6, F 7, G 7 | 1·75 |
| 21b |  | I (P)E | I (P)E |  |  |  |  |  |  |  |  |  |  |  |  |  | H 8 | 2·50 |

## KING EDWARD VII. 1d., TYPE M1. Co-extensive Rule (Plates 22a to 34a)

| | Bottom row, Stamp No. | | | | | | | | | | | | 12th stamp, Row No. | | | | | Positional piece |
|---|---|---|---|---|---|---|---|---|---|---|---|---|---|---|---|---|---|---|
| **Plate** | 1 | 2 | 3 | 4 | 5 | 6 | 7 | 8 | 9 | 10 | 11 | 12 | 17 | 18 | 19 | 20 | Controls | Prices from |
| **22a** | | | | ¾ PE | | | | | | | | | | | | | D 4 | 3·00 |
| **22b** | | 1 PE | | ¾ PE | | | | | | | | | | | | | D 4 | 3·00 |
| **23a** | | | | < E(N) | | | | | | | | | | | | | D 4, D 5, E 5, E 6, F 6, F 7, G 7 | 2·50 |
| **23b** | | | 1 P | < E(N) | | | | | | | | | | | | | G 8, H 8 | 2·50 |
| **24a** | | | | | 1 PE | | | | | | | | | | | | D 4, D 5, E 5, E 6, F 6 | 2·50 |
| **24b** | | ½ NN | | | 1 PE | | | | | | | | | | | | F 6 | 2·50 |
| **25a** | | | | | | 1 (N)E | | | | | | | | | | | D 4, D 5 | 3·00 |
| **25b** | | | | | | 1 (N)E | | | | | | ¾ PE | | | | | E 5, G 8, H 8, J 10 | 1·00 |
| **26a** | | | | | | 1 (O)N | | | | | | | | | | | D 4 | 3·00 |
| **26b** | | | | | | 1 (O)N | | | | | 1 P | | | | | | E 5, G 8, H 8 | 1·00 |
| **26c** | | ½ NE | | | | 1 (O)N | | | | | 1 P | | | | | | H 8 | 3·00 |
| **27** | | | | | | | 1 N(N) | | | | | | | | | | D 4, D 5, E 5, E 6, F 6 | 2·50 |
| **28a** | | | | | | | | 1¼ P | | | | | | | | | D 4, D 5, E 5 | 3·00 |
| **28b** | 1 PE | | | | | | | 1¼ P | | | | | | | | | E 6 | 3·00 |
| **30** | | | | | | | | | | | | crack NE | | | | | D 4, D 5, E 5 | 9·00 |
| **31** | | 1½ NE | | | | | | | | | | | | | | | D 4, F 7, G 7, G 8, H 8 | 4·50 |
| **33a** | | | | | | 2 NE | | | | | | | | | | | D 5, E 5, G 8, H 8 | 4·50 |
| **33b** | | | | | | 2 NE | | | | ½ P | | | | | | | J 10 | 4·50 |
| **34a** | | | | | | | | | | | ½ NE | | | | | | D 5, E 5, E 6, G 8, H 8, I 9, I 10, J 10 | 1·25 |

**KING EDWARD VII. 1d., TYPE M1. Co-extensive Rule (Plates 34b to 44)**

| Plate | Bottom row, Stamp No. | | | | | | | | | | | | 12th stamp, Row No. | | | | Controls | Positional piece Prices from |
|---|---|---|---|---|---|---|---|---|---|---|---|---|---|---|---|---|---|---|
| | 1 | 2 | 3 | 4 | 5 | 6 | 7 | 8 | 9 | 10 | 11 | 12 | 17 | 18 | 19 | 20 | | |
| 34b | | | | | | | | | 1 o PEN | | ↑ NE | | | | | | J 10, A 11 (14) (w) | 1·25 |
| 34c | | | | | | | | | 1 o PEN | | ↑ NE | | | | | 1 5 mm. | A 11 (14) (w) | 1·75 |
| 34d | | | | | | | | | 1 o PEN | | ↑ NE | | | | 1 8½ mm. | 1 5 mm. | A 11 (15×14) | 2·00 |
| 35 | | ↑ EP | | | | | | | | | | | | | | | E 5, G 7, G 8, H 8 | 2·00 |
| 36 | | | | | | 0 Y | | 1 (P)E | ◡ | | | | | | | | E 5, E 6, F 6, F 7, G 7, G 8 | 3·00 |
| 37 | | | | | | | | | | ↑ PE | | | | | | | E 5 | 1·50 |
| 38a | | 1 PE | | | | | | | | | | | | | | | E 6, F 6 | 4·00 |
| 38b | | 1 PE | | | | | 2 NN | | | | | | | | | | F 6, F 7, G 7 | 4·00 |
| 39a | 0 EP | | | 2 PEN | | | | | | | | | | | | | F 6, F 7, G 7, G 8, H 8 | 2·50 |
| 39b | 0 EP | | | | | | | | | | | | | | | | H 8 | 3·00 |
| 40a | | 2 PE | | | | | | | | | | | | | | | F 6, F 7, G 7 | 2·50 |
| 40b | | 2 PE | | | 2 EPE | | | | | | | | | | | | G 7 | 3·00 |
| 41a | | | | | V (P)E | | | | | | | | | | | | F 6, F 7, G 7 | 2·50 |
| 41b | | | | ↑ (P)E | V (P)E | | | | | | | | | | | | G 8, H 8 | 3·00 |
| 42 | | | | | | 1 (O)N | | | | | | | | | | | F 6, F 7, G 8 | 2·50 |
| 43a | | | | | | | ↑ Y | | | | | | | | | | F 6, F 7, G 7 | 2·50 |
| 43b | 1 P | | | | | | ↑ Y | | | | | | | | | | H 8 | 4·00 |
| 44 | | | | | 1 P | | | | | | | | | | | | G 7, G 8, I 9 | 2·50 |

# KING EDWARD VII. 1d., TYPE M1. Co-extensive Rule (Plates 45a to 53b)

| Plate | | Bottom row, Stamp No. | | | | | | | | | | | 12th stamp, Row No. | | | | Controls | Positional piece Prices from |
| --- | --- | --- | --- | --- | --- | --- | --- | --- | --- | --- | --- | --- | --- | --- | --- | --- | --- | --- |
| | 1 | 2 | 3 | 4 | 5 | 6 | 7 | 8 | 9 | 10 | 11 | 12 | 17 | 18 | 19 | 20 | | |
| 45a | | | | | | 2 ON | | | | | | | | | | | G 7 | 4·00 |
| 45b | | | | | | 2 ON | | | | | | | | | | | G 8 | 4·50 |
| 46a | | | | ) | | 2 NE | | | | &#124; | | | | | | | G 8, H 8, H 9 | 4·00 |
| 46b | | | | ) | ½ 1 ½ NEP | 2 NE | | | ) | | | | | | | | I 9 | 4·50 |
| 47a | | | | | 1 P | | 1 NY | | | | | | | | | | H 8 | 2·50 |
| 47b | | | | | 1 P | | 1 NY | | | | | | | | | | H 9, I 9 | 2·50 |
| 47c | | | | | | | 1 NY | | | Y | | | | | | | I 9 | 3·00 |
| 48a | | | | | | | | 1½ P | | | | | | | | | H 8, H 9, I 9 | 2·50 |
| 48b | | | | | | | 1½ (E)N | 1½ P | | ½ NY | | | | | | | J 10 | 3·00 |
| 49 | ½ PE | | | | | | | | | | | | | | | | H 8, H 9, I 9 | 1·75 |
| 50a | 1½ EP | | | | | | | | | | | | | | | | H 8 | 2·50 |
| 50b | 1½ EP | | | 1 EP | | | | | | | | | | | | | H 8, H 9, I 9, I 10 | 2·00 |
| 51a | | ½ PE | | | | | | | | | | | | | | | H 8, H 9, I 9, I 10 | 3·50 |
| 51b | ½ EP | ½ PE | | | | | | | | | | | | | | | J 10 | 4·00 |
| 52a | | | 1 PE | | | | | | | | | | | | | | H 8, H 9, I 9, J 10 | 2·50 |
| 52b | ½ (N)E | | 1 PE | | | | | | | | | | | | | | J 10 | 3·00 |
| 53a | | | | 1 (P)E | | | | | | | | | | | | | H 8 | 2·50 |
| 53b | | | ∨ EN | 1 (P)E | | ½ (O)N | | | | | | | | | | | H 8 | 2·50 |

## KING EDWARD VII. 1d., TYPE M1. Co-extensive Rule (Plates 54a to 64)

| Plate | Bottom row, Stamp No. 1 | 2 | 3 | 4 | 5 | 6 | 7 | 8 | 9 | 10 | 11 | 12 | 12th stamp, Row No. 17 | 18 | 19 | 20 | Control | Positional piece Prices from |
|---|---|---|---|---|---|---|---|---|---|---|---|---|---|---|---|---|---|---|
| 54a | | | | | ¹(P)E | | | ½½(P)E | | | | | | | | | H 8, H 9 | 4·00 |
| 54b | | | | ¹PE | ¹(P)E | | | | | | | | | | | | J 10 | 4·00 |
| 55 | | | | | | | | | | | | ¹EP | | | | | H 8 | 1·50 |
| 56 | | | | | (N)N | ²N(E) | | | | | | o | | | | | I 9, J 10 | 3·00 |
| 57a | | | | | | | | | | | | o | | | | | I 9 | 3·00 |
| 57b | | | | | ²PEN | ²N(E) | ½NY | ¹EP | | | | | | | | | I 10 | 3·00 |
| 58a | | | | | | | ½NY | | | | | | | | | | I 9, I 10, J 10 | 3·00 |
| 58b | | | | | | | ½NY | ²EPE | | | | | | | | | A 11 (15×14) | 4·50 |
| 59 | ½N(N) | | | | | 2∨ ON | | | | | | | | | | | I 9, J 10 | 3·50 |
| 60 | | ½PE | | | | | | | | | | | | | | | I 10, J 10 | 2·00 |
| 61a | | | | ½EP | | | | | | | | | | | | | I 10, J 10 | 2·00 |
| 61b | | | | ½EP | ¹EP | | | | ¹NN | | | | ¹ 8½ mm. | | | | A 11 (14) (c), A 11 (15×14) | 5·00 |
| 62a | | | | | ¹EP | | | | | | | | | | | | I 10, J 10 | 3·50 |
| 62b | | | | | | | | | | | ¹PE | | | | ¹ 12 mm. | | A 11 (14) (c & w), A 11 (15×14) | 4·00 |
| 62c | | | | | ¹EP | | | | | | ¹PE | | | ¹ 11 mm. | ¹ 12 mm. | | A 11 (14) (w) | 5·00 |
| 63a | | | ½NE | | | | | | | | | | ¹ 2½ mm. | | | | J 10, A 11 (14) | 2·50 |
| 63b | | | ½NE | | | | | | | | | | ¹ 2½ mm. | | | ¹ 9½ mm. | A 11 (14) (w), A 11 (15×14) | 1·50 |
| 64 | | | | | | | ¹EN | | | ½∨ NY | | | | | | | J 10 | 2·50 |

157

## KING EDWARD VII. 1d., TYPE M1. Co-extensive Rule (Plates 65 to 71)

| Plate | Bottom row, Stamp No. | | | | | | | | | | | | 12th stamp, Row No. | | | | Control | Positional piece Prices from |
|---|---|---|---|---|---|---|---|---|---|---|---|---|---|---|---|---|---|---|
| | 1 | 2 | 3 | 4 | 5 | 6 | 7 | 8 | 9 | 10 | 11 | 12 | 17 | 18 | 19 | 20 | | |
| 65 | | | | | | | $\frac{4}{\text{EN}}$ | | | | | | | | | | J 10 | 2·50 |
| 66a | | | | | | | | $\frac{4}{\text{P}}$ | | | | | | | | | J 10 | 3·00 |
| 66b | | | | | | | | $\frac{4}{\text{P}}$ | | $\frac{1}{\text{EP}}$ | | | | $\frac{1}{10\frac{1}{2}}$ mm. | | | A 11 (14) (w) | 3·50 |
| 67 | | | | | | | | | | | $\frac{\text{V}}{\text{PE}}$ | | | | | | J 10 | 2·00 |
| 71 | | | | | | cut filled in | | | | | | | | | | | C 4 | 5·00 |

158

## KING EDWARD VII.   1½d., TYPE M2

### The Head Plates

#### (a) With continuous marginal rule

Plate

1   Cut under 2nd stamp.   Square dots in corner
   of interpane rules.
2   Cut under 1st stamp
3   No marking

#### (b) With co-extensive marginal rule

4   Minute diagonal nick under centre of 2nd stamp
5   (a) cut preceded by a nick under 2nd stamp
   (b) V cut added under 5th stamp.   Broad date
      cuts under 11th stamp, bottom pane
6   (a) cut under 12th stamp.   Rule under 2nd
      stamp worn
   (b) cut under 12th stamp filled up.   Cut pre-
      ceded by a nick added under 1st stamp
   (c) cut and nick under 1st stamp filled up.
      Dots added above and below 12th vertical
      rows in both panes.   Narrow thin date cuts
      added to right of 1 under 12th stamp
7   (a) diagonal cut under 8th stamp.   Rule to right
      of 20th row thin.   Dots added above and
      below 12th vertical rows in both panes.
      Date cuts under d of 11th stamp
   (b) cuts under 8th and 11th stamps filled up.
      Date cuts added under 12th stamp to left
      of figure 1
8   Date cuts under 1 of 12th stamp, broader and
   thicker than on plate 7b.   Dots added above and
   below 12th vertical rows of both panes

### The Duty Plates

#### (a) With continuous marginal rule at sides of panes only

Plate

1   (a) rule at right of 20th row slopes down from
      left to right
   (b) rule at left of 20th row became thin and
      defective
2   Rule at right of 20th row rounded at the
   bottom.   Rule at left of 20th row tapered
   at the end

#### (b) With continuous marginal rule all round panes with breaks in vertical rows after every 3rd stamp

3   (a) no marking
   (b) break at top of rule to left of rows 2 and 20.
      Rule below 2nd stamp bulges

#### (c) With co-extensive rule round the panes. Break under 2nd stamp, with extra breaks, below 4th, 6th, 7th and 9th stamps in bottom row, and 1 to right of the 2nd and 19th row

4   (a) rule under 12th stamp defective
   (b) rule under 12th built up and has splayed
      end at right
   (c) rule under 12th repaired

### Printing Series

| Series | Date | Head Plate | Duty Plate | Paper | Position | | | Price |
|---|---|---|---|---|---|---|---|---|
| De la Rue | | | | | | | | |
| 1st | 1902 | 1 | 1a | Ordinary | S.W. corner pair | .. | .. | 10·00 |
| 2nd | 1902 | 2 | 2 | Ordinary | S.W. corner pair | ·· | .. | 10·00 |
| 3rd | 1903/4 | 2 | 3a | Ordinary | S.W. corner pair | .. | .. | 4·50 |
| 4th | 1905 | 2 | 3a | Chalky | S.W. corner pair | .. | .. | 4·00 |
| 5th | 1906/7 | 3 | 1a | Chalky | S.W. corner pair | .. | .. | 4·00 |
| 6th | 1907/9 | 4 | 1a | Chalky | S.W. corner pair | .. | .. | 4·00 |
| | | 4 | 1b | Chalky | S.W. corner pair | .. | .. | 4·00 |
| | | 5a | 1a | Chalky | S.W. corner pair | .. | .. | 4·00 |
| 7th | 1909/10 | 6a | 3a | Chalky | S.E. corner pair | .. | .. | 4·00 |
| | | 6b | 3a | Chalky | S.W. corner pair | .. | .. | 4·00 |
| | | 6b | 3b | Chalky | S.W. corner pair | .. | .. | 4·00 |
| Somerset House | | | | | | | | |
| With 1911 date cuts under 11th stamp, bottom pane only | | | | | | | | |
| 8th | July 1911 | 5b | 3b | Ordinary | S.E. corner pair | .. | .. | 6·00 |
| 9th | Sept. 1911 | 7a | 3b | Ordinary | S.E. corner pair | .. | .. | 3·50 |
| With 1912 date cuts under 12th stamp, bottom pane only | | | | | | | | |
| 10th | Feb.-May 1912 | 7b | 4a b or c | Ordinary | S.E. corner pair | .. | .. | 4·50 |
| 11th | May-Oct. 1912 | 8 | 4c | Ordinary | S.E. corner pair | .. | .. | 3·50 |
| 12th | Oct. 1912 | 6c | 4c | Ordinary | S.E. corner pair | .. | .. | 4·00 |

## KING EDWARD VII.   2d., TYPE M3

### The Head Plates

(a) With continuous marginal rule

Plate

1  Cut under 1st stamp
2  Cut under 2nd stamp
3  No marking.  Line thinned under 2nd stamp

(b) With co-extensive marginal rule

4  (a) cut under right of 7th stamp in addition to normal break.  S.W. corner piece comparatively large and protruding beyond vertical line
   (b) date cuts added under left of 2 on 11th stamp bottom row
   (c) coloured dots added above and below 12th vertical rows in both panes
   (d) diagonal cut added below 11th stamp in bottom row of *both panes*
5  No marking.  S.W. corner piece comparatively small and not protruding beyond vertical line
6  Two date dots in rule below 12th stamp in bottom row.  Coloured dots above and below 12th vertical rows in both panes

### The Duty Plates

(a) With marginal rule of short bars

These bars become much worn during the life-time of the plates, and in many cases eventually disappeared.  The plate markings given here are valid even for the latest printings.

Plate

1  Bar below 1st stamp in bottom row 11 mm. long.  Bar to right of 20th row faint.  A sloping cut appeared in the bar below the upper pane under the 10th stamp during the 8th series
2  Bar below 1st stamp in bottom row 12 mm. long.  Bar to right of 20th row intact

(b) With marginal rule fully co-extensive.

3  No marking.

### Printing Series

| Series | Date | Head Plate | Duty Plate | Paper | Position | | Price |
|---|---|---|---|---|---|---|---|
| De la Rue | | | | | | | |
| 1st | 1902 | 1 | 1 | Ordinary | S.W. corner pair  .. | .. | 6·00 |
| | | 2 | 2 | Ordinary | S.W. corner pair  .. | .. | 6·00 |
| 2nd | 1903 | 1 | 1 | Ordinary | S.W. corner pair  .. | .. | 6·50 |
| | | 2 | 2 | Ordinary | S.W. corner pair  .. | .. | 6·50 |
| 3rd | 1905 | 1 | 1 | Chalky | S.W. corner pair  .. | .. | 4·50 |
| | | 2 | 2 | Chalky | S.W. corner pair  .. | .. | 4·50 |
| | | 3 | 1 | Chalky | S.W. corner pair  .. | .. | 4·50 |
| | | 3 | 2 | Chalky | S.W. corner pair  .. | .. | 5·00 |
| 4th | 1907/10 | 4a | 1 | Chalky | S.W. corner pair  .. | .. | 5·00 |
| | | 5 | 1 | Chalky | S.W. corner pair  .. | .. | 5·00 |
| 5th | July 1910 | 3 | 2 | Chalky | S.W. corner pair  .. | .. | 4·50 |
| 6th | 1910 | 5 | 1 | Chalky | S.W. corner pair  .. | .. | 4·50 |

Somerset House

With 1911 date cuts under 11th stamp, bottom pane only

| | | | | | | | |
|---|---|---|---|---|---|---|---|
| 7th | Aug. 1911 | 4b | 1 | Ordinary | S.E. corner pair  .. | .. | 5·00 |
| | | 4c | 1 | Ordinary | S.E. corner pair  .. | .. | 5·00 |
| 8th | Nov. 1911 | 4d | 1 | Ordinary | S.E. corner pair  .. | .. | 4·00 |

With 1912 date cuts under 12th stamp, bottom pane only

| | | | | | | | |
|---|---|---|---|---|---|---|---|
| 9th | March 1912 | 6 | 3 | Ordinary | S.E. corner pair  .. | .. | 3·50 |

## KING EDWARD VII.   2½d., TYPE M5

### The Plates

(a) With continuous marginal rule

Plate

1  Diagonal cut and nick under ½ of 1st stamp
2  (a) Cut preceded by nick under ½ of 2nd stamp
   (b) Added cut below ½ of 1st stamp
3  (a) Cut under 2 of 3rd stamp
   (b) Added cut under ½ of 11th stamp.  2 cuts in vertical rule right of interpane margin
4  Cut under ½ of 4th stamp.  Rule at right of row 19 broken during 5th series
5  Thin cut between 2 and ½ of 1st stamp

(b) With co-extensive marginal rule

6  Thin cut under 2 of 1st stamp
7  Thick cut between 2 and ½ of 2nd stamp
8  No marking

## Printing Series

| Series | Date | Plate | Perf. | Position | | | | Price |
|---|---|---|---|---|---|---|---|---|
| De la Rue | | | | | | | | |
| 1st | 1902/6 | 1 | 14 | S.W. corner pair | .. | .. | .. | 2·00 |
| | | 2a | 14 | S.W. corner pair | .. | .. | .. | 2·00 |
| | | 2b | 14 | S.W. corner pair | .. | .. | .. | — |
| | | 3a | 14 | S.W. corner strip of 3 | | .. | .. | 3·00 |
| | | 4 | 14 | S.W. corner strip of 4 | | .. | .. | 4·00 |
| | | 5 | 14 | S.W. corner pair | .. | .. | .. | 2·00 |
| 2nd | 1907/10 | 6 | 14 | S.W. corner pair | .. | .. | .. | 2·00 |
| | | 7 | 14 | S.W. corner pair | .. | .. | .. | 2·00 |
| | | 8 | 14 | S.W. corner pair | .. | .. | .. | 2·00 |
| Harrison & Sons | | | | | | | | |
| 3rd | July 1911 | 6 | 14 | S.W. corner pair | .. | .. | .. | 6·00 |
| | | 7 | 14 | S.W. corner pair | .. | .. | .. | 8·00 |
| 4th | Sept. 1911 | 3b | 14 | S.E. or S.W. corner strip of 3 | | | .. | 10·00 |
| | | 5 | 14 | S.W. corner pair | .. | .. | | 8·00 |
| 5th | Oct. 1911 | 3b | 15 × 14 | S.E. or S.W. corner strip of 3 | | | .. | 3·00 |
| | | 4 | 15 × 14 | S.W. corner strip of 4 | | .. | .. | 4·00 |
| | | 5 | 15 × 14 | S.W. corner pair | .. | .. | .. | 3·00 |
| | | 6 | 15 × 14 | S.W. corner pair | .. | .. | .. | 3·00 |

## KING EDWARD VII.  3d., TYPE M6
### The Plates

With continuous marginal rule

Plate
1  Cut under 1st stamp
2  Cut under 2nd stamp
3  Cut under 3rd stamp
4  Cut under 4th stamp under EN
5  Cut under 4th stamp under VE

## Printing Series

| Series | Date | Plate | Paper | Position | | | | Price |
|---|---|---|---|---|---|---|---|---|
| De la Rue | | | | | | | | |
| 1st | 1902/5 | 1 | Ordinary | S.W. corner pair | .. | .. | .. | 5·00 |
| | | 2 | Ordinary | S.W. corner pair | .. | .. | .. | 5·00 |
| | | 3 | Ordinary | S.W. corner strip of 3 | | .. | .. | 8·00 |
| | | 4 | Ordinary | S.W. corner strip of 4 | | .. | .. | 10·00 |
| 2nd | Jan. 1906 | 1 | Chalky | S.W. corner pair | .. | .. | .. | 4·00 |
| | | 2 | Chalky | S.W. corner pair | .. | .. | .. | 4·00 |
| | | 3 | Chalky | S.W. corner strip of 3 | | .. | .. | 5·00 |
| | | 4 | Chalky | S.W. corner strip of 4 | | .. | .. | 6·00 |
| | | 5 | Chalky | S.W. corner strip of 4 | | .. | .. | 40·00 |
| Harrison & Sons | | | | | | | | |
| 3rd | Sept. 1911 | 4 | 14 | S.W. corner strip of 4 | | .. | .. | 30·00 |
| | | 5 | 14 | S.W. corner strip of 4 | | .. | .. | 40·00 |
| 4th | Sept. 1911 | 1 | 15 × 14 | S.W. corner pair | .. | .. | .. | 2·00 |
| | | 4 | 15 × 14 | S.W. corner strip of 4 | | .. | .. | 3·50 |
| | | 5 | 15 × 14 | S.W. corner strip of 4 | | .. | .. | 8·00 |

## KING EDWARD VII.  4d. GREEN AND BROWN, TYPE M7
### The Head Plates

(a) With continuous marginal rule

1  (a) Cut under 1st stamp.  Scoops in bottom rule between 10th and 11th and 11th and 12th stamps.
      All corners of rule cut away except at S.E. corner of upper pane.  Line of rule irregular at ends
      at S.W. and S.E. corners of the sheet.
   (b) All corners cut away
   (c) Rule to right of 19th and 20th rows broken away
2  (a) Cut under 2nd stamp.  Lines of rule regular at S.W. and S.E. corners of sheet
   (b) Added broad cut under 11th stamp
3  No marking, all corners complete.  Defect under 2nd stamp bottom row

(b) With co-extensive marginal rule

4  Cut under 12th stamp.  Scoop in rule under 2nd stamp
5  Broad cut under 11th stamp.  Small scoop in outside of rule right of 19th row

## The Duty Plates

With continuous marginal rule

Plate
1  The rules at the S.W. corner of the lower pane are comparatively thick
2  The rules at the S.W. corner of the lower pane are comparatively thin

### Printing Series

| Series | Date | Head Plate | Duty Plate | Paper | Position | | Price |
|---|---|---|---|---|---|---|---|
| De la Rue | | | | | | | |
| 1st | 1902/5 | 1a | 1 | Ordinary | S.E. corner pair | .. | 8.00 |
| | | 1b | 1 | Ordinary | S.W. corner pair | .. | 7.00 |
| | | 1c | 1 | Ordinary | S.E. corner pair | .. | 7.00 |
| | | 2a | 2 | Ordinary | S.W. corner pair | .. | 7.00 |
| 2nd | 1906 | 3 | 1 | Chalky | S.W. corner pair | .. | 5.00 |
| 3rd | 1906/9 | 2b | 1 | Chalky | S.E. corner pair | .. | 5.00 |
| 4th | 1906/9 | 4 | 2 | Chalky | S.E. corner pair | .. | 5.00 |
| 5th | 1906/9 | 5 | 2 | Chalky | S.E. corner pair | .. | 5.00 |

## KING EDWARD VII.   4d. ORANGE, TYPE M7
### The Plates

With co-extensive rule

Plate
1  (a) no marking
   (b) fine half cut under 1st stamp bottom row
2  Fine half cut under 2nd stamp bottom row
3  Fine half cut under 3rd stamp bottom row
4  Fine half cut under 4th stamp bottom row

### Printing Series

| Series | Date | Plate | Perf. | Position | | | Price |
|---|---|---|---|---|---|---|---|
| De la Rue | | | | | | | |
| 6th | 1909/11 | 1a | 14 | S.W. corner strip of 4 | .. | .. | 10•00 |
| | | 1b | 14 | S.W. corner pair | .. | .. | 3.00 |
| | | 2 | 14 | S.W. corner pair | .. | .. | 3.00 |
| | | 3 | 14 | S.W. corner strip of 3 | .. | .. | 4.00 |
| | | 4 | 14 | S.W. corner strip of 4 | .. | .. | 6.00 |
| Harrison & Sons | | | | | | | |
| 7th | July 1911 | 1b | 14 | S.W. corner pair | .. | .. | 20.00 |
| | | 2 | 14 | S.W. corner pair | .. | .. | 20.00 |
| 8th | Nov. 1911 | 1b | 15 × 14 | S.W. corner pair | .. | .. | 2.50 |
| | | 2 | 15 × 14 | S.W. corner pair | .. | .. | 2.50 |
| | | 4 | 15 × 14 | S.W. corner strip of 4 | .. | .. | 3.50 |

## KING EDWARD VII.   5d., TYPE M8

### The Head Plates

(a) With continuous marginal rule

Plate
1  Cut under 1st stamp
2  (a) cut under 2nd stamp
   (b) cut under 2nd stamp filled up
   (a) no marking
   (b) date cuts under the 11th stamp in bottom
       row of lower pane under the harp. Cut
       under 7th stamp. Purple dots above and
       below 12th vertical row in both panes

(b) With co-extensive marginal rule

3  No marking. Square dots in corner of interpane
   rules
5  No marking
   (a) date cuts under 11th stamp bottom row
       both panes. Purple dots above and below
       12th vertical row of both panes
   (b) date cuts under 11th stamp in both panes
       filled up, and date cuts added under harp
       of the 12th stamp in lower pane only
   (c) coloured dots removed
   (d) added dot in rule at right of 20th row

### The Duty Plates

(a) With short blue bars

Plate
1  1st bar in bottom margin more to the right in
   relation to the value tablet than on Plate 2
2  1st bar in bottom margin more to the left in
   relation to the value tablet than on Plate 1

There is a white dot in the base of the 5 in the
left value tablet of stamp No. 240 in the sheets in
all De la Rue printings from Duty Plate 2.

(b) With continuous rule

3  Bulge in line under 2nd stamp. Cut in rule at
   right of 19th row
4  No marking

## Printing Series

| Series | Date | Head Plate | Duty Plate | Paper | Position | | | Price |
|--------|------|------------|------------|-------|----------|---|---|-------|
| De la Rue | | | | | | | | |
| 1st | 1902/5 | 1 | 1 | Ordinary | S.W. corner pair | .. | .. | 5·00 |
| | | 2a | 2 | Ordinary | S.W. corner pair | .. | .. | 6·00 |
| | | 2b | 2 | Ordinary | S.W. corner pair | .. | .. | 6·00 |
| 2nd | 1905 | 1 | 1 | Chalky | S.W. corner pair | .. | .. | 5·00 |
| | | 2b | 2 | Chalky | S.W. corner pair | .. | .. | 5·00 |
| 3rd | 1907 | 3 | 2 | Chalky | Corner pair | .. | .. | 60·00 |
| 4th | 1909/10 | 1 | 3 | Chalky | S.W. corner pair | .. | .. | 5·00 |
| | | 4a | 4 | Chalky | S.W. corner pair | .. | .. | 6·00 |

### Somerset House

With 1911 date cuts under 11th stamp

| Series | Date | Head Plate | Duty Plate | Paper | Position | | Top pane | Bottom pane |
|--------|------|------------|------------|-------|----------|---|----------|-------------|
| 5th | Aug. 1911 | 4b | 3 | Ordinary | S.E. corner pair | .. | † | 4·00 |
| 6th | Feb. 1912 | 5a | 3 | Ordinary | S.E. corner pair | .. | 4·50 | 4·50 |

With 1912 date cuts under 12th stamp, bottom pane only

| Series | Date | Head Plate | Duty Plate | Paper | Position | | | Price |
|--------|------|------------|------------|-------|----------|---|---|-------|
| 7th | April 1912 | 5b | 3 | Ordinary | S.E. corner pair | .. | † | 14·00 |
| 8th | Feb. 1913 | 5c | 3 | Ordinary | S.E. corner pair | .. | † | 8·00 |
| 9th | March 1913 | 5d | 3 | Ordinary | S.E. corner pair | .. | † | 4·50 |

The 7th series shows varieties *f.* and *g.*   Some sheets from the 8th series show variety *h.*


# KING EDWARD VII.  6d., TYPE M1

## The Plates

With continuous marginal rule

Plate

1  Cut under PE of 1st stamp
2  (a) ¾ cut under P of 2nd stamp
   (b) ½ cut added under 4th stamp
   (c) cut under 2nd enlarged to a pyramid shape
   (d) cut under 2nd improved to thin straight cut.   Purple dots added above and below 12th vertical row of both panes.   Date cuts added under E of 12th stamp.   White dot in rule at right of 19th row. Stamp 132 with broken frame
   (e) coloured dots removed.   White dot in 19th row filled up.   White dot added in rule at right of 18th row
   (f) broken frame on stamp 132 repaired
3  Thin cut under P of 3rd stamp
4  Thin cut to right of P on 1st stamp and cut to left of P on 4th stamp
5  Cut between X and P on 3rd stamp and cut under P of 4th stamp
6  ¾ cut under 1st E of 3rd stamp


With co-extensive marginal rule

7  (a) cut under X of 1st stamp
   (b) date cuts under EN of 11th stamp.   Purple dots added above and below 12th vertical rows of both panes
8  (a) cut under 1st E of 2nd stamp and cut under P of 4th stamp
   (b) date cuts under CE of 11th stamp.   Purple dots added above and below 12th vertical rows of both panes
   (c) cut under 4th stamp filled up.   Date cuts under 11th stamp filled up.   Thin date cuts added under EN of 12th stamp sometimes faint and obscure
   (d) new date cuts made under P of 12th stamp.   White dot in vertical rule to right of 20th row
   (e) as above, but the date cuts of (b) also showing, due to the filling having fallen out
   (f) as (d) but white dot to right of 20th row filled up  and added white dot in rule to right of 19th row
9  (a) thin cut under E of 1st stamp.   Corner piece of rule at S.W. corner of lower pane joined to the vertical rule to left of 20th row
   (b) thin date cuts under E of 12th stamp.   Purple dots added above and below 12th vertical rows of both panes
   (c) white dots added in rule to right of 20th row
   (d) white dot to right of 20th row filled up, and white dot added in rule to right of 19th row
   (e) white dot to right of 19th row filled up and white dot added in rule to right of 18th row.   Purple dots above and below 12th vertical rows removed
   (f) as (e) but cut under 1st stamp filled up
   (g) as (f) but double cuts at top and bottom of rule to right of interpane gutter
10  Thin date cuts under P of 12th stamp.   Small white dot in left of rule to right of 18th row.   No breaks under 6th and 7th stamps in bottom row
11  Thin date cuts to left of P on 12th stamp.   Small white dot in middle of rule to right of 18th row. No breaks under 6th and 7th stamps in bottom row

## Printing Series

| Series | Date | Plate | Paper | Position | | | Price |
|--------|------|-------|-------|----------|---|---|-------|
| De la Rue | | | | | | | |
| 1st | 1902/5 | 1 | Ordinary | S.W. corner pair .. | .. | .. | 4·00 |
| | | 2a | Ordinary | S.W. corner pair .. | .. | .. | 4·00 |
| | | 3 | Ordinary | S.W. corner strip of 3 | .. | .. | 5·00 |
| | | 4 | Ordinary | S.W. corner strip of 4 | .. | .. | 6·00 |
| 2nd | 1905 | 1 | Chalky | S.W. corner pair .. | .. | .. | 4·00 |
| | | 2a | Chalky | S.W. corner strip of 4 | .. | .. | 6·00 |
| | | 2b | Chalky | S.W. corner strip of 4 | .. | .. | 6·00 |
| | | 2c | Chalky | S.W. corner strip of 3 | .. | .. | 7·00 |
| | | 3 | Chalky | S.W. corner strip of 3 | .. | .. | 8·00 |
| | | 4 | Chalky | S.W. corner strip of 4 | .. | .. | 6·00 |
| | | 5 | Chalky | S.W. corner strip of 4 | .. | .. | 6·50 |
| | | 6 | Chalky | S.W. corner strip of 3 | .. | .. | 5·00 |
| 3rd | 1907/10 | 7a | Chalky | S.W. corner pair .. | .. | .. | 5·00 |
| | | 8a | Chalky | S.W. corner pair .. | .. | .. | 8·00 |
| | | 9a | Chalky | S.W. corner pair .. | .. | .. | 8·00 |

### Somerset House
With 1911 date cuts under 11th stamp, bottom pane only

| Series | Date | Plate | Paper | Position | | | Price |
|--------|------|-------|-------|----------|---|---|-------|
| 4th | 1911 | 7b | Ordinary | S.E. corner pair .. | .. | .. | 4·00 |
| | | 7b | Chalky | S.E. corner pair .. | .. | .. | — |
| | | 8b | Ordinary | S.E. corner pair .. | .. | .. | 4·00 |
| | | 8b | Chalky | S.E. corner pair .. | .. | .. | £300 |

With 1912 date cuts under 12th stamp, bottom pane only

| Series | Date | Plate | Paper | Position | | | Price |
|--------|------|-------|-------|----------|---|---|-------|
| 5th | March 1912 | 8c | Ordinary | S.E. corner pair .. | .. | .. | 7·00 |
| | | 9b | Ordinary | S.E. corner pair .. | .. | .. | 7·00 |
| 6th | May 1912 | 8d | Ordinary | S.E. corner pair .. | .. | .. | 6·00 |
| | | 8e | Ordinary | S.E. corner pair .. | .. | .. | 50·00 |
| | | 9c | Ordinary | S.E. corner pair .. | .. | .. | 6·00 |
| 7th | May/June 1912 | 2d | Ordinary | S.E. corner block of 4 | .. | .. | 5·00 |
| | | 8f | Ordinary | S.E. corner pair .. | .. | .. | 25·00 |
| | | 9d | Ordinary | S.E. corner block of 4 | .. | .. | 5·00 |
| 8th | Oct. 1912 | 2e | Ordinary | S.E. corner block of 6 | .. | .. | 8·00 |
| | | 9e | Ordinary | S.E. corner block of 6 | .. | .. | 5·00 |
| 9th | Nov. 1912 | 10 | Ordinary | S.E. corner block of 6 | .. | .. | 5·00 |
| | | 11 | Ordinary | S.E. corner block of 6 | .. | .. | 5·00 |
| 10th | March 1913 | 10 | Ordinary | S.E. corner block of 6 | .. | .. | 5·00 |
| | | 11 | Ordinary | S.E. corner block of 6 | .. | .. | 5·00 |
| | | 10 | Coated | S.E. corner block of 6 | .. | .. | 90·00 |
| | | 11 | Coated | S.E. corner block of 6 | .. | .. | 90·00 |
| 11th | June 1913 | 9f | Plate glazed | S.E. corner block of 6 | .. | .. | 15·00 |
| | | 10 | Plate glazed | S.E. corner block of 6 | .. | .. | 15·00 |
| 12th | July 1913 | 9g | Chalky | S.E. corner block of 6 | .. | .. | 18·00 |
| | | 10 | Chalky | S.E. corner block of 6 | .. | .. | 18·00 |

## KING EDWARD VII.   7d., TYPE M9
### The Plates
With co-extensive marginal rule

Plate
1  (a) fine cut under 1st stamp
   (b) date cuts added under RE of 12th stamp
2  (a) fine cut under 2nd stamp
   (b) date cuts added under & R of 12th stamp
3  (a) no marking
   (b) fine date cuts added under & on 12th stamp

## Printing Series

| Series | Date | Plate | Position | | | Price |
|--------|------|-------|----------|---|---|-------|
| De la Rue | | | | | | |
| 1st | 1910 | 1a | S.W. corner pair .. | .. | .. | 2·00 |
| | | 2a | S.W. corner pair .. | .. | .. | 2·00 |
| | | 3a | S.W. corner pair .. | .. | .. | 6·00 |

### Somerset House
With 1912 date cuts under 12th stamp, bottom pane only

| Series | Date | Plate | Position | | | Price |
|--------|------|-------|----------|---|---|-------|
| 2nd | 1912 | 2b | S.E. corner pair .. | .. | .. | 5·00 |
| 3rd | 1912 | 2b | S.E. corner pair .. | .. | .. | 3·50 |
| 4th | Dec. 1912 | 1b | S.E. corner pair .. | .. | .. | 3·00 |
| 5th | May 1913 | 3b | S.E. corner pair .. | .. | .. | 3·50 |

In the 2nd series the printing impressions are very coarse.

## KING EDWARD VII.   9d., TYPE M10
### The Head Plates

Plate
1  (a) cut over 1st stamp in top row of pane A.   Cut below 2nd stamp in bottom row pane G
   (b) white dot added in vertical rule to left of 1st stamp in top row of pane F
   (c) double purple date dots added in margin below 4th stamp in bottom row of panes D and H
   (d) date dots of state (c) removed.   Broad date cuts added below 4th stamp in bottom row of panes D
       and H.   Those in pane H are more to the right than those in pane D
   (e) date cuts of state (d) filled up.   Fine date cuts added below 5th stamp in bottom row of panes D
       and H.   Those in pane H are broader and more to the right than those in pane D
   (f) cut added above 1st stamp in top row of pane E
2  Cut over 2nd stamp in top row of pane A.   Cut below 1st stamp bottom row pane G
3  Serrated date cuts below 5th stamp in bottom row of panes D and H, those in pane H being more
   to the right than those in pane D

### The Duty Plates

Plate
1  (a) crack in marginal rule left of 1st stamp top row pane B.   A small crack also appeared to the left
       of the 1st stamp in the bottom row of pane B
   (b) Thin cut added above 4th stamp top row pane B.   Later a dot was added over the 5th stamp in
       top row of pane B
2  No marking.   This plate was free from cracks and flaws

### Printing Series

| Series | Date | Head Plate | Duty Plate | Paper | Position | | N.W. of pane A | S.W. of pane G |
|---|---|---|---|---|---|---|---|---|
| De la Rue | | | | | | | | |
| | | | | | | | **Price** | |
| 1st | 1902/5 | 1a | 1a | Ordinary | Corner pair | .. | 10·00 | 10·00 |
| | | 2 | 2 | Ordinary | Corner pair | .. | 10·00 | 10·00 |
| 2nd | 1905/10 | 1a | 1a | Chalky | Corner pair | .. | 7·00 | 7·00 |
| | | 2 | 2 | Chalky | Corner pair | .. | 7·00 | 7·00 |

Somerset House

Without date cuts

| | | | | | | | Pane D | Pane H |
|---|---|---|---|---|---|---|---|---|
| 3rd | July 1911 | 1b | 1a | Ordinary | S.E. corner pair | .. | 30·00 | 30·00 |
| | | 2 | 2 | Ordinary | S.E. corner pair | .. | 30·00 | 30·00 |

With 1911 date dots under 4th stamp

| 4th | Sept. 1911 | 1c | 1a | Ordinary | S.E. corner pair | .. | 45·00 | 40·00 |
|---|---|---|---|---|---|---|---|---|

With 1911 date cuts under 4th stamp

| 5th | Oct. 1911 | 1d | 1a | Ordinary | S.E. corner pair | .. | 7·00 | 7·00 |
|---|---|---|---|---|---|---|---|---|

With 1912 date cuts under 5th stamp

| 6th | Mar. 1912 | 1e | 1b | Ordinary | S.E. corner pair | .. | 6·00 | 6·00 |
|---|---|---|---|---|---|---|---|---|
| 7th | Jan. 1913 | 3 | 2 | Ordinary | S.E. corner pair | .. | 5·50 | 5·50 |

## KING EDWARD VII.   10d., TYPE M11
### The Head Plates

Plate
1  (a) cut under 1st stamp bottom row Z pane.   Break below X pane between 4th and 5th stamps.
       Breaks were made in the rule between 4th and 5th and 8th and 9th stamps in the bottom row of
       both X and Z panes
   (b) cut added under 8th stamp bottom row X pane and Z pane.   Date cuts added under 11th stamp
       bottom row X and Z panes, those in the Z pane being more sloping
   (c) cut under 1st stamp in Z pane, and cut under 9th stamp in X and Z panes filled up.   Date cuts
       in X and Z panes filled up.   Thin date cuts added under 12th row of X and Z panes, those in the
       Z pane being more to the left than those in X pane
2  Cut under 2nd stamp bottom row Z pane.   Breaks were made in the rule between 4th and 5th and the
   8th and 9th stamps in the bottom rows on both the X and Z panes

### The Duty Plate

Plate
1  No marking

## Printing Series

| Series | Date | Head Plate | Duty Plate | Colour | Paper | Position | | Price |
|--------|------|-----------|-----------|--------|-------|----------|--|-------|
| De la Rue | | | | | | | | |
| | | | | | | | | Pane Z |
| 1st | 1902/4 | 1a | 1 | Carmine | Ordinary | S.W. corner pair | .. | .. 6·00 |
| | | 2 | 1 | Carmine | Ordinary | S.W. corner pair | .. | .. 6·00 |
| 2nd | 1905/9 | 1a | 1 | Carmine | Chalky | S.W. corner pair | .. | .. 10·00 |
| | | 2 | 1 | Carmine | Chalky | S.W. corner pair | .. | .. 10·00 |
| 3rd | 1910 | 2 | 1 | Scarlet | Chalky | S.W. corner pair | .. | .. 14·00 |

Somerset House

With 1911 date cuts under 11th stamp

| Series | Date | Head Plate | Duty Plate | Colour | Paper | Position | Pane X | Pane Z |
|--------|------|-----------|-----------|--------|-------|----------|--------|--------|
| 4th | 1911 | 1b | 1 | Scarlet | Ordinary | S.E. corner pair | 10·00 | 10·00 |

With 1912 date cuts under 12th stamp

| Series | Date | Head Plate | Duty Plate | Colour | Paper | Position | | |
|--------|------|-----------|-----------|--------|-------|----------|--|--|
| 5th | 1912 | 1c | 1 | Carmine | Ordinary | S.E. corner pair | 8·00 | 8·00 |

## KING EDWARD VII.  1s., TYPE M12

### The Head Plates

With continuous rule round the panes, all corners cut away.
Breaks in top and bottom rules between 4th and 5th and 8th and 9th vertical rows

Plate

1  (a) cut under 1st stamp
   (b) wide date cuts added under 11th stamp bottom row of both panes
   (c) cuts of (a) and (b) filled up.  Added thin date cuts under 12th stamp bottom row both panes
2  Cut under 2nd stamp

### The Frame Plates

With continuous rule round the panes, all corners cut away.

Plate

1  (a) cut under 1st stamp bottom row lower pane. S.W. corner rules joined by thin semi-circular line
   (b) line at S.W. corner cut away
2  Cut under 2nd stamp bottom row lower pane

With continuous rule not cut away at the corners.

3  (a) no plate cut
   (b) red dots added in the margins above and below 12th vertical row of both panes
   (c) red dots in state (b) removed

## Printing Series

| Series | Date | Head Plate | Frame Plate | Colour | Paper | Position | | Price |
|--------|------|-----------|-----------|--------|-------|----------|--|-------|
| De la Rue | | | | | | | | |
| 1st | 1902/4 | 1a | 1 | Carmine | Ordinary | S.W. corner pair | .. | 7·00 |
| | | 2 | 2 | Carmine | Ordinary | S.W. corner pair | .. | 7·00 |
| 2nd | 1905/9 | 1a | 1a & 1b | Carmine | Chalky | S.W. corner pair | .. | 12·00 |
| | | 1a | 3a | Carmine | Chalky | S.W. corner pair | .. | — |
| | | 2 | 2 | Carmine | Chalky | S.W. corner pair | .. | 12·00 |
| 3rd | 1910 | 2 | 3a | Scarlet | Chalky | S.W. corner pair | .. | 6·00 |
| | | 1a | 3a | Scarlet | Chalky | S.W. corner pair | .. | 8·00 |

Somerset House

Without date cuts

| Series | Date | Head Plate | Frame Plate | Colour | Paper | Position | Top pane | Bottom pane |
|--------|------|-----------|-----------|--------|-------|----------|----------|-------------|
| 4th | July 1911 | 1a | 3a | Scarlet | Ordinary | S.E. corner pair | 30·00 | 30·00 |

With 1911 date cuts under 11th stamp

| Series | Date | Head Plate | Frame Plate | Colour | Paper | Position | Top pane | Bottom pane |
|--------|------|-----------|-----------|--------|-------|----------|----------|-------------|
| 5th | Oct. 1911 | 1b | 3a | Scarlet | Ordinary | S.E. corner pair | 20·00 | 20·00 |
| | | 1b | 3b | Scarlet | Ordinary | S.E. corner pair | 18·00 | 18·00 |

With 1912 date cuts under 12th stamp

| Series | Date | Head Plate | Frame Plate | Colour | Paper | Position | Top pane | Bottom pane |
|--------|------|-----------|-----------|--------|-------|----------|----------|-------------|
| 6th | April 1912 | 1c | 3b | Carmine | Ordinary | S.E. corner pair | 4·50 | 4·50 |
| 7th | Dec. 1912 | 1c | 3c | Carmine | Ordinary | S.E. corner pair | 4·50 | 4·50 |

## KING EDWARD VII.   2s. 6d., TYPE M13
### The Plate
Plate
1  (a) no marking
   (b) coloured dots added in the margins above and below the last vertical rows in each pane.   Cuts added
       under the 7th stamp bottom row of both panes, those in the lower pane being thicker and broader
   (c) cuts under 7th stamps filled up and cuts added under 8th stamp bottom row of both panes
   (d) added white dot in the marginal rule at right of corner stamp both panes

### Printing Series

| Series | Date | Plate | Paper | Position | | | | Price | |
|--------|------|-------|-------|----------|---|---|---|-------|---|
| De la Rue | | | | | | | | | |
| | | | | | | | | Top pane | Bottom pane |
| 1st | 1902 | 1a | Ordinary | S.E. corner pair | .. | .. | .. | 40·00 | 40·00 |
| 2nd | 1905 | 1a | Chalky | S.E. corner pair | .. | .. | .. | 40·00 | 40·00 |
| Somerset House | | | | | | | | | |
| With 1911 date cuts under 7th stamp | | | | | | | | | |
| 3rd | 1911 | 1b | Ordinary | S.E. corner pair | | | | | |
| | | | | Dull greyish purple (F) | .. | | .. | 60·00 | 60·00 |
| | | | | Dull reddish purple | | .. | .. | 35·00 | 35·00 |
| With 1912 date cuts under 8th stamp | | | | | | | | | |
| 4th | 1912 | 1c | Ordinary | S.E. corner pair | .. | .. | .. | 35·00 | 35·00 |
| 5th | 1913 | 1d | Plate glazed | S.E. corner pair | .. | .. | .. | 35·00 | 35·00 |

## KING EDWARD VII.   5s., TYPE M14
### The Plate
Plate
1  (a) no marking
   (b) added small carmine dots in the margins above and below the last vertical rows of both panes.
       Date cuts added under the 7th stamp in the bottom row of both panes.   Top pane cuts very fine
       and small, lower pane cuts thicker and broader.
   (c) date cuts in state (b) removed and cuts made under the 8th stamp in the bottom row of both panes

### Printing Series

| Series | Date | Plate | | Position | | | | Price | |
|--------|------|-------|---|----------|---|---|---|-------|---|
| De la Rue | | | | | | | | | |
| | | | | | | | | Top pane | Bottom pane |
| 1st | 1902/10 | 1a | | S.E. corner pair | .. | .. | .. | 45·00 | 45·00 |
| Somerset House | | | | | | | | | |
| With 1911 date cuts under 7th stamp | | | | | | | | | |
| 2nd | Feb. 1912 | 1b | | S.E. corner pair | .. | .. | .. | 40·00 | 40·00 |
| With 1912 date cuts under 8th stamp | | | | | | | | | |
| 3rd | Oct. 1912 | 1c | | S.E. corner pair | .. | .. | .. | 40·00 | 40·00 |

## KING EDWARD VII.   10s., TYPE M15

### The Plate

Plate

1   (a) no marking
   (b) blue dots added in the margins above and below the last vertical row in each pane.  Upper pane with very fine cuts added under the gutter between the 7th and 8th stamps, in the bottom row (sometimes almost entirely removed during perforation).  Lower pane cuts are larger and appear under the corner square of the 7th stamp bottom row
   (c) cuts in state (b) filled up, and cuts made under the last stamp in the bottom row of both panes

### Printing Series

| Series | Date | Plate | Position | | | | Price | |
|--------|------|-------|----------|--|--|--|-------|--|
| De la Rue | | | | | | | Top pane | Bottom pane |
| 1st | 1902/10 | 1a | S.E. corner pair | .. | .. | .. | 75·00 | 75·00 |
| Somerset House | | | | | | | | |
| With 1911 date cuts under 7th stamp | | | | | | | | |
| 2nd | Jan. 1912 | 1b | S.E. corner pair | .. | .. | .. | £150 | £100 |
| With 1912 date cuts under 8th stamp | | | | | | | | |
| 3rd | July 1912 | 1c | S.E. corner pair | .. | .. | .. | 75·00 | 75·00 |

## KING EDWARD VII. £1, TYPE M16

### The Plate

Plate

1   (a) no marking
   (b) date cuts added under the 4th stamp bottom row of both panes
   (c) cuts in state (b) filled up and a white dot made in the rules above and below the last stamps in the 4th vertical rows of both panes

### Printing Series

| Series | Date | Plate | Position | | | | Price | |
|--------|------|-------|----------|--|--|--|-------|--|
| De la Rue | | | | | | | Top pane | Bottom pane |
| 1st | 1902/10 | 1a | S.E. corner single | .. | .. | .. | £150 | £150 |
| Somerset House | | | | | | | | |
| With 1911 date cuts under 3rd stamp | | | | | | | | |
| 2nd | Sept. 1911 | 1b | S.E. corner single | .. | .. | .. | £160 | £160 |
| With 1912 date dot under 4th stamp | | | | | | | | |
| 3rd | April 1912 | 1c | S.E. or N.E. corner single | .. | | .. | £150 | £150 |

# King George V, Typographed

Much research work initiated by the late Lt.-Col. Stanton is chronicled as an appendix to the *Stamps of Great Britain, Part IV*, published by the Royal Philatelic Society. Our lists incorporate the result of ten years' study of new discoveries by the Great Britain Philatelic Society.

This has necessitated much regrouping and re-numbering, but as far as possible we have kept to the same arbitrary plate numbers as were first laid down in the R.P.S. book. New discoveries are still being made, and the list may need to be amended from time to time.

## 1911-12

### KING GEORGE V. ½d., TYPE N1, DIE 1A

| Plate | Marking | | Plate | Marking |
|---|---|---|---|---|
| 1 | No marking | | 5 | Cut 18th right side, 10 mm. |
| 2 | Curved cut 20th right side | | 6 | Half dot (left) 17th right side, 13½ mm. |
| 3 | Cut 19th right side, 11½ mm. | | 7 | Dot (breaking left) 18th right side, 13½ mm. |
| 4 | Cut 19th right side, 8¾ mm. | | | |

#### Control Schedule

| Plate | Control | | | | Price | Plate | Control | | | | Price |
|---|---|---|---|---|---|---|---|---|---|---|---|
| 1 | A 11 | .. | .. | .. | 12·00 | 5 | A 11 | .. | .. | .. | 12·00 |
| 2 | A 11 | .. | .. | .. | 12·00 | 6 | A 11 | .. | .. | .. | 12·00 |
| 3 | A 11 | .. | .. | .. | 10·00 | 7 | A 11 | .. | .. | .. | 18·00 |
| 4 | A 11 | .. | .. | .. | 12·00 | | | | | | |

### KING GEORGE V. ½d., TYPE N1, DIE 1B

Master Plate flaw (A) 19th left side 2 minute nicks either side, 8 mm.

| | | | | |
|---|---|---|---|---|
| 1a | Minute dot at left under 3rd; cut 20th left side, 13 mm; 20th right side, 11¾ mm. | | 10a | (A) Cut under P of 11th |
| 1b | Added cut 17th left side | | 10b | Added cut 19th left side, 10½ mm; cut 19th right side, 12½ mm. |
| 2 | Cut 20th left side, 12½ mm. | | 11a | Cut under FP of 12th. Rule under 2nd thinner at right |
| 3 | Cut 17th left side, 9¾ mm. | | | |
| 4 | Cut 20th right side, 8¼ mm. | | 11b | Added cut 17th right side |
| 5 | Double cut 17th left side; cut under PE of 12th; cut 17th right side | | 12 | Cut under HA of 12th; cut 20th right side, 12½ mm. |
| 6 | Cut 17th left side, 12½ mm.   Cuts 19th and 17th right side | | 13 | (A) Cut 18th left side, 14½ mm. |
| | | | 14 | Oval cut 18th right side, 10½ mm. |
| 7 | Cut under 11th; cut 20th right side | | 15 | Cut 20th right side, 11½ mm; cut 19th right side, 17½ mm; oval cut 18th right side, 10½ mm. |
| 8 | Cut 18th left side, 11¾ mm. | | | |
| 9 | (A) Cut 20th left side, 12½ mm. Cut 19th left side, 13½ mm. | | 16 | Cut 20th right side, 10 mm. |

#### Control Schedule

| Plate | Control | | | | Price | Plate | Control | | | | Price |
|---|---|---|---|---|---|---|---|---|---|---|---|
| 1a | A 11 | .. | .. | .. | 80 | 10a | A 11 | .. | .. | .. | 3·00 |
| 1b | A 11 | .. | .. | .. | 2·00 | 10b | A 11 | .. | .. | .. | 1·25 |
| 2 | A 11 | .. | .. | .. | 80 | 11a | A 11 | .. | .. | .. | 1·25 |
| 3 | A 11 | .. | .. | .. | 2·50 | 11b | A 11 | .. | .. | .. | 3·00 |
| 4 | A 11 | .. | .. | .. | 3·00 | 12 | A 11 | .. | .. | .. | 2·50 |
| 5 | A 11 | .. | .. | .. | 5·00 | 13 | A 11 | .. | .. | .. | 2·50 |
| 6 | A 11 | .. | .. | .. | 2·50 | 14 | A 11 | .. | .. | .. | 3·00 |
| 7 | A 11 | .. | .. | .. | 2·00 | 15 | A 11 | .. | .. | .. | 4·50 |
| 8 | A 11 | .. | .. | .. | 3·00 | 16 | A 11 | .. | .. | .. | 3·00 |
| 9 | A 11 | .. | .. | .. | 1·50 | | | | | | |

### KING GEORGE V. ½d., TYPE N2, DIE 2

| Plate | Marking | | Plate | Marking |
|---|---|---|---|---|
| 1a | Small dot under P of 5th | | 13 | Big oval dot (top) under FP of 8th; two fine diagonal cuts 20th left side, 5 mm. forming an open 'V' |
| 1b | Added dot under E of 12th | | | |
| 2 | Small dot under LF of 6th | | | |
| 3 | Big double dot under (N)N of 7th | | 14 | Small dot under PE of 9th; base of 20th left side partly bevelled off |
| 4 | Pear dot under FP of 8th | | | |
| 5 | Small dot under FP of 9th | | 15 | Minute nick under NY of 9th; dot (base) under PE of 11th |
| 6 | Small dot under P of 10th; base of 20th left side completely bevelled off | | | |
| | | | 16a | Dot under FP of 1st, horizontal dash under HALFP of 2nd; dot under NN of 12th |
| 7 | Small dot under F of 11th | | | |
| 8 | Small dot (base) under FP of 12th | | 16b | Added cut under A of 12th |
| 9 | Minute dot 20th left side, 6 mm. | | 17 | ½ cut (base) and dot under N(N)Y of 12th |
| 10a | Big dot under F of 5th | | 18 | Long dot under HA of 12th |
| 10b | Added single fine diagonal cut 20th left side, 5 mm.  Sometimes showing as a fine 'V' cut | | 19 | 20th left side bent |
| | | | 20 | ¾ cut (base) under PE of 9th |
| 11 | Big dot under HA of 6th; fine 'X' cut in 20th left side | | 21 | ½ cut (base) under N(N) of 10th |
| | | | 22 | Small dot (top) under F of 12th |
| 12 | Big dot under AL of 7th; fine horizontal 'V' cut in 20th left side, 6¼ mm. | | 23 | Dot under PE of 12th |
| | | | 24 | No marking |

## Control Schedule

All Wmk. Crown unless marked (s) Simple Cypher or (m) Multiple Cypher

| Plate | Controls | Price | Plate | Controls | Price |
|---|---|---|---|---|---|
| 1a | B 11, B 12 | 75 | 13 | B 12, B 12 (s), B 12 (m), B 13 (s) | 70 |
| 1b | B 13 (s) | 1·50 | 14 | B 12 | 1·50 |
| 2 | B 11, B 12 | 80 | 15 | B 12, B 12 (s), B 12 (m) | 1·75 |
| 3 | B 11, B 12 | 1·40 | 16a | B 12, B 12 (m) | 70 |
| 4 | B 11, B 12, B 12 (s), B 13 (s) | 2·00 | 16b | B 12 (s), B 12 (m), B 13 (s) | 2·00 |
| 5 | B 11, B 12, B 13 (s) | 2·00 | 17 | None, B 12, B 12 (s), B 13 (s) | 4·00 |
| 6 | B 11, B 12 | 70 | 18 | B 12, B 12 (s), B 12 (m) | 4·00 |
| 7 | B 11, B 12 | 2·25 | 19 | B 12 (s), B 13 (s) | 1·25 |
| 8 | B 11, B 12, B 12 (s), B 12 (m), B 13 (s) | 1·75 | 20 | B 12 (s), B 13 (s) | 1·50 |
| 9 | B 12 (m) | 35·00 | 21 | B 12 (s), B 13 (s) | 2·25 |
| 10a | B 12 | 1·25 | 22 | B 12 (s), B 13 (s) | 3·00 |
| 10b | B 12, B 12 (s), B 12 (m) | 70 | 23 | B 12 (s), B 13 (s) | 3·50 |
| 11 | B 12, B 12 (s), B 12 (m) | 70 | 24 | B 13 (s) | 4·50 |
| 12 | B 12, B 12 (s), B 12 (m) | 80 | | | |

## KING GEORGE V.   1d., TYPE N3, DIE 1A

| Plate | Marking |
|---|---|
| 1a | Dot 19th right side |
| 1b | Added cut under EP of 2nd; cut under NN of 7th |
| 2 | Cut under P of 1st |
| 3 | Dot 20th right side, 12½ mm.  Rule broken under EP of 11th in later printings |
| 4a | No marking |
| 4b | 'U' mark under E of 3rd |
| 5 | Dot 18th right side, 10½ mm |
| 6 | Dot 17th right side, 9½ mm. |
| 7 | Cut 20th right side, 13½ mm. |
| 8 | Cut under E of 11th |

| Plate | Marking |
|---|---|
| 9a | ½ dot (outer) 20th right side, 10 mm.  Small dot (breaking inner) 20th left side, 8¾ mm. |
| 9b | Added dot under (N)E of 11th |
| 10 | Cut 19th right side, 10½ mm; left of 11th rule cut away |
| 11 | Cut under E of 9th |
| 12a | ½ dot (inner) 19th right side, 10 mm. |
| 12b | Added cut under (P)E of 11th |
| 13a | Nick (outer) 20th right side, 13 mm. |
| 13b | Added dot 18th right side, 10½ mm; dot 18th left side, 12½ mm. |
| 13c | Added cut under (P)E of 10th |

### Control Schedule

| Plate | Control | Price | Plate | Control | Price |
|---|---|---|---|---|---|
| 1a | A. 11 | 8·00 | 9a | A 11 | 1·35 |
| 1b | A 11 | 15·00 | 9b | A 11 | 2·50 |
| 2 | A 11 | 8·00 | 10 | A 11 | 1·75 |
| 3 | A 11 | 1·25 | 11 | A 11 | 5·00 |
| 4a | A 11 | 12·00 | 12a | A 11 | 2·00 |
| 4b | A 11 | 10·00 | 12b | A 11 | 2·50 |
| 5 | A 11 | 4·50 | 13a | A 11 | 1·00 |
| 6 | A 11 | 6·00 | 13b | A 11 | 9·00 |
| 7 | A 11 | 6·50 | 13c | A 11 | 6·00 |
| 8 | A 11 | 4·00 | | | |

## KING GEORGE V.   1d., TYPE N3, DIE 1B

| Plate | Marking |
|---|---|
| 1 | No marking |
| 2 | Cut 20th right side, 9 mm. |
| 3a | No marking |
| 3b | Added oval cut 20th right side, 11½ mm. |
| 3c | Added cut 17th right side |
| 4 | Cut 20th right side, 14½ mm. |
| 5 | Cut 20th right side, 13½ mm. |
| 6 | ½ dot (outer) 20th right side, 12 mm. |
| 7 | Cut under P(E) of 12th; cut 20th right side, 10 mm. |
| 8a | ½ cut (base) under (N)E of 11th; cut 19th right side, 14 mm. |

| Plate | Marking |
|---|---|
| 8b | Added cut 20th right side, 11¾ mm. |
| 9a | No marking |
| 9b | Added cut 19th right side, 16 mm. |
| 10 | Cut 19th right side, 11½ mm. |
| 11 | Cut 19th right side, 9 mm. |
| 12 | Cut 19th right side, 8 mm. |
| 13 | Cut 18th right side |
| 14 | Cut 17th right side, 9 mm. |
| 15a | No marking |
| 15b | Added minute dot under (P)E of 9th |
| 16 | Cut 17th left side, 16 mm. |

### Control Schedule

| Plate | Control | Price | Plate | Control | Price |
|---|---|---|---|---|---|
| 1 | A 11 | — | 9a | A. 11 | 3·00 |
| 2 | A 11 | 50 | 9b | A 11 | 2·00 |
| 3a | A. 11 | 3·00 | 10 | A 11 | 1·50 |
| 3b | A 11 | 50 | 11 | A 11 | 50 |
| 3c | A 11 | 3·00 | 12 | A 11 | 75 |
| 4 | A 11 | 70 | 13 | A 11 | 3·00 |
| 5 | A 11 | 70 | 14 | A 11 | 4·50 |
| 6 | A 11 | 75 | 15a | A. 11 | 3·00 |
| 7 | A 11 | 50 | 15b | A 11 | 3·25 |
| 8a | A 11 | 50 | 16 | A 11 | 10·00 |
| 8b | A 11 | 2·00 | | | |

## KING GEORGE V.  1d., TYPE N4, DIE 2

Minute dot at left under 1st is a master plate flaw

| Plate | Marking |
|---|---|
| 1a | No marking |
| 1b | Added dot under EP of 5th |
| 1c | Added cut under right serif of P of 11th |
| 2a | No marking |
| 2b | Added dot (base) under NE of 6th |
| 3a | No marking |
| 3b. | Added dot under NN of 7th |
| 4a | Scoop (base) under right of 8th |
| 4b | Added dot under N(E) of 8th |
| 5a | No marking |
| 5b | Added dot under PE of 9th |
| 6a | Dot above 1st in top row |
| 6b | Added dot under PE of 1st; added dot under EP of 10th |
| 7a | No marking |
| 7b | Added dot under E(P) of 11th |

| Plate | Marking |
|---|---|
| 8a | No marking |
| 8b | Added dot under EP of 12th |
| 9a | Dash under PE of 11th |
| 9b | Added dot under EP of 11th |
| 10a | Dash under PE of 12th |
| 10b | Added dot under (N)E of 12th |
| 11 | Cut under PE of 9th |
| 12 | ½ cut under PE of 10th |
| 13 | Cut under P of 11th |
| 14 | Cut under (P)E of 12th |
| 15 | Small dot 19th right side, 9¼ mm. |
| 16a | Two small dots 20th right side, 10½, 16 mm. |
| 16b | Added dot under P of 12th |
| 17 | Dot under P of 9th |
| 18 | Dot under PE of 10th |

### Control Schedule

All Wmk. Crown unless marked (s) Simple Cypher or (m) Multiple Cypher

| Plate | Controls | | | | Price | Plate | Controls | | | | Price |
|---|---|---|---|---|---|---|---|---|---|---|---|
| 1a | B 11 | .. | .. | .. | — | 8a | B. 11, B. 12 | | .. | .. | — |
| 1b | B 11 | .. | .. | .. | 6·00 | 8b | B 11, B 12 | .. | .. | .. | 25 |
| 1c | B 12 | .. | .. | .. | 10·00 | 9a | B 12 | .. | .. | .. | 6·00 |
| 2a | B. 12 | .. | .. | .. | — | 9b | B 12 | .. | .. | .. | 2·25 |
| 2b | B 11, B 12 | .. | .. | .. | 5·00 | 10a | B 12 | .. | .. | .. | 5·00 |
| 3a | B 11 | .. | .. | .. | — | 10b | B 12 | .. | .. | .. | 50 |
| 3b | B 11, B 12 | .. | .. | .. | 5·00 | 11 | B 12, B 12 (s), B 12 (m), B 13 (s) | .. | 50 |
| 4a | B 11 | .. | .. | .. | 6·00 | 12 | B 12, B 12 (s), B 12 (m), B 13 (s) | .. | 25 |
| 4b | B 11, B 12 | .. | .. | .. | 4·50 | 13 | B 12, B 12 (s), B 12 (m) | | .. | 25 |
| 5a | B 11 | .. | .. | .. | — | 14 | B 12 | .. | .. | .. | 60 |
| 5b | B 11 | .. | .. | .. | 6·50 | 15 | B 12, B 13 (s) | .. | .. | .. | 75 |
| 6a | B. 11, B. 12 | .. | .. | .. | — | 16a | B 12, B 12 (s), B 12 (m) | .. | 30 |
| 6b | B 11, B 12 | .. | .. | .. | 25 | 16b | B 13 (s) | .. | .. | .. | 30 |
| 7a | B 11 | .. | .. | .. | — | 17 | B 13 (s) | .. | .. | .. | 1·25 |
| 7b | B 11, B 12 | .. | .. | .. | 25 | 18 | B 13 (s) | .. | .. | .. | 75 |

## 1912-26

## KING GEORGE V.  ½d., TYPE N6. WMK. SIMPLE CYPHER, W.14.  HARRISON

| Plate | Marking |
|---|---|
| 1a | Dot above 1st in upper and lower panes; minute dot under H of 2nd |
| 1b | Dots above first filled in; added cut under N(N) of 1st |
| 2a | Dot above 2nd in upper and lower panes; indents at base of 1st and 12th |
| 2b | Dots above 2nd filled in; added large dot bulging (sometimes breaking) base under FP of 3rd |
| 2c | Added dot under E of 3rd |
| 3a | Dot above 3rd in upper and lower panes |
| 3b | Dots above 3rd filled in; added small dot 17th left side, 11 mm. |
| 3c | Added big cut under P of 1st |
| 4a | Dot above 4th in upper and lower panes |
| 4b | Dots above 4th filled in; added sloping cut (base) under FP of 4th; small dot 18th left side, 12½ mm. |
| 5 | Dot (top) under H of 1st |
| 6a | Dot (top) under PE of 1st; indent (top) under EN of 3rd; ½ cut (top) to left of H of 6th |
| 6b | Added dot under N(N) of 1st |
| 7a | ½ cut (base) under LF of 1st; small dot 20th left side, 13¾ mm. |
| 7b | Added dot under PE of 2nd |
| 8 | ½ cut (top) under LF of 2nd |
| 9a | Irregular cut under E of 3rd |
| 9b | Added ½ nick 20th left side (slanting down to outer edge) 22–21½ mm. |
| 9c | Added 2 dots 20th left side, 10, 12 mm. |
| 10a | Small dot 19th left side, 10½ mm. |
| 10b | Added small dot under A of 1st |
| 11a | Cut within rule at left of 9th |
| 11b | Added cut 20th left side, 12¾ mm. |

| Plate | Marking |
|---|---|
| 12a | Dash at right of 2nd. Scoop (top) above 1st top row |
| 12b | Added dot under PE of 3rd |
| 12c | Added sloping cut under FP of 3rd |
| 13a | Dot under FP of 1st |
| 13b | Added dot under PE of 1st |
| 13c | Added dot (inner) 20th left side, 9¾ mm. |
| 13d | Added dot under PE of 2nd |
| 14a | Dot under P of 2nd |
| 14b | Added dot (top) under EN of 2nd |
| 14c | Added dot under LF of 3rd; added dot at left above 1st top row; ½ dot (outer) 18th left side, 12½ mm. |
| 14d | Added ½ dot (top) under P of 3rd; added nick and ½ dot (inner) 18th left side, 6½, 10 mm. |
| 15. | Dot under PE of 1st |
| 16a | Dot under PE of 2nd |
| 16b | Added 2 dots 19th left side, 11, 14 mm. |
| 16c | Added cut under N(N) of 1st |
| 17 | Dot (top) under P of 3rd |
| 18 | Dot under FP of 4th |
| 19 | 3 dots (left dot minute) under LFPE of 2nd |
| 20a | 3 dots (centre dot minute) under LFP of 3rd |
| 20b | Added dot under A of 1st |
| 21a | 2 dots (top/base) under FPE of 4th |
| 21b | Added cut under LF of 3rd |
| 22 | 2 dots (base/top) under FPE of 4th |
| 23a | Dot under H of 1st |
| 23b | Added cut under HA of 4th |
| 24 | Dot under H of 2nd |
| 25 | Dot under H of 3rd |
| 26 | Dot under H of 4th |
| 27 | 2 dots under NN of 1st |
| 28a | 2 small dots under PEN of 2nd |

½d., Type **N6**, Wmk. **W.14**.  Harrison—*continued*

| Plate | Marking |
|---|---|

28b  Added dot under P of 1st
29    2 dots under ALF of 3rd
30    2 dots under HALF of 4th
31a   Double ½ cut (top/base) under HA of 2nd
31b   Added dot covering base of above cut
32a   Tiny dot under P of 1st
32b   Added fine double cut under PE of 3rd; small dot 17th right side, 16 mm.
33    Tiny dot under PE of 3rd
34a   Cut under PE of 1st
34b   Added dot under NN of 9th
35    Cut under E of 2nd
36a   Cut under P of 3rd
36b   Added 3 dots under HALFP of 3rd
37    Cut under F of 4th; minute ½ cut (outer) 20th right side, 6 mm.
38a   4 dots from left to under right of F of 4th
38b   Added dot (breaking base) under PE of 1st; dot 20th left side, 11½ mm; 2 dots 17th left side, 7, 11¾ mm.
39    Withdrawn
40    Small, slightly ovoid dot (central) under PE of 1st
41    Dot, barely bulging top, under P of 2nd; right of rule under 3rd has small downward projection
42    Dot (breaking base) under FP of 1st. Scoop (outer) 2nd left side.
43a   Very fine ¼ cut (base) under (N)N of 3rd
43b   Added ½ dot (top) under E of 10th
44    Dot (bulging and later breaking base) under right serif of P of 2nd
45a   Large dot 19th right side, 7¼ mm.
45b   Added small dot 20th left side, 11½ mm.
46a   Cut under N(N) of 1st
46b   Added cut 20th right side, 11½ mm; large dot (breaking outer) 18th right side, 11 mm.
47    Dot (central) under right serif of P of 2nd; 2 dots 19th left side, both breaking outer, 4½, 8½ mm.
48    Large oval dot (breaking base) under PE of 1st. Two minute dots under LF, NN of 2nd; two minute dots under A, N(N) of 5th. Base 20th left side damaged (outer).
49a   Dot (breaking top) under PE of 9th
49b   Added small, slightly ovoid dot (base) under right serif of P of 2nd
50    Dot (bulging—later breaking) base under right serif of P of 2nd
51a   Large dot 17th right side, 9 mm.
51b   Added dot under PE of 1st
52a   Large dot under E of 9th
52b   Added small dot 20th left side, 14 mm.
53a   Small dot 17th right side, 4½ mm.
53b   Added slanting cut 19th right side, 4 mm.
54a   Dot 19th left side, 10 mm.
54b   Added dot (top) under FP of 2nd

54c   Added dot under E of 2nd
55    Dot (base) under F of 1st
56    Small dot (central) 18th right side, 11½ mm; small dot (inner) 17th right side, 10 mm.
57a   Large dot (later breaking inner) 17th right side, 11 mm.
57b   Added ½ dot (top) under N(N) of 9th
58    Base of 20th right side bevelled off; dot 17th right side, 9½ mm.
59    19th left side scooped out (outer) 8–12 mm. with vertical dash to right of it
60a   Dot under F of 10th
60b   Added 4 dots under AL, FP, and 2 touching each other under E of 3rd
61a   Nick (outer) 19th right side, 14½ mm; ½ dot (outer) 19th left side, 6¾ mm.
61b   Added dot (top) under FP of 9th
61c   Added 4 dots from left end to left of F of 4th
63a   Large dot (breaking outer) 18th right side, 10 mm; dot (breaking inner) 3rd right side, 11½ mm.
63b   Added small dot (central) 17th right side, 10 mm.
64    3 dots breaking inner 19th right side, 5½, 7½, 10½ mm.
65a   Small double dot 18th right side, 11½ mm.
65b   Added dot, breaking base, under PE of 10th
65c   Added dot 19th right side, 9 mm.
66a   Small dot (central) 19th left side, 9½ mm. Dot (breaking inner) 2nd left side, 10½ mm.
66b   Added 2 fine cuts 19th left side, 11¾, 13½ mm.
67    Small dot inner 18th right side, 11 mm.
68    Dot 1st left side, 11½ mm. Dot inner 20th left side, 11½ mm.
69    2 cuts 19th left side, 7, 9½ mm.
70    ½ dot (base) under P and nick under NY both of 4th
71    Large oval dot breaking top and bottom under PE of 2nd; 20th left side thins towards base
72    Oval dot under FP of 3rd; base of 19th right side bevelled off
73    No marking
74    Oval dot (widely breaking top) to right of P of 2nd; ½ dot (inner) 17th right side, 12 mm.
75    Large oval dot either bulging or just breaking top, under PE of 2nd
76    Small dot (outer) 18th left side, 11 mm.
77    2 large dots 19th left side, 11, 13½ mm.
78    5 cuts under HALF of 12th; minute fine nick (outer) 19th left side, 8¼ mm.
79    Base of 2nd rule cut away from under ENNY to right end
80    Large dot (central) 19th left side, 9½ mm.
81    ½ cut and ½ dot (outer) 19th left side, 11, 13½ mm; cut 18th left side, 13½ mm.
82    Small dot (outer) 20th left side, 11½ mm.
83    2 small cuts under NN of 11th

# KING GEORGE V. ½d., TYPE N6. Wmk. Simple Cypher, W.14. Harrison (Plates 1a to 9b)

| Plate | 17 | 18 | 19 | 20 | 1 | 2 | 3 | 4 | 5 | 6 | 7 | 8 | 9 | 10 | 11 | 12 | Controls | Prices from |
|---|---|---|---|---|---|---|---|---|---|---|---|---|---|---|---|---|---|---|
| 1a |  |  |  |  |  | O/H |  |  |  |  |  |  |  |  |  |  | B 13 | 20 |
| 1b |  |  |  |  | I/N(N) | O/H |  |  |  |  |  |  |  |  |  |  | C 13, C 14, D 14 | 20 |
| 2a |  |  |  |  | < |  |  |  |  |  |  |  |  |  |  | < | B 13 | 20 |
| 2b |  |  |  |  | < |  | O/FP |  |  |  |  |  |  |  |  | < | C 13, C 14, D 14 | 20 |
| 2c |  |  |  |  | < |  | OO/FPE |  |  |  |  |  |  |  |  | < | E 14 | 30 |
| 3a |  |  |  |  |  |  |  |  |  |  |  |  |  |  |  |  | B 13 | 1·50 |
| 3b | O |  |  |  |  |  |  |  |  |  |  |  |  |  |  |  | C 13 | 1·00 |
| 3c | O |  |  |  | I/P |  |  |  |  |  |  |  |  |  |  |  | C 13, C 14, D 14 | 20 |
| 4a |  |  |  |  |  |  |  |  |  |  |  |  |  |  |  |  | B 13 | 1·50 |
| 4b |  | O |  |  |  |  |  | >/FP |  |  |  |  |  |  |  |  | C 13, C 14, D 14 | 35 |
| 5 |  |  |  |  | O/H |  |  |  |  |  |  |  |  |  |  |  | C 13, C 14, D 14 | 20 |
| 6a |  |  |  |  | O/PE |  | </EN |  |  | ½/H |  |  |  |  |  |  | C 13, C 14 | 20 |
| 6b |  |  |  |  | OO/PEN |  | </EN |  |  | ½/H |  |  |  |  |  |  | E 14, F 15, G 15 | 20 |
| 7a |  |  |  |  | ½/LF |  |  |  |  |  |  |  |  |  |  |  | C 13, C 14, D 14 | 20 |
| 7b |  |  |  | O | ½/LF | O/PE |  |  |  |  |  |  |  |  |  |  | D 14 | 35 |
| 8 |  |  |  | O |  | ½/LF | I/E |  |  |  |  |  |  |  |  |  | C 13, C 14, D 14 | 20 |
| 9a |  |  |  |  |  |  |  |  |  |  |  |  |  |  |  |  | C 13 | 20 |
| 9b |  |  |  | ½/< |  |  | I/E |  |  |  |  |  |  |  |  |  | C 13, C 14 | 20 |

# KING GEORGE V. ½d., TYPE N6. Wmk. Simple Cypher, W.14. Harrison (Plates 9c to 16a)

| Plate | 17 | 18 | 19 | 20 | 1 | 2 | 3 | 4 | 5 | 6 | 7 | 8 | 9 | 10 | 11 | 12 | Controls | Prices from |
|---|---|---|---|---|---|---|---|---|---|---|---|---|---|---|---|---|---|---|
| 9c | | | | ∨ 00½ | | | I E | | | | | | | | | | E 14 | 75 |
| 10a | | | o | | | | | | | | | | | | | | C 13, C 14, D 14 | 30 |
| 10b | | | o | | o A | | | | | | | | | | | | F 15, G 15 | 35 |
| 11a | | | | | | | | | | | | | I | | | | C 13, C 14 | 1·25 |
| 11b | | | | I | | | | | | | | | I | | | | C 14, D 14 | 25 |
| 12a | | | | | | \| | | | | | | | | | | | C 14, D 14 | 20 |
| 12b | | | | | | \| | o PE | | | | | | | | | | D 14, E 14 | 25 |
| 12c | | | | | | \| | o∨ PEFP | | | | | | | | | | E 14 | 25 |
| 13a | | | | | o FP | | | | | | | | | | | | D 14, E 14 | 20 |
| 13b | | | | | oo FPE | | | | | | | | | | | | E 14 | 35 |
| 13c | | | | o | oo FPE | | | | | | | | | | | | E 14 | 35 |
| 13d | | | | o | oo FPE | o PE | | | | | | | | | | | E 14, F 15 | 35 |
| 14a | | | | | | o P | | | | | | | | | | | D 14, E 14 | 25 |
| 14b | | | | | | oo PEN | | | | | | | | | | | E 14, F 15 | 25 |
| 14c | | ½o | | | | oo PEN | o LF | | | | | | | | | | F 15 | 55 |
| 14d | | ∨ ½o | | | | oo PEN | oo LFP | | | | | | | | | | G 15 | 55 |
| 15 | | | | | o PE | | | | | | | | | | | | E 14, F 15 | 20 |
| 16a | | | | | | o PE | | | | | | | | | | | E 14 | 55 |

*1st Stamp, Row No.* (columns 17–20) — *Bottom row, Stamp No.* (columns 1–12) — *Positional piece*

# KING GEORGE V. ½d., TYPE N6. Wmk Simple Cypher, W.14. Harrison (Plates 16b to 28b)

| Plate | 1st stamp, Row No. | | | | Bottom row, Stamp No. | | | | | | | | | | | | Controls | Positional piece Prices from |
|---|---|---|---|---|---|---|---|---|---|---|---|---|---|---|---|---|---|---|
| | 17 | 18 | 19 | 20 | 1 | 2 | 3 | 4 | 5 | 6 | 7 | 8 | 9 | 10 | 11 | 12 | | |
| 16b | | | oo | | | o PE | | | | | | | | | | | E 14, F 15 | 40 |
| 16c | | | oo | | I N(N) | o PE | | | | | | | | | | | G 15, H 16 | 40 |
| 17 | | | | | | | o P | | | | | | | | | | E 14, F 15 | 20 |
| 18 | | | | | | | | o FP | | | | | | | | | E 14, F 15 | 40 |
| 19 | | | | | | ooo LFPE | | | | | | | | | | | E 14, F 15, G 15 | 25 |
| 20a | | | | | | | ooo LFP | | | | | | | | | | E 14, F 15, G 15 | 25 |
| 20b | | | | | o A | | ooo LFP | | | | | | | | | | ? | — |
| 21a | | | | | | | | oo FPE | | | | | | | | | E 14, F 15, G 15 | 1·25 |
| 21b | | | | | | | I LF | oo FPE | | | | | | | | | ? | — |
| 22 | | | | | | | | oo FPE | | | | | | | | | E 14, F 15 | 1·00 |
| 23a | | | | | o H | | | | | | | | | | | | F 15, G 15 | 40 |
| 23b | | | | | o H | | | I HA | | | | | | | | | G 15, H 16 | 1·25 |
| 24 | | | | | | o H | o H | | | | | | | | | | F 15, G 15 | 20 |
| 25 | | | | | | | | o H | | | | | | | | | F 15, G 15, H 16 | 20 |
| 26 | | | | | | | | | | | | | | | | | F 15, G 15 | 75 |
| 27 | | | | | oo NN | | | | | | | | | | | | G 15, H 16, I 16 | 20 |
| 28a | | | | | | oo PEN | | | | | | | | | | | G 15, H 16, I 16, J 17 | 25 |
| 28b | | | | | o P | oo PNE | | | | | | | | | | | J 17 | 25 |

# KING GEORGE V. ½d., TYPE N6. Wmk. Simple Cypher, W.14. Harrison (Plates 29 to 42)

| Plate | 1st stamp, Row No. | | | | Bottom row, Stamp No. | | | | | | | | 12th stamp, Row No. | | | | Controls | Positional piece Prices from |
|---|---|---|---|---|---|---|---|---|---|---|---|---|---|---|---|---|---|---|
| | 17 | 18 | 19 | 20 | 1 | 2 | 3 | 4 | 9 | 10 | 11 | 12 | 17 | 18 | 19 | 20 | | |
| 29 | | | | | | | OO ALF | | | | | | | | | | G 15, H 16, J 17 | 25 |
| 30 | | | | | | ‡‡ HA | | OO HALF | | | | | | | | | G 15, H 16, I 16 | 1·40 |
| 31a | | | | | | ‡‡O HA | | | | | | | | | | | G 15, H 16, I 16, J 17 | 20 |
| 31b | | | | | O P | | | | | | | | | | | | J 17 | 25 |
| 32a | | | | | O P | | | | | | | | | | | | H 16 | 1·50 |
| 32b | | | | | | | 2 PE | | | | | | O | | | | H 16, I 16, J 17 | 20 |
| 33 | | | | | | | O PE | | | | | | | | | | H 16, I 16, J 17 | 25 |
| 34a | | | | | I PE | | | | | | | | | | | | H 16, I 16 | 20 |
| 34b | | | | | I PE | | | | O NN | | | | | | | | J 17 | 2·25 |
| 35 | | | | | | I E | | | | | | | | | | | H 16, I 16, J 17 | 20 |
| 36a | | | | | | | | | | | | | | | | | H 16 | 25 |
| 36b | | | | | | | OOO I HALFP | | | | | | | | | | I 16, J 17 | 25 |
| 37 | | | | | | | | I F | | | | | | | | ‡ | H 16, I 16 | 1·40 |
| 38a | | | | | | | | OOOO F | | | | | | | | | I 16, J 17 | 1·25 |
| 38b | OO | | | O | O PE | | | OOOO F | | | | | | | | | J 17 | 4·00 |
| 39 | | | | | | | | | | | | | | | | | Withdrawn | † |
| 40 | | | | | O PE | | | | | | | | | | | | J 17 | 60 |
| 41 | | | | | | O P | | | | | | | | | | | J 17 | 60 |
| 42 | | | | | O FP | | &#124; | | | | | | | | | | J 17, K 17, K 18, M 18, M 19, N 19 | 60 |

# KING GEORGE V. ½d., TYPE N6. Wmk. Simple Cypher, W.14. Harrison (Plates 43a to 54a)

| Plate | 1st stamp, Row No. 17 | 18 | 19 | 20 | Bottom row, Stamp No. 1 | 2 | 3 | 4 | 9 | 12th stamp, Row No. .10 | 11 | 12 | 17 | 18 | 19 | 20 | Controls | Prices from |
|---|---|---|---|---|---|---|---|---|---|---|---|---|---|---|---|---|---|---|
| 43a | | | | | | | (N)N | | | | | | | | | | J 17, K 17 | 50 |
| 43b | | | | | | | (N)N | | | o E | | | | | | | K 17, K 18, L 18, M 18 | 2·50 |
| 44 | | | | | | o P | | | | | | | | | | | K 17, K 18 | 75 |
| 45a | | | | | | | | | | | | | | | o | | J 17, K 17, K 18 | 2·00 |
| 45b | | | | o | | | | | | | | | | | o | | L 18, M 18 | 1·25 |
| 46a | | | | | I N(N) | | | | | | | | | | | | J 17 | 35 |
| 46b | | | | | I N(N) | | | | | | | | | o | | I | J 17, K 17, K 18, L 18, M 19 | 2·00 |
| 47 | | | oo | | | | | | | | | | | | | | J 17 | 75 |
| 48 | | | | ▬ | o PE | oo LFN | | | | | | | | | | | Q 21, R 21, T 22, U 22, U 23 | 20 |
| 49a | | | | | | | | | o PE | | | | | | | | J 17 | 3·00 |
| 49b | | | | | | o P | | | o PE | | | | o | | | | K 17, K 18, M 19 | 75 |
| 50 | | | | | | o P | | | | | | | o | | | | J 17, K 18 | 55 |
| 51a | | | | | o PE | | | | | | | | | | | | K 17, K 18, M 18 | 5·00 |
| 51b | | | | | | | | | | | | | | | | | M 19, N 19 | 3·00 |
| 52a | | | | o | | | | | o E | | | | o | | | | K 17, L 18, M 18 | 3·00 |
| 52b | | | | | | | | | o E | | | | o | | | | M 19, N 19 | 60 |
| 53a | | | | | | | | | | | | | | | | | M 18 | 6·00 |
| 53b | | | | | | | | | | | | | | | ∧ | | M 19, N 19 | 5·00 |
| 54a | | | o | | | | | | | | | | | | | | L 18, M 18, M 19 | 60 |

# KING GEORGE V. ½d., TYPE N6. Wmk. Simple Cypher, W.14. Harrison (Plates 54b to 65c)

| Plate | 1st stamp, Row No. | | | | bottom row, Stamp No. | | | | | | | | 12th stamp, Row No. | | | | Controls | Positional piece Prices from |
|---|---|---|---|---|---|---|---|---|---|---|---|---|---|---|---|---|---|---|
| | 17 | 18 | 19 | 20 | 1 | 2 | 3 | 4 | 9 | 10 | 11 | 12 | 17 | 18 | 19 | 20 | | |
| 54b | | | o | | | o FP | | | | | | | | | | | M 19 | 50 |
| 54c | | | o | | | oo FPE | | | | | | | | | | | N 19 | 40 |
| 55 | | | | | o F | | | | | | | | | | | | M 19, N 19, O 19, P 20, Q 20, Q 21 | 30 |
| 56 | | | | | | | | | | | | | o | | | | M 19, N 19, O 19, P 20 | 4·00 |
| 57a | | | | | | | | | ½o N | | | | o | | | | K 17, K 18 | 5·00 |
| 57b | | | | | | | | | | | | | o | | | | M 19 | 5·50 |
| 58 | | | | | | | | | | | | | o | | | | O 19, Q 21, U 22 | 2·50 |
| 59 | | | ɔ | | | | | | | | | | | | | | M 19, N 19, O 19, O 20, P 20 | 60 |
| 60a | | | | | | | | | | o F | | | | | | | M 19 | 4·00 |
| 60b | | | | | | | oooo ALF | | | | | | | | | | N 19 | 50 |
| 61a | | | ½o | | | | | | o FP | | | | | | | | M 19 | 75 |
| 61b | | | ½o | | | | | | o FP | | | | | | < | | M 19 | 5·00 |
| 61c | | | ½o | | | | | oooo F | | | | | | | < | | N 19, P 20, Q 20 | 1·25 |
| 63a | | | | | | | | | | | | | | | < | | M 18 | 5·00 |
| 63b | | | | | | | | | | | | | o | o | | | N 19 | 7·00 |
| 64 | | | | | | | | | | | | | | | ooo | | U 23 | 5·00 |
| 65a | | | | | | | | | | | | | | oo | | | M 18 | 5·00 |
| 65b | | | | | | | | | | o PE | | | | oo | | | M 19 | 4·00 |
| 65c | | | o | | | | | | | o PE | | | | oo | | | N 19, O 19, P 20, Q 20, Q 21 | 1·50 |

## KING GEORGE V. ½d., TYPE N6. Wmk. Simple Cypher, W.14. Harrison (plates 66a to 83)

| Plate | 1st stamp, Row No. 17 | 18 | 19 | 20 | Bottom row, Stamp No. 1 | 2 | 3 | 4 | 9 | 10 | 11 | 12 | 12th stamp, Row No. 17 | 18 | 19 | 20 | Controls | Prices from |
|---|---|---|---|---|---|---|---|---|---|---|---|---|---|---|---|---|---|---|
| 66a | | | o | | | | | | | | | | | | | | O 19, O 20, P 20 | 60 |
| 66b | | | 20 | | | | | | | | | | | | | | P 20, Q 21, T 22, U 22, U 23 | 60 |
| 67 | | | | o | | | | | | | | | | o | | | O 20, P 20 | 4·00 |
| 68 | | | | | | | | ½o ∧ PNY | | | | | | | | | P 20, Q 20, R 21, S 21, S 22, T 22, U 22, U 23 | 30 |
| 69 | | | 2 | | | o PE | | | | | | | | | | | Q 20, Q 21 | 1·40 |
| 70 | | | | | | | | | | | | | | | | | Q 21, R 21, S 21, S 22, T 22, U 22 | 1·25 |
| 71 | | | | \| | | | | | | | | | | | | | Q 21, R 21, S 21, S 22, U 22, U 23, V 23 | 30 |
| 72 | | | | | | | o FP | | | | | | | | \| | | Q 21, R 21, S 21, S 22, T 22, U 22, V 23 | 30 |
| 73 | | | | | | | | | | | | | | | | | V 23 | 6·50 |
| 74 | | | | | | o P | | | | | | | ½o | | | | R 21, T 22, U 22, U 23, V 23 | 30 |
| 75 | | | | | | o PE | | | | | | | | | | | R 21, T 22, U 22, U 23 | 35 |
| 76 | | o | | | | | | | | | | | | | | | S 21, T 22 | 2·50 |
| 77 | | | oo | | | | | | | | | | | | | | U 22, U 23, V 23 | 1·25 |
| 78 | | | ∧ | | | | | | | | | 5 HAL. | | | | | U 23, V 23, W 23, W 24 | 6·00 |
| 79 | | | | | | ENNY | | | | | | | | | | | U 23, V 23 | 1·25 |
| 80 | | | o | | | | | | | | | | | | | | U 23, V 23 | 1·00 |
| 81 | | I | ½o | | | | | | | | | | | | | | U 23, V 23, W 23, W 24 | 70 |
| 82 | | | | o | | | | | | | 2 NN | | | | | | V 23 | 75 |
| 83 | | | | | | | | | | | | | | | | | V 23, W 23 | 5·00 |

## KING GEORGE V. ½d., TYPE N6.    WMK. BLOCK CYPHER, W.15.    WATERLOW

| Plate | Marking |
|---|---|
| 1 | Large dot (top) under N(N) of 3rd |
| 2 | Dot (base) under EN of 1st |
| 3 | Minute dot (inner) 20th left side, 10½ mm. |
| 4 | Tiny dot 19th left side, 8 mm. |
| 5 | (a) Dot (base) under PE of 2nd |
|   | (b) Projection below rule under L of 1st; ½ dot (outer) 19th left side, 13 mm. |
| 6 | As for Harrison Plate 79 but with added 4 large dots 19th right side |
| 7 | As for Harrison Plate 80 |
| 8 | ½ dot (top) under E of 3rd |
| 9 | Dot (breaking outer) 18th left side, 12 mm. |
| 10 | ½ dot (top) under F of 4th |
| 11 | ½ dot and ½ cut (top) under E of 2nd |
| 12 | ½ dot (top) under PE of 3rd; rule 19th left side damaged (top) |
| 13 | Split at right end of rule under 2nd. Dot (inner) 19th left side, 7½ mm. |
| 14 | 2 large dots under PEN of 3rd |
| 15 | Dot (outer) 20th left side, 6½ mm. |
| 16 | As for Harrison Plate 83 with small ½ cut (base) under L of 1st |
| 17 | 2 dots 19th left side, 10½ mm., 13½ mm. |
| 18 | Dot under F of 2nd |
| 19 | Large dot (outer) 20th left side, 11 mm. Indent (base) under 11th |
| 20 | Dot (base) under FP of 1st |
| 21 | Dot under P of 3rd |
| 22 | Small dot 20th left side, 11½ mm. |
| 23 | Large dot 19th left side, 12 mm. Tiny dots under F of 7th and A of 12th |
| 24 | Nick at left of 3rd rule |
| 25 | Minute dot at base of 20th left side |
| 26 | Indistinct dot 19th left side, 16 mm. Dot (top) under FP of 11th |
| 27 | Nick at right of 2nd |
| 28 | Dot (central) above 3rd top row. Minute dot 20th left side, 7½ mm. |

| Plate | Marking |
|---|---|
| 29 | ½ dot (outer) 19th left side, 11 mm. Gash below 8th |
| 30 | Indents (base) under H and L of 1st |
| 31 | Left end of 1st rule very thick and curves upwards. Top of 20th left bevelled (outer) |
| 32 | Cut at top of 1st left side with dot halfway down. Dot above 4th top row |
| 33 | Very fine cut 19th left side, 13 mm. |
| 34 | As for Harrison Plate 78 |
| 35 | Rule 19th right side has projection at base. 2 internal cuts under F of 12th |
| 36 | Dot 19th left side, 13¼ mm. |
| 37 | Nick bottom left corner of 8th. Dot 20th right side, 2½ mm. |
| 38 | Dot extreme right of rule under 11th |
| 39 | Tiny dot 19th right side, 18½ mm. |
| 40 | Small dot at top of both 19th and 20th rules at right side |
| 41 | Small dot 18th left side, 13 mm. |
| 42 | Dot and small dot 3rd left side. Scoop (outer) 4th right side |
| 43 | Dot 4th left side. 2 tiny dots 1st right side |
| 44 | Tiny dot above 1st top row. Dot (to right) above 3rd top row. Dot (top) 4th right side |
| 45 | Large and small dots 3rd left side, 11½ mm. 4th right side damaged |
| 46 | Tiny dot under LF of 3rd |
| 47 | Dot (breaking top) under P(E) and nick under (N)N of 3rd |
| 48 | No marking |
| 49 | Small vertical nick at top of 20th right side |
| 50 | 20th left side ragged and thickens at base. 7th rule thins at left |
| 51 | Minute dot 20th right side, 8 mm. |
| 52 | As for Harrison Plate 64 |
| 53 | Tiny half dot (outer) 17th left side, 8 mm. |

# KING GEORGE V. ½d., TYPE N6. Wmk. Block Cypher, W.15. Waterlow (Plates 1 to 18)

| Plate | 1st stamp, Row No. | | | | Bottom row, Stamp No. | | | | | | | | | | | | Controls | Positional piece. Prices from |
|---|---|---|---|---|---|---|---|---|---|---|---|---|---|---|---|---|---|---|
| | 17 | 18 | 19 | 20 | 1 | 2 | 3 | 4 | 5 | 6 | 7 | 8 | 9 | 10 | 11 | 12 | | |
| 1 | | | | | o / EN | | o / N(N) | | | | | | | | | | A 24, B 24, C 25, D 25 | 25 |
| 2 | | | | o | | | | | | | | | | | | | A 24, C 25, D 25 | 25 |
| 3 | | | o | | | | | | | | | | | | | | A 24, B 24, C 25 | 25 |
| 4 | | | o | | | | | | | | | | | | | | A 24, E 26, F 26, H 27 | 40 |
| 5 | | | ½o / 2 | | ∧ / L | o / PE | | | | | | | | | | | A 24, B 24, C 25, D 25, E 26 | 45 |
| 6 | | | o | | | ENNY | | | | | | | | | | | B 24, C 25, D 25, E 26 | 35 |
| 7 | | | | | | | | | | | | | | | | | B 24, C 25 | 60 |
| 8 | | o | | | | 1½o / E | ½o / E | | | | | | | | | | C 25, D 25, E 26, G 27, I 28, J 28, K 29 | 25 |
| 9 | | | o | | | \| | | | | | | | | | | | B 24, C 25 | 1·25 |
| 10 | | | | | | | | ½o / F | | | | | | | | | C 24, J 28, K 29 | 60 |
| 11 | | | o | | | 1½o / E | | | | | | | | | | | D 24, E 26, F 26, G 27, I 28 | 25 |
| 12 | | | \| | | | | ½o / PE | | | | | | | | | | D 24, F 26, G 27, H 27, I 28 | 25 |
| 13 | | | o | | | | oo / PEN | | | | | | | | | | E 26, F 26, G 27, H 27, I 28 | 25 |
| 14 | | | | o | | \| | | | | | | | | | | | F 26, G 27, H 27 | 25 |
| 15 | | | | | | | | | | | | | | | | | F 26, G 27, H 27 | 25 |
| 16 | | | | | ½o / L | | | | | | | | | | 2 / NN | | F 26, G 27 | 25 |
| 17 | | | oo | | | | | | | | | | | | | | D 25, F 26, G 27 | 60 |
| 18 | | | | | | o / F | | | | | | | | | | | I 28, J 28, K 29, L 29 | 30 |

181

# KING GEORGE V. ½d., TYPE N6.  Wmk. Block Cypher, W.15.  Waterlow (Plates 19 to 36)

| Plate | 17 | 18 | 19 | 20 | 1 | 2 | 3 | 4 | 5 | 6 | 7 | 8 | 9 | 10 | 11 | 12 | Controls | Prices from |
|---|---|---|---|---|---|---|---|---|---|---|---|---|---|---|---|---|---|---|
| 19 |  |  |  | o |  |  |  |  |  |  |  |  |  |  | ∧ |  | I 28, J 28, K 29, L 29, N 30 | 25 |
| 20 |  |  |  |  | o FP |  |  |  |  |  |  |  |  |  |  |  | I 28, J 28, K 29, L 29 | 25 |
| 21 |  |  |  |  |  |  | o P |  |  |  |  |  |  |  |  |  | I 28, J 28, K 29, L 29 | 25 |
| 22 |  |  |  | o |  |  |  |  |  |  |  |  |  |  |  |  | J 28, K 29, L 29, N 30 | 35 |
| 23 |  |  | o |  |  |  |  |  |  |  | o F |  |  |  |  | o A | I 28, J 28, K 29, L 29, M 30, N 30 | 60 |
| 24 |  |  |  |  |  |  | ∧ |  |  |  |  |  |  |  |  |  | M 30, N 30, Q 32 | 55 |
| 25 |  |  | o | o |  |  |  |  |  |  |  |  |  |  |  |  | M 30, N 30, O 31, Q 32 | 55 |
| 26 |  |  | o |  |  |  |  |  |  |  |  |  |  |  | o FP |  | N 30, O 31, P 31 | 40 |
| 27 |  |  |  |  |  | ∧ |  |  |  |  |  |  |  |  |  |  | P 31, Q 32, R 32, S 33, T 33 | 25 |
| 28 |  |  |  | o |  |  |  |  |  |  |  | | |  |  |  |  | N 30, P 31 | 75 |
| 29 |  |  | ↑o |  |  |  |  |  |  |  |  | | |  |  |  |  | Q 32, R 32, S 33, T 33 | 75 |
| 30 |  |  |  |  | ∧ HL |  |  |  |  |  |  |  |  |  |  |  | U 34 (H), V 34 (H) | 1·25 |
| 31 |  |  |  | | |  |  |  |  |  |  |  |  |  |  |  |  | U 34 (H), V 34 (H) | 80 |
| 32 |  |  |  |  |  |  |  |  |  |  |  |  |  |  |  |  | U 34 (W) | 6·00 |
| 33 |  |  | I |  |  |  |  |  |  |  |  |  |  |  |  |  | V 34 (H) | 1·75 |
| 34 |  |  | ∧ |  |  |  |  |  |  |  |  |  |  |  |  | 5 HAL | E 26 | 6·00 |
| 35 |  |  |  |  |  |  |  |  |  |  |  |  |  |  |  | 2 F | D 25 | 5·50 |
| 36 |  |  | o |  |  |  |  |  |  |  |  |  |  |  |  |  | K 29, M 30 | 1·75 |

# KING GEORGE V. ½d., TYPE N6. Wmk. Block Cypher, W.15. Waterlow (Plates 37 to 53)

| Plate | 1st stamp, Row No. | | | | Bottom row, Stamp No. | | | | | | | | 12th stamp, Row No. | | | | Controls | Positional piece Prices from |
|---|---|---|---|---|---|---|---|---|---|---|---|---|---|---|---|---|---|---|
| | 17 | 18 | 19 | 20 | 1 | 2 | 3 | 8 | 9 | 10 | 11 | 12 | 17 | 18 | 19 | 20 | | |
| 37 | | | | | | | | ∧ | | | | | | | | o | P 31, Q 32 | 5·00 |
| 38 | | | | | | | | | | | o | | | | | | Q 32 | 4·50 |
| 39 | | | | | | | | | | | | | | | o | | R 32 | 4·50 |
| 40 | | | | | | | | | | | | | | | o | o | T 33 | 4·50 |
| 41 | | o | | | | | | | | | | | | | | | A 24 | 2·25 |
| 42 | | | | | | | | | | | | | | | | | H 27 | 6·00 |
| 43 | | | | | | | | | | | | | | | | | G 27, I 28 | 8·00 |
| 44 | | | | | | | | | | | | | | | | | N 30 | 8·00 |
| 45 | | | | | | | | | | | | | | | | | F 26 | 8·00 |
| 46 | | | | | | | o L.F | | | | | | | | | | A 24 | 75 |
| 47 | | | | | | | o P(N)N ∧ | | | | | | | | | | K 29 | 1·50 |
| 48 | | | | | | | | | | | | | | | | | U 34 (W) V 34 (H) | 35·00 25 |
| 49 | | | | | | | | | | | | | | | | ∧ | U 34 (W) U 34 (H) | 45·00 2·50 |
| 50 | | | | │ | | | | | | | | | | | | | U 34 (H), V 34 (H) | 25 |
| 51 | | | | | | | | | | | | | | | | o | V 34 (H) | 1·50 |
| 52 | | | | | | | | | | | | | | | ooo | | D 25 | 7·00 |
| 53 | ½o | | | | | | | | | | | | | | | | F 26, G 27 | 5·00 |

**183**

**KING GEORGE V.   1d., TYPE N5.   WMK. SIMPLE CYPHER, W.14.   HARRISON**

Plate          Marking

1   No marking
2a  Dot under left serif of P 1st
2b  Added $\frac{1}{2}$ dot (inner) and dot 20th left side,
    8 mm.
3a  Dot under E(N) of 2nd
3b  Added two dots under O(N)E of 3rd
3c  Added dot and $\frac{1}{2}$ dot (outer) 20th left side,
    $10\frac{1}{2}$ mm.
4a  Small dot under P of 3rd
4b  Added minute dot at left, under 3rd
5a  Dot under P of 4th
5b  Added dot under N(N) of 4th
5c  Added dot under N(E) of 1st
6a  Dot under PE of 1st
6b  Added dot under N(E) of 1st. Dot 18th right
    side, 10 mm.  Rule under 11th thin
7   Dot under P of 3rd.  $\frac{1}{2}$ dot (inner) 17th left
    side, $12\frac{1}{2}$ mm.  Dot 17th right side, 10 mm.
    Nick left base of 12th.  Rule under 11th thin
8a  Slanting internal cut under PE of 1st
8b  Added small dot under (P)E of 5th
8c  Added $\frac{1}{2}$ dot (inner) and dot bulging (inner)
    20th left side, $8\frac{1}{2}$, 7 mm.
9   Dot 20th left side, $13\frac{1}{2}$ mm.
10a 2 big dots under (O)N, E(N) of 2nd
10B Added long dot under EP of 2nd
11a Dot (breaking right) 18th right side, 10 mm.
11b Added small dot 18th right side, $4\frac{3}{4}$ mm., the
    original dot now bulging right
12  Dot (central) 18th right side, 12 mm.
13  Long dot (breaking right) 19th left side, 8 mm.
14a Dot 19th left side, 12 mm.  Two internal cuts
    to left of O and under O of 2nd
14b Added two internal cuts under NE and P of
    2nd
15  Dot 17th right side, $8\frac{3}{4}$ mm.
16  Small dot 20th left side, $7\frac{3}{4}$ mm.  Dot 18th
    right side, 11 mm.  Top 19th left side bevelled
17  Triangular dot under E(N) of 2nd
18  Triangular dot under P of 3rd
19  Irregular dot, which is large and sometimes
    plain, but at other times hardly visible (top)
    under EN of 4th.  Small dot above 11th
    upper pane
20  Small dot 18th right side, 11 mm.  Rule
    thinner at top
21  Dot 18th right side, $7\frac{1}{2}$ mm.
22  Dot (bulging right) 17th right side, 11 mm.
23  $\frac{1}{2}$ cut (base) and $\frac{1}{2}$ dot (top) under (N)N of 1st
24  2 small dots under ONE of 2nd
25  Two small dots at left and under PE of 4th
26  Dot breaking left 18th right side, $11\frac{3}{4}$ mm.
27  Small dot 18th right side, 12 mm.
28  Dot (right) 18th right side, 11 mm.
29a Dot (left) 20th left side, $12\frac{1}{2}$ mm.
29b Added cut to left of O of 1st.  Added large
    dot to left of O of 4th
30  Flat oval dot under EN of 1st
31  Dot (breaking base) under EP of 2nd
32a $\frac{3}{4}$ dot (base) left of O of 3rd
32b Added large dot 20th left side, 10 mm.
33  Dot under O of 4th.  Dot 18th right side,
    $12\frac{1}{4}$ mm.  Base of 10th damaged at right
34  Dot 18th right side, $8\frac{1}{2}$ mm.
35  Minute nick under NY of 11th; dot 17th right
    side, 10 mm.  (Smaller and more regular
    than Pl. 7)
36  Curved dot under PEN of 1st (breaking base)
37a Dot 20th left side, $8\frac{3}{4}$ mm.  Right end of
    rule under 3rd damaged
37b Added slanting $\frac{3}{4}$ cut (base) under PE of
    3rd
37c Added wide $\frac{3}{4}$ cut (base) under PEN of 2nd
38a Curved dot under PE of 3rd
38b Added dot 19th left side, 11 mm.
39a Curved dot under E(P) of 3rd
39b Added curved dot under PE of 4th
40a Dot under (N)E of 3rd; dot under P of 7th; dot
    18th left side, 13 mm.  Dot 19th side,
    11 mm. (breaking inner)
40b Added dot 17th left side, $11\frac{1}{4}$ mm.

41  Dot under N(E) of 4th.  Dot under P of 8th
    $\frac{1}{2}$ dot (inner) 17th left side, 12 mm.
42a Dot under P of 6th
42b Added dot under EN of 1st and under EN
    of 2nd
43  Horizontal gash (base) under PE of 1st
44  Dot under P of 1st.  Dot under P of 5th
    Dot 20th left side, $10\frac{1}{2}$ mm.  Dot 17th left
    side, 14 mm.
45  Large dot breaking base under EN of 2nd.
    Dot 20th left side, 10 mm.  Dot 19th left
    side, $12\frac{1}{2}$ mm.
46a Curved dot under NE of 3rd
46b Added large irregular curved dot under EPE
    of 1st
47  Small dot under P of 2nd
48  Curved dot under N(N) of 2nd.  Dot under
    NE of 3rd which later became larger oval dot
    (breaking base)
49  Dot under NE of 2nd; minute dot under ON
    of 12th.  X cut 20th left side, 12–14 mm.
50  Large $\frac{1}{2}$ dot (base) under PE of 2nd.  Dot
    19th left side, 10 mm.
51  $\frac{1}{2}$ dot (top) under PE of 3rd
52  Dot under PE of 1st
53a Large dot (breaking top) under EP of 3rd.
    Long dot 19th right side, 11 mm.  Cut 15th
    left side, $12\frac{1}{4}$ mm.  Rules at sides thick.
53b Added large dot (breaking base) under EN
    of 1st
54  Indent (base) under ON of 5th.  Dot (breaking
    inner) 19th left side, 10 mm.
55  Dot 20th left side, $11\frac{1}{2}$ mm.  The rule is 23
    mm. high (see Plate 119)
56a Small oval dot under PE of 1st.  Base (outer)
    20th left side rounded
56b Added dot (top) under (N)E of 3rd
57  Dash under EN and dot under (N)N of 1st.
    Dot and irregular $\frac{1}{2}$ cut (base) under EP of
    2nd.  Dot (base) under NE of 3rd.  4 cuts
    19th right side, $9\frac{1}{2}$–11 mm.
58  Large dot (breaking top) under PEN of 2nd
59  Oval cut under EP of 2nd.  Nick (base) at
    right end of 10th
60  Dot under P of 2nd.  2 oval cuts under PE
    of 3rd
61a Dot and oval dot under EPE of 2nd.  Large
    dot (breaking top) under NE of 4th
61b Added large dot (top) under N(N) of 4th
62  Irregular dot with spur breaking base under
    E(P) of 4th
63  Dot under EP and dash to the right of Y
    of 4th.  Nick (outer) 20th left side, 10 mm.
    Dot 17th left side, $15\frac{1}{4}$ mm.  Base 20th left
    side bevelled.  $\frac{1}{4}$ dot (top) above 1st top row
    to right of rule
64  Inverted V cut (base) under (P)E of 2nd
65a Indent (base) under NN of 11th
65b Added diagonal cut with internal nick below
    it 18th right side, 10 mm., $9\frac{1}{2}$ mm.
66  X cut 17th right side, $14\frac{1}{2}$ mm.  X cut and
    straight cut 18th right side, $13\frac{1}{2}$, $12\frac{1}{2}$ mm.
67a 2 dots over 2 cuts 19th right side, 9, 13 mm.
    Rule under 11th thinner.  Dot (top) under
    P of 3rd
67b Added X cut 17th right side, 10 mm.  X cut
    18th right side, $10\frac{1}{2}$ mm.
68a Dot (breaking base) under P of 1st
68b Added half dot (breaking base) under NE
    of 2nd
68c Added 3 dots under PE, NN to right of Y
    of 11th
69a Dot (base) under PE of 1st
69b Added dot 20th left side, $13\frac{3}{4}$ mm.
70a Dot under EN of 2nd
70b Added two irregular dots breaking top and
    base under (P)E of 3rd
71  $\frac{1}{2}$ dot (top) under PE of 10th; small dot 18th
    right side, 6 mm.
72  Nick (base) at right end of 11th
73a Dot 18th right side, $9\frac{1}{2}$ mm.

1d., Type **N5**, Wmk. **W.14**, Harrison—*continued*

| Plate | Marking |
|---|---|
| 73b | Added dot under (N)N of 1st; added ½ dot (inner) 20th left side, 9¼ mm. |
| 74 | Dot (base) under EP of 2nd. Dot (central) 19th left side, 14 mm. |
| 75a | Dot (sometimes breaking base) to left of P of 10th. 2 dots, left of O and under (N)E of 2nd |
| 75b | Added slanting ½ cut 18th right side (inner) |
| 76 | Diagonal cut 19th right side, 14–13 mm. Thin tapering cut, 13 mm. (forming a rudimentary V) |
| 77a | Dot under (P)E of 1st. ½ dot (inner) 20th left side, 11¾ mm. |
| 77b | Added dot (outer) 19th left side, 13¼ mm. |
| 78 | Cut at right of 1st |
| 79 | Dot under EP of 1st |
| 80a | Dot under EN of 2nd; dot 19th left side, 10½ mm. |
| 80b | Added four dots under EN, NY of 11th |
| 81 | Dot under (N)E of 10th |
| 82 | Dot (top) under EP of 2nd |
| 83 | Dot 20th left side breaking outer, 10½ mm. Rule 20th left bevelled at base. Tiny nick (base) under EP of 4th |
| 84 | ½ dot (base) at extreme left of 11th |
| 85 | Dot 19th left side, 10½ mm. |
| 86 | Cut under (P)E of 2nd. Two tall dots 2nd left side, 10, 14½ mm. |
| 87a | Dot (breaking inner) 20th right side, 12 mm. |
| 87b | Added dot under PE of 10th |
| 88a | Dot 17th right side, 3 mm. |
| 88b | Added dot 19th left side, 7 mm. |
| 89 | Dot (inner) 18th right side, 9¾ mm. |
| 90 | Tall dot 17th right side, 12½ mm. |
| 91 | Dot 18th right side 9½ mm.; minute nick 19th right side, 12¾ mm. |
| 92 | 3 cuts 20th right side, 8, 12½, 17 mm. Small dot 17th right side, 5½ mm. Minute dot 20th left side, 6½ mm. |
| 93 | 4 half cuts (outer) 20th right side, 5, 8¾, 12¼, 15½ mm. |
| 94 | Tiny dot (inner) 20th left side, 12 mm. |
| 95 | Large dot (breaking left) 18th right side, 11½ mm. |
| 96 | Left of 12th thinner |
| 97a | ½ dot (base) under (P)E of 1st |
| 97b | Added dot joined to tiny dot, 20th left side, 9½ mm. |
| 98 | Vacant |
| 99 | Tall dot 20th right side, 12 mm. (Waterlow Plate 3) |
| 100 | Dot 20th left side, 13½ mm.; two small cuts left of O and under O of 3rd |
| 101 | Fine tall dot 19th left side, 8¼ mm. (Waterlow Plate 5) |
| 102 | Thick irregular cut 19th right side, 14¼–13 mm., thin tapering cut, 13 mm. (Rather similar to Plate 76, but the upper cut is thicker and longer) |
| 103 | Dot 18th right side 10 mm.; fine diagonal cut 19th right side with outer part of rule indented, 10 mm. |
| 104 | Thin X cut over diagonal cut 17th right side, 7 mm. Internal crescent cut 20th left side, 11 mm. |
| 105 | Dot breaking top under right serif of P of 9th |
| 106 | Large oval ½ dot (top) under PE of 9th |
| 107 | Dot (base) under EP of 9th |
| 108 | Dot (base) under P of 9th (bulging base). Rules at sides, particularly the left, very irregular |
| 109 | Cut 15th left side, 12½ mm. Rules at sides thinner than Plate 53 |
| 110 | Cut 16th left side, 12 mm. |
| 111 | Tiny dot under PE of 3rd. Rule 19th left side very thick. Rule 20th left side tapers slightly at base |
| 112 | Small dot (inner) 18th left side, 11 mm. Small dot under P of 2nd. Dot under PE of 3rd. Nick (inner) 18th right side, 21 mm. |
| 113 | Minute nick 19th right side, 16 mm. Tall dot (breaking left) 18th right side, 12 mm. |
| 114a | Cut with central dot under O of 3rd. Tiny dot above 5th top row |
| 114b | Added two cuts with central dots, 20th left side, 13, 17½ mm. (Waterlow Plate 1) |
| 115 | Small dot 18th right side, 16 mm. |
| 116 | Dot 18th right side, 10 mm. |
| 117 | Dot 17th right side, 12 mm.; dot 18th right side, 14 mm. ½ dot (top) above 1st top row to left of rule |
| 118 | Tiny ½ dot (outer) 20th right side, 5½ mm. Large irregular dot 19th left side, 10¾ mm. (Waterlow Plate 4) |
| 119 | Dot (breaking inner) 20th left side, 11½ mm. The rule is 22¾ mm. high (to distinguish from plate 55) |
| 120 | Minute nick (outer) 20th left side, 2½ mm. (Waterlow Plate 6) |
| 121 | Small dot 20th left side, 11¾ mm. Rule damaged 15th right side. Tiny dot above 3rd top row |

# KING GEORGE V. 1d., TYPE N5. Wmk. Simple Cypher, W.14. Harrison (Plates 1 to 9)

| Plate | 1st stamp, Row No. | | | | Bottom row, Stamp No. | | | | | | | | 12th stamp, Row No. | | | | Controls | Positional piece Prices from |
|---|---|---|---|---|---|---|---|---|---|---|---|---|---|---|---|---|---|---|
| | 17 | 18 | 19 | 20 | 1 | 2 | 3 | 4 | 5 | 6 | 7 | 8 | 17 | 18 | 19 | 20 | | |
| 1 | | | | | | | | | | | | | | | | | ? | — |
| 2a | | | | | O / P | | | | | | | | | | | | C 12, C 13 | 60 |
| 2b | | | | $\frac{1}{2}$OO | O / P | | | | | | | | | | | | C 13 | 60 |
| 3a | | | | | | O / EN | | | | | | | | | | | C 12, C 13 | 1·50 |
| 3b | | | | | | O / EN | O / O(N)E | | | | | | | | | | C 13 | 2·50 |
| 3c | | | | O$\frac{1}{2}$O | | O / EN | O / O(N)E | | | | | | | | | | C 13 | 1·25 |
| 4a | | | | | | | O / P | | | | | | | | | | C 12, C 13 | 1·50 |
| 4b | | | | | | | OO / P | | | | | | | | | | C 13, C 14 | 1·25 |
| 5a | | | | | | | | O / P | | | | | | | | | C 12, C 13 | 1·50 |
| 5b | | | | | | | | OO / PN | | | | | | | | | C 13 | 2·00 |
| 5c | | | | | O / N(E) | | | OO / PN | | | | | | | | | C 13, C 14 | 1·25 |
| 6a | | | | | O / PE | | | | | | | | | | | | C 12 | 1·50 |
| 6b | | | | | OO / PEN | | O / P | | | | | | | O | | | C 12, C 13 | 1·50 |
| 7 | $\frac{1}{2}$O | | | | | | | | | | | | O | | | | C 12, C 13 | 55 |
| 8a | | | | | ∧ / PE | | | | | | | | | | | | C 13 | 2·50 |
| 8b | | | | | ∧ / PE | | | | O / (P)E | | | | | | | | C 13 | 1·30 |
| 8c | | | | $\frac{1}{2}$OO | ∧ / PE | | | | O / (P)E | | | | | | | | C 13, C 14 | 1·60 |
| 9 | | | | O | | | | | | | | | | | | | C 13, D 14 | 1·60 |

# KING GEORGE V. 1d., TYPE N5. Wmk. Simple Cypher, W.14. Harrison (Plates 10a to 24)

| Plate | 1st stamp, Row No. | | | | Bottom row, Stamp No. | | | | | | | | 12th stamp, Row No. | | | | Controls | Prices from |
|---|---|---|---|---|---|---|---|---|---|---|---|---|---|---|---|---|---|---|
| | 17 | 18 | 19 | 20 | 1 | 2 | 3 | 4 | 5 | 6 | 7 | 8 | 17 | 18 | 19 | 20 | | |
| 10a | | | | | | oo NE | | | | | | | | | | | C 13 | 1·30 |
| 10b | | | | | | ooo NEP | | | | | | | | | | | E 14 | — |
| 11a | | | | | | | | | | | | | | o | | | C 13 | 2·50 |
| 11b | | | | | | | | | | | | | | oo | | | C 13 | 2·00 |
| 12 | | | | | | | | | | | | | | o | | | C 13, C 14, D 14, E 14 | 1·75 |
| 13 | | | o | | | 2 O | | | | | | | | | | | C 14, D 14 | 2·50 |
| 14a | | | o | | | 4 ONE | | | | | | | | | | | C 14, D 14 | 2·50 |
| 14b | | | o | | | | | | | | | | | | | | E 14 | 3·00 |
| 15 | | | | | | | | | | | | | o | | | | C 13, C 14, D 14, E 14 | 1·50 |
| 16 | | | | o | | | | | | | | | | o | | | C 13, D 14, E 14, F 15 | 1·40 |
| 17 | | | │ | | | o E(N) | | | | | | | | | | | D 14, E 14 | 1·50 |
| 18 | | | | | | | o P | | | | | | | | | | D 14, E 14 | 1·50 |
| 19 | | | | | | | | o EN | | | | | | | | | C 14, D 14, E 14 | 1·20 |
| 20 | | | | | | | | | | | | | | o | | | D 14 | 2·50 |
| 21 | | | | | | | | | | | | | | o | | | D 14 | 3·00 |
| 22 | | | | | 1½o (N)N | | | | | | | | o | | | | D 14, E 14 | 2·50 |
| 23 | | | | | | | | | | | | | | | | | E 14 | 2·75 |
| 24 | | | | | | oo ONE | | | | | | | | | | | E 14 | 2·75 |

187

# KING GEORGE V. 1d., TYPE N5. Wmk. Simple Cypher, W.14. Harrison (Plates 25 to 38a)

| Plate | 1st stamp, Row No. | | | | Bottom row, Stamp No. | | | | | | | | 12th stamp, Row No. | | | | Controls | Positional piece Prices from |
|---|---|---|---|---|---|---|---|---|---|---|---|---|---|---|---|---|---|---|
| | 17 | 18 | 19 | 20 | 1 | 2 | 3 | 4 | 5 | 6 | 7 | 8 | 17 | 18 | 19 | 20 | | |
| 25 | | | | | | | | oo / PE | | | | | | | | | C 13, D 14, E 14 | 2·00 |
| 26 | | | | | | | | | | | | | | o | | | E 14 | 2·25 |
| 27 | | | | | | | | | | | | | | o | | | E 14 | 1·50 |
| 28 | | | | | | | | | | | | | | o | | | E 14 | 2·50 |
| 29a | | | | o | | | | o o | | | | | | | | | E 14 | 3·00 |
| 29b | | | | o | 1 / O | | | | | | | | | | | | F 15, G 15 | 1·60 |
| 30 | | | | | o / EN | | | | | | | | | | | | F 15, H 16 | 3·00 |
| 31 | | | | | | o / EP | | | | | | | | | | | F 15, H 16 | 2·75 |
| 32a | | | | | | | ¾ / O | | | | | | | | | | F 15 | 2·50 |
| 32b | | | | o | | | ¾ / O | | | | | | | | | | G 15 | 2·50 |
| 33 | | | | | | | | o o | | | | | | o | | | F 15, G 15 | 2·50 |
| 34 | | | | | | | | | | | | | | o | | | F 15 | 2·75 |
| 35 | | | | | | | | | | | | | o | | | | F 15, G 15 | 3·50 |
| 36 | | | | | o / PEN | | | | | | | | | | | | G 15, H 16 | 3·00 |
| 37a | | | | o | | | | | | | | | | | | | E 14, F 15, G 15 | 3·00 |
| 37b | | | | o | | ¾> / PEN | ¾> / PE | | | | | | | | | | G 15 | 4·50 |
| 37c | | | | o | | | o / PE | | | | | | | | | | G 15, H 16 | 3·00 |
| 38a | | | | | | | o / PE | | | | | | | | | | G 15, H 16, I 16 | 2·50 |

# KING GEORGE V. 1d., TYPE N5. Wmk. Simple Cypher, W.14. Harrison (Plates 38b to 51)

| Plate | 1st stamp, Row No. | | | | Bottom row, Stamp No. | | | | | | | | | | | | Controls | Prices from |
|---|---|---|---|---|---|---|---|---|---|---|---|---|---|---|---|---|---|---|
| | 17 | 18 | 19 | 20 | 1 | 2 | 3 | 4 | 5 | 6 | 7 | 8 | 9 | 10 | 11 | 12 | | |
| 38b | | | | | | | o/PE | | | | | | | | | | I 16 | 4·50 |
| 39a | | | o | | | | | | | | | | | | | | G 15 | 4·25 |
| 39b | | | | | | | o/E(P) | | | | | | | | | | G 15, H 16 | 3·00 |
| 40a | | o | o | | | | o/E(P) | o/PE | | | o/P | | | | | | G 15, H 16 | 4·50 |
| 40b | o | o | o | | | | o/(N)E | | | | o/P | | | | | | H 16, I 16 | 4·25 |
| 41 | ⅓o | | | | | | | o/N(E) | | | | o/P | | | | | G 15, H 16, I 16 | 2·50 |
| 42a | | | | | o/EN | | | | | o/P | | | | | | | G 15 | 3·00 |
| 42b | | | | | | o/EN | | | | o/P | | | | | | | G 15, H 16 | 2·50 |
| 43 | | | | o | PE | | | | | | | | | | | | C 14, D 14 | 3·75 |
| 44 | o | | | o | o/P | | | | o/P | | | | | | | | G 15, H 16 | 3·50 |
| 45 | | | o | o | | o/EN | o/NE | | | | | | | | | | H 16 | 5·50 |
| 46a | | | | | | | o/NE | | | | | | | | | | H 16 | 3·00 |
| 46b | | | | | o/EPE | | | | | | | | | | | | I 16 | 4·50 |
| 47 | | | | | | o/P | | | | | | | | | | | I 16 | 5·00 |
| 48 | | | | | | o/N(N) | o/NE | | | | | | | | | | I 16 | 5·00 |
| 49 | | | | X | | o/NE | | | | | | | | | | o/ON | I 16, J 17, K 17 | 1·50 |
| 50 | | | o | | | ½o/PE | | | | | | | | | | | I 16 | 5·50 |
| 51 | | | | | | | ½o/PE | | | | | | | | | | I 16, J 17 | 4·00 |

# KING GEORGE V.  1d., TYPE N5.  Wmk. Simple Cypher, W.14.  Harrison (Plates 52 to 65b)

| Plate | 1st stamp, Row No. 17 | 18 | 19 | 20 | Bottom row, Stamp No. 1 | 2 | 3 | 4 | 5 | 10 | 11 | 12 | 12th stamp, Row No. 17 | 18 | 19 | 20 | Controls | Positional piece Prices from |
|---|---|---|---|---|---|---|---|---|---|---|---|---|---|---|---|---|---|---|
| 52 | | | | | °PE | | | | | | | | | | | | F 15, G 15 | 2·50 |
| 53a | | | | | | | °EP | | | | | | | | ○ | | I 16, J 17 | 2·00 |
| 53b | | | | | °EN | | °EP | | | | | | | | ○ | | J 17 | 5·50 |
| 54 | | | ○ | | | | | | ∧ON | | | | | | | | I 16 | 5·00 |
| 55 | | | | ○ | | | | | | | | | | | | | G 15, H 16, I 16, J 17 | 4·00 |
| 56a | | | | | °PE | | | | | | | | | | | | J 17 | 4·50 |
| 56b | | | | | °PE | °½EP | (N)°E | | | | | | | | | | J 17 | 3·75 |
| 57 | | | | | °(N)N | °PEN | °NE | | | | | | | | 4 | | J 17 | 75 |
| 58 | | | | | | 1 EP | | | | | | | | | | | J 17 | 3·00 |
| 59 | | | | | | | | | | ∧ | | | | | | | J 17 | 75 |
| 60 | | | | | | °P | 2 PE | | | | | | | | | | J 17 | 3·00 |
| 61a | | | | | | °°EPE | | °NE | | | | | | | | | J 17 | 4·50 |
| 61b | | | | | | °°EPE | | °°NNE | | | | | | | | | J 17 | 3·00 |
| 62 | | | | | | | | °E(P) | | | | | | | | | J 17 | 4·50 |
| 63 | ○ | | | ∧ | | | | °EP | | | | | | ∧< | | | J 17, K 17, K 18 | 2·50 |
| 64 | | | | | | ∧(P)E | | | | | | | | | | | G 15 | 4·00 |
| 65a | | | | | | | | | | | ∧NN | | | | | | J 17, K 17, K 18 | 80 |
| 65b | | | | | | | | | | | ∧NN | | | | | | K 18 | 4·00 |

# KING GEORGE V. 1d., TYPE N5. Wmk. Simple Cypher, W.14. Harrison (Plates 66 to 76)

| Plate | 1st stamp, Row No. 17 | 18 | 19 | 20 | Bottom row, Stamp No. 1 | 2 | 3 | 4 | 9 | 10 | 11 | 12 | 12th stamp, Row No. 17 | 18 | 19 | 20 | Controls | Positional piece Prices from |
|---|---|---|---|---|---|---|---|---|---|---|---|---|---|---|---|---|---|---|
| 66 | | | | | | | | | | | | | X | X1 | | | J 17, K 17 | 6·00 |
| 67a | | | | | | | o P | | | | \| | | | | oo 2 | | J 17 | 75 |
| 67b | | | | | | | o P | | | | \| | | X | X | oo 2 | | J 17, K 17 | 5·00 |
| 68a | | | | | o P | †o NE | | | | | | | | | | | K 17 | 4·50 |
| 68b | | | | | o P | †o NE | | | | | | | | | | | K 18 | 4·50 |
| 68c | | | | | o P | | | | | | ooo PNN | | | | | | N 19, P 20 | 35 |
| 69a | | | | | o PE | | | | | | | | | | | | J 17 | 3·00 |
| 69b | | | | o | o PE | | | | | | | | | | | | K 17, M 18 | 2·50 |
| 70a | | | | | | o EN | | | | | | | | | | | K 17 | 4·50 |
| 70b | | | | | | o EN | oo (P)E | | | | | | | | | | K 18, L 18, M 19 | 1·50 |
| 71 | | | | | | | | | | †o PE | | | | o | | | K 17, K 18, M 19 | 55 |
| 72 | | | | | | | | | | | ∧ | | | | | | K 17, K 18 | 90 |
| 73a | | | | | | | | | | | | | | o | | | J 17, K 17, M 19 | 1·50 |
| 73b | | | o | †o | o (N)N | | | | | | | | | o | | | P 20, N 19 | 1·75 |
| 74 | | | | | | o EP | | | | o P | | | | | | | K 18, L 18, M 18 | 2·50 |
| 75a | | | | | | o O(N)E | | | | o P | | | | | | | K 18, L 18, N 19, O 19 | 1·50 |
| 75b | | | | | | o O(N)E | | | | | | | | † | | | O 20, R 21, S 21 | 2·50 |
| 76 | | | | | | | | | | | | | | | ∧ | | J 17, K 17, K 18 | 1·75 |

# KING GEORGE V. 1d., TYPE N5. Wmk. Simple Cypher, W.14. Harrison (Plates 77a to 90)

| Plate | 1st stamp, Row No. | | | | Bottom row, Stamp No. | | | | | | | | 12th stamp, Row No. | | | | Controls | Positional piece Prices from |
|---|---|---|---|---|---|---|---|---|---|---|---|---|---|---|---|---|---|---|
| | 17 | 18 | 19 | 20 | 1 | 2 | 3 | 4 | 9 | 10 | 11 | 12 | 17 | 18 | 19 | 20 | | |
| 77a | | | | ½o | o (P)E | | | | | | | | | | | | K 18 | 3·50 |
| 77b | | | o | ½o | o (P)E | | | | | | | | | | | | M 19 | 3·50 |
| 78 | | | | | 1 | | | | | | | | | | | | M 19, N 19, O 19 | 3·50 |
| 79 | | | | | o EP | | | | | | | | | | | | N 19, O 19 | 3·00 |
| 80a | | | o | | | o EN | | | | | | | | | | | K 18, N 19 | 3·00 |
| 80b | | | o | | | o EN | | | | | oooo ENY | | | | | | N 19, P 20 | 35 |
| 81 | | | | | | | | | | o (N)E | | | | | | | N 19 | 50 |
| 82 | | | | | | o EP | | | | | | | | | | | N 19 | 3·00 |
| 83 | | | | o | | | | ∧ EP | | | | | | | | | S 22 | 3·50 |
| 84 | | | o | | | 1 (P)E | | | | | ½o | | | | | | N 19 | 1·75 |
| 85 | | | | | | | | | | | | | | | | | P 20, Q 20 | 2·50 |
| 86 | | | | | | | | | | | | | | | | | S 22, T 22, W 23 | 2·50 |
| 87a | | | | | | | | | | o PE | | | | | | o | P 22, Q 20, Q 21, R 21 | 50 |
| 87b | | | | | | | | | | | | | | | | o | R 21, S 21, S 22, T 22, U 22 | 50 |
| 88a | | | | | | | | | | | | | o | | | | P 20 | 4·50 |
| 88b | | | o | | | | | | | | | | o | | | | Q 21 | 4·50 |
| 89 | | | | | | | | | | | | | | o | | | R 21 | 4·50 |
| 90 | | | | | | | | | | | | | o | | | | O 20 | 4·50 |

## KING GEORGE V. 1d., TYPE N5. Wmk. Simple Cypher, W.14. Harrison (Plates 91 to 107)

| Plate | 1st stamp, Row No. | | | | Bottom row, Stamp No. | | | | | | | | 12th stamp, Row No. | | | | Controls | Prices from Positional piece |
|---|---|---|---|---|---|---|---|---|---|---|---|---|---|---|---|---|---|---|
| | 17 | 18 | 19 | 20 | 1 | 2 | 3 | 4 | 9 | 10 | 11 | 12 | 17 | 18 | 19 | 20 | | |
| 91 | | | | | | | | | | | | | o | o | ∧ | | S 22, T 22, U 23 | 75 |
| 92 | | | | o | | | | | | | | | o | | | 3 | T 22, U 22, U 23, V 23 | 60 |
| 93 | | | | o | | | | | | | | | o | | | ½½½½ | T 22, U 22, U 23, V 23 | 60 |
| 94 | | | | | | | | | | | | | | | | | S 22, T 22 | 2·50 |
| 95 | | | | | | | | | | | | | | | | | P 20 | 4·00 |
| 96 | | | | | | | | | | | | | | o | | | S 21, T 22 | 1·00 |
| 97a | | | | | ½o(P)E | | | | | | | | | | | | ? | 4·50 |
| 97b | | | | oo | ½o(P)E | | | | | | | \| | | | | | S 22, U 22, U 23 | 2·50 |
| 98 | | | | | | | | | | | | | | | | | | † |
| 99 | | | | | | | 2 o | | | | | | | | | o | W 23, W 24 | 1·25 |
| 100 | | | o | o | | | | | | | | | | | | | ? | 4·50 |
| 101 | | | | | | | | | | | | ∧ | | | 2 | | V 23, W 23, W 24 | 1·25 |
| 102 | | | | | | | | | | | | | | | | | J 17 | 2·00 |
| 103 | | | | | | | | | | | | | | o | ∧ ∧ | | L 18, M 18 | 1·40 |
| 104 | | | | I | | | | | o P | | | | × | | | | J 17, L 18, M 18 | 5·00 |
| 105 | | | | | | | | | | | | | | | | | K 17, K 18, L 18 | 1·50 |
| 106 | | | | | | | | | ½o PE | | | | | | | | T 22 | 2·50 |
| 107 | | | | | | | | | o EP | | | | | | | | K 18, L 18 | 2·75 |

# KING GEORGE V. 1d., TYPE N5. Wmk. Simple Cypher, W.14. Harrison (Plates 108 to 121)

| Plate | 1st stamp, Row No. | | | | Bottom row, Stamp No. | | | | | | | | 12th stamp, Row No. | | | | Controls | Prices from | Positional piece |
|---|---|---|---|---|---|---|---|---|---|---|---|---|---|---|---|---|---|---|---|
| | 17 | 18 | 19 | 20 | 1 | 2 | 3 | 4 | 9 | 10 | 11 | 12 | 17 | 18 | 19 | 20 | | | |
| 108 | | | | | | | | | o/P | | | | | | | | N 19 | 1·25 | |
| 109 | | | | | | | | | | | | | | | | | I 16 | 9·00 | |
| 110 | | | | | | | | | | | | | | | | | H 16 | 9·00 | |
| 111 | | | \| | \| | | o/P | o/PE | | | | | | | | | | J 17 | 4·00 | |
| 112 | | o | | | | o/P | o/PE | | | | | | | < | | | K 17 | 4·50 | |
| 113 | | | | | | | | | | | | | | o | < | | Q 21, R 21 | 60 | |
| 114a | | | | | | | I/O | | | | | | | | | | S 22 | 5·50 | |
| 114b | | | | 2 | | | I/O | | | | | | | | | | V 23 | 5·50 | |
| 115 | | | | | | | | | | | | | | o | | | W 23 | 4·00 | |
| 116 | | | | | | | | | | | | | | o | | | U 22 | 3·50 | |
| 117 | | | o | | | | | | | | | | o | | | | V 23, W 24 | 4·50 | |
| 118 | | | | | | | | | | | | | | o | | ½o | V 23, W 23 | 1·50 | |
| 119 | | | | o | | | | | | | | | | | | | O 20 | 4·00 | |
| 120 | | | | < | | | | | | | | | | | | | W 24 | 4·50 | |
| 121 | | | | o | | | | | | | | | | | | | V 23 | 4·00 | |

194

## KING GEORGE V. 1d., TYPE N5. WMK. BLOCK CYPHER, W.15. WATERLOW

| Plate | Marking |
|---|---|
| 1 | Two cuts 20th left side, 13, 17½ mm. (Harrison Plate 114b) |
| 2 | Small dot at right of 11th |
| 3 | Dot (inner) 20th right side, 12 mm. Irregular dot 11–12 mm. 20th left side. Nick (base) under (N)N of 4th. Damage to left base of rule under 11th (Harrison Plate 99) |
| 4 | Dot 19th left side, 10¾ mm. Tiny half dot (outer), 20th right side 5½ mm. (Harrison Plate 118) |
| 5 | Dot 19th left side, 8¼ mm. (Harrison Plate 101) |
| 6 | ½ cut (outer) 18th left side, 7½ mm. Nick 20th left side (outer), 2½ mm. Small ½ cut base under left of 9th. Large double dot breaking both sides. 18th right side, 12 mm. (Harrison Plate 120) |
| 7 | Large ½ dot (breaking inner) 19th left side, 13 mm. Indent (base) under (N)N of 8th |
| 8 | Dot 17th right side, 11 mm. |
| 9 | Dot 17th right side, 7½ mm. Rule 15th left side damaged (centre). Cut 20th left side, 14½ mm. Nick (top) 6th under P |
| 10 | Dot 20th left side, 12 mm. Tiny dot 17th right side, 7½ mm. |
| 11 | Rule 19th left side damaged (outer). Minute dot 17th right side, 14 mm. |
| 12 | Dot 17th left side, 10½ mm. |
| 13 | Dot under EP of 1st |
| 14 | Dot 18th left side, 12½ mm. Rule 19th left bevelled at base |
| 15 | 20th left side severely damaged at left and broken near base |
| 16 | Left at 10th broken away at base |
| 17 | Horizontal dash at left of 11th |
| 18 | Nick 3rd right side, 6½ mm. Small nick at left base of 6th No other marking on sheet |
| 19 | Dot 4th left side, 11½ mm. 20th left side irregular. 12th right side bevelled at base |
| 20 | Cut 4th left side, 11 mm. Tiny nick 20th left side, 17½ mm. Scoop 6th right side |
| 21 | Minute dot to right of Y of 2nd. No other marking on sheet |
| 22 | Tiny dot and double dot 1st left side, 20½, 11 mm. ½ dot at right end of 3rd. Dot over 4th, and ½ dot at right of 5th all top row |
| 23 | Nick at left of 11th |
| 24 | Base of 20th right side bent in |
| 25 | As for Harrison Plate 117 |

## KING GEORGE V. 1d., TYPE N5. Wmk. Block Cypher, W.15. Waterlow. (Plates 1 to 18)

| Plate | 1st stamp, Row No. | | | | Bottom row, Stamp No. | | | | | | | | | 12th stamp, Row No. | | | Controls | Positional piece Prices from |
|---|---|---|---|---|---|---|---|---|---|---|---|---|---|---|---|---|---|---|
| | 17 | 18 | 19 | 20 | 1 | 2 | 3 | 4 | 6 | 8 | 9 | 10 | 11 | 17 | 18 | 20 | | |
| 1 | | | | 2 | | | 1 o | | | | | | | | | | C 25, E 26 | 4·50 |
| 2 | | | | | | | | | | | | | o | | | | F 26, G 27 | 75 |
| 3 | | | | o | | | | (N)N | | | | | | | | o | F 26, G 27 | 80 |
| 4 | | | o | | | | | | | | | | † | | | ½o | F 26, G 27, H 27 | 80 |
| 5 | | | o | | | | | | | | | | | | | | C 25 | 5·50 |
| 6 | | † | ½o | < | | | | | | | | | | | oo | | C 25, D 25, E 26 | 4·50 |
| 7 | | | | | | | | | | (N)N | | | | | | | E 26 | 5·50 |
| 8 | | | | | | | | | | | | | | o | | | F 26 | 5·50 |
| 9 | | | | 1 | | | | | P | | | | | o | | | B 24, C 25 | 5·50 |
| 10 | | | | o | | | | | | | | | | o | | | A 24, B 24 | 4·50 |
| 11 | | | | | | | | | | | | | | o | | | B 24 | 4·50 |
| 12 | o | | | | o EP | | | | | | | | | | | | B 24, C 25, H 27 | 4·50 |
| 13 | | | | | | | | | | | | | | | | | F 26, G 27 | 4·50 |
| 14 | | o | | | | | | | | | | | | | | | A 24 | 6·00 |
| 15 | | | | \| | | | | | | | | | | | | | M 30 | 5·00 |
| 16 | | | | | | | | | | | | \| | | | | | K 29, L 29, M 30, N 30 | 75 |
| 17 | | | \| | | | | | | | | | | | | | | Q 32, R 32, S 33, T 33 | 75 |
| 18 | | | | | | | < | | < | | | | | | | | K 29 | 6·00 |

196

# KING GEORGE V. 1d., TYPE N5. Wmk. Block Cypher, W.15. Waterlow (Plates 19 to 25)

| Plate | 1st stamp, Row No. | | | | Bottom row, Stamp No. | | | | | | | | | 12th stamp, Row No. | | | Controls | Prices from |
|---|---|---|---|---|---|---|---|---|---|---|---|---|---|---|---|---|---|---|
| | 17 | 18 | 19 | 20 | 1 | 2 | 3 | 4 | 6 | 8 | 9 | 10 | 11 | 17 | 18 | 20 | | |
| 19 | | | | │ | | | | | | | | | | | | | L 29 | 6·50 |
| 20 | | | | ∧ | | | | | | | | | | | | | M 30 | 6·50 |
| 21 | | | | | | O̶Y | | | | | | | | | | | J 28 | 5·50 |
| 22 | | | | | | | ½O | | | | | | | | | | ? | 6·00 |
| 23 | | | | | | | | | | | | | ∧ | | | | U 34 (H), V 34 (H) | 50 |
| 24 | | | | | | | | | | | | | | | | │ | U 34 (W) | 50·00 |
| 25 | | | | | | | | | | | | | | O | O | | C 25 | 9·00 |

## KING GEORGE V.   1½d., TYPE N6.   WMK. SIMPLE CYPHER, W.14.   HARRISON

| Plate | Marking |
|---|---|
| 1a | Dot above 1st in upper and lower panes |
| 1b | Dots above 1st filled in |
| 2a | Dot above 2nd in upper and lower panes; scoop under THR of 10th.   1st right side split at top |
| 2b | Dots above 2nd filled in |
| 2c | Added minute dot under L of 1st |
| 2d | Added very fine cut 1st top row. Added dot 20th right side, 11½ mm. |
| 3a | Dot above 3rd in upper and lower panes |
| 3b | Dots above 3rd filled in |
| 3c | Added minute dot under L of 2nd.   Large internal cut 18th right side, 5–10 mm |
| 3d | Added very fine cut 2nd top row |
| 3e | Added dot 19th right side, 8½ mm. |
| 4a | Dot above 4th in upper and lower panes |
| 4b | Dots above 4th filled in |
| 5a | Dot (base) to left of T of 1st |
| 5b | Added ½ dot (inner) 19th left side, 6¼ mm. |
| 6a | Large dot (breaking base) to left of T of 2nd |
| 6b | Added fine ½ cut (base) under P of 2nd; added dot under AL of 9th |
| 7 | Dot (top) to left of T of 3rd.  Nick (outer) 3rd left side, 21 mm. |
| 8a | Dot (base) to left of T of 4th |
| 8b | Added ½ cut (outer) 19th left side, 9½ mm. Added fine ½ cut (base) under FP of 2nd |
| 9 | Large dot (bulging top) under T of 1st |
| 10a | 2 dots 19th left side, 8½, 9 mm. Lower dot breaking outer |
| 10b | Added tiny nick (base) under H of 2nd |
| 11 | Dot 20th left side, 11½ mm. Crack (outer) 11th right side |
| 12a | 2 cuts 20th left side, 5½, 7 mm. Minute dot under F of 12th |
| 12b | Added dot under A of 9th |
| 13a | 2 cuts 19th left side, 7, 8 mm. Rules 18th, 19th and 20th left irregular.  ½ dot (base) under F of 11th |
| 13b | Added nick (base) under HA of 2nd |
| 14a | Cut 20th left side, 10 mm.  Fine cut under H of 1st |
| 14b | Cut under H filled in |
| 15a | ½ cut 17th left side, 7½ mm. |
| 15b | Added dot under AL of 2nd |
| 16a | Dot 17th left side, 11½ mm. |
| 16b | Added small dot under A of 3rd.  Added cut 18th right side, 10½ mm. |
| 17 | Large dot (breaking base) under H(A) of 1st |
| 18 | Large oval dot under L of 2nd (breaking base). Tall oval dot 19th left side, 11½ mm., usually breaking right, sometimes left as well |
| 19 | Nick (inner) 19th left side, 10½ mm. |

| Plate | Marking |
|---|---|
| 20a | Cut 20th left side, 6½ mm. |
| 20b | Added ½ cut under TH of 1st |
| 21 | Large ½ dot (base) under L of 2nd. Fine ½ cut (base) under L of 11th |
| 22 | Double dot under A of 10th |
| 23 | No marking |
| 24a | Dot (outer) 19th left side, 6½ mm  Double dot under A of 9th |
| 24b | Added nick (base) under EN of 2nd.  *Note* Rule at 19th left is thicker and measures 23 mm.  See Plate 27 |
| 25 | Cut 19th left side, 5½ mm. |
| 26 | Oval (blurred) cut 20th left side, 15 mm. |
| 27 | Small dot (outer) 19th left side, 6¾ mm. *Note* Rule at 19th left measures 22¾ mm. See Plate 24.  On late printings from U 23, the rule under 1st is broken at bottom left |
| 28 | Small dot under A of 4th |
| 29 | ½ dot (outer) 20th right side, 21 mm. |
| 30 | No marking on lower pane.  ½ cut (outer) 3rd right side, 10 mm. |
| 31 | ½ dot (inner) 19th left side, 12 mm. |
| 32 | Dot 17th left side, 11 mm.  ½ dot (outer) 20th left side, 9 mm.  Lower end of 20th left side thinner. Dot and ½ dot above 1st top row |
| 33 | ½ dot (outer) 20th left side, 10½ mm. |
| 34 | Dot (inner) 20th left side, 13 mm. |
| 35 | Small dot 20th left side, 9 mm. |
| 36 | Oval cut 17th right side, 9½ mm. |
| 37 | Small nick (base) to left of T of 2nd |
| 38 | Tall dot 19th left side, 10½ mm |
| 39 | Dot (outer) 20th left side, 11½ mm.  ½ dot (outer) 19th left side, 10 mm. |
| 40 | 2 cuts 18th right side, 8¾, 10½ mm. |
| 41 | ½ dot (outer) 20th left side, 5 mm. (Waterlow Plate 10) |
| 42 | Outer side of 20th left side damaged 4–5 mm |
| 43 | Small ½ dot (base) under A of 4th.  Nick (outer) 7 mm. and tiny dot 11 mm. both 17th left side. (Waterlow Plate 11) |
| 44a | Small dot (inner) 18th left side, 9½ mm. |
| 44b | Added dot under H of 10th; added tiny dots under HR and (E)E of 11th |
| 45 | Small ½ dot (inner) 20th right side, 12 mm. Tiny dot below EE of 12th |
| 46 | Dot (outer) at foot of 1st right side.  Small dot 18th right side, 12½ mm.  Dot (outer) 20th right side, 7 mm. |
| 47 | Dot 19th right side, 12 mm., also internal nick, 10 mm. Tiny dot under A of 10th. Small dot 13th left side, 9 mm. Small ½ dot (outer) 15th left side, 15 mm. |

# KING GEORGE V. 1½d., TYPE N6. Wmk. Simple Cypher, W.14. Harrison (Plates 1a to 7)

| Plate | 1st stamp, Row No. | | | | Bottom row, Stamp No. | | | | | | | | 12th stamp, Row No. | | | | Controls | Positional piece Prices from |
|---|---|---|---|---|---|---|---|---|---|---|---|---|---|---|---|---|---|---|
| | 17 | 18 | 19 | 20 | 1 | 2 | 3 | 4 | 9 | 10 | 11 | 12 | 17 | 18 | 19 | 20 | | |
| 1a | | | | | | | | | | | | | | | | | A.12 | 1·25 |
| 1b | | | | | | | | | | | | | | | | | C.13 | 50 |
| 2a | | | | | O/L | | | | | | | | | | | | A.12 | 75 |
| 2b | | | | | O/L | | | | | ⌣THR | | | | | | | C.13, D.14 | 50 |
| 2c | | | | | | O/L | | | | ⌣THR | | | | | | | F.15, G.15, H.16, J.17 | 40 |
| 2d | | | | | | O/L | | | | ⌣THR | | | | | | o | J.17, K.18, L.18, (K).18 | 1·50 |
| 3a | | | | | | O/L | | | | ⌣THR | | | | | | | A.12 | 1·00 |
| 3b | | | | | | | | | | | | | | 1 | | | C.13, D.14 | 45 |
| 3c | | | | | | | | | | | | | | 1 | | | F.15, G.15 | 45 |
| 3d | | | | | | | | | | | | | | 1 | o | | H.16 | 1·25 |
| 3e | | | | | | | | | | | | | | | | | J.17, K.18, L.18 | 1·50 |
| 4a | | | | | | | | | | | | | | | | | A.12 | 1·50 |
| 4b | | | | | | | | | O/AL | | | | | | | | K.18 | 1·50 |
| 5a | | | | | O/T | | | | | | | | | | | | K.18, L.18, M.18, M.19 | 50 |
| 5b | | | O/10 | | O/T | | | | | | | | | | | | M.19 | 2·50 |
| 6a | | | | | | O/T | | | | | | | | | | | K.18, L.18 | 50 |
| 6b | | | | | | IO/PT | | | | | | | | | | | M.18, M.19 | 45 |
| 7 | | | | | | | O/T | | | | | | | | | | K.18, L.18, M.19, N.19 | 40 |

KING GEORGE V. 1½d., TYPE N6.   Wmk. Simple Cypher, W.14.   Harrison (Plates 8a to 18)

| Plate | 1st stamp, Row No. | | | | Bottom row, Stamp No. | | | | | | | | 12th stamp, Row No. | | | | Controls | Positional piece / Prices from |
|---|---|---|---|---|---|---|---|---|---|---|---|---|---|---|---|---|---|---|
| | 17 | 18 | 19 | 20 | 1 | 2 | 3 | 4 | 9 | 10 | 11 | 12 | 17 | 18 | 19 | 20 | | |
| 8a | | | | | | | | | | | | | | | | | K 18 | 2·50 |
| 8b | | | † | | | $\frac{3}{4}$FP | | O/T | | | | | | | | | M 19, N 19, T 22 | 60 |
| 9 | | | | | O/T | | | | | | | | | | | | L 18, M 18, M 19 | 55 |
| 10a | | | oo | | | | | | | | | | | | | | L 18 | 1·25 |
| 10b | | | oo | | | | | | | | | | | | | | N 19 | 1·25 |
| 11 | | | | o | | $\wedge$H | | | | | | | | | | | L 18, M 19, N 19 | 45 |
| 12a | | | | 2 | | | | | O/A | | | O/F | | | | | L 18, O 19 | 1·50 |
| 12b | | | | 2 | | | | | | | $\frac{O}{F}$ | O/F | | | | | Q 21, T 22 | 1·00 |
| 13a | | \| | 2 | | | $\wedge$HA | | | | | $\frac{O}{F}$ | | | | | | L 18, M 18, M 19, N 19 | 85 |
| 13b | | \| | 2 | | | | | | | | $\frac{O}{F}$ | | | | | | N 19 | 85 |
| 14a | | | | I | I/H | | | | | | | | | | | | M 18 | 85 |
| 14b | | | | I | | | | | | | | | | | | | M 19, (M) 19, N 19 | 50 |
| 15a | † | | | | | | | | | | | | | | | | M 19 | 7·00 |
| 15b | † | | | | | O/AL | | | | | | | | | | | M 19, N 19 | 45 |
| 16a | o | | | | | | O/A | | | | | | | | | | L 18 | 8·00 |
| 16b | o | | | | O/H(A) | | | | | | | | | I | | | M 19 | 75 |
| 17 | | | | | | | | | | | | | | | | | N 19, O 19, O 20, T 22, V 23 | 45 |
| 18 | | | o | | | O/L | | | | | | | | | | | N 19, O 19, O 20, Q 21, T 22, U 23, V 23 | 45 |

# KING GEORGE V. 1½d., TYPE N6. Wmk. Simple Cypher, W.14. Harrison (Plates 19 to 34)

| Plate | 1st stamp, Row No. | | | | Bottom row, Stamp No. | | | | | | | | 12th stamp, Row No. | | | | Controls | Positional piece Prices from |
|---|---|---|---|---|---|---|---|---|---|---|---|---|---|---|---|---|---|---|
| | 17 | 18 | 19 | 20 | 1 | 2 | 3 | 4 | 9 | 10 | 11 | 12 | 17 | 18 | 19 | 20 | | |
| 19 | | | ∧ | | | | | | | | | | | | | | M 18, N 19, Q 21 | 1·25 |
| 20a | | | | 1 | ¼ TH | | | | | | | | | | | | N 19, O 19, Q 20, Q 21, T 22, U 22, U 23 | 45 |
| 20b | | | | 1 | | O L | | | | | | | | | | | U 23, V 23 | 1·00 |
| 21 | | | | | | | | | | OO A | ¼ L | | | | | | N 19, O 19, O 20, Q 20, Q 21 | 3·50 |
| 22 | | | | | | | | | | | | | | | | | T 22 | — |
| 23 | | | | | | | | | | | | | | | | | M 18 | 60 |
| 24a | | | 0 | | | | | | OO A | | | | | | | | O 19, O 20, Q 21 | 75 |
| 24b | | | 0 | | | ∧ EN | | | OO A | | | | | | | | Q 21, T 22 | 80 |
| 25 | | | 1 | | | | | | | | | | | | | | O 19, Q 20, T 22, U 22, U 23 | 45 |
| 26 | | | | 1 | | | | | | | | | | | | | O 19, O 20, Q 21, T 22 | 75 |
| 27 | | | 0 | | | | | O A | | | | | | | | | T 22, U 22, U 23 | 5·00 |
| 28 | | | | | | | | | | | | | | | | | M 19 | 5·00 |
| 29 | | | | | | | | | | | | | | | | 10 | Q 21 | 5·00 |
| 30 | | | | | | | | | | | | | | | | | N 19 | — |
| 31 | 0 | | | | | | | | | | | | | | | | T 22, U 22, U 23 | 1·75 |
| 32 | | | | 10 | | | | | | | | | | | | | T 22, U 22, U 23 | 45 |
| 33 | | | | 10 | | | | | | | | | | | | | T 22, U 22, U 23 | 45 |
| 34 | | | | 0 | | | | | | | | | | | | | T 22, U 22, U 23 | 45 |

# KING GEORGE V. 1½d., TYPE N6. Wmk. Simple Cypher, W.14. Harrison (Plates 35 to 47)

| Plate | 1st stamp, Row No. | | | | Bottom row, Stamp No. | | | | | | | | 12th stamp, Row No. | | | | Controls | Positional piece Prices from |
|---|---|---|---|---|---|---|---|---|---|---|---|---|---|---|---|---|---|---|
| | 17 | 18 | 19 | 20 | 1 | 2 | 3 | 4 | 9 | 10 | 11 | 12 | 17 | 18 | 19 | 20 | | |
| 35 | | | | o | | | | | | | | | | | | | T 22, V 23 | 50 |
| 36 | | | | | | | | | | | | | 1 | | | | T 22 | 10·00 |
| 37 | | | | | | $\overset{\wedge}{\mathrm{T}}$ | | | | | | | | | | | V 23, W 23 | 1·25 |
| 38 | | | o | | | | | | | | | | | | | | V 23, W 23, W 24 | 2·00 |
| 39 | | | ½o | o | | | | | | | | | | | | | U 23, V 23, W 23 | 1·50 |
| 40 | | | | | | | | | | | | | | 2 | | | Q 20, V 23, W 23 | 8·00 |
| 41 | | | | ½o | | | | $\overset{½\mathrm{o}}{\mathrm{A}}$ | | | | | | | | | V 23, W 23 | 50 |
| 42 | | | | | | | | | | | | | | | | | V 23, W 23 | 60 |
| 43 | $\overset{\mathrm{o}}{\wedge}$ | | | \| | | | | | | | | | | | | | V 23 | 5·00 |
| 44a | | o | | | | | | | | $\overset{\mathrm{o}}{\mathrm{H(A)}}$ | $\overset{\mathrm{oo}}{\mathrm{HRE}}$ | $\overset{\mathrm{o}}{\mathrm{EE}}$ | | | | | L 18, M 18 | 3·50 |
| 44b | | o | | | | | | | | | | | | | | | M 19 | 4·50 |
| 45 | | | | | | | | | | | | | | o | | ½o | V 23, W 23 | 2·50 |
| 46 | | | | | | | | | | | | | | o | $\overset{\mathrm{o}}{\wedge}$ | o | W 23 | 5·00 |
| 47 | | | | | | | | | | $\overset{\mathrm{o}}{\mathrm{A}}$ | | | | | | | V 23 | 6·50 |

## KING GEORGE V. 1½d., TYPE N6. WMK. BLOCK CYPHER, W.15. WATERLOW

| Plate | Marking |
|---|---|
| 1 | Dot (base) under PE of 1st |
| 2 | Small dot (base) under HA of 2nd |
| 3 | Small dot (base) under AL of 3rd |
| 4 | Small dot 20th left side, 14½ mm. |
| 5 | Small dot 19th left side, 16 mm. |
| 6 | ½ dot (outer) and full dot 18th left side, 21, 10 mm. |
| 7 | 19th outer left side scooped out 4–6 mm. Dot 18th right side, 13 mm. |
| 8 | Nick (outer) 19th left side, 8½ mm. Dot under F of 4th. Dot 20th right side |
| 9 | Dot and ½ dot (inner) 19th left side, 9½, 10½ mm. |
| 10 | ½ dot (outer) 20th left side, 5 mm. 19th left side badly scored (outer) (Harrison Plate 41) |
| 11 | ½ dot (base) under A of 4th (Harrison Plate 43) |
| 12 | Line under 1st bevelled at left. Nick (outer) base of 20th right side. Large dot 4th left side |
| 13 | Dot 20th left side, 11 mm. |
| 14 | Oval dot 19th left side, 8 mm. |
| 15 | 19th left side bulges in middle. 20th left side thins at base |
| 16 | Large dot 1st left side, 12 mm. Dot at left over 1st top row. Base of 20th left side bent inwards |
| 17 | Dot 20th left side, 10 mm. |
| 18 | Fine dot (inner) 20th left side, 11 mm. |
| 19 | Nick (outer) 19th left side, 14 mm. |
| 20a | Large dot (top) under LF of 1st |
| 20b | Added fine dot under EN of 3rd |
| 21a | Dot (top) under AL of 2nd |
| 21b | Added dot 20th left side, 10 mm. |
| 21c | Added minute dot under A of 1st |
| 22a | Notch (base) to right of (C)E of 2nd. Base of 19th left side bevelled 1–2 mm. |
| 22b | Added minute dot under L of 1st |
| 23 | Minute dot under EH of 2nd |
| 24 | Tiny dot under F of 3rd |
| 25 | Tiny dot under L of 4th |
| 26 | Large and small dot 20th left side. Both 6½ mm. |
| 27 | Dot 19th left side, 8 mm. Small nick (base) under FP of 3rd |
| 28 | Two minute dots under HA of 1st (usually visible). Two minute dots under NC of 2nd |
| 29 | Double nick at left of 2nd |
| 30 | Scratch under NC of 3rd |
| 31a | Double notch (base) under EN of 2nd |
| 31b | Added notch (base) under FP of 2nd |
| 32 | Vertical score 20th left side |
| 33 | ½ dot (base) under HA of 3rd |
| 34 | Small dot (top) under HA of 3rd. 19th left damaged (outer), 8–10 mm. |
| 35 | Oval dot under EE of 3rd |
| 36 | Dot (base) under HR of 3rd |
| 37 | 2 dots, top and bottom, 20th left side, 19½, 3 mm. |
| 38 | 2 dots, top and bottom, 19th left side, 21, 3 mm. |
| 39 | No marking. 20th left side thick and irregular |
| 40 | 2 dots top and bottom, 20th left side, 21, 2 mm. |
| 41 | 2 dots top and bottom, 19th left side, 20½, 1½ mm. Cut 18th left side, 11 mm. |
| 42 | Base of 20th left side bends inwards. |
| 43 | Small dot 20th right side, 6½ mm. |
| 44 | Internal cut 17th left side, 7½ mm. |
| 45 | 2 internal cuts 15th right side at top |
| 46 | 20th left side tapers from 8 mm. to base |
| 47a | Internal score 19th left side, 17–19 mm. |
| 47b | Added dot 19th left side, 16½ mm. |
| 48 | Tiny nick under base of N of 3rd |
| 49 | Small dot under C of 1st |
| 50 | Small dot 17th right side, 14½ mm. |
| 51 | Dot 16th left side, 10 mm. |
| 52 | 19th left side damaged (outer), 7½–11 mm. |
| 53 | Dot over 1st in upper row. Dot 1st left side, 11 mm. |
| 54 | Tiny dots under E(E) of 12th and 20th right side (inner), 12 mm. |
| 55 | Dot 17th left side, 10½ mm. Minute dot under HA of 11th. Two dots 19th right side, 7, 9½ mm. |
| 56 | Tiny dot 15th left side, 16 mm. Scoop (outer) 16th left side, 16–20 mm. |

## KING GEORGE V. 1½d., TYPE N6. Wmk. Block Cypher, W.15. Waterlow (Plates 1 to 18)

| Plate | 1st stamp, Row No. | | | | Bottom row, Stamp No. | | | | | | | | 12th stamp, Row No. | | | | Controls | Positional piece Prices from |
|---|---|---|---|---|---|---|---|---|---|---|---|---|---|---|---|---|---|---|
| | 17 | 18 | 19 | 20 | 1 | 2 | 3 | 4 | 9 | 10 | 11 | 12 | 17 | 18 | 19 | 20 | | |
| 1 | | | | | o PE | | | | | | | | | | | | A 24, B 24, C 25, D 25 | 30 |
| 2 | | | | | | o HA | | | | | | | | | | | A 24, B 24, C 25, D 25 | 30 |
| 3 | | | | | | | o AL | | | | | | | | | | A 24, B 24, C 25, D 25, F 26 | 30 |
| 4 | | | | o | | | | | | | | | | | | | A 24, B 24 | 30 |
| 5 | | | o | | | | | | | | | | | | | | A 24 | 70 |
| 6 | | ½oo | | | | | | | | | | | | o | | | A 24 | 2·50 |
| 7 | | | ⊃ | | | | | | | | | | | | | | B 24, C 25, D 25 | 60 |
| 8 | | | ∧ | | | | | o F | | | | | | | | o | B 24, C 25, E 26 | 70 |
| 9 | | | o½o | ½o | | | | | | | | | | | | | C 25, D 25 | 75 |
| 10 | | | | | | | | | | | | | | | | | C 25, D 25, F 26 | 75 |
| 11 | | | | | | | | ½o A | | | | | | | | | D 25, E 26 | 70 |
| 12 | | | | | | | | | | | | | | | | ∧ | E 26, F 26, G 27 | 35 |
| 13 | | | | o | | | | | | | | | | | | | E 26, F 26, G 27, H 27, I 28 | 30 |
| 14 | | | o | | | | | | | | | | | | | | E 26, F 26, G 27 | 60 |
| 15 | | | \| | \| | | | | | | | | | | | | | E 26 (SH) E 26, H 27, I 28 | 75 |
| 16 | | | | \| | | | | | | | | | | | | | F 26, G 27 | 60 |
| 17 | | | | o | | | | | | | | | | | | | H 27, I 28 | 90 |
| 18 | | | | o | | | | | | | | | | | | | H 27, I 28, J 28 | 30 |

# KING GEORGE V. 1½d., TYPE N6. Wmk. Block Cypher, W.15. Waterlow (Plates 19 to 31b)

| Plate | 1st stamp, Row No. | | | | Bottom row, Stamp No. | | | | | | | | 12th stamp, Row No. | | | | Controls | Prices from |
|---|---|---|---|---|---|---|---|---|---|---|---|---|---|---|---|---|---|---|
| | 17 | 18 | 19 | 20 | 1 | 2 | 3 | 4 | 9 | 10 | 11 | 12 | 17 | 18 | 19 | 20 | | |
| 19 | | | ∧ | | | | | | | | | | | | | | | E 26, I 28, J 28 | 1·00 |
| 20a | | | | | o/LF | | | | | | | | | | | | | J 28, K 29, L 29 | 40 |
| 20b | | | | | o/LF | | o/EN | | | | | | | | | | | M 30 | 60 |
| 21a | | | | | | o/AL | | | | | | | | | | | | J 28, K 29, L 29 | 50 |
| 21b | | | | o | | o/AL | | | | | | | | | | | | L 29, O 31 | 75 |
| 21c | | | | o | o/A | o/AL | | | | | | | | | | | | O 31 | 80 |
| 22a | | | | ▌ | | ∧(C)E | | | | | | | | | | | | J 28, K 29 | 60 |
| 22b | | | | ▌ | o/L | ∧(C)E | | | | | | | | | | | | L 29, M 30 | 60 |
| 23 | | | | | | o/EH | | | | | | | | | | | | L 29 | 75 |
| 24 | | | | | | | o/F | | | | | | | | | | | L 29, M 30 | 75 |
| 25 | | | | | | | | o/L | | | | | | | | | | L 29 | 1·25 |
| 26 | | | | oo | | | | | | | | | | | | | | M 30, N 30 | 50 |
| 27 | | | o | | | | ∧/FP | | | | | | | | | | | M 30, N 30, O 31 | 75 |
| 28 | | | | | oo/HA | oo/NC | | | | | | | | | | | | B 24, M 30, N 30, O 31, Q 32, R 32 | 40 |
| 29 | | | | | | ∧∧ | | | | | | | | | | | | N 30, O 31, P 31, Q 32, R 32 | 30 |
| 30 | | | | | | | | | | | | | | | | | | N 30 | 1·00 |
| 31a | | | | | | ∧∧/EN | | | | | | | | | | | | O 31, P 31 | 55 |
| 31b | | | | | | ∧∧∧/ENF | | | | | | | | | | | | Q 32 | 75 |

# KING GEORGE V. 1½d., TYPE N6. Wmk. Block Cypher, W.15. Waterlow (Plates 32 to 48)

| Plate | 1st stamp, Row No. | | | | Bottom row, Stamp No. | | | | | | | | 12th stamp, Row No. | | | | Controls | Positional piece — Prices from |
|---|---|---|---|---|---|---|---|---|---|---|---|---|---|---|---|---|---|---|
| | 17 | 18 | 19 | 20 | 1 | 2 | 3 | 4 | 9 | 10 | 11 | 12 | 17 | 18 | 19 | 20 | | |
| 32 | | | | \| | | | | | | | | | | | | | O 31, P 31, Q 32, R 32 | 45 |
| 33 | | | | | | | | | | | | | | | | | S 33 | 1·50 |
| 34 | | | \| | | | | °HA | | | | | | | | | | S 33, T 33 | 40 |
| 35 | | | | | | | °HA | | | | | | | | | | S 33, T 33 | 40 |
| 36 | | | | | | | °EE | | | | | | | | | | S 33, T 33 | 45 |
| 37 | | | | oo | | | °HR | | | | | | | | | | S 33, T 33 | 1·50 |
| 38 | | | oo | | | | | | | | | | | | | | T 33<br>U 34 (H), V 34 (H)<br>U 34 (W) | 2·00<br>1·75<br>18·00 |
| 39 | | | | oo | | | | | | | | | | | | | U 34 (H), V 34 (H)<br>T 33<br>U 34 (W) | 40<br>42·00<br>— |
| 40 | | | | oo | | | | | | | | | | | | | U 34 (H), V 34 (H)<br>T 33 | 1·50<br>1·50 |
| 41 | | I | oo | | | | | | | | | | | | | | U 34 (H)<br>T 33 | 2·25<br>2·50 |
| 42 | | | | \| | | | | | | | | | | | | | U 34 (H), V 34 (H) | 40 |
| 43 | | | | | | | | | | | | | | | | o | B 24, C 25, D 25, F 26 | 1·50 |
| 44 | I | | | | | | | | | | | | | | | | B 24 | 2·50 |
| 45 | | | | | | | | | | | | | | | | | F 26 | 6·00 |
| 46 | | | | \| | | | | | | | | | | | | | P 31 | 1·25 |
| 47a | | | | \| | | | | | | | | | | | | | J 28 | 1·50 |
| 47b | | | o | \| | | | | | | | | | | | | | L 29, M 30 | 1·50 |
| 48 | | | | | | | ∧N | | | | | | | | | | A 24 | 55 |

# KING GEORGE V. 1½d., TYPE N6. Wmk. Block Cypher, W.15. Waterlow (Plates 49 to 56)

| | 1st stamp, Row No. | | | | Bottom row, Stamp No. | | | | | | | | 12th stamp, Row No. | | | | | Positional piece |
| Plate | 17 | 18 | 19 | 20 | 1 | 2 | 3 | 4 | 9 | 10 | 11 | 12 | 17 | 18 | 19 | 20 | Controls | Prices from |
|---|---|---|---|---|---|---|---|---|---|---|---|---|---|---|---|---|---|---|
| 49 | | | | | °C | | | | | | | | | | | | S 33 | 65 |
| 50 | | | | | | | | | | | | | o | | | | B 24 | 5·00 |
| 51 | | | — | | | | | | | | | | | | | | J 28 | 5·00 |
| 52 | | | | | | | | | | | | | | | | | R 32, S 33 | 2·00 |
| 53 | | | | | | | | | | | | °E(E) | | | | | ? | 5·50 |
| 54 | | | | | | | | | | | °HA | | | | | o | D 25 | 4·00 |
| 55 | o | | | | | | | | | | | | | | oo | | D 25 | 5·50 |
| 56 | | | | | | | | | | | | | | | | | E 26 | 5·00 |

## KING GEORGE V. 2d., TYPE N7. WMK. SIMPLE CYPHER, W.14. HARRISON

### A. Die I

This value departed from the normal usage in the setting of the marginal rules. The settings are:—

A  All rules fully co-extensive; rule under 6th vertical row very long (20 mm.). (Plates 1, 2, 3, 4 and 5.)

B  Cuts above and below 6th and 7th vertical rows; no cuts between 6th and 7th rows. (Plates 7, 10, 13 and 19.)

C  As Setting B but cuts have been filled in. (Plates 9 and 18.)

D  As Setting A, but rule under 6th vertical row measures 19½ mm. (Plates 8, 11 and 21.)

E  As Setting D, but rule under 6th vertical row measures 19 mm. This setting shows signs of having cuts above and below 6th and 7th vertical rows filled in. (Plate 20.)

The settings of the remaining plates (6, 12, 14, 15, 16 and 17) are not known.

| Plate | Marking |
|---|---|
| 1 | No marking |
| 2a | Dot above 6th in upper and lower panes; dash under E of 2nd |
| 2b | Dash under E repaired, but traces showing at bottom of rule |
| 2c | Added tall oval dot 19th left side, 12 mm. Later this dot breaks left and right edges of rule |
| 3 | Dot above 8th in upper pane only; cut under PE of 1st |
| 4 | Cut under WO of 2nd |
| 5a | Dot above 2nd in upper and lower panes. 20th left side shows a slight bulge in the centre and a progressive thickening towards the base |
| 5b | Dots above 2nd filled in |
| 6 | Large dot 20th left side bulging rule at right, 12 mm. |
| 7a | Dot 19th left side, 11 mm. |
| 7b | Dot now breaking right side of rule; added dot 19th left side (breaking left), 7½ mm. Dot to right of 4th in top row |
| 8a | Fine dot 20th left side, 13 mm. |
| 8b | 18th left side damaged slightly at left; added dot 20th left side, 14 mm. |

| Plate | Marking |
|---|---|
| 9a | Nick (inner) 20th left side, 2 mm. Dot 17th right side, 9⅛ mm. |
| 9b | Added oblique dot 20th left side, 14½ mm. |
| 10 | Dot 18th right side, 8 mm. |
| 11 | Dot 17th right side, 10½ mm. ½ dot (outer) 18th left side, 11½ mm. |
| 12 | Outer base of 19th left side bevelled off. Nick (outer) 20th left side, 10 mm. |
| 13 | Tall dot 19th left side, 11½–12 mm., usually breaking rule at left and bulging rule slightly at right |
| 14 | Scoop (outer) 19th left side, 8½–11 mm.; outer frame of stamp 19/1 broken opposite left value tablet |
| 15 | Elongated dot 19th left side, 11 mm. |
| 16 | Nick (base) under W of 1st; nick (outer) 19th left side, 2 mm. |
| 17a | Oval cut 20th left side, 11¾ mm. |
| 17b | Added three tiny dots 1st right side |
| 18a | ½ dot (outer) 18th right side, 18 mm. |
| 18b | Added ½ dot (inner) 20th left side, 8 mm. |
| 19 | Tall oval dot 19th left side breaking right and usually left, 14½ mm. Dot (inner) 18th right side, 11 mm. Dot 20th right side, 10 mm. |
| 20 | Double dot 17th left side, 13½ mm. |

### B. Die II

| Plate | Marking |
|---|---|
| 1 | Oval dot 19th left side, sometimes breaking rule at left and right, 13 mm. |
| 2 | Dot (outer) 20th left side, 14¼ mm.; ½ dot (base) under P of 1st |
| 3 | Lower part of 20th left side slightly tapered; dot (top) under OP of 9th; dot (breaking inner) |

| Plate | Marking |
|---|---|
| | 17th right side, 12½ mm. (Waterlow Plate 17) |
| 4 | Dot 20th left side, 13 mm. (Waterlow Plate 4) |
| 5 | Dot 19th left side, 12½ mm.; scratch 20th left side (not always visible) (Waterlow Plate 5) |
| 6 | Dot under P of 10th; dot (central) 18th right side, 13 mm. (Waterlow Plate 18) |

# KING GEORGE V. 2d., TYPE N7. Wmk. Simple Cypher, W. 14. Harrison

## A. Die I (Plates 1 to 8b)

| Plate | 1st stamp, Row No. | | | | Bottom row, Stamp No. | | | | | | | | 12th stamp, Row No. | | | | Controls | Prices from |
|---|---|---|---|---|---|---|---|---|---|---|---|---|---|---|---|---|---|---|
| | 17 | 18 | 19 | 20 | 12 | 11 | 10 | 9 | 4 | 3 | 2 | 1 | 17 | 18 | 19 | 20 | | |
| 1 | | | | | | | | | | | | | | | | | None; D 14 | 3·50; 40 |
| 2a | | | | | | | | | | | E | | | | | | C. 13, O 20, P 20 | 30 |
| 2b | | | o | | | | | | | | | | | | | | P 20, Q 20, Q 21, R 21 | 1·50 |
| 2c | | | | | | | | | | | | | | | | | R 21, S 21 | 75 |
| 3 | | | | | | | | | | | | ¹ PE | | | | | None; C 14, D 14, F 15, G 15, H 16, I 16, J 17, K 17, L 18, M 19, N 19, O 19, P 20, Q 20 | 2·25; 30 |
| 4 | | | | | | | | | | | ¹ WO | | | | | | None; C 14, D 14, F 15, G 15, H 16, I 16, J 17, K 17, N 19, O 19, O 20, P 20 | 2·50; 30 |
| 5a | | | | \| | | | | | | | | | | | | | C. 13 | 45 |
| 5b | | | | | | | | | | | | | | | | | J 17, K 17, M 19, N 19, O 20, P 20, Q 20 | 30 |
| 6 | | | | o | | | | | | | | | | | | | O 20, P 20, Q 20, Q 21, S 22 | 45 |
| 7a | | | o | | | | | | | | | | | | | | P 20 | 2·25 |
| 7b | | | oo | | | | | | | | | | | | | | P 20, Q 20, Q 21, S 21 | 75 |
| 8a | | | | o | | | | | | | | | | | | | P 20 | 70 |
| 8b | | \| | | oo | | | | | | | | | | | | | P 20, Q 20, Q 21, R 21, S 21 | 30 |

# KING GEORGE V. 2d., TYPE N7. Wmk. Simple Cypher, W.14. Harrison

## A. Die I (Plates 9a to 20)

| Plate | 1st stamp, Row No. | | | | Bottom row, Stamp No. | | | | | | | | 12th stamp, Row No. | | | | Controls | Prices from |
|---|---|---|---|---|---|---|---|---|---|---|---|---|---|---|---|---|---|---|
| | 17 | 18 | 19 | 20 | 1 | 2 | 3 | 4 | 9 | 10 | 11 | 12 | 17 | 18 | 19 | 20 | | |
| 9a | | | | ∧ | | | | | | | | | o | | | | P 20, Q 20 | 50 |
| 9b | | | | ∧ o | | | | | | | | | o | | | | Q 21, R 21, S 22, T 22 | 60 |
| 10 | | | | | | | | | | | | | | o | | | R 21 | 6·00 |
| 11 | | ½o | | | | | | | | | | | o | | | | R 21 | 5·00 |
| 12 | | | ❘ | ∧ | | | | | | | | | | | | | P 20, Q 21, R 21, S 21, S 22, T 22 | 60 |
| 13 | | | o | | | | | | | | | | | | | | O 22, P 20, Q 20, Q 21 | 1·25 |
| 14 | | | ) | | | | | | | | | | | | | | Q 21 | 4·00 |
| 15 | | | o | | | | | | | | | | | | | | Q 21, R 21, T 22 | 1·50 |
| 16 | | | ∧ | | ∧w | | | | | | | | | | | | Q 21, R 21, S 21, S 22, T 22 | 60 |
| 17a | | | | I | | | | | | | | | | | | | R 21, S 21, S 22 | 60 |
| 17b | | | | I | | | | | | | | | | | | | T 22 | — |
| 18a | | | | | | | | | | | | | | ½o | | | O 20 | 5·50 |
| 18b | | | | ½o | | | | | | | | | | ½o | | | R 21, S 21, S 22, T 22 | 60 |
| 19 | | | o | | | | | | | | | | | o | | o | R 21, S 21, S 22, T 22 | 1·50 |
| 20 | oo | | | | | | | | | | | | | | | | P 20 | 4·00 |

## KING GEORGE V. 2d., TYPE N7. Wmk. Simple Cypher, W.14. Harrison

## B. Die II (Plates 1 to 6)

| Plate | 1st stamp, Row No. | | | | Bottom row, Stamp No. | | | | | | | | 12th stamp, Row No. | | | | Controls | Positional piece Prices from |
|---|---|---|---|---|---|---|---|---|---|---|---|---|---|---|---|---|---|---|
| | 17 | 18 | 19 | 20 | 1 | 2 | 3 | 4 | 9 | 10 | 11 | 12 | 17 | 18 | 19 | 20 | | |
| 1 | | | o | | ½o P | | | | | | | | | | | | S 21, S 22, T 22, U 22, U 23, V 23 | 1·50 |
| 2 | | | | o | | | | | | | | | | | | | S 21, S 22, T 22, U 22, U 23 | 80 |
| 3 | | | | \| | | | | | o OP | | | | o | | | | S 21, S 22, T 22. W 23, W 24 | 80 |
| 4 | | | o | | | | | | | | | | | | | | T 22, U 23, V 23, W 23, W 24 | 80 |
| 5 | | | | | | | | | | o P | | | | | | | T 22, U 23, V 23; W 23, W 24 | 1·50 |
| 6 | | | | | | | | | | | | | | o | | | S 22, T 22 | 5·00 |

**KING GEORGE V. 2d., TYPE N7. WMK. BLOCK CYPHER, W.15. WATERLOW DIE II**

Plate        Marking

1   Base of 20th left side rounded off
2   Left of rule under 1st pointed below; base of rule under 12th irregular and bevelled at left; large dot 18th right side, 11 mm.
3   Minute dot 20th left side, 11½ mm.; rule under 1st slightly scooped out under OP
4   Dot 20th left side, 13 mm. (Harrison Plate 4)
5a   Dot 19th left side, 13 mm. (Harrison Plate 5)
5b   Added minute dot under P of 2nd
6   Dot 19th left side breaking right, 9 mm. Base of rules under 1st, 2nd and 3rd very irregular
7   Lower portion of 19th left side shows internal damage; ½ dot (inner) 20th left side, 11 mm., with minute dot to left of it
8   Flaw in base of 19th left side; dot with offshoot dot above and to right of it 20th left side, 13 mm.; nick to left of 1st at base

Plate        Marking

9   Dot 19th left side, 11¾ mm.; minute dot (base) under P of 2nd
10   Large dot (breaking top) under P of 1st
11   ½ dot (top) under P of 2nd
12   Dot 19th left side, 11½ mm. Nicks (base) at left and right of 2nd
13   Dot 20th left side, 12 mm.
14   Two dots 19th left side, 11, 13 mm.; indent (base) under and to right of E of 2nd
15   No marking
16   Indent (base) under C of 1st
17   Dot (top) under OP of 9th; dot (breaking inner) 17th right side, 12½ mm. (Harrison Plate 3)
18   Dot under P of 10th; dot (central) 18th right side, 13 mm.; rule under 2nd appears thinner than those under 1st and 3rd. (Harrison Plate 6)

# KING GEORGE V. 2d., TYPE N7. Wmk. Block Cypher, W.15. Waterlow, Die II

| Plate | 1st stamp, Row No. | | | | Bottom row, Stamp No. | | | | | | | | 12th stamp, Row No. | | | | Controls | Positional piece Prices from |
|---|---|---|---|---|---|---|---|---|---|---|---|---|---|---|---|---|---|---|
| | 17 | 18 | 19 | 20 | 1 | 2 | 3 | 4 | 9 | 10 | 11 | 12 | 17 | 18 | 19 | 20 | | |
| 1 | | | | \| | | | | | | | | | | | | | A 24, B 24, C 25 | 50 |
| 2 | | | | \| | o/OP | | | | | | | \| | | o | | | F 26, L 29, M 30, N 30, P 31, Q 32, R 32 | 50 |
| 3 | | | | o | | | | | | | | | | | | | B 24, D 25, F 26, H 27, I 28, K 29, L 29 | 50 |
| 4 | | | | o | | | | | | | | | | | | | B 24, C 25, D 25, E 26, | 50 |
| 5a | | | o | | | | | | | | | | | | | | B 24, D 25, E 26, I 28, J 28 | 1·25 |
| 5b | | | o | | | o/P | | | | | | | | | | | J 28, K 29, L 29 | 1·50 |
| 6 | | | o | | | \| | \| | | | | | | | | | | F 26, G 27, H 27, I 28, J 28 | 1·25 |
| 7 | | | | ½o/o | ∧ | | | | | | | | | | | | F 26, G 27, H 27, K 29, L 29, M 30 | 50 |
| 8 | | | | oo | | | | | | | | | | | | | J 28, K 29, L 29 | 50 |
| 9 | | | o | | | o/P | | | | | | | | | | | J 28, K 29, L 29 | 1·50 |
| 10 | | | | | o/P | | | | | | | | | | | | M 30, N 30, O 31, P 31 | 50 |
| 11 | | | | | | ½o/P | | | | | | | | | | | M 30, N 30, O 31, P 31, Q 32, R 32 | 50 |
| 12 | | | | o | | ∧∧ | | | | | | | | | | | U 34 (H), N 30, Q 32, R 32, S 33, T 33 | 2·00 |
| 13 | | | | | | | | | | | | | | | | | N 30, O 31, R 32, T 33 | 1·00 |
| 14 | | | oo | | | ∧/E | | | | | | | | | | | O 31, Q 32, R 32, S 33, T 33 | 60 |
| 15 | o | | | | ∧/C | | | | | | | | | | | | U 34 (H), V 34 (H) | 1·50 |
| 16 | | | | | | | | | o/OP | | | | | | | | V 34 (H) | 1·25 |
| 17 | | | | \| | | | | | | o/p | | | | o | | | E 26 | 60 |
| 18 | | | | \| | | | | | | | | | | o | | | D 25 | 7·00 |
| | | | | | | | | | | | | | | | | | | 6·00 |

213

# KING GEORGE V. 2½d., TYPE N5. WMK. SIMPLE CYPHER, W.14. HARRISON

| Plate | Marking |
|---|---|
| 1a | Dot above 1st in upper and lower panes |
| 1b | Dots above 1st filled in |
| 1c | Added nick (outer) 3rd left side |
| 1d | Added oval dot under 2nd |
| 2a | Dots above 2nd in upper and lower panes |
| 2b | Dots above 2nd filled in |
| 2c | Added oval dot under P of 1st |
| 3a | Added oval dot under 4th in upper and lower panes |
| 3b | Dots above 4th in upper and lower panes. 19th right side damaged (outer) 20th left side bent inwards at base. 19th right |
| 4a | Dots above 5th in upper and lower panes. 20th right side damaged |
| 4b | Dots above 5th filled in |
| 5 | Minute nick at left of 1st. Tiny nick top right of 2nd |

| Plate | Marking |
|---|---|
| 6 | 19th right side damaged (inner). Small ½ dot (base) under 12th. 12th left side bevelled; nick (outer) 14th left side |
| 7a | No marking. Tiny nick (top) of 1st beneath Y. (Hardly visible on M19) |
| 7b | 20th left side bevelled at base |
| 8a | 1st left side bevelled at top; rule under 7th thins at right |
| 8b | Added circular dot under P of 1st. (Waterlow Plate 6) |
| 9a | No marking |
| 9b | Added ½ dot (base) under FP of 2nd |
| 10 | Cut under (P)E of 1st. (Waterlow Plate 15) |
| 11a | Base of 12th worn, with nick (central) at top |
| 11b | Added cut under F of 2nd. (Waterlow Plate 4) |
| 12 | 4th and 9th rules right side bevelled |

## (Plates 1a to 4b)

| Plate | 1st stamp, Row No. | | Bottom row, Stamp No. | | | | | | | | | | | | 12th stamp, Row No. | | Controls | Prices from |
|---|---|---|---|---|---|---|---|---|---|---|---|---|---|---|---|---|---|---|
| | 19 | 20 | 1 | 2 | 3 | 4 | 5 | 6 | 7 | 8 | 9 | 10 | 11 | 12 | 19 | 20 | | |
| 1a | | | | | | | | | | | | | | | | | A.12 | 1·50 |
| 1b | | | | | | | | | | | | | | | | | C.13 | 75 |
| 1c | | | | | | | | | | | | | | | | | I.16 | — |
| 1d | | | | o | | | | | | | | | | | | | I.16, J.17 | 1·25 |
| 2a | | | | | | | | | | | | | | | | | A.12 | 2·00 |
| 2b | | | | | | | | | | | | | | | | | I.16 | — |
| 2c | | | o P | | | | | | | | | | | | | | I.16, J.17 | 1·25 |
| 3a | | | | | | | | | | | | | | | | | A.12 | 3·50 |
| 3b | | ] | | | | | | | | | | | | | | | C.13 | 50 |
| 4a | | | | | | | | | | | | | | | | ] | A.12 | 6·00 |
| 4b | | | | | | | | | | | | | | | | | D.14, E.14 | 2·00 |

# KING GEORGE V. 2½d., TYPE N5. Wmk. Simple Cypher, W.14. Harrison (Plates 5 to 12)

| Plate | 1st stamp, Row No. | | Bottom row, Stamp No. | | | | | | | | | | | | 12th stamp, Row No. | | Controls | Positional piece Prices from |
|---|---|---|---|---|---|---|---|---|---|---|---|---|---|---|---|---|---|---|
| | 19 | 20 | 1 | 2 | 3 | 4 | 5 | 6 | 7 | 8 | 9 | 10 | 11 | 12 | 19 | 20 | | |
| 5 | | \| | ∧ | | | | | | | | | | | | | | H 16 | 70 |
| 6 | | | | ∧ | | | | | | | | | | ½o | | | C 14, G 15 | 2·00 |
| 7a | | | | | | | | | | | | | | | | | K 17, L 18, M 18, M 19 | 75 |
| 7b | | | | | | | | | | | | | | | \| | | O 19, O 20, Q 21 | 65 |
| 8a | | | O P | | | | | | \| | | | | | | | | J 17, K 17, M 19, N 19 | 1·25 |
| 8b | | | | | | | | | \| | | | | | | | | N 19, O 19, P 20, Q 21, R 21, S 22, T 22 | 75 |
| 9a | | | | | | | | | | | | | | | | | M 18, N 19 | 1·25 |
| 9b | | | | ½o F P | | | | | | | | | | | | | N 19, O 20, Q 21, R 21 | 65 |
| 10 | | | | | | | | | | | | | | \| | | | S 21, T 22, U 23, V 23 | 65 |
| 11a | | | I (P)E | | | | | | | | | | | \| | | | R 21 | 2·25 |
| 11b | | | | I F | | | | | | | | | | | | | S 21, S 22, T 22, U 23, V 23 | 65 |
| 12 | | | | | | | | | | | | | | | | | G 15 | — |

## KING GEORGE V. 2½d., TYPE N5. WMK. BLOCK CYPHER, W.15.   WATERLOW

| Plate | Marking |
|---|---|
| 1a | Tiny dot 19th right side; nick (base) to right of 8th |
| 1b | Added dot 19th left side (inner), 12 mm. |
| 2 | 20th left side very thick and irregular rule under 1st curves slightly upwards towards left end. Large dot 2nd left side |
| 3 | Dot (inner) 20th left side, 13½ mm. |
| 4 | Cut under F of 2nd. (Harrison Plate 1b) |
| 5 | Large dot (outer) 19th left side, 11½ mm. |
| 6 | Circular dot under P of 1st. (Harrison Plate 8b) |
| 7 | Dot 20th left side, 10½ mm. |
| 8 | Small dot 19th left side, 11 mm. |
| 9 | 20th left side bends in at base; rule under 1st splays out at left end; minute dot under Y of 2nd |
| 10 | Dot 20th left side, 7 mm.; minute dot at right of 2nd |
| 11 | Scratch in rule under Y of 1st |
| 12 | Dot 19th left side, 10½ mm. |
| 13 | Base of 20th left side has an inward projection |
| 14 | No marking |
| 15 | Cut under (P)E of 1st. (Harrison Plate 10) |

# KING GEORGE V. 2½d., TYPE N5. Wmk. Block Cypher, W.15. Waterlow (Plates 1a to 15)

| Plate | 1st stamp, Row No. | | Bottom row, Stamp No. | | | | | | | | | | | | 12th stamp, Row No. | | Controls | Positional piece Prices from |
|---|---|---|---|---|---|---|---|---|---|---|---|---|---|---|---|---|---|---|
| | 19 | 20 | 1 | 2 | 3 | 4 | 5 | 6 | 7 | 8 | 9 | 10 | 11 | 12 | 19 | 20 | | |
| 1a | o | | | | | | | | | ∧ | | | | | o | | B 24, C 25 | 1·50 |
| 1b | o | | | | | | | | | ∧ | | | | | o | | D 25 | 2·50 |
| 2 | | o | — | | | | | | | | | | | | | | M 30, N 30, Q 32, R 32, S 33 | 1·00 |
| 3 | | o | | I F | | | | | | | | | | | | | D 25, E 26, G 27 | 1·00 |
| 4 | o | | | | | | | | | | | | | — | | | E 26, G 27, I 28 | 1·00 |
| 5 | | o | | | | | | | | | | | | | | | G 27 | 2·00 |
| 6 | o | | o P | | | | | | — | | | | | | | | G 27, H 27 | 2·00 |
| 7 | | | | | | | | | | | | | | | | | I 28 | 2·00 |
| 8 | o | | | | | | | | | | | | | | | | I 28 | 3·00 |
| 9 | | o | — | o Y | | | | | | | | | | | | | Q 32, R 32, S 33 | 1·00 |
| 10 | o | | | o | | | | | | | | | | | | | K 29 | 1·75 |
| 11 | | | Y | | | | | | | | | | | | | | V 34 (H), T 33 | 1·25 1·00 |
| 12 | o | | — | | | | | | | | | | | | | | K 29 | 3·75 |
| 13 | | — | | | | | | | | | | | | | | | V 34 (H), W 35 (H), Q 32, T 33 | 2·00 |
| 14 | | | | | | | | | | | | | | | | | I 28, M 30, N 30 | 1·75 |
| 15 | | | I (P)E | | | | | | | | | | | | | | V 34 (H), W 35 (H) | 2·00 |

# KING GEORGE V. 3d., TYPE N7. WMK. SIMPLE CYPHER, W.14. HARRISON

| Plate | Marking |
|---|---|
| 1a | Dot at left and dot (central) above 1st in upper pane; dot (central) above 1st in lower pane |
| 1b | Dots above 1st filled in |
| 1c | Added dot at right of 1st in upper and lower panes |
| 2a | Dot above 2nd in upper and lower panes. Minute ¼ dot under right of 5th |
| 2b | Dots above 2nd filled in |
| 2c | Added cut 20th left side, 12½ mm. |
| 3a | Dot above 3rd in upper and lower panes |
| 3b | Dots above 3rd filled in |
| 4a | Dot above 4th in upper and lower panes |
| 4b | Dots above 4th filled in |
| 4c | Further dot cut above 6th in upper and lower panes |
| 5 | Diamond cut under EP of 2nd. Minute dot under EN of 11th |
| 6a | No marking |

| Plate | Marking |
|---|---|
| 6b | Added cut under E(E) of 1st |
| 7a | ¼ dot (outer) 14th right side, 3 mm. |
| 7b | Added cut under EP of 2nd |
| 8a | Base of 20th right side bevelled |
| 8b | Added nick (outer) 19th left side, 5¾ mm. |
| 9 | ¼ dot (inner) 20th left side, 12¾ mm. (Waterlow Plate 4) |
| 10 | Dot 19th left side, 13 mm. (Waterlow Plate 3) |
| 11 | Base 17th right side bevelled. Damage (base) under REEP of 8th |
| 12a | Rule under 2nd damaged and broken away at bottom right. Cut above 11th top row |
| 12b | Left of line under 3rd broken at base. Added horizontal dash under PE of 2nd |
| 13a | Cut above 12th top row |
| 13b | Added large ½ dot (base) under EP of 1st |

**(Plates 1a to 3b)**

| Plate | 1st stamp, Row No. | | | | Bottom row, Stamp No. | | | | | | | | | | | | Positional piece | |
|---|---|---|---|---|---|---|---|---|---|---|---|---|---|---|---|---|---|---|
| | 17 | 18 | 19 | 20 | 1 | 2 | 3 | 4 | 5 | 6 | 7 | 8 | 9 | 10 | 11 | 12 | Controls | Prices from |
| 1a | | | | | | | | | | | | | | | | | A. 12 (close) | 2·00 |
| 1b | | | | | | | | | | | | | | | | | C 13 | — |
| 1c | | | | | | | | | | | | | | | | | C. 13, F 15, H 16, I 16 | 3·00 |
| 2a | | | | | | | | | 1/10 | | | | | | | | B. 13 | 1·75 |
| 2b | | | | | | | | | 1/10 | | | | | | | | C 13, D 14 | — |
| 2c | | | | 1 | | | | | | | | | | | | | E 14, F 15, H 16, I 16 | 65 |
| 3a | | | | | | | | | | | | | | | | | A. 12 (close), A. 12 (wide) | 1·75 |
| 3b | | | | | | | | | | | | | | | | | F 15, G 15 | 1·75 |

**KING GEORGE V. 3d., TYPE N7. Wmk. Simple Cypher, W.14. Harrison (Plates 4a to 13b)**

|  | 1st stamp, Row No. | | | | Bottom row, Stamp No. | | | | | | | | | | | | Positional Piece |
| Plate | 17 | 18 | 19 | 20 | 1 | 2 | 3 | 4 | 5 | 6 | 7 | 8 | 9 | 10 | 11 | 12 | Controls | Prices from |
|---|---|---|---|---|---|---|---|---|---|---|---|---|---|---|---|---|---|---|
| 4a |  |  |  |  |  |  |  |  |  |  |  |  |  |  |  |  | A. 12 (wide) | 4·00 |
| 4b |  |  |  |  |  |  |  |  |  |  |  |  |  |  |  |  | C 13 | — |
| 4c |  |  |  |  |  |  |  |  |  |  |  |  |  |  |  |  | C. 13, F 15 | 3·00 |
| 5 |  |  |  |  |  | I EP |  |  |  |  |  |  |  |  | O EN |  | M 18, N 19, O 20, P 20, Q 21, T 22, U 23, V 23 | 75 |
| 6a |  |  |  |  |  |  |  |  |  |  |  |  |  |  |  |  | Q 21, R 21 | — |
| 6b |  |  |  |  | I E(E) |  |  |  |  |  |  |  |  |  |  |  | R 21 | 2·00 |
| 7a |  |  |  |  |  |  |  |  |  |  |  |  |  |  |  |  | Q 21, R 21 | — |
| 7b |  |  |  |  |  | I EP |  |  |  |  |  |  |  |  |  |  | R 21 | 2·00 |
| 8a |  |  |  |  |  |  |  |  |  |  |  |  |  |  |  | — | S 21, S 22, T 22 | 75 |
| 8b |  |  | Λ | ½o |  |  |  |  |  |  |  |  |  |  |  | — | U 22 | 2·00 |
| 9 |  |  |  |  |  |  |  |  |  |  |  |  |  |  |  |  | U 22, U 23, V 23, W 23 | 75 |
| 10 |  |  | o |  |  |  |  |  |  |  |  |  |  |  |  |  | U 22, U 23, V 23, W 23 | 1·50 |
| 11 |  |  |  |  |  |  |  |  |  |  |  | REEP |  |  |  |  | S 21, S 22, T 22, U 22, U 23 | — |
| 12a |  |  |  |  |  |  |  |  |  |  |  |  |  |  |  |  | J 17, L 18 | 1·00 |
| 12b |  |  |  |  |  | PE |  |  |  |  |  |  |  |  |  |  | M 18, N 19, Q 21 | 1·25 |
| 13a |  |  |  |  |  |  |  |  |  |  |  |  |  |  |  |  | L 18, M 18 | — |
| 13b |  |  |  |  | ½o EP |  |  |  |  |  |  |  |  |  |  |  | M 18, N 19, O 19, O 20, P 20 | 1·00 |

# KING GEORGE V. 3d., TYPE N7. WMK. BLOCK CYPHER, W.15. WATERLOW

| Plate | Marking |
|---|---|
| 1a | Tiny nick (base) to right of 2nd |
| 1b | Added cut 20th left side, 10 mm. |
| 2 | 20th left side heavy and irregular |
| 3 | Dot 19th left side, 13 mm. (Harrison Plate 10 |
| 4 | ¼ dot (inner) 20th left side, 12¾ mm. (Harrison Plate 9) |

| Plate | Marking |
|---|---|
| 5 | Tiny dot 20th left side, 11 mm. |
| 6 | Tiny dot (inner) 19th left side, 9 mm. |
| 7 | No marking.  20th left side irregular |
| 8 | No marking.  20th left side sharply defined |

| Plate | 1st stamp, Row No. | | | | Bottom row, Stamp No. | | | | | | | | | | | | Controls | Positional piece Prices from: |
|---|---|---|---|---|---|---|---|---|---|---|---|---|---|---|---|---|---|---|
| | 17 | 18 | 19 | 20 | 1 | 2 | 3 | 4 | 5 | 6 | 7 | 8 | 9 | 10 | 11 | 12 | | |
| 1a | | | | | | ∧ | | | | | | | | | | | B 24 | 1·50 |
| 1b | | | | I | | ∧ | | | | | | | | | | | B 24, C 25, D 25 | 1·00 |
| 2 | | | | \| | | | | | | | | | | | | | B 24, C 25 | 1·00 |
| 3 | | | o | | | | | | | | | | | | | | V 34 (H)<br>D 25, E 26, G 27,<br>R 32 | 2·00<br>2·00 |
| 4 | | | | 10 | | | | | | | | | | | | | V 34 (H)<br>E 26, G 27, I 28,<br>K 29, M 30, P 31,<br>R 32 | 1·25<br>1·00 |
| 5 | | | | o | | | | | | | | | | | | | E 26, G 27, I 28,<br>K 29, M 30, N 30,<br>P 31, S 33, T 33 | 1·00 |
| 6 | | | o | | | | | | | | | | | | | | I 28, K 29, M 30,<br>N 30, P 31 | 2·50 |
| 7 | | | | \| | | | | | | | | | | | | | M 30, N 30, P 31,<br>R 32, S 33, T 33 | 1·00 |
| 8 | | | | | | | | | | | | | | | | | S 33, T 33 | 1·00 |

# KING GEORGE V. 4d., TYPE N8. WMK. SIMPLE CYPHER, W.14. HARRISON

| Plate | Marking |
|---|---|
| 1a | Dot above 1st in upper and lower panes |
| 1b | Dots above 1st filled in |
| 1c | Added small dot under RP of 1st |
| 1d | Dot under RP enlarged |
| 1e | Rule under 3rd bevelled off at left |
| 2a | Dot above 2nd in upper and lower panes |

| Plate | Marking |
|---|---|
| 2b | Dots above 2nd and filled in |
| 2c | Added small dot under RP of 2nd |
| 2d | Dot under RP enlarged (Waterlow Plate 8) |
| 3 | No marking |
| 4 | Dot under RP of 1st. (Rule under 3rd not bevelled) (Waterlow Plate 4) |

| Plate | 1st stamp, Row No. | | | | Bottom row, Stamp No. | | | | | | | | 12th stamp, Row No. | | | | Controls | Prices from |
|---|---|---|---|---|---|---|---|---|---|---|---|---|---|---|---|---|---|---|
| | 17 | 18 | 19 | 20 | 1 | 2 | 3 | 4 | 9 | 10 | 11 | 12 | 17 | 18 | 19 | 20 | | |
| 1a | | | | | | | | | | | | | | | | | B. 13 | 1·50 |
| 1b | | | | | | | | | | | | | | | | | | — |
| 1c | | | | | °RP | | | | | | | | | | | | F 15, G 15 | 80 |
| 1d | | | | | °RP | | | | | | | | | | | | G 15, H 16, I 16 | 80 |
| 1e | | | | | °RP | | \| | | | | | | | | | | I 16, J 17, K 17, K 18, O 20, Q 21, R 21, S 21, S 22, T 22, U 22 | 1·00 |
| 2a | | | | | | | | | | | | | | | | | B. 13 | 1·50 |
| 2b | | | | | | °RP | | | | | | | | | | | | — |
| 2c | | | | | | °RP | | | | | | | | | | | F 15, G 15 | 90 |
| 2d | | | | | | | | | | | | | | | | | G 15, H 16, I 16, J 17, K 18, M 18, N 19, O 20, Q 21, R 21, S 21, S 22, T 22, U 22, U 23, V 23 | 80 |
| 3 | | | | | | | | | | | | | | | | | I 16, J 17, M 18 | 90 |
| 4 | | | | | °RP | | | | | | | | | | | | N 19, R 21, S 21, U 23, V 23 | 85 |

# KING GEORGE V. 4d., TYPE N8. WMK. BLOCK CYPHER, W.15. WATERLOW

| Plate | Marking |
|---|---|
| 1a | 2 diagonal cuts 20th right side, 4,7 mm. Base of 2nd bevelled at right |
| 1b | Base of 2nd repaired |
| 2a | Base of 20th left side splays out to left. (outer) 4th left side, 12½ mm. |
| 2b | Added tiny dot under P of 11th |
| 3 | 2 cuts 20th left side 17, 18¼ mm. |

Base ½ dot

| Plate | Marking |
|---|---|
| 4 | Dot under RP of 1st (Harrison Plate 4) |
| 5 | Dot at top of 19th left side |
| 6 | No marking |
| 7 | No marking, 20th left side irregular. Rule under 1st, 2nd and 3rd thinner than Plate 6 |
| 8 | Dot under RP of 2nd (Harrison Plate 2d) |

| Plate | 1st stamp, Row No. | | | | Bottom row, Stamp No. | | | | | | | | 12th stamp, Row No. | | | | Controls | Prices from |
|---|---|---|---|---|---|---|---|---|---|---|---|---|---|---|---|---|---|---|
| | 17 | 18 | 19 | 20 | 1 | 2 | 3 | 4 | 9 | 10 | 11 | 12 | 17 | 18 | 19 | 20 | | Positional piece |
| 1a | | | | | | \| | | | | | | | | | | 2 | B 24, C 25, E 26 | 1·50 |
| 1b | | | | \| | | | | | | | | | | | | | G 27, I 28, K 29, Q 32, R 32, T 33 | 1·50 |
| 2a | | | | \| | | | | | | | | | | | | | B 24, C 25, E 26, G 27 | 1·50 |
| 2b | | | | 2 | | | | | | | o/P | | | | | | K 29, M 30, O 31, | 1·50 |
| 3 | | | o | | | | | | | | | | | | | | E 26, G 27, I 28, K 29, M 30, O 31 | 1·50 |
| 4 | | | | | o/RP | | | | | | | | | | | | Q 32 | 3·00 |
| 5 | | | o | | | | | | | | | | | | | | V 34 (H), W 35 (H), O 31, Q 32, R 32, T 33 | 1·50 / 2·50 |
| 6 | | | | | | | | | | | | | | | | | V 34 (H), R 32 | 1·50 / 1·50 |
| 7 | | | | | | o/RP | \| | | | | | | | | | \| | V 34 (H), X 35 (H) | 1·75 |
| 8 | | | | | | | | | | | | | | | | | X 35 (H) | 1·50 |

## KING GEORGE V. 5d., TYPE N8. WMK. SIMPLE CYPHER, W.14. HARRISON

| Plate | Marking |
|---|---|
| 1a | Dot above 1st in upper and lower panes |
| 1b | Dots above 1st filled in |
| 1c | Added 1½ sloping cuts under EN of 1st |
| 2a | Dot above 2nd in upper and lower panes |

| Plate | Marking |
|---|---|
| 2b | Dots above 2nd and filled in |
| 2c | Added sloping cut under P of 2nd |
| 3 | Tiny diagonal internal cut, 14 mm. 19th right side. (Waterlow Plate 1) |

| Plate | 1st stamp, Row No. | | | | Bottom row, Stamp No. | | | | | | | | | | 12th stamp, Row No. | | Controls | Prices from |
|---|---|---|---|---|---|---|---|---|---|---|---|---|---|---|---|---|---|---|
| | 17 | 18 | 19 | 20 | 1 | 2 | 3 | 4 | 9 | 10 | 11 | 12 | 17 | 18 | 19 | 20 | | Positional piece |
| 1a | | | | | | | | | | | | | | | | | B. 13 | 1·25 |
| 1b | | | | | | | | | | | | | | | | | C 14, D 14, F 15, G 15, H 16 | — |
| 1c | | | | | 1½ EN | | | | | | | | | | | | H 16, I 16, J 17, K 17, L 18, N 19, O 19, Q 21, R 21 | 1·00 |
| 2a | | | | | | | | | | | | | | | | | B. 13 | 2·00 |
| 2b | | | | | | | | | | | | | | | | | C 14, D 14, F 15, G 15, H 16 | — |
| 2c | | | | | | ∧ P | | | | | | | | | | | H 16, I 16, J 17, K 17, L 18, Q 21, S 21, S 22 | 1·50 |
| 3 | | | | | | | | | | | | | | | 1 | | Q 21, R 21, S 22, T 22, U 23, V 23 | 1·50 |

## KING GEORGE V. 5d., TYPE N8. WMK. BLOCK CYPHER, W.15. WATERLOW

| Plate | Marking |
|---|---|
| 1a | No marking. Tiny diagonal internal cut, 14 mm. 19th right side. (Harrison Plate 3 |
| 1b | Added dot 19th left side, 10 mm. |

| Plate | Marking |
|---|---|
| 2a | Base of 20th left side slightly bent inwards |
| 2b | Added dot 20th left side, 14 mm. |

| Plate | 1st stamp, Row No. 17 | 18 | 19 | 20 | Bottom row, Stamp No. 1 | 2 | 3 | 4 | 9 | 10 | 11 | 12 | 12th stamp, Row No. 17 | 18 | 19 | 20 | Controls | Prices from |
|---|---|---|---|---|---|---|---|---|---|---|---|---|---|---|---|---|---|---|
| 1a | | | | | | | | | | | | | | | I | | A 24, C 25 | 4·00 |
| 1b | | | o | | | | | | | | | | | | I | | C 25, F 26, H 27, I 28, K 29, L 29, M 30, O 31, Q 32, S 33, T 33, U 34 (H), V 34 (H), X 35 (H) | 3·50 |
| | | | | | | | | | | | | | | | | | | 3·50 |
| 2a | | | | \| | | | | | | | | | | | | | C 25 | 3·00 |
| 2b | | | o | \| | | | | | | | | | | | | | C 25, F 26, H 27, I 28, K 29, L 29, M 30, O 31, Q 32, S 33, T 33, U 34 (W), U 34 (H), V 34 (H), X 35 (H) | 2·00 |
| | | | | | | | | | | | | | | | | | | 18·00 |
| | | | | | | | | | | | | | | | | | | 2·50 |

## KING GEORGE V.   6d., TYPE N8

### A. Somerset House

Plates with interpane margin.

Plate markings such as those used by Harrison and Waterlow were not used at Somerset House, and plating can only be accomplished by the study of fortuitous marks.   It seems that the 6d. stamps were printed in pairs of plates and these were marked above the top rows of the panes with a dot above the 1st or 2nd stamps to signify the position in the press.

| Plate | Marking |
|---|---|
| 1 | Dot above 1st in upper and lower panes<br>20th right side thick and mis-shapen |
| 2 | Dot above 2nd in upper and lower panes |
| 3a | Dot above 1st in upper and lower panes<br>No marking |
| 3b | Small dot below (P)E of 2nd |
| 4 | Dot above 2nd in upper and lower panes<br>Base of 20th left side splayed out |
| 5 | Dot above 1st in upper and lower panes<br>Rule under 2nd very thick |
| 6 | Dot above 2nd in upper pane (to left of rule)<br>Small projection under X of 1st |
| 7 | No marking<br>No dots in upper rows |

| Plate | Marking |
|---|---|
| 8 | Scoop above 1st top row<br>Minute dot under EN of 2nd |
| 9 | Rule under 1st thin at left and thick at right<br>Rules under 2nd and 3rd irregular |
| 10 | No marking.  Thin rules |
| 11 | Nick under N of 2nd |
| 12 | Scoop (base) to left of 2nd |
| 13 | Protrusion top of 1st under C |
| 14 | Two small diagonal nicks under PE, C of 2nd |
| 15 | Minute dot under P of 2nd |
| 16 | Tiny nick under to left of S of 2nd; rule under 1st thinner at left |
| 17 | Nick (top) under I of 1st |
| 18 | No marking<br>Thick rules |

### Control Schedule

Chalk-surfaced paper.   Wmk. Simple Cypher, **W.14**

| Plate | Controls | | | Price | Plate | Controls | | | Price |
|---|---|---|---|---|---|---|---|---|---|
| 1 | C. 13 (dull purple) .. | .. | .. | 4·00 | 3b | L. 18, N. 19, O. 19, P. 20, Q. 20 | .. | | 1·00 |
| 2 | C. 13 (dull purple) .. | .. | .. | 4·50 | 4 | I. 16, J. 17, K. 17, Q. 20, R. 21, S. 21 | | | 1·00 |
| | | | | | 5 | L. 18, M. 18, N. 19, O. 19 .. | | .. | 1·25 |
| 1 | C. 13, D. 14, F. 15, G. 15, H. 16, I. 16 | | | 1·00 | 6 | S. 21, T. 22, U. 22, V. 23, W. 23, | | | |
| 2 | C. 13, D. 14, F. 15, G. 15, H. 16 | | .. | 1·00 | | A. 24, B. 24 .. | .. | .. | 1·25 |
| 3a | J. 17, K. 17 | .. | .. | 1·00 | 7 | V. 23, A. 24, B. 24 .. | .. | .. | 1·25 |

Chalk-surfaced paper.   Wmk. Block Cypher, **W.15**

| | | | | | | | | | | | |
|---|---|---|---|---|---|---|---|---|---|---|---|
| 6 | B. 24 | .. | .. | .. | .. | 3·00 | 8 | C. 25, D. 25 .. | .. | .. | .. | 2·50 |

Ordinary paper.   Wmk. Block Cypher, **W.15**

| Plate | Controls | | | Price | Plate | Controls | | | Price |
|---|---|---|---|---|---|---|---|---|---|
| 8 | D. 25, E. 26, F. 26, G. 27, H. 27 | .. | | 1·50 | 13 | K. 29, L. 29, M. 30, N. 30, R. 32 | .. | | 1·00 |
| 9 | G. 27, H. 27, I. 28, J. 28, K. 29, | | | | 14 | N. 30, O. 31, P. 31 | .. | .. | 1·25 |
| | M. 30, P. 31 .. | .. | .. | .. | 2·50 | 15 | O. 31, T. 33 .. | .. | .. | 1·25 |
| 10 | E. 26, F. 26, G. 27, I. 28, K. 29 | .. | | 1·50 | 16 | R. 32, S. 33, T. 33 .. | .. | .. | 1·25 |
| 11 | E. 26, J. 28, K. 29 .. | .. | .. | 2·00 | 17 | S. 33, T. 33 .. | .. | .. | 1·50 |
| 12 | K. 29, L. 29, M. 30, N. 30 .. | .. | 2·00 | 18 | Q. 32, S. 33, T. 33 .. | .. | .. | 1·00 |

### B. Harrison

| Plate | Marking |
|---|---|
| 19a | No marking |
| 19b | Rule under 3rd shows progressive wear to right<br>(base).   Finally showing nick under N |
| 20 | 19th and 20th left sides bevelled at their<br>adjacent ends |

| Plate | Marking |
|---|---|
| 21 | 2 cuts 1st left side |
| 22 | Rules 19th and 20th left side thin |
| 23 | Cut 1st left side; shallow nick (base) under CE<br>of 1st; horizontal mark in 2nd, under E(N) |

### Control Schedule

Ordinary paper.   Wmk. Block Cypher, **W.15**

| Plate | Controls | | | Price | Plate | Controls | | | Price |
|---|---|---|---|---|---|---|---|---|---|
| 16 | V 34, W 35, X 35, Z 36 | .. | .. | 1·50 | 21 | X 35, Z 36, A 37, B 37, C 38, D 38 | | | 2·50 |
| 19a | V 34, W 35 .. | .. | .. | .. | 1·50 | 22 | Z 36, A 37, C 38 | .. | .. | .. | 1·25 |
| 19b | X 35, Y 36, Z 36 | .. | .. | .. | 1·00 | 23 | Z 36, A 37, B 37, C 38, D 38 | .. | 1·00 |
| 20 | X 35, Y 36, Z 36, A 37 | .. | .. | 1·00 | | | | | |

Chalk-surfaced paper.   Wmk. Block Cypher, **W.15**

| | | | | | | | | | | | | |
|---|---|---|---|---|---|---|---|---|---|---|---|---|
| 16 | Y 36 .. | .. | .. | .. | .. | 10·00 | 19b | Z 36 .. | .. | .. | .. | 2·50 |
| 19b | Y 36 .. | .. | .. | .. | .. | 10·00 | | | | | | |

## KING GEORGE V.   7d., TYPE N8.   WMK. SIMPLE CYPHER, W.14.   HARRISON

| Plate | Marking |
|---|---|
| 1a | Dots above 1st in upper and lower panes<br>Dot above 5th in lower pane |
| 1b | Dots filled in |

| Plate | Marking |
|---|---|
| 1c | Added small dot under (VE)N of 1st<br>Thin half cut above 1st top row |
| 2a | No marking |
| 2b | Added small dot under NP of 2nd |

### Control Schedule

Both plates (i.e. 1a, 1b and 2a) were at press with controls C. 13, C 13 and D 14, and are not easily distinguishable.

| Plate | Control | Price | Plate | Control | Price |
|---|---|---|---|---|---|
| 1c | F 15, G 15, H 16, J 17, L 18 | .. 2·50 | 2b | F 15, G 15, H 16 .. .. .. | 4·00 |

## KING GEORGE V.   8d., TYPE N8.   WMK. SIMPLE CYPHER, W.14.   HARRISON

| Plate | Marking | Plate | Marking |
|---|---|---|---|
| 1a | Dot above 1st in upper and lower panes | 1b | Dots filled in |

### Control Schedule

| Plate | Controls | Price | Plate | Controls | Price |
|---|---|---|---|---|---|
| 1a | C. 13 .. .. .. .. .. | 2·50 | 1b | D 14, F 15, G 15, H 16, I 16, J 17, K 18 .. .. .. .. | 2·50 |

## KING GEORGE V.   9d. AGATE and 9d. OLIVE-GREEN, TYPE N9.   WMK. SIMPLE CYPHER, W.14.   HARRISON

| Plate | Marking | Plate | Marking |
|---|---|---|---|
| 1a | Dot above 1st in upper and lower panes | 1f | Added dot (top) under EN of 1st |
| 1b | Dots above 1st filled in | 2a | Dot above 2nd in upper and lower panes |
| | Minute dot in rule under PE of 3rd | 2b | Added tiny nick (outer) 19th left side, 13 mm. |
| 1c | Dot under 3rd now filled in.  Flaw in base o | 3a | Small internal nick 19th left side, 11–12 mm. |
| | rule under CE of 1st | | Small cut under first N of 4th |
| 1d | Flaw at base of 1st repaired | 3b | Added dot (base) under P of 2nd |
| 1e | Added nick top (outer) 20th left side | | |

### Control Schedule

| Plate | Controls | Price | Plate | Controls | Price |
|---|---|---|---|---|---|
| 1a | B. 13 .. .. .. .. .. | 2·50 | 2a | B. 13, K 17, L 18, N 19, O 19, O 20, | |
| 1b | E 14, F 15, G 15 .. .. .. | 6·00 | | P 20, Q 20 .. .. .. .. | 6·00 |
| 1c | G15, H 16, I 16, J 17 .. .. | 2·50 | 2b | R 21, S 21, S 22 .. .. .. | 6·00 |
| 1d | J 17, K 17, .. .. .. | 2·50 | | T 22, U 23, V 23 .. .. .. | 25·00 |
| 1e | L 18, N 19 .. .. .. | 2·50 | 3a | K 18, L 18, N 19 .. .. .. | 6·00 |
| 1f | N 19, O 20, S 21 .. .. .. | 2·50 | 3b | N 19, O 19, O 20, P 20, Q 20, R 21, | |
| | T 22, U 23 .. .. .. .. | 15·00 | | S 21, S 22 .. .. .. .. | 6·00 |
| | | | | T 22, U 23, V 23 .. .. .. | 25·00 |

## KING GEORGE V.   9d. OLIVE-GREEN, TYPE N9.   WMK. BLOCK CYPHER, W.15

| Plate | Marking | Plate | Marking |
|---|---|---|---|
| 1 | Irregular cuts 19th left side, 11 mm. | 3 | Minute dot 19th left side, 11 mm. |
| 2 | Sloping internal cut 20th left side, 13mm. | 4 | No marking.  Thick rules at left |
| | After re-chroming in 1926, this cut got pro- | 5 | No marking.  Thin rules at left |
| | gressively smaller, finally showing as a tiny | | |
| | dot | | |

### Control Schedule

#### A. Waterlow

| Plate | Controls | Price |
|---|---|---|
| 1 | A 24, C 25, F 26, I 28, J 28, L 29, N 30, P 31, R 32, T 33  .. .. | 6·00 |
| 2 | A 24, C 25, F 26, I 28, J 28, L 29, N 30, P 31, R 32, T 33  .. .. | 3·00 |

#### B. Harrison provisional printing

| Plate | Controls | Price |
|---|---|---|
| 1 | V 34, W 35 .. .. .. .. | 9·00 |
| 2 | V 34, W 35, X 35 .. .. .. | 3·00 |
| 3 | V 34, W 35 .. .. .. .. | 4·50 |
| 4 | W 35, X 35 .. .. .. .. | 3·00 |
| 5 | X 35 .. .. .. .. .. | 3·00 |

## KING GEORGE V.   10d., TYPE N9.   WMK. SIMPLE CYPHER, W.14.   HARRISON

| Plate | Marking | Plate | Marking |
|---|---|---|---|
| 1a | Base of 20th left side bends inwards; dot above | 1c | Added large dot under P of 2nd |
| | 1st in upper and lower panes | 2a | No marking.  Base of 16th right side bevelled |
| 1b | Dots above 1st filled in.  Two minute dots | 2b | Added large dot under PE of 1st |
| | under PE of 1st | | |

### Control Schedule

| Plate | Controls | Price | Plate | Controls | Price |
|---|---|---|---|---|---|
| 1a | C. 13 .. .. .. .. .. | 5·00 | 2a | D 14, G 15, K 18, M 19 .. .. | 5·00 |
| 1b | D 14, F 15, G 15, H 16, I 16, J 17, K 18, M 19 .. .. .. .. | 5·00 | 2b | M 19, O 19, Q 21, S 21, S 22, T 22, U 23 .. .. .. .. .. | 4·00 |
| 1c | M 19, Q 21, S 21 ,S 22 .. .. | 5·00 | | | |

## KING GEORGE V.  10d., TYPE N9.    WMK. BLOCK CYPHER. W.15

| Plate | Marking | | Plate | Marking |
|---|---|---|---|---|
| 1c | As for Harrison | | 3 | Dot and minute dot 1st left side, 18, 22½ mm· |
| 2b | As for Harrison | | | |

### Control Schedule

Waterlow printings 1924-33

| Plate | Controls | Price | | Plate | Controls | Price |
|---|---|---|---|---|---|---|
| 1c | A 24, D 25, F 26, G 27, J 28, L 29, O 31, Q 32, S 33  ..    ..    .. | 5·00 | | 2b | A 24, D 25, F 26, G 27, J 28, L 29 Q 31, Q 32, S 33   ..    ..    .. | 4·00 |
| | | | | 3 | G 27 ..    ..    ..    ..    .. | 4·00 |

Waterlow provisional printing 1934

| Plate | Controls | Price |
|---|---|---|
| 1c | U 34 ..    ..    ..    ..    .. | 22·00 |

Harrison provisional printings 1934

| Plate | Controls | Price | | Plate | Controls | Price |
|---|---|---|---|---|---|---|
| 1c | V 34 ..    ..    ..    ..    .. | 3·50 | | 3 | W 35    ..    ..    ..    .. | 3·00 |
| 2b | U 34, V 34, W 35  ..    ..    .. | 3·00 | | | | |

## KING GEORGE V.  1s., TYPE N9.    WMK. SIMPLE CYPHER, W.14.    HARRISON

| Plate | Marking | | Plate | Marking |
|---|---|---|---|---|
| 1a | Dots above 1st in upper and lower panes Rule 20th left side thick and rounded outer base corner | | 2c | Added cut under S of 2nd |
| 1b | 20th left side now shows a nick base (outer). Dots above 1st filled in | | 3 | Tiny nick (outer) 19th left side, 4 mm. |
| | | | 4 | Cut 19th left side, 18¾ mm. (Waterlow Plate 2) |
| 2a | Dot above 2nd in upper and lower panes Rule 20th left side irregular | | 5a | Tiny nick (inner) 19th left side, 14 mm. |
| 2b | Dots above 2nd filled in.  Nick 19th right side (outer), 10½ mm. | | 5b | Added dash at left of 2nd |
| | | | 5c | Added cut under S of 1st.  (Waterlow Plate 5) |
| | | | 6 | No marking |

### Control Schedule

| Plate | Controls | Price | | Plate | Controls | Price |
|---|---|---|---|---|---|---|
| 1a | C. 13 ..    ..    ..    ..    .. | 2·00 | | 4 | R 21, S 21, S 22, T 22, U 22, U 23, V 23 ..    ..    ..    ..    .. | 5·00 |
| 1b | D 14, E 14, F 15, G 15, H 16, I 16, J 17, M 19, O 19, O 20    ..    .. | 2·00 | | 5a | J 17, K 17, L 18   ..    ..    .. | 5·50 |
| 2a | C. 13 ..    ..    ..    ..    .. | 2·00 | | 5b | M 19 ..    ..    ..    ..    .. | 7·00 |
| 2b | D 14, E 14, F 15, G 15, H 16, I 16, J 17, M 19   ..    ..    ..    .. | 3·00 | | 5c | M 19, N 19, O 19, O 20, P 20, Q 20, R 21, V 23 ..    ..    ..    .. | 2·00 |
| 2c | M 19, N 19, O 19, O 20    ..    .. | 3·00 | | 6 | V 23 ..    ..    ..    ..    .. | 7·00 |
| 3 | O 20, P 20, Q 20, R 21, S 21, S 22, T 22, U 22, U 23  ..    ..    .. | 5·00 | | | | |

## KING GEORGE V.  1s., TYPE N.9.    WMK. BLOCK CYPHER, W.15

| Plate | Marking | | Plate | Marking |
|---|---|---|---|---|
| 1 | No marking | | 4a | ½ dot (inner) 19th left side, 13 mm.;  small nicks at each end of rule under 2nd |
| 2 | Cut 19th left side, 18½ mm. (Harrison Plate 4) | | | |
| 3a | Dot 20th left side, 12½ mm. | | 4b | Added dot (outer) 19th left side, 6 mm. |
| 3b | Added large dot 20th left side | | 5 | Cut under S of 1st. (Harrison Plate 5c) |

### Control Schedule

Waterlow printings 1924-33

| Plate | Controls | Price | | Plate | Controls | Price |
|---|---|---|---|---|---|---|
| 1 | A 24, B 24, D 25    ..    ..    .. | 7·00 | | 3b | R 32, S 33 ..    ..    ..    .. | 4·50 |
| 2 | A 24, B 24, D 28    ..    ..    .. | 7·00 | | 4a | F 26, H 27, I 28, J 28, K 29, L 29, N 30, P 31, R 32, S 33   ..    .. | 7·00 |
| 3a | F 26, H 27, I 28, J 28, K 29, L 29, N 30, P 31, R 32    ..    ..    .. | 4·00 | | 4b | S 33 ..    ..    ..    ..    .. | 9·00 |

Waterlow provisional printing 1934

| Plate | Controls | Price | | Plate | Controls | Price |
|---|---|---|---|---|---|---|
| 3b | U 34 ..    ..    ..    ..    .. | 50·00 | | 4b | U 34 .    ..    ..    ..    .. | 25·00 |

Harrison provisional printings 1934-35

| Plate | Controls | Price | | Plate | Controls | Price |
|---|---|---|---|---|---|---|
| 3b | U 34, V 34, W 35, X 35  ..    .. | 4·00 | | 5 | W 35, X 35 ..    ..    ..    .. | 4·50 |
| 4b | U 34, V 34  ..    ..    ..    .. | 7·00 | | | | |

# Post Office Booklets of Stamps

## SERIES 1—2s. BOOKLETS

### King Edward VII

The first fourteen editions were without a number on the cover, each edition being identifiable by some feature peculiar to itself and, for the sake of convenience, these early editions are referred to by numbers in brackets, viz., No. (1) to No. (14). After this the printing contract was awarded to Harrison & Sons who instituted the numbering of the booklets on the cover, starting with No. 8.

For all the King Edward VII editions, i.e., Nos. (1) to (7) an additional ½d. was charged for the booklet itself in addition to the price of the stamps. No. (1) was sold over the counter for 2s. 0½d.; Nos. (2) to (7) contained only 1s. 11½d. worth of stamps, one of the stamps on one of the ½d. panes being printed with a green cross. Since that time no charge has ever been made for any British Post Office booklet of stamps other than the price of the stamps it contained.

Type 1

Type 2

**1904 (March).** The first booklet issued contained four panes of six, i.e., 24 × 1d. K.E. VII stamps, printed by De la Rue, with watermark Crown, normal or inverted. It was bound with staples in a red cover bearing the Edwardian P.O. cypher and interleaved with plain grease proof paper. Booklet issued: No. (1). (Type 1.)

**1906 (June).** As before, but make-up changed to include 12 × 1d. and 23 × ½d. stamps and one green cross. Booklet issued: No. (2). (Type 2.)

**1907 (August).** As before, but make-up changed to include 18 × 1d. and 11 × ½d. and one green cross. Booklet issued: No. (3).

**1908.** As before, but interleaves used for Post Office notices printed in red. Booklet issued: No. (4).

**1909.** As before, but interleaves of plain white paper printed on one side with trade advertisements in green. Booklets issued: No. (5)—third advertisement Chas. Baker & Co. and No. (6)—third advertisement Brimsdown lamps.

**1911.** As before, but containing stamps printed by Harrison & Sons and showing a larger Post Office cypher on cover. Interleaves printed on one side with Post Office notices in green. Booklet issued: No. (7).

### King George V

**1911 (August).** As before, but make-up changed to include 18 × 1d. and 12 × ½d. stamps of the new reign (Die 1B) with watermark Crown, normal or inverted. Interleaves printed on both sides with trade advertisements in green. Georgian Post Office cypher on cover. Booklet issued: No. (8)—first advertisement Aitchison & Co.; No. (9)—first advertisement Gresham Fire and Accident Insurance Society; and No. (10)—first advertisement Empire Hotels.

Type 3                                                    Type 4

**1912 (April).** Cover redrawn to allow space for inland postage rates, otherwise as before. Booklets issued: No. (11)—first advertisement Marsuma Cigarettes and No. (12)—first advertisement Palethorpes Sausages. (Type 3.)

**1912 (September).** As before, but stamps (Die 1b) with watermark Simple Cypher. Booklet issued: No. (13).

**1912 (November).** As before, but with redesigned cover showing foreign and colonial as well as inland rates of postage. Booklet No. (14). (Type 4.)

**1913 (January).** As before, but bearing booklet number on the cover. Booklets issued: Nos. 8 and 9.

**1913 (April).** As before, but containing stamps of the 1912-22 issue with watermark Simple Cypher, normal or inverted. Booklets issued: Nos. 10 to 35.

**1915 (November).** As before, except lower panel of front cover, which was changed to show " NEW RATES OF POSTAGE ". Booklets issued: Nos. 36 to 42.

**1916 (May).** As before, but advertisements on interleaves printed in black instead of green. Booklets issued: Nos. 43, 44 and 45.

**1916 (July).** As before, but colour of cover changed from red to orange. Booklets issued: Nos. 46 to 64.

NOTE.—From Booklet No. 62, the booklets were stitched instead of stapled.

Type 5

**1917 (September).** As before, but rates of postage transferred to an interleaf and the lower panel of the front cover used for a trade advertisement. Booklets issued: Nos. 65 to 81. (Type 5.)

**1918 (October).** Series 1 was replaced by Series 2.

# SERIES 2—3s. and 3s. 6d. BOOKLETS

King George V

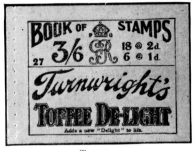

Type 6                                          Type 7

**1918 (October).**   The minimum inland postage rate having been increased from 1d. to 1½d., a new series was introduced to replace Series 1, containing 12 × 1½d.; 12 × 1d. and 12 × ½d. stamps of the 1912-22 issue with watermark Simple Cypher, normal or inverted. Bound in orange covers and fully interleaved.   Booklets issued: Nos. 1 to 11.

**1919 (July).**   Make-up altered to contain 18 × 1½d., 6 × 1d. and 6 × ½d.   Otherwise as before.   Booklets issued: Nos. 12 to 26.   (Type 6.)

**1920 (July).**   With the increase of the minimum inland postage rate from 1½d. to 2d., the make-up was changed to 18 × 2d. and 6 × 1d., and the price was increased from 3s. to 3s. 6d.   Otherwise as before.   Booklets issued: Nos. 27 to 32.   (Type 7.)

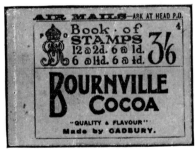

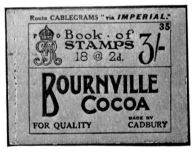

Type 8                                          Type 9

**1921 (April).**   Make-up changed to 12 × 2d.; 6 × 1d.; 6 × 1½d. and 6 × ½d. Booklets issued: Nos. 33, 34, 36 and 38. (Type 8.)

**1921 (April).**   An experimental booklet bound in blue covers was issued containing 18 × 2d. stamps (Die I), which sold at 3s. concurrently with the 3s. 6d. booklets.   Booklets issued: Nos. 35 and 37.   (Type 9.)

**1921 (August).**   Series 2 was replaced by Series 3.

## SERIES 3—3s. 6d. and 3s. BOOKLETS

King George V

**1921 (August).**   A new series was introduced to replace Series 2, containing 12 × 2d. (Die I or Die II); 6 × 1½d., 6 × 1d. and 6 × ½d. stamps of the 1912-22 issue with watermark Simple Cypher, normal or inverted.   Bound in orange-red covers, fully interleaved and costing 3s. 6d.   Booklets issued: Nos. 1 to 11 and 14 to 18.   (Type 8.)

**1921 (December).**   An experimental booklet bound in blue covers, similar to Nos. 35 and 37 of Series 2, was issued containing 18 × 2d. stamps (Die II), costing 3s. and sold concurrently with the 3s. 6d. books.   Booklets issued: Nos. 12 and 13.   (Type 9.)

Type 10

**1922 (May).** With the reduction of the minimum inland postage rate from 2d. to 1½d., the make-up was changed to include 18 × 1½d.; 6 × 1d. and 6 × ½d. Bound in scarlet covers and fully interleaved. Booklets issued: Nos. 19, 20, 22, 23, 25 to 54. (Type 10.)

**1922 (June).** An experimental booklet was issued bound in blue covers, similar to Nos. 12 and 13, but containing 24 × 1½d. stamps. Sold concurrently with Nos. 20, 22, 23 and 25. Booklets issued: Nos. 21 and 24.

**1924 (February).** As before (No. 54) but containing stamps with the Block Cypher watermark printed by Waterlow & Sons. Booklets issued: Nos. 55 to 167. (Type 10.)

**1929 (May).** As before, but cover of special design printed in red on buff and containing stamps of the P.U.C. issue. Booklets issued: 168 to 172. (Type 12.)

**1929 (August).** As No. 167, with stamps with the Block Cypher watermark printed by Waterlow & Sons. Booklets issued: Nos. 173 to 190. (Type 10.)

**1930 (May).** As before, but Air Mail label included. Booklets issued: Nos. 191 to 273.

**1934 (March).** As before, but containing stamps with the Block Cypher watermark printed by Harrison & Sons. Booklets issued: Nos. 274 to 288.

**1935 (January).** As before, but containing stamps of the photogravure issue intermediate size. Booklets issued: Nos. 289 to 293.

**1935 (May).** Silver Jubilee issue of booklets larger in size than the normal with cover of special design printed in red on buff, containing 20 × 1½d.; 4 × 1d. and 4 × ½d. Silver Jubilee stamps, watermark Block Cypher, normal or inverted. Booklets issued: Nos. 294 to 297. (Type 13.)

**1935 (July).** As No. 293, but containing stamps of the photogravure issue small size. Booklets issued: Nos. 298 to 319. (Type 10.)

### King Edward VIII

**1936 (November).** As before, except for the K.E.VIII cypher on the cover and without " P " and " O " on either side of crown, and containing stamps of the new reign. Booklets issued: Nos. 320 to 332.

### King George VI

**1937 (August).** As King Edward VIII, except for K.G.VI cypher on the cover and containing stamps of the new reign in the original dark colours. Booklets issued: Nos 333 to 343.

**1938 (April).** As before, but with redesigned front cover showing GPO emblem instead of royal cypher. Booklets issued: Nos. 344 to 377 (Type 14.)

**1940 (May).** This series was replaced by Series 7.

## SERIES 4—2s. BOOKLETS

A new series was introduced, bound in blue covers, selling at 2s., concurrently with Series 3. A feature of this series (except the Special Jubilee booklets) and of Series 5, is the first pane of 1½d. stamps, which contained only four postage stamps. The remaining two spaces, i.e., those on the left next to the margin, being printed with trade advertisements or postal notices.

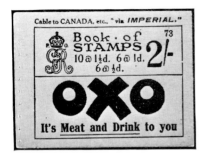

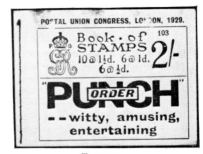

Type 11                           Type 12

### King George V

**1924 (February).** Containing 10 × 1½d., 6 × 1d. and 6 × ½d. stamps of the 1912–1922 issue with Simple Cypher watermark, normal or inverted. Booklets issued: Nos. 1 and 2. (Type 11.)

**1924 (June).** As before, but containing stamps with the Block Cypher watermark printed by Waterlow & Sons. Booklets issued: Nos. 3 to 102. (Type 11.)

*Varieties*

**1924 (June).** The *se-tenant* advertisements were accidentally inverted. Booklet No. 8.

**1924 (September).** The upper *se-tenant* advertisement was deliberately inverted. Booklet No. 12.

**1924 (November).** Some of the advertisement panes were printed on paper with watermark sideways. Booklet No. 15. (Booklets containing these are very rare.)

**1927 (November).** The upper *se-tenant* advertisement was deliberately inverted. Booklet No. 67.

**1929 (May).** As before, but cover of special design printed in blue on buff and containing stamps of the P.U.C. issue. Booklets issued: Nos. 103 to 107. (Type 12.)

**1929 (July).** As No. 102, containing stamps with the Block Cypher watermark printed by Waterlow & Sons. Booklets issued: Nos. 108 to 254. (Type 11.)

*Varieties*

**1931 (September).** The *se-tenant* advertisements were printed in green. Booklet No. 171.

**1933 (October).** As a trial the covers were printed on unglazed paper of a deeper blue. Booklet No. 242.

**1934 (February).** As before, but containing stamps with the Block Cypher watermark printed by Harrison & Sons. Booklets issued: Nos. 255 to 287. (Type 11.)

**1935 (January).** As before, but containing stamps of the photogravure issue intermediate size with the *se-tenant* advertisements printed in brown. Booklets issued: Nos. 288 to 297. (From Booklet No. 289 an interleaf Air Mail label was included.)

Type 13

**1935 (May).** Silver Jubilee issue of booklets larger in size than the normal with cover of special design printed in blue on buff, containing 12 × 1½d., 4 × 1d. and 4 × ½d. and no *se-tenant* advertisements. Booklets issued: Nos. 298 to 304. (Type 13.)

**1935 (July).** As No. 297, but containing stamps of the photogravure issue small size with *se-tenant* advertisements printed in black. Booklets issued: Nos. 305 to 353. (Type 11.)

### King Edward VIII

**1936 (October).**  As before, except for the K.E.VIII cypher on the cover and containing stamps of the new reign.  Booklets issued: Nos. 354 to 385.

### King George VI

**1937 (August).**  As before, except for the K.G.VI cypher on the cover and containing stamps of the new reign in the original dark colours.  Booklets issued: Nos. 386 to 412.

Type 14

**1938 (April).**  As before, but with redesigned front cover showing GPO emblem instead of royal cypher.  Booklets issued: Nos. 413 to 508.  (Type 14.)

**1940 (May).**  This series was replaced by Series 7.

## SERIES 5—5s. BOOKLETS

### King George V

Type 15

The letters " P " and " O " are on either side of crown
on the King George V booklets, as shown in Type 10

**1931 (August).**  A new series was introduced, bound in green covers, selling at 5s. concurrently with Series 3 and 4, and containing 34 × 1½d.; 6 × 1d. and 6 × ½d. stamps with Block Cypher watermark printed by Waterlow & Son, the first 1½d. pane being similar to that in Series 4 and having four postage stamps and two *se-tenant* advertisements. Booklets issued: No. 1.  (Type 15.)

**1932 (June).**  As before, but with buff covers.  Booklets issued: Nos. 2 to 6.  (From Booklet No. 4 an interleaf Air Mail label was included.)

**1934 (July).**  As before, but containing stamps with the Block Cypher watermark printed by Harrison & Sons.  Booklets issued: Nos. 7 and 8.

**1935 (February).**  As before, but with stamps of the photogravure issue intermediate size and with *se-tenant* advertisements printed in brown.  Booklet issued: No. 9.

**1935 (July).**  As before, but with stamps of the photogravure issue small size and with the *se-tenant* advertisements printed in black.  Booklets issued: Nos. 10 to 15.

**King Edward VIII**
**1937 (March).** As before, but with the K.E.VIII cypher on the cover and containing stamps of the new reign. Booklets issued: Nos. 16 and 17.

**King George VI**
**1937 (August).** As before, but with K.G.VI cypher on the cover and containing stamps of the new reign in the original dark colours. Booklets issued: Nos. 18 to 20.

Type 16

**1938 (May).** As before, but with redesigned front cover showing GPO emblem instead of royal cypher. Booklets issued: Nos. 21 to 29. (Type 16.)
**1940 (July).** This series was replaced by Series 8.

## SERIES 6—6d. and 1s. BOOKLETS SOLD IN SLOT-MACHINES

This series consists of booklets sold from Post Office slot-machines. None of the booklets in this series was dated or numbered.

**Sub-Series A. 6d. Booklets**
**King Edward VIII**
**1936.** Booklets containing 4 × 1½d. stamps, in small panes of two, were obtainable from slot-machines placed outside 40 of the larger London Post Offices. No interleaves and stamps either watermark normal or inverted. Bound in buff unglazed covers.

**King George VI**
**1938 (January).** As before, but containing stamps of the new reign in the original dark colours, with watermark normal or inverted. With or without interleaf.

**Sub-Series B. 6d. Booklets**
**King George VI**
**1938 (February).** Make-up changed to contain 2 × 1½d.; 2 × 1d. and 2 × ½d. stamps in the original dark colours, with watermark normal or inverted. Bound in plain pink unglazed covers, with or without interleaves.

**Sub-Series C. 6d. Booklets**
**King George VI**
**1940 (June).** Make-up changed to contain 4 × 1d. and 4 × ½d. stamps in the original dark colours in panes of four with watermark sideways, either with margin at top of stamps or at bottom; bound in pale green plain covers with interleaves. Booklets obtainable only from a slot-machine placed inside the G.P.O., King Edward Building, E.C.1.

**Sub-Series D. 1s. Booklets**
**King George VI**
**1947 (December).** Make-up changed to contain 4 × ½d.; 4 × 1d. and 4 × 1½d. stamps in the pale shades in panes of two, all with watermark normal. Bound in plain unglazed cream covers without interleaves.
**1951 (May).** As before, but containing stamps in the changed colours.

## Sub-Series E. 1s. Booklets
### King George VI

**1951.** Make-up changed to contain $4 \times \frac{1}{2}$d.; $4 \times 1$d. and $4 \times 1\frac{1}{2}$d. stamps of the pale shades in panes of four with watermark normal. Cover cream. A very rare booklet.

**1951 (May).** As before, but stamps in the new colours all watermark normal, margin either at the top or at the bottom. These booklets were on sale outside the Festival of Britain Post Office on the South Bank.

**1952 (December).** As before, but with printed covers with stamps either watermark normal or inverted and with margins only at the top. At first available at Paignton head office, but later at other places. Back cover printed: " $1\frac{1}{2}$d. Minimum postage rate for inland printed papers ".

**1953 (September).** As before with Inland Letter rate on inside cover corrected in ink.

**1954.** As before, with Inland Postage rates correctly printed. GPO emblem with St. Edward's crown and oval frame on the front cover and new notice on the back cover: " Minimum Foreign Letter Rate FOURPENCE ".

## SERIES 7—2s. 6d. BOOKLETS
### King George VI

Type 17

Type 18

**1940 (June).** The minimum inland postage rate having been increased from $1\frac{1}{2}$d. to $2\frac{1}{2}$d., a new series of booklets was introduced to replace Series 3 and 4, containing $6 \times 2\frac{1}{2}$d.; $6 \times 2$d. and $6 \times \frac{1}{2}$d. stamps in the dark colours. Fully interleaved and bound in red covers to use up surplus card left over from Series 3. Booklets issued: Nos. 1 to 7. (Type 17.)

**1940 (September).** As before, but covers changed to blue to use up surplus card left over from Series 4. Booklets issued: Nos. 8 to 13.

**1940 (October).** As before, but with glazed green covers of changed design. Booklets issued: Nos. 14 to 94. (Type 18.)

**1942 (March).** As before, but containing stamps in the pale shades. Booklets issued: Nos. 95 to 146 (part).

**1942 (October).** As before, but with unglazed green covers. Booklets issued: Nos. 146 (part) to 214.

Type 19

**1943 (August).** After Booklets No. 214, the booklets were no longer numbered, but were dated with the month of issue. At the same time commercial advertising ceased, covers and interleaves being used for Post Office slogans. Changed cover design, with GPO emblem in centre. (Type 19.)

*Varieties*

**1943 (October).** As before, with Forces parcel rates correctly printed.

**1943 (November).** As before, with thinner and rougher interleaving.

**1943 (December).** As before, but booklets with or without interleaving.

**1944 (September).** As before, all booklets now without interleaves.

**1951 (May).** As before, but containing stamps in the new colours.

**1951 (June).** The minimum printed paper rate was increased to 1½d., and as the rate shown in the booklet was incorrect, the correct rate was printed on the cover in red also on part of the July edition.

**1951 (July).** As for May, but with corrected printed paper rate.

**1952 (March).** Make-up changed to contain 6 × 2½d.; 6 × 1½d.; 3 × 1d. and 6 × ½d. The 1d. pane comprised three stamps in the top row and a Post Office notice in the lower row reading " MINIMUM INLAND PRINTED PAPER RATE 1½D." and measuring 17 mm. high (PPR 17 mm.). Otherwise as before.

## SERIES 8—5s. BOOKLETS

### King George VI

**1940 (July).** The minimum inland postage rate having been raised from 1½d. to 2½d., a new series of 5s. booklets was introduced to replace Series 5, containing 18 × 2½d.; 6 × 2d. and 6 × ½d. stamps in the original dark colours. Bound in glazed buff covers and fully interleaved. Booklets issued: Nos. 1 to 16 (part). (Type 16.)

**1942 (March).** During the life of Booklet No. 16 stamps in the pale shades were brought into use. Otherwise as before. Booklets issued: Nos. 16 (part) to 29 (part).

**1943 (February).** As before, but cover changed to rough unglazed buff. Booklets issued: Nos. 29 (part) to 36.

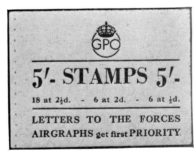

Type 20

Type 21

**1943 (September).** As before, but with changed cover design with GPO emblem in centre. Booklets dated and no longer numbered. Commercial advertising ceased and interleaves were used for war slogans. (Type 20.)

In the earlier printing an error in the Forces parcel rate—the 3 lb. rate being shown as 6d. instead of 9d.—was corrected with a hand stamp, but this was later correctly printed

**1944 (April).** As before, but with changed cover design. (Type 21.)

**1944 (August).** The cover reverted to the September, 1943, design, and interleaves were discontinued altogether.

**1951 (May).** As before, but containing stamps in the new colours.

**1952 (March).** Make-up changed to contain 18 × 2½d.; 6 × 1½d.; 3 × 1d. and 6 × ½d., the 1d. pane having three stamps in the top row and Post Office notice in the lower row reading " MINIMUM INLAND PRINTED PAPER RATE 1½d." and measuring 17 mm. high (PPR 17 mm.). Otherwise as before.

**1953 (January).** Make-up again altered to include the 2d. value and containing 12 × 2½d.; 6 × 2d.; 6 × 1½d.; 6 × 1d. and 6 × ½d. Otherwise as before.

## KING EDWARD VII

| Cat. No. | Cover Type | Face Value | Booklet Nos. | Date | Colour | Series | Price |
|---|---|---|---|---|---|---|---|
| **Wmk. Crown** | | | | | | | |
| B1 | 1 | 2/0½d. | (1) | 1904 | Red | 1 | 6·00 |
| B2 | 2 | 2/– | (2) | 1906 | Red | 1 | 14·00 |
| B3 | 2 | 2/– | (3) | 1907 | Red | 1 | 12·00 |
| B4 | 2 | 2/– | (4) | 1908 | Red | 1 | 17·00 |
| B5 | 2 | 2/– | (5) & (6) | 1909 | Red | 1 | 12·00 |
| B6 | 2 | 2/– | (7) | 1911 | Red | 1 | 25·00 |

## KING GEORGE V

| | | | | | | | |
|---|---|---|---|---|---|---|---|
| **Types N1 and N3. Die 1B. Wmk. Crown** | | | | | | | |
| B7 | 2 | 2/– | (8) (9) & (10) | 1911 | Red | 1 | 12·00 |
| B8 | 3 | 2/– | (11) & (12) | 1912 | Red | 1 | 18·00 |
| **Types N1 and N3. Die 1B. Wmk. Simple Cypher** | | | | | | | |
| B 9 | 3 | 2/– | (13) | 1912 | Red | 1 | 8·00 |
| B10 | 4 | 2/– | (14) | 1912 | Red | 1 | 11·00 |
| B11 | 4 | 2/– | 8–9 | 1912 | Red | 1 | 9·00 |
| **Types N5, N6 and N7. Wmk. Simple Cypher** | | | | | | | |
| B12 | 4 | 2/– | 10–35 | 1913 | Red | 1 | 4·00 |
| B13 | 4 | 2/– | 36–42 | 1915 | Red | 1 | 4·50 |
| B14 | 4 | 2/– | 43–45 | 1916 | Red | 1 | 5·00 |
| B15 | 4 | 2/– | 46–64 | 1916 | Orange | 1 | 4·00 |
| B16 | 5 | 2/– | 65–81 | 1917 | Orange | 1 | 4·00 |
| B17 | 11 | 2/– | 1–2 | 1924 | Blue | 4 | 18·00 |
| B18 | 6 | 3/– | 1–11 | 1918 | Orange | 2 | 7·00 |
| B19 | 6 | 3/– | 12–26 | 1919 | Orange | 2 | 6·00 |
| B20 | 9 | 3/– (Die I) | 35 & 37 | 1921 | Blue | 2 | 11·00 |
| B21 | 9 | 3/– (Die II) | 12–13 | 1921 | Blue | 3 | 15·00 |
| B22 | 10 | 3/– | 21 & 24 | 1922 | Blue | 3 | 22·00 |
| B23 | 10 | 3/– | 19–20, 22–23 & 25–54 | 1922 | Scarlet | 3 | 8·00 |
| B24 | 7 | 3/6 | 27–32 | 1920 | Orange | 2 | 10·00 |
| B25 | 8 | 3/6 | 33–34, 36 & 38 | 1921 | Orange-red | 2 | 12·00 |
| B25a | 8 | 3/6 (Die I or Die II) | 1–11 14–18 | 1921 | Orange-red | 3 | 12·00 |
| **1924 Wmk. Block Cypher. Printed by Waterlow & Son** | | | | | | | |
| B26 | 11 | 2/– | 3–102 & 108–254 | 1924/29 | Blue | 4 | 10·00 |
| B27 | 10 | 3/– | 55–167 & 173–273 | 1924/30 | Scarlet | 3 | 3·50 |
| B28 | 15 | 5/– | 1 | 1931 | Green | 5 | 25·00 |
| B29 | 15 | 5/– | 2–6 | 1932 | Buff | 5 | 8·00 |
| **1929 Postal Union Congress Issue** | | | | | | | |
| B30 | 12 | 2/– | 103–107 | 1929 | Blue/*buff* | 4 | 20·00 |
| B31 | 12 | 3/– | 168–172 | 1929 | Red/*buff* | 3 | 12·00 |
| **1934 Wmk. Block Cypher. Printed by Harrison & Sons** | | | | | | | |
| B32 | 11 | 2/– | 255–287 | 1934 | Blue | 4 | 10·00 |
| B33 | 10 | 3/– | 274–288 | 1934 | Scarlet | 3 | 4·50 |
| B34 | 15 | 5/– | 7–8 | 1934 | Buff | 5 | 12·00 |
| **1935 (January) Photogravure in the Intermediate Forma** | | | | | | | |
| B35 | 11 | 2/– | 288–297 | 1935 | Blue | 4 | 20·00 |
| B36 | 10 | 3/– | 289–293 | 1935 | Scarlet | 3 | 14·00 |
| B37 | 15 | 5/– | 9 | 1935 | Buff | 5 | 25·00 |
| **1935 (May) Silver Jubilee Issue** | | | | | | | |
| B38 | 13 | 2/– | 298–304 | 1935 | Blue/*buff* | 4 | 7·00 |
| B39 | 13 | 3/– | 294–297 | 1935 | Red/*buff* | 3 | 9·00 |
| **1935 (July) Photogravure in the Small Forma** | | | | | | | |
| B40 | 11 | 2/– | 305–353 | 1935 | Blue | 4 | 4·50 |
| B41 | 10 | 3/– | 298–319 | 1935 | Scarlet | 3 | 3·00 |
| B42 | 15 | 5/– | 10–15 | 1935 | Buff | 5 | 6·00 |

**236**

## KING EDWARD VIII

| Cat. No. | Cover Type | Face Value | Bookle: Nos | Date | Colour | Series | Price |
|---|---|---|---|---|---|---|---|
| **1936** | | | | | | | |
| B43 | 11 | 2/– | 354–385 | 1936 | Blue | 4 | 2·00 |
| B44 | 10 | 3/– | 320–332 | 1936 | Scarlet | 3 | 1·25 |
| B45 | 15 | 5/– | 16–17 | 1937 | Buff | 5 | 3·50 |

## KING GEORGE VI

**1937-40 Dark colours**

| Cat. No. | Cover Type | Face Value | Bookle: Nos | Date | Colour | Series | Price |
|---|---|---|---|---|---|---|---|
| B46 | 11 | 2/– | 386–412 | 1937 | Blue | 4 | 5·00 |
| B47 | 14 | 2/– | 413–508 | 1938 | Blue | 4 | 4·00 |
| B48 | 10 | 3/– | 333–343 | 1937 | Scarlet | 3 | 4·00 |
| B49 | 14 | 3/– | 344–377 | 1938 | Scarlet | 3 | 3·50 |
| B50 | 15 | 5/– | 18–20 | 1937 | Buff | 5 | 14·00 |
| B51 | 16 | 5/– | 21–29 | 1938 | Buff | 5 | 10·00 |
| B52 | 16 | 5/– | 1–16 | 1940 | Buff | 8 | 10·00 |
| B53 | 17 | 2/6 | 1–7 | 1940 | Scarlet | 7 | 9·00 |
| B54 | 17 | 2/6 | 8–13 | 1940 | Blue | 7 | 9·00 |
| B55 | 18 | 2/6 | 14–94 | 1940 | Green | 7 | 6·00 |

**1942 Pale Colours**
  (a) Glazed covers

| | | | | | | | |
|---|---|---|---|---|---|---|---|
| B56 | 18 | 2/6 | 95–146 | 1942 | Green | 7 | 4·50 |
| B57 | 16 | 5/– | 16–29 | 1942 | Buff | 8 | 8·00 |

  (b) Unglazed covers

| | | | | | | | |
|---|---|---|---|---|---|---|---|
| B58 | 18 | 2/6 | 146–214 | 1942 | Green | 7 | 4·00 |
| B59 | 16 | 5/– | 29–36 | 1943 | Buff | 8 | 8·00 |

## BOOKLETS SOLD IN SLOT-MACHINES (Series 6)

None of the books in this series is dated or numbered.

| Cat. No. | Face value | | Date | Colour | Sub-Series | Price |
|---|---|---|---|---|---|---|
| **King Edward VIII** | | | | | | |
| B60 | 6d. | | 1936 | Buff | A | 1·25 |
| **King George VI. Dark Colours** | | | | | | |
| B61 | 6d. | | 1938 | Buff | A | 1·25 |
| a. | | Ditto with interleaf | | | | 1·25 |
| B62 | 6d. | | 1938 | Pink | B | 3·50 |
| a. | | Ditto with interleaves | | | | 3·50 |
| B63 | 6d. | Bound at top | 1940 | Green | C | 4·00 |
| a. | | Bound at bottom | | | | 4·00 |
| **King George VI. Pale Colours** | | | | | | |
| B64 | 1/– | | 1947 | Cream | D | 60 |
| B65 | 1/– | | 1949 | Cream | E | — |
| **King George VI. New Colours** | | | | | | |
| B66 | 1/– | | 1951 | Cream | D | 50 |
| B67 | 1/– | Bound at top | 1951 | Cream | E | 60 |
| a. | | Bound at bottom | | | | 60 |
| B68 | 1/– | | 1952 | Printed covers | E | 60 |
| a. | | Manuscript deletion | 1953 | | | 60 |
| B69 | 1/– | | 1954 | Printed covers | E | 1·00 |

## DATED 2s. 6d. and 5s. BOOKLETS

**King George VI**

| Cat. No. | Cover Type | Face Value | Date | Colour | Series | *From* |
|---|---|---|---|---|---|---|
| **1943 Pale Colours** | | | | | | |
| B70 | 19 | 2/6 | 1943 | Green | 7 | 1·25 |

|  |  |  |  |
|---|---|---|---|
| 1943 | August–December. | 1948 | January–December. |
| 1944 | January–December. | 1949 | January–August. |
| 1945 | January–December. | | October–December. |
| 1946 | January–December. | 1950 | January–December. |
| 1947 | January–December. | 1951 | January–Fedruary. |

**237**

| Cat. No. | Cover Type | Face Value | Date | Colour | Series | *From* |
|---|---|---|---|---|---|---|
| **1943 Pale Colours** | | | | | | |
| B71 | 20 | 5/– (April, June 1944 Type 21) | 1943 | Buff | 8 | 1·50 |

1943  September, October, November, December.
1944  February, March, April, June, August, October, November.
1945  January, February, April, June, August, October, December.
1946  January, March, May, June, August, October, December.
1947  February, April, June, August, October, December.
1948  February, April, June, July, August, October, December.
1949  February, April, June, August, September, October, December.
1950  February, April, June, August, October, December.

| | | | | | | |
|---|---|---|---|---|---|---|
| **1951 New Colours** | | | | | | |
| B72 | 19 | 2/6 | 1951 | Green | 7 | 1·25 |

1951  May–December.
1952  January–February.

| | | | | | | |
|---|---|---|---|---|---|---|
| B73 | 19 | 2/6 New make-up | 1952 | Green | 7 | 1·50 |

1952  March–December.
1953  January–May.

| | | | | | | |
|---|---|---|---|---|---|---|
| B74 | 20 | 5/– | 1951 | Buff | 8 | 1·50 |

1951  May, July, September, November.
1952  January.

| | | | | | | |
|---|---|---|---|---|---|---|
| B75 | 20 | 5/– New make-up | 1952 | Buff | 8 | 1·75 |

1952  March, May, July, September, November.

| | | | | | | |
|---|---|---|---|---|---|---|
| B76 | 20 | 5/– Make-up changed again | 1953 | Buff | 8 | 2·00 |

1953  January, March.

# Advertisement Panes

Advertisement Pane

The advertisements are printed in black, unless otherwise stated. Prices are for complete booklet panes of four stamps and two labels *se-tenant*. The prices are the same for water-mark upright or inverted. Blocks showing two stamps and two advertisements *se-tenant* can be supplied at half these prices.

## 1924-34. Typographed

### 1924. 1½d. RED-BROWN, TYPE N6, WMK. TYPE W.14

Printed by Harrison & Sons

1. Stamp Auctions, Harmer, Rooke, expert advice free
   Millennium Oat-Flakes .. .. 10·00

2. Millennium Oat-Flakes
   Stamp Auctions, Harmer, Rooke,
   expert advice free .. .. .. 10·00

### 1924-34. 1½d. RED-BROWN, TYPE N6, WMK. TYPE W.15

I. Printed by Waterlow & Sons

(a) The G.P.O. advertisements

3. Air Mails (enquire)
   Cable via Imperial .. .. .. 6·00
4. Air Mails (enquire) (*inverted*)
   Cable via Imperial (*inverted*) .. 12·00
5. Air Mails (enquire)
   Telephone Service .. .. .. 6·00
6. Cable via Imperial
   Air Mails (enquire) .. .. .. 6·00
7. Cable via Imperial
   Telephone Service .. .. .. 6·00
8. via Empiradio
   Cable via Imperial .. .. .. 7·00

9. via Empiradio
   Telephone Service .. .. .. 8·00
10. Saving is Simple
    Home Safe (*Setting 1*) .. .. 6·00
11. Telephone Service
    Air Mails (enquire) .. .. .. 6·00
12. Telephone Service
    Air Mails, letters and parcels
    (*Setting 1*) .. .. .. .. 6·00
13. Telephone Service
    Cable via Imperial .. .. .. 6·00

(b) Commercial advertisements

*J. & J. Cash Ltd., Coventry*

14. Cash's names. The best method of
    marking personal and household linen
    List of styles. J. & J. Cash .. 6·00
15. Cash's washing ribbons. Ideal for
    shoulder straps
    Book of ribbons. J. & J. Cash .. 7·00
    *With this booklet pane, J. & J. Cash started
    the practice of printing the booklet number on
    their advertisements. This pane exists with-
    out number, also with Nos. 144, 152, 160,
    163, 167 and 175.*

16. Cash's names. The best method of
    marking all linen
    Cash's booklet. " Lose less linen ",
    J. & J. Cash (150) .. .. .. 11·00
17. Cash's lingerie ribbons. Ideal for
    shoulder straps
    Book of ribbons. J. & J. Cash (181) 8·00
17a. ditto, but with Cash's in larger type
    (185) .. .. .. .. .. 8·00
18. Cash's " Lose less linen " book
    Free booklet. J. & J. Cash (3, 196) 11·00

19. Cash's " Safety first.  Cash's names "
    booklet (237)
    Free booklet.  J. &. J. Cash (*Setting 1*)   11·00
20. Cash's satin lingerie ribbons
    Cash's ribbon booklet.  J. & J. Cash
    (Nos. 190, 207, 225, 229 and 2)   ..   7·00
21. Cash's satin lingerie ribbons
    Samples (*central*) of Cash's ribbons,
    J. & J. Cash (Nos. 243 and 249)
    (*Setting 1*)   ..   ..   ..   ..   8·00

*Castell Bros., London, E.C.1*

22. Bodiam.  Use it with pride
    Bodiam.  Castell Bros.   ..   ..   7·00
23. Castletone fashionable writing paper
    Castell Bros. ..   ..   ..   11·00
24. Castletone Stationery
    Castell Bros. ..   ..   ..   11·00
25. Bodiam.  (*Six named colours*)
    Bodiam Castell Bros.   ..   ..   11·00
26. Pepys Stationery.  Bodiam Castletone
    Royal York.  Stonehenge ..   ..   8·00

*Cruise departments*

27. American Holiday £40
    ss. Minnekahda.  Atlantic Transport
    Co.   ..   ..   ..   ..   8·00
28. Holiday Trips £40.  Tourist 3rd Cabin
    only (*in 4 lines*)
    ss. Minnekahda and Minnesota
    Atlantic Transport Co. Ltd.   ..   8·00
29. Holiday Trips £40.  Tourist 3rd Cabin
    (*in 2 lines*)
    ss. Minnekahda and Minnesota
    Atlantic Transport Line   ..   ..   10·00
30. Holiday Trips £40.  Tourist 3rd Cabin
    only (*in 3 lines*)
    ss. Minnekahda and Minnesota
    Atlantic Transport Line   ..   ..   10·00
31. Your holiday problem solved.
    £39 15s. od. (*upright*)
    Atlantic Transport Line (*sideways*)   10·00
32. South Africa for Sunshine
    Union Castle Line   ..   ..   10·00
33. Your 3 weeks holiday.  A trip to New
    York £38
    White Star Line   ..   ..   11·00
34. Your 3 weeks holiday.  Why not a
    trip?  £38
    White Star Line   ..   ..   11·00
35. Your 3 weeks holiday. Take a trip. £38
    White Star Line   ..   ..   7·00
36. Your Holiday.  Cruise British by White
    Star
    The Cruise Department   ..   ..   10·00
37. 33 Spring and Summer Cruises
    White Star Line   ..   ..   9·00

*John Knight Ltd.*

38. Have YOU tried Knight's Castile
    John Knight Ltd.   ..   ..   10·00
39. For a limited period, Knight's Castile
    Robinson and Cleaver Ltd.   ..   10·00
40. Soap picture, Knight's Castile
    Knight picture, Knight's Castile   ..   10·00
41. Try the three perfumes of Knight's
    Castile
    Three visitors' tablets (*small type*)   ..   10·00
42. Try the three perfumes of Knight's
    Castile
    Three visitors' tablets (*large type*)   ..   10·00
43. Knight's Castile, delicately perfumed
    A British soap   ..   ..   10·00
44. You ought to try ' zyxt '
    John Knight Ltd.   ..   ..   10·00
45. What is your week-end job?  ' ZYXT '
    John Knight Ltd.   ..   ..   10·00
46. Whatever your week-end job, ' ZYXT '
    John Knight Ltd.   ..   ..   11·00

47. Picture of zyxt
    ' zyxt ' is 4d. a tablet   ..   ..   11·00
48. Knight's Castile, new artistic pack
    John Knight Ltd.   ..   ..   10·00
49. Free to users of Family Health Soap
    John Knight Ltd.   ..   ..   11·00
50. Royal Primrose Soap
    John Knight Ltd.   ..   ..   11·00
51. Have you had your copy of the new
    list of British Gifts.  Family Health
    Soap
    John Knight Ltd.   ..   ..   10·00
52. Family Health and Hustler Too!
    John Knight Ltd.   ..   ..   10·00
53. John Knight Ltd.
    Family Health and Hustler Too!  ..   10·00
54. Have YOU tried Shavallo?
    John Knight Ltd.   ..   ..   10·00
55. To obtain real luxury in shaving,
    Shavallo
    21 days for 2d.  SHAVALLO   ..   10·00
56. Why not try Shavallo shaving cream?
    John Knight Ltd.   ..   ..   10·00
57. John Knight's Shavallo 1/-
    It's British   ..   ..   ..   10·00

*Sundry*

58. If interested in Billiards
    The Billiard Player ..   ..   11·00
59. Bring the breath of the pine forest, etc.
    Cleaver's Terebene
    F. S. Cleaver, Twickenham..   ..   9·00
60. Have YOU tried Cleaver's Terebene?
    F. S. Cleaver, London   ..   ..   9·00
61. Desti cigarettes
    Silmos Lollies   ..   ..   9·00
62. Desti cigarettes
    Telephone Service   ..   ..   10·00
63. Dutton's shorthand
    Reginald P. O. Dutton   ..   ..   11·00
64. Buy Gillette blades
    The blade with a shave in it   ..   11·00
65. Garden work for amateurs
    Cable via Imperial ..   ..   10·00
66. Gaze's all weather tennis courts (*sideways*)
    Send to Harmer, Rooke, Auctions
    (*upright*)   ..   ..   ..   7·00
67. Glastonbury's
    Soft Sheepskin Shoes   ..   ..   9·00
68. Gospo
    Cable via Imperial ..   ..   7·00
69. Auctions, Harmer, Rooke, cash ad-
    vanced, 69 Fleet Street (*inverted*)
    Harmer Rooke, Auctions (*upright*) ..   10·00
70. Note new address, Harmer Rooke
    Stamp collectors should visit 188/189
    Strand W.C.2..   ..   ..   11·00
71. Auctions, Harmer, Rooke, cash ad-
    vanced, 188 Strand (*inverted*)
    Harmer, Rooke, Auctions (*upright*)   10·00
72. Best seats (*sideways*)
    Keith Prowse (*sideways*)   ..   ..   11·00
73. La Corona, Havana Cigars
    Acknowledged the world over   ..   11·00
74. India Rubber Sponge (*in green*)
    R. G. McKinlay (*in green*) ..   ..   25·00
75. Millennium Oat-Flakes
    Wright's Coal Tar Soap   ..   ..   6·00
76. Pitman's correspondence course
    Pitman's W.C.1   ..   ..   11·00
77. Pomeroy skin food.  Helps the plain
    Mrs. Pomeroy   ..   ..   10·00
78. Pomeroy skin food.  Trial size jar
    Superfluous hair.  Mrs. Pomeroy ..   10·00
79. Poultry World.  Free copy
    Poultry World, 27 Stamford Street,
    S.E.1 ..   ..   ..   ..   11·00
80. H.T. Battery
    Ripaults Ltd.   ..   ..   ..   7·00
81. Robinson and Cleaver famous for linen
    handkerchiefs
    Hemstitched Handkerchiefs   ..   7·00

82. Robinson and Cleaver famous for Irish
    Linens
    Ladies' Linen Hemstitched Handker-
    chiefs  ..    ..    ..    ..    10·00
83. Scarborough's Hotels
    Cable via Imperial ..    ..    ..    7·00
84. Scarborough's Hotels
    Harmer, Rooke weekly Stamp
    Auctions    ..    ..    ..    ..    8·00
85. Scarborough's Hotels
    Wright's Coal Tar Soap    ..    ..    8·00

86. Wireless World.  Free copy
    Complete foreign programmes.
    Wireless World    ..    ..    ..    11·00
87. Save the outside wrappers.  Wright's
    Coal Tar Soap
    Wright to the Proprietors, 46 South-
    wark Street, S.E.1 ..    ..    ..    10·00
88. Wright's Coal Tar Soap
    Telephone Service ..    ..    ..    10·00
89. Wright's Lysol
    Air Mail, letters and parcels    ..    10·00

## II. Printed by Harrison & Sons (1934)

90. Telephone Service (*Setting 2*)
    Air Mails, letters and parcels    ..    6·00
    (*Bolder setting. Line under " Installed free "
    has only three loops*)
91. Saving is Simple
    Home Safe  ..    ..    ..    ..    6·00
    (*Setting 2.  Larger type than Setting 1*)
92. Cash's satin lingerie ribbons
    Samples (*central*) of Cash's ribbons,
    J. & J. Cash (Nos. 257, 275, 285, 4
    and 5)    ..    ..    ..    ..    6·50
    (*Setting 2.  Bolder type than Setting 1*)
93. Cash's " Safety first.  Cash's names "
    booklet
    Free booklet J. & J. Cash (Nos. 263
    and 7)    ..    ..    ..    ..    10·00
    (*Setting 2.  Bolder type than Setting 1*)
94. Pepys Stationery
    Ruskin Linen    ..    ..    ..    11·00
95. Pepys Stationery.  Castletone
    Castells, London    ..    ..    ..    11·00
96. Pepys Stationery.  Bodiam in white
    and six colours
    Just added: Bodiam Grey.  Castells    7·00

97. For every woman. Bodiam in 7 colours
    Pepys Stationery    ..    ..    ..    11·00
98. For every woman, Bodiam.  For every
    man, Royal York
    White and azure.  Pepys Stationery
    Productions ..    ..    ..    ..    11·00
99. Kargo.  (Card Golf)
    Castell Bros. (Pepys Stationery)    ..    11·00
100. " Cruises " (with picture of a sailor)
    White Star Line    ..    ..    ..    10·00
101. Poultry World.  Free copy
    Poultry World, 31 Stamford Street,
    S.E.1 ..    ..    ..    ..    ..    11·00
102. Shavallo for a swift smooth shave
    Shavallo, Barbers use it    ..    ..    6·50
103. corot models.  33, old bond street
    corot.  33, old bond street ..    ..    10·00
104. corot models.  33, old bond street, sb. 19
    corot.  33, old bond street    ..    ..    10·00
105. corot models.  33, old bond street
    corot (dept s.b 20) 33, old bond street    11·00

# 1929.  Postal Union Congress

## 1½d. PURPLE-BROWN, TYPE N.19, WMK. TYPE W.15

106. Cash's washing Ribbons
    J. & J. Cash Ltd.  ..    ..    ..    10·00
107. Cleaver's Terebene
    F. S. Cleaver & Sons Ltd. ..    ..    10·00
108. Stamp Collectors
    Desti Ltd.  ..    ..    ..    ..    10·00

109. Holiday trips £40 Tourist 3rd Cabin
    only (*in 3 lines*)
    Atlantic Transport Line    ..    ..    10·00
110. Telephone Service
    Air Mails, Letters & Parcels    ..    10·00

# 1934-35.  Photogravure

## 1934.  1½d. RED-BROWN, TYPE N11.  INTERMEDIATE FORMAT

The advertisements were etched on the cylinder, and therefore appear in red-brown.

111. Cash's satin lingerie ribbons
    Samples of Cash's ribbons.
    J. & J. Cash Ltd.  ..    ..    ..    12·00
112. For Safety of Capital
    Amalgamated Fixed Trust ..    ..    10·00
113. For Safety of Capital
    Commercial Fixed Trust    ..    ..    10·00

114. For Safety of Capital
    National Fixed Trust    ..    ..    10·00
115. Saving is Simple
    Home Safe  ..    ..    ..    ..    12·00
116. Telephone Service
    Air Mails, Letters & Parcels    ..    12·00

## 1935.  1½d. RED-BROWN, TYPE N11.  SMALL FORMAT

The advertisements were typographed after the stamps had been printed, and appear in black.

117. Cash's " Lose less Linen " book
    Free booklet J. & J. Cash (No. 318)..    8·00
118. Cash's satin lingerie ribbons
    Samples (*central*) of Cash's ribbons.
    J. & J. Cash (No. 306)    ..    ..    4·00
119. Cash's satin lingerie ribbons
    Samples (*in text*) of Cash's ribbons.
    " Attach this to a " J. & J. Cash (Nos.
    323, 331, 335, 342 or 348)  ..    ..    2·25
120. Cash's satin lingerie ribbons
    Samples (*in text*) of Cash's ribbons.
    " Attach this to a post- ".  J. & J.
    Cash (No. 312)    ..    ..    ..    4·00

121. Number One Bond
    Pepys Stationery    ..    ..    ..    4·50
122. Kargo 2/6 per pack
    Castell Bros. (Pepys Stationery)    ..    4·00
123. Drages fine furniture
    50 months to pay  ..    ..    ..    4·50
124. For Safety of Capital
    Amalgamated Fixed Trust ..    ..    1·75
125. For Safety of Capital
    Century Fixed Trust (pointer) (*in
    large type*)    ..    ..    ..    ..    4·00
126. For Safety of Capital
    Century Fixed Trust (pointer) (*in
    small type*)  ..    ..    ..    ..    4·00

127. For Safety of Capital
Century Fixed Trust (see last page)    2·00
128. For Safety of Capital
Commercial Fixed Trust    ..    ..    2·00
129. For Safety of Capital
National Fixed Trust    ..    ..    2·00
130. For Safety of Capital
Universal Fixed Trust (Pointer) (in
large type)    ..    ..    ..    ..    3·50

131. For Safety of Capital
Universal Fixed Trust (see last page)    3·00
a. Advertisement transposed    30·00
132. Saving is Simple
Home Safe    ..    ..    ..    ..    8·00
133. Telephone Service
Air Mails, letters and parcels (with
" Installed Free " deleted by hand-
stamp)..    ..    ..    ..    ..    12·00

## 1936.  King Edward VIII

### 1½d.  RED-BROWN, TYPE P1

134. Cash's " Lose less Linen " book
Free booklet. J. & J. Cash (No. 364)    3·00
135. Cash's names for marking all linen
Free booklet. J. & J. Cash (No. 372)    3·00
136. Cash's satin lingerie ribbons
Samples (in text) of Cash's ribbons.
" Attach this to a ".  J. & J. Cash
(Nos. 357, 379)    ..    ..    ..    1·50
137. Number One Bond
Castell Bros. ..    ..    ..    ..    3·00
138. Ruskin Linen
Castell Bros. ..    ..    ..    ..    3·00
139. Kargo.  2/6 per pack.
Castell Bros. ..    ..    ..    ..    3·00
140. Drages 50 pay-way
Free book.  Drages ..    ..    ..    1·50
141. Everitt's
Everitt's    ..    ..    ..    ..    3·00

142. For Safety of Capital
Century Fixed Trust (see last page)    2·50
143. For Safety of Capital
Universal Fixed Trust (see last page)    1·50
144. Spread your Capital (diagonal)
Century Fixed Trust (diagonal)    ..    1·50
145. Spread your Capital (diagonal)
Universal Fixed Trust (diagonal)    ..    1·50
146. Stamp Collectors
Chas. Nissen ..    ..    ..    ..    3·00
147. Saving is Simple
Home Safe    ..    ..    ..    ..    1·25
148. Come on the telephone
Air Mails, letters and parcels    ..    1·25
149. Your friends are on the telephone
Air Mails, letters and parcels    ..    1·25

## 1937.  King George VI

### 1½d.  RED-BROWN, TYPE Q1

150. Cash's name tapes
J. & J. Cash Ltd. (No. 405)    ..    6·00
151. Cash's satin lingerie ribbons
Booklet containing samples (No. 453)    6·00
152. Cash's satin lingerie ribbons
Booklet containing patterns (Nos.
459, 467, 473, 482, 492, 498)    ..    1·75
153. Cash's satin lingerie ribbons
Samples o í Cash's ribbons (Nos. 21,
389, 395, 410, 416, 424, 430, 441, 448,
460)    ..    ..    ..    ..    ..    1·75
154. Fontana Note
Wm. Collins, Sons & Co. Ltd.    ..    6·00
155. Drages.  50 Pay-Way
Drages Ltd. ..    ..    ..    ..    4·00
156. Drages.  Terms to suit YOU
Drages Ltd. ..    ..    ..    ..    1·75

157. Saving is Simple (small " is ")
Home Safe    ..    ..    ..    ..    1·75
158. Saving is Simple (large " is ")
Home Safe    ..    ..    ..    ..    1·75
159. Send your good wishes
by Greeting Telegram    ..    ..    1·75
160. You can reach your
friends at sea by Radio Telegram    ..    1·75
161. Atlantic Holidays
Cunard White Star ..    ..    ..    6·00
162. Post Early
In the Day    ..    ..    ..    2·50
163. Commander Stephen (sideways)
King-Hall (sideways)    ..    ..    6·00
164. Times Furnishing Company
London, W.C.1    ..    ..    ..    6·00

# Photogravure Booklet Panes with Cylinder Numbers

Booklet Pane with Cylinder Number

Unless otherwise stated all panes with cylinder numbers have upright watermarks. For notes about Perforation Types see Appendix I.

## 1934-35. King George V

### INTERMEDIATE FORMAT

| Value | Cyl. No. | | | Perf. Type B3 | B4 | Cyl. No. | | | | | Perf. Type B3A | B4A |
|---|---|---|---|---|---|---|---|---|---|---|---|---|
| ½d. | E 1 | .. | .. | 4·50 | — | E 1. | .. | .. | .. | .. | 4·50 | — |
| 1d. | F 1 | .. | .. | 4·50 | † | F 1. | .. | .. | .. | .. | 4·50 | † |
| 1½d. | G 4 | .. | .. | 4·50 | — | G 4. | .. | .. | .. | .. | 4·50 | — |

### 1½d. Advertisement Panes

The advertisement number is the number given to the advertisement pane in Appendix L.

| Cyl. No. | Advert. No. | | | Perf. Type B3 | B4 | Cyl. No. | Advert. No. | | | Perf. Type B3A | B4A |
|---|---|---|---|---|---|---|---|---|---|---|---|
| G 7 | 115 | .. | .. | 15·00 | † | G 7. | 116 | .. | .. | 15·00 | — |
| G 9 | 114 | .. | .. | 12·00 | † | G 9. | 111 | .. | .. | 15·00 | † |
| G 10 | 112 | .. | .. | 12·00 | † | G 10. | 113 | .. | .. | 12·00 | † |
| G 15 | 114 | .. | .. | 12·00 | † | G 15. | 113 | .. | .. | 12·00 | — |
| G 16 | 114 | .. | .. | 12·00 | 15·00 | G 16. | 112 | .. | .. | 12·00 | 15·00 |
| G 17 | 113 | .. | .. | 15·00 | — | G 17. | 113 | .. | .. | 15·00 | — |

### SMALL FORMAT

| Value | Cyl. No. | | | Perf. Type B3 | B4 | Cyl. No. | | | Perf. Type B3A | B4A | B4B |
|---|---|---|---|---|---|---|---|---|---|---|---|
| ½d. | E 4 | .. | .. | 1·25 | — | E 4. | .. | .. | 1·25 | 2·00 | † |
| | Wmk. inverted | .. | .. | — | — | | Wmk. inverted | .. | — | † | † |
| ½d. | E 5 | .. | .. | 1·25 | † | E 5. | .. | .. | 1·25 | † | — |
| ½d. | E 6 | .. | .. | 1·25 | † | E 6. | .. | .. | 1·25 | † | 1·25 |
| 1d. | F 6 | .. | .. | 1·25 | 2·00 | F 6. | .. | .. | 1·25 | 2·00 | † |
| 1d. | F 7 | .. | .. | 1·25 | — | F 7. | .. | .. | 1·25 | — | 1·25 |
| 1½d. | G 20 | .. | .. | 1·25 | — | G 20. | .. | .. | 1·25 | 1·50 | † |
| 1½d. | G 24 | .. | .. | 1·25 | — | G 24. | .. | .. | See advert. panes | | |
| 1½d. | G 27 | .. | .. | † | — | G 27. | .. | .. | — | — | † |
| 1½d. | G 30 | .. | .. | 1·25 | † | G 30. | .. | .. | 1·25 | † | 1·25 |
| 1½d. | G 31 | .. | .. | 2·00 | † | G 31. | .. | .. | 2·00 | † | † |

**243**

## 1½d. Advertisement Panes

| Cyl. No. | Advert. No. | B3 | B4 | B3A | B4A | B4B |
|---|---|---|---|---|---|---|
| G 24 | 113 | † | † | — | † | † |
| G 24 | 118 | † | † | 6·00 | † | † |
| G 24 | 128 | † | † | 4·00 | † | † |
| G 24 | 129 | † | † | 4·00 | † | † |
| G 24 | 132 | † | † | 14·00 | † | † |
| G 24 | 133 | † | † | 20·00 | † | † |
| G 26 | 99 | — | † | — | † | † |
| G 26 | 117‡ | † | † | † | † | † |
| G 26 | 119 (No. 323) | 4·00 | — | 4·00 | † | † |
| G 26 | 120 | † | † | 6·00 | 7·00 | † |
| G 26 | 121 | 6·00 | † | 6·00 | † | † |
|  | Wmk. inverted | 20·00 | † | — | † | † |
| G 26 | 122 | 5·00 | † | 5·00 | † | † |
| G 26 | 124 | 4·00 | 5·00 | 4·00 | — | † |
| G 26 | 128 | 4·00 | 4·50 | 4·00 | 4·50 | † |
|  | Wmk. inverted | — | † | — | † | † |
| G 26 | 129 | 4·00 | — | 4·00 | 4·50 | † |
| G 28 | 119 (No. 331) | 4·00 | † | 4·00 | † | † |
|  | (No. 335) | 4·00 | † | 4·00 | † | † |
|  | (No. 342) | 4·00 | † | 4·25 | † | 4·00 |
|  | (No. 348) | 5·00 | † | 6·00 | † | † |
| G 28 | 123 | 6·00 | † | 4·00 | † | † |
| G 28 | 124 | 4·00 | † | 4·00 | † | 4·50 |
| G 28 | 125 | 6·00 | † | 5·50 | † | 6·00 |
| G 28 | 126 | 6·00 | † | 6·00 | † | † |
| G 28 | 127 | 4·00 | † | 4·00 | † | 4·50 |
| G 28 | 128 | 4·00 | † | 4·00 | † | † |
| G 28 | 129 | 4·00 | † | 4·00 | † | 4·50 |
| G 28 | 130 | 6·00 | † | 6·00 | † | † |
| G 28 | 131 | 6·00 | † | 6·00 | † | 5·50 |

‡ No examples of cylinder G 26 with advertisement No. 117 have been found.

# 1936.  King Edward VIII

| Value | Cyl. No. | B3 | B4 | B3A | B4A | B4B |
|---|---|---|---|---|---|---|
| ½d. | E 2 | 60 | — | 60 | — | 1·00 |
|  | E 4 | 80 | † | 80 | † | † |
| 1d. | F 3 | 60 | — | 60 | 3·00 | 80 |
|  | F 6 / *F 6. | † | † | — | † | † |
| 1½d. | G 4 | 2·00 | † | 1·75 | — | † |
|  | G 5 (i) / G 5. | 60 | — | 60 | 1·50 | 1·00 |
|  | G 5 (ii) | 80 | 1·75 |  |  |  |

State (ii) of G 5 shows a flaw in the margin at left of stamp No. 1.

* This is an "abnormal". For explanation see note under "Printing" on page 89.

## 1½d. Advertisement Panes

| Cyl. No. | Advert. No. | B3 | B3A | B4B |
|---|---|---|---|---|
| G 7 | 134 | 4·00 | 4·00 | † |
| G 7 | 135 | 4·00 | 4·00 | † |
| G 7 | 136 (No. 357) | 2·50 | 2·50 | † |
|  | (No. 379) | 2·50 | 2·50 |  |
| G 7 | 137 | 4·00 | 4·00 | † |
| G 7 | 138 | 4·00 | 4·00 | 4·50 |
| G 7 | 139 | 4·00 | 4·00 | † |
| G 7 | 140 | 2·50 | 2·50 | 3·00 |
| G 7 | 141 | 4·00 | 4·00 | † |
| G 7 | 142 | 3·25 | 3·00 | † |
| G 7 | 143 | 2·75 | 2·75 | † |
| G 7 | 144 | 2·75 | 2·75 | † |
| G 7 | 145 | 2·75 | 2·75 | † |
| G 7 | 146 | 4·00 | 4·00 | † |
| G 7 | 147 | 2·50 | 2·50 | 2·75 |
| G 7 | 148 | 2·50 | 2·50 | 2·75 |
| G 7 | 149 | 2·50 | 2·50 | 2·75 |

# King George VI
## Panes of six
### ½d. GREEN, No. Q1

| Cyl. No. | | | | Perf. Type B3 | B4 | Cyl. No. | | | B3A | B4A | B4B |
|---|---|---|---|---|---|---|---|---|---|---|---|
| E 2 | .. | .. | .. | 60 | † | E 2. | .. | .. | 60 | † | 60 |
| Wmk. inverted | .. | .. | | 7·00 | † | Wmk. inverted | .. | | 7·00 | † | 7·00 |
| E 5 | .. | .. | .. | 60 | † | E 5. | .. | .. | 60 | † | 60 |
| E 10 | .. | .. | .. | 60 | 2·00 | E 10. | .. | .. | 60 | 2·00 | 60 |
| E 18 | .. | .. | .. | 60 | † | E 18. | .. | .. | 60 | † | 60 |
| E 19 | .. | .. | .. | † | 60 | E 19. | .. | .. | † | † | † |
| E 22 | .. | .. | .. | † | 60 | E 22. | .. | .. | † | † | † |
| E 28 | .. | .. | .. | † | 60 | E 28. | .. | .. | † | † | † |
| E 29 | .. | .. | .. | † | 60 | E 29. | .. | .. | † | † | † |
| E 35 | .. | .. | .. | 60 | † | E 35. | .. | .. | 1·00 | † | 60 |
| E 36 | .. | .. | .. | 60 | † | E 36. | .. | .. | 60 | † | † |
| E 38 | .. | .. | .. | † | 60 | E 38. | .. | .. | † | † | † |
| E 39 | .. | .. | .. | † | 60 | E 39. | .. | .. | † | † | † |
| E 41 | .. | .. | .. | † | 70 | E 41. | .. | .. | † | † | † |
| E 42 | .. | .. | .. | † | 60 | E 42. | .. | .. | † | † | † |
| E 43 | .. | .. | .. | † | — | E 43. | .. | .. | † | † | † |
| E 45 | .. | .. | .. | † | 60 | E 45. | .. | .. | † | † | † |
| E 46 | .. | .. | .. | † | 70 | E 46. | .. | .. | † | † | † |
| E 48 | .. | .. | .. | † | 60 | E 48. | .. | .. | † | † | † |
| E 49 | .. | .. | .. | † | 70 | E 49. | .. | .. | † | † | † |
| E 50 | .. | .. | .. | † | 70 | E 50. | .. | .. | † | † | † |

In cylinder E 42 only the " 2 " shows and a small part of " 4 ", so that it can easily be taken for E2.

### ½d. PALE GREEN, No. Q2

| Cyl. No. | | | | Perf. Type B3 | B4 | Cyl. No. | | | B3A | B6 | B5 |
|---|---|---|---|---|---|---|---|---|---|---|---|
| E 53 | .. | .. | .. | † | 60 | E 53. | .. | .. | † | † | † |
| E 56 | .. | .. | .. | † | 60 | E 56. | .. | .. | † | † | † |
| E 58 | .. | .. | .. | † | 60 | E 58. | .. | .. | † | † | † |
| E 59 | .. | .. | .. | † | 60 | E 59. | .. | .. | † | † | † |
| E 62 | .. | .. | .. | † | 60 | E 62. | .. | .. | † | † | † |
| E 65 | .. | .. | .. | † | 60 | E 65. | .. | .. | 60 | — | 60 |
| E 66 | .. | .. | .. | † | 60 | E 66. | .. | .. | † | 60 | — |
| E 67 | .. | .. | .. | † | 60 | E 67. | .. | .. | † | 60 | † |
| E 68 | .. | .. | .. | † | 60 | E 68. | .. | .. | † | 60 | † |
| E 70 | .. | .. | .. | † | 50 | E 70. | .. | .. | † | 50 | † |
| E 71 | .. | .. | .. | † | 50 | E 71. | .. | .. | † | 50 | † |
| E 72 | .. | .. | .. | † | 50 | E 72. | .. | .. | † | 50 | † |
| E 73 | .. | .. | .. | † | 50 | E 73. | .. | .. | † | 50 | † |
| E 75 | .. | .. | .. | † | 50 | E 75. | .. | .. | † | 50 | † |
| E 76 | .. | .. | .. | † | 50 | E 76. | .. | .. | † | 50 | † |
| E 77 | .. | .. | .. | † | 50 | E 77. | .. | .. | † | 50 | † |
| E 78 | .. | .. | .. | † | 50 | E 78. | .. | .. | † | 50 | † |
| E 79 | .. | .. | .. | † | 50 | E 79. | .. | .. | † | 50 | † |
| E 80 | .. | .. | .. | † | 50 | E 80. | .. | .. | † | 50 | † |
| E 81 | .. | .. | .. | † | 50 | E 81. | .. | .. | † | 50 | † |
| E 82 | .. | .. | .. | † | 70 | E 82. | .. | .. | † | 70 | † |
| E 83 | .. | .. | .. | † | 50 | E 83. | .. | .. | † | 50 | † |

### ½d. ORANGE, No. Q3

| Cyl. No. | | | | Perf. Type B3 | B4 | Cyl. No. | | | B3A | B6 | B5 |
|---|---|---|---|---|---|---|---|---|---|---|---|
| E 82 | .. | .. | .. | † | 55 | E 82. | .. | .. | † | 55 | † |
| E 83 | .. | .. | .. | † | 70 | E 83. | .. | .. | † | 70 | † |
| E 84 | .. | .. | .. | † | 45 | E 84. | .. | .. | † | 45 | † |
| E 85 | .. | .. | .. | † | 45 | E 85. | .. | .. | † | 45 | † |

### 1d. SCARLET, No. Q4

| Cyl. No. | | | | B3 | B4 | Cyl. No. | | | B3A | B4B | B4B |
|---|---|---|---|---|---|---|---|---|---|---|---|
| F 1 | .. | .. | .. | 1·25 | † | F 1. | .. | .. | 1·25 | † | 1·25 |
| F 3 | .. | .. | .. | 1·25 | † | F 3. | .. | .. | 1·25 | — | 1·25 |
| F 4 | .. | .. | .. | 1·25 | † | F 4. | .. | .. | 1·25 | † | 1·25 |
| F 5 | .. | .. | .. | 1·25 | † | F 5. | .. | .. | 1·25 | † | 1·25 |
| F 7 | .. | .. | .. | † | 1·25 | F 7. | .. | .. | † | † | † |
| F 9 | .. | .. | .. | † | 1·25 | F 9. | .. | .. | † | † | † |
| F 10 | .. | .. | .. | 1·25 | † | F 10. | .. | .. | 1·25 | † | † |
| F 14 | .. | .. | .. | † | 1·25 | F 14. | .. | .. | † | † | † |
| F 15 | .. | .. | .. | † | 1·25 | F 15. | .. | .. | † | † | † |
| F 16 | .. | .. | .. | † | 1·50 | F 16. | .. | .. | † | † | † |

### 1d. ULTRAMARINE, No. Q6

| Cyl. No. | | | | B3 | B4 | Cyl. No. | | | B3A | B6 | B5 |
|---|---|---|---|---|---|---|---|---|---|---|---|
| F 8 | .. | .. | | † | 60 | F 8. | .. | .. | † | 60 | † |

## 1½d. RED-BROWN, No. Q7

| Cyl. No. | | | | | Perf. Type B3 | B4 | Cyl. No. | | | | B3A | Perf. Type B4A | B4B |
|---|---|---|---|---|---|---|---|---|---|---|---|---|---|
| G 8 | .. | .. | .. | .. | 65 | 1·50 | G 8... | .. | .. | .. | 65 | 1·50 | 65 |
| G 19 | .. | .. | .. | .. | 65 | † | G 19... | .. | .. | .. | 65 | † | 65 |
| G 20 | .. | .. | .. | .. | 65 | † | G 20... | .. | .. | .. | 65 | † | 65 |
| G 28 | .. | .. | .. | .. | 65 | † | G 28... | .. | .. | .. | 65 | † | 65 |
| G 29 | .. | .. | .. | .. | † | — | G 29... | .. | .. | .. | † | † | † |
| G 30 | .. | .. | .. | .. | † | 65 | G 30... | .. | .. | .. | † | † | † |
| G 34 | .. | .. | .. | .. | † | 65 | G 34... | .. | .. | .. | † | † | † |
| G 36 | .. | .. | .. | .. | † | 65 | G 36... | .. | .. | .. | † | † | † |
| G 40 | .. | .. | .. | .. | † | 65 | G 40... | .. | .. | .. | † | † | † |
| G 44 | .. | .. | .. | .. | † | 65 | G 44... | .. | .. | .. | † | † | † |
| G 45 | .. | .. | .. | .. | † | 65 | G 45... | .. | .. | .. | † | † | † |
| G 48 | .. | .. | .. | .. | † | 1·25 | G 48... | .. | .. | .. | † | † | † |
| G 49 | .. | .. | .. | .. | 65 | † | G 49... | .. | .. | .. | 65 | † | † |
| G 50 | .. | .. | .. | .. | 65 | † | G 50... | .. | .. | .. | 65 | † | 70 |
| G 57 | .. | .. | .. | .. | † | 65 | G 57... | .. | .. | .. | † | † | † |
| G 58 | .. | .. | .. | .. | † | 65 | G 58... | .. | .. | .. | † | † | † |
| G 61 | .. | .. | .. | .. | † | 2·00 | G 61... | .. | .. | .. | † | † | † |
| G 69 | .. | .. | .. | .. | † | 65 | G 69... | .. | .. | .. | † | † | † |
| G 71 | .. | .. | .. | .. | † | 70 | G 71... | .. | .. | .. | † | † | † |

## 1½d. GREEN, No. Q9

| Cyl. No. | | | | | Perf. Type B3 | B4 | Cyl. No. | | | | B3A | Perf. Type B6 | B5 |
|---|---|---|---|---|---|---|---|---|---|---|---|---|---|
| G 4 | .. | .. | .. | .. | † | 50 | G 4. | .. | .. | .. | † | 50 | † |

## 2d. ORANGE, No. Q10

| H 1 | .. | .. | .. | .. | † | 2·75 | H 1. | .. | .. | .. | † | † | † |
|---|---|---|---|---|---|---|---|---|---|---|---|---|---|
| H 2 | .. | .. | .. | .. | † | 2·75 | H 2. | .. | .. | .. | † | † | † |
| H 4 | .. | .. | .. | .. | † | 3·00 | H 4. | .. | .. | .. | † | † | † |
| H 5 | .. | .. | .. | .. | † | 3·00 | H 5. | .. | .. | .. | † | † | † |
| H 6 | .. | .. | .. | .. | † | 3·00 | H 6. | .. | .. | .. | † | † | † |
| H 7 | .. | .. | .. | .. | † | 3·00 | H 7. | .. | .. | .. | † | † | † |

## 2d. PALE ORANGE, No. Q17

| H 10 | .. | .. | .. | .. | † | 60 | H 10. | .. | .. | † | † | † |
|---|---|---|---|---|---|---|---|---|---|---|---|---|
| H 11 | .. | .. | .. | .. | † | 65 | H 11. | .. | .. | † | † | † |
| H 14 | .. | .. | .. | .. | † | 60 | H 14. | .. | .. | † | † | † |
| H 15 | .. | .. | .. | .. | † | 60 | H 15. | .. | .. | † | † | † |
| H 16 | .. | .. | .. | .. | † | 60 | H 16. | .. | .. | † | † | † |
| H 17 | .. | .. | .. | .. | † | 15·00 | H 17. | .. | .. | † | † | † |
| H 18 | .. | .. | .. | .. | † | 60 | H 18. | .. | .. | † | † | † |
| H 20 | .. | .. | .. | .. | 90 | 60 | H 20. | .. | .. | 90 | 90 | 60 |
| H 22 | .. | .. | .. | .. | † | 90 | H 22. | .. | .. | † | 90 | 90 |
| H 23 | .. | .. | .. | .. | † | 60 | H 23. | .. | .. | † | 60 | † |
| H 24 | .. | .. | .. | .. | † | 60 | H 24. | .. | .. | † | 60 | † |
| H 25 | .. | .. | .. | .. | † | 1·25 | H 25. | .. | .. | † | 1·25 | † |
| H 26 | .. | .. | .. | .. | † | 1·25 | H 26. | .. | .. | † | 1·25 | † |
| H 28 | .. | .. | .. | .. | † | 50 | H 28. | .. | .. | † | 50 | † |
| H 29 | .. | .. | .. | .. | † | 50 | H 29. | .. | .. | † | 50 | † |
| H 31 | .. | .. | .. | .. | † | 50 | H 31. | .. | .. | † | 50 | † |
| H 32 | .. | .. | .. | .. | † | 50 | H 32. | .. | .. | † | 50 | † |
| H 34 | .. | .. | .. | .. | † | 60 | H 34. | .. | .. | † | 60 | † |
| H 41 | .. | .. | .. | .. | † | 65 | H 41. | .. | .. | † | 65 | † |
| H 45 | .. | .. | .. | .. | † | 50 | H 45. | .. | .. | † | 50 | † |
| H 46 | .. | .. | .. | .. | † | 60 | H 46. | .. | .. | † | 60 | † |
| H 47 | .. | .. | .. | .. | † | 1·50 | H 47. | .. | .. | † | 1·50 | † |

## 2d. RED-BROWN, No. Q12

| H 41 | .. | .. | .. | .. | † | 1·00 | H 41. | .. | .. | † | 1·00 | † |
|---|---|---|---|---|---|---|---|---|---|---|---|---|
| H 47 | .. | .. | .. | .. | † | 1·00 | H 47. | .. | .. | † | 1·00 | † |
| H 48 | .. | .. | .. | .. | † | 3·50 | H 48. | .. | .. | † | 3·50 | † |

## 2½d. ULTRAMARINE, No. Q13

| J 3 | .. | .. | .. | .. | † | 2·75 | J 3. | .. | .. | .. | † | † | † |
|---|---|---|---|---|---|---|---|---|---|---|---|---|---|
| J 5 | .. | .. | .. | .. | † | 2·75 | J 5. | .. | .. | .. | † | † | † |
| J 7 | .. | .. | .. | .. | † | 2·75 | J 7. | .. | .. | .. | † | † | † |
| J 10 | .. | .. | .. | .. | † | 2·75 | J 10. | .. | .. | .. | † | † | † |

| Cyl. No. | Perf. Type B3 | B4 | | Cyl. No. | B3A | Perf. Type B6 | B5 |
|---|---|---|---|---|---|---|---|

### 2½d. LIGHT ULTRAMARINE, No. Q14

| Cyl. No. | B3 | B4 | Cyl. No. | B3A | B6 | B5 |
|---|---|---|---|---|---|---|
| J 15 | † | 1·00 | J 15. | † | † | † |
| J 16 | † | 1·00 | J 16. | † | † | † |
| J 17 | † | 1·00 | J 17. | † | † | † |
| J 18 | † | 1·00 | J 18. | † | † | † |
| J 20 | † | 1·00 | J 20. | † | † | † |
| J 21 | † | 1·00 | J 21. | † | † | † |
| J 23 | 80 | 80 | J 23. | 80 | † | 80 |
| J 25 | 2·00 | 80 | J 25. | 2·00 | † | 80 |
| J 28 | 80 | 1·00 | J 28. | 80 | † | 1·00 |
| J 29 | † | 80 | J 29. | † | 80 | 1·00 |
| J 30 | † | 80 | J 30. | † | 1·00 | 80 |
| J 31 | † | 80 | J 31. | † | 80 | † |
| J 32 | † | 80 | J 32. | † | 80 | † |
| J 34 | † | 80 | J 34. | † | 80 | † |
| J 35 | † | 80 | J 35. | † | 80 | † |
| J 39 | † | 80 | J 39. | † | 80 | † |
| J 43 | † | 2·00 | J 43. | † | 2·00 | † |
| J 45 | † | 80 | J 45. | † | 75 | † |
| J 48 | † | 80 | J 48. | † | 75 | † |
| J 49 | † | 80 | J 49. | † | 75 | † |
| J 50 | † | 80 | J 50. | † | 75 | † |
| J 51 | † | 1·00 | J 51. | † | 1·00 | † |
| J 52 | † | 80 | J 52. | † | 75 | † |
| J 53 | † | 80 | J 53. | † | 75 | † |
| J 54 | † | 80 | J 54. | † | 75 | † |
| J 58 | † | 80 | J 58. | † | 75 | † |
| J 59 | † | 80 | J 59. | † | 75 | † |
| J 60 | † | 80 | J 60. | † | 75 | † |
| J 61 | † | 80 | J 61. | † | 75 | † |
| J 62 | † | 1·00 | J 62. | † | 1·00 | † |
| J 65 | † | 2·00 | J 65. | † | 2·00 | † |

### 2½d. SCARLET, No. Q15

| Cyl. No. | B3 | B4 | Cyl. No. | B3A | B6 | B5 |
|---|---|---|---|---|---|---|
| J 62 | † | 80 | J 62. | † | 80 | † |
| J 66 | † | 80 | J 66. | † | 80 | † |
| J 67 | † | 80 | J 67. | † | 80 | † |
| J 68 | † | 2·00 | J 68. | † | 2·00 | † |
| J 69 | † | 1·00 | J 69. | † | 1·00 | † |
| J 70 | † | 80 | J 70. | † | 80 | † |

### Panes of six with two advertisement labels
### 1½d. RED-BROWN, No. Q7

| Cyl. No. | Advert. No. | Perf. Type B3 | B4 | Cyl. No. | Advert. No. | B3A | Perf. Type B4A | B4B |
|---|---|---|---|---|---|---|---|---|
| G 10 | 153 (No. 389) | 3·25 | † | G 10. | 153 (No. 389) | 3·25 | † | 3·25 |
| | 154 | 8·00 | † | | 154 | 6·50 | † | † |
| | Wmk. inverted | 8·00 | † | | Wmk. inverted | 6·50 | † | † |
| | 155 | 6·50 | † | | 155 | † | † | 6·50 |
| | Wmk. inverted | 5·00 | † | | Wmk. inverted | † | † | 5·00 |
| | 156 | 2·50 | † | | 156 | † | † | 2·50 |
| | 157 | 9·00 | † | | 157 | 9·00 | † | 9·00 |
| | Wmk. inverted | 7·00 | † | | Wmk. inverted | † | † | 7·00 |
| | 158 | † | † | | 158 | † | — | † |
| G 18 | 150 (No. 405) | † | † | G 18. | 150 (No. 405) | 7·00 | † | † |
| | 153 (No. 21) | 2·75 | † | | 153 (No. 21) | 2·75 | † | † |
| | (No. 395) | † | † | | (No. 395) | 2·75 | † | † |
| | (No. 410) | 2·75 | † | | (No. 410) | 2·75 | † | † |
| | (No. 416) | 2·75 | † | | (No. 416) | 2·75 | † | † |
| | (No. 424) | 2·75 | † | | (No. 424) | 2·75 | † | † |
| | (No. 430) | 2·75 | † | | (No. 430) | 2·75 | † | † |
| | (No. 448) | 3·25 | † | | (No. 448) | 3·25 | † | † |
| | 156 | 2·25 | 3·25 | | 156 | 2·75 | † | 3·25 |
| | 157 | 2·75 | † | | 157 | 3·25 | † | — |
| | 158 | 2·25 | † | | 158 | 2·25 | — | 2·50 |
| | 159 | 2·25 | † | | 159 | 2·25 | † | 2·50 |
| | 160 | 2·25 | † | | 160 | 2·25 | † | 2·50 |
| | 161 | 6·50 | † | | 161 | † | † | 7·00 |

### Single Pane Cylinders

| Cyl. No. | Advert. | B3 | B4 | Cyl. No. | Advert. | B3A | B4A | B4B |
|---|---|---|---|---|---|---|---|---|
| G 29 | 157‡ | † | 5·50 | G 29. | 157 | † | † | † |
| | 159 | † | 2·25 | | 159 | † | † | † |
| | 160‡ | † | 5·50 | | 160 | † | † | † |
| | 160 | † | 5·50 | | | | | |

‡The cylinder number was originally engraved incorrectly on the advertisement pane. This was later erased and re-engraved in its correct position in the margin.

| Cyl. No. | Advert. No. | | | Perf. Type B4 | B4A |
|---|---|---|---|---|---|
| G 37 | 153 (No. 441) | .. | .. | 2·25 | 2·25 |
|  | (No. 448) | .. | .. | 2·25 | 2·25 |
|  | 157 | .. | .. | 2·25 | 2·25 |
|  | 158 | .. | .. | 2·25 | 2·25 |
|  | 159 | .. | .. | 2·25 | 2·25 |
|  | 160 | .. | .. | 2·25 | 2·25 |
| G 41 | 151 (No. 453) | .. | .. | 5·50 | † |
|  | 152 (No. 459) | .. | .. | 2·25 | † |
|  | 159 | .. | .. | 2·25 | † |
|  | 160 | .. | .. | 2·25 | † |
|  | 162 | .. | .. | 6·50 | † |
| G 46 | 152 (No. 467) | .. | .. | 2·75 | † |
|  | (No. 473) | .. | .. | 3·00 | † |
|  | 158 | .. | .. | — | † |
|  | 159 | .. | .. | 2·75 | † |
|  | 160 | .. | .. | 2·75 | † |

| Cyl. No. | Advert. No. | | | Perf. Type B3A | B4 |
|---|---|---|---|---|---|
| G 46 | 162 | .. | .. | † | 2·50 |
|  | 163 | .. | .. | † | 6·50 |
|  | 164 | .. | .. | † | 6·50 |
| G 59 | 152 (No. 482) | .. | .. | 3·25 | † |
|  | (No. 492) | .. | .. | 3·25 | † |
|  | 158 | .. | .. | 3·75 | † |
|  | 159 | .. | .. | 2·75 | † |
|  | 162 | .. | .. | 2·75 | † |
| G 67 | 159 | .. | .. | 4·25 | † |
| G 70 | 152 (No. 498) | .. | .. | 2·50 | † |
|  | 158 | .. | .. | 2·25 | † |
|  | 159 | .. | .. | 2·50 | † |
|  | 162 | .. | .. | 2·50 | † |

## 1d. ULTRAMARINE, No. Q6

Pane with three labels

| Advert. | Cyl. No. | Perf. Type B4 | Cyl No. | Perf. Type B5 |
|---|---|---|---|---|
| Minimum Inland Paper Rate 1½d. (17 mm.) | F 5 | 55 | F 5. | 55 |
| Ditto (15 mm.) | F 7 | 4·50 | F 7. | 4·50 |
| Shorthand in 1 week .. .. .. .. | F 7 | 3·25 | F 7. | 3·25 |

## Panes of four

Watermark sideways.   1937 Colours

| Value | Cyl. No. | | | Perf. Type B3 |
|---|---|---|---|---|
| ½d. No. Q1 | A 40 | .. | .. | 3·25 |
| 1d. No. Q4 | B 17 | .. | .. | 9·00 |

## Panes of two

1937 colours

| Value | Cyl. No. | | Perf. Type B3 | B4 | Cyl. No. | | | | Perf. Type B3A | B4B |
|---|---|---|---|---|---|---|---|---|---|---|
| ½d. No. Q1 | E 2 | .. | † | 1·60 | E 2. | .. | .. | .. | 1·60 | 2·25 |
|  | E 10 | .. | † | 1·60 | E 10. | .. | .. | .. | 1·60 | † |
|  | E 18 | .. | 2·25 | 1·60 | | | | | | |
|  | E 28 | .. | † | 2·25 | | | | | | |
| 1d. No. Q4 | F 1 | .. | † | 1·60 | F 1. | .. | .. | .. | 1·60 | 2·25 |
|  | F 5 | .. | † | 1·60 | F 5. | .. | .. | .. | 1·60 | † |
|  | F 15 | .. | † | 2·25 | | | | | | |
| 1½d. No. Q7 | G 19 | .. | † | 1·60 | G 19. | .. | .. | .. | 1·60 | 2·25 |
|  | G 20 | .. | † | 1·60 | G 20. | .. | .. | .. | 1·75 | † |
|  | G 28 | .. | 2·75 | 1·60 | | | | | | |
|  | G 50 | .. | 3·00 | 2·25 | | | | | | |

1947 pale colours

| Value | Cyl. No. | | | Perf. Type 5 | Cyl. No. | | | | Perf. Type 5 |
|---|---|---|---|---|---|---|---|---|---|
| ½d. No. Q2 | 137 | .. | .. | 25 | 137. | .. | .. | .. | 25 |
|  | 147 | .. | .. | 1·75 | 147. | .. | .. | .. | † |
|  | 150 | .. | .. | 25 | 150. | .. | .. | .. | 25 |
| 1d. No. Q5 | 157 | .. | .. | 25 | 157. | .. | .. | .. | 25 |
|  | 159 | .. | .. | † | 159. | .. | .. | .. | 60 |
|  | 160 | .. | .. | 25 | 160. | .. | .. | .. | 25 |
|  | 172 | .. | .. | 40 | 172. | .. | .. | .. | 60 |
|  | 175 | .. | .. | 45 | 175. | .. | .. | .. | 40 |
|  | 179 | .. | .. | 60 | 179. | .. | .. | .. | 60 |
| 1½d. No. Q8 | 185 | .. | .. | 45 | 185. | .. | .. | .. | 45 |
|  | 187 | .. | .. | 45 | 187. | .. | .. | .. | 45 |

1951 colours

| Value | Cyl. No. | | | Perf. Type 5 | Cyl. No. | | | | Perf. Type 5 |
|---|---|---|---|---|---|---|---|---|---|
| ½d. No. Q3 | 151 | .. | .. | † | 151. | .. | .. | .. | 20 |
|  | 153 | .. | .. | 20 | 153. | .. | .. | .. | 20 |
|  | 154 | .. | .. | 20 | 154. | .. | .. | .. | † |
|  | 155 | .. | .. | 20 | 155. | .. | .. | .. | † |
| 1d. No. Q6 | 191 | .. | .. | † | 191. | .. | .. | .. | 20 |
|  | 192 | .. | .. | 20 | 192. | .. | .. | .. | 20 |
| 1½d. No. Q9 | 192 | .. | .. | † | 192. | .. | .. | .. | 20 |
|  | 194 | .. | .. | 20 | 194. | .. | .. | .. | † |
|  | 195 | .. | .. | † | 195. | .. | .. | .. | 70 |
|  | 196 | .. | .. | † | 196. | .. | .. | .. | 40 |
|  | 199 | .. | .. | † | 199. | .. | .. | .. | 30 |

# Cylinder Numbers, Controls and Perforation Types

**INTRODUCTION.** The lists which follow cover the photogravure definitive issues of the reigns of King George V, King Edward VIII and King George VI. The lists of the commemorative issues are given immediately after the listing of the stamps in Sections N 4 and Q 3.

For descriptions of Perforation Types see Appendix I and for further notes about controls and prices see pages 86–87.

## King George V

### LARGE FORMAT

Control under the 2nd stamp bottom row. Cylinder number at left of 20th row.

*Prices are for corner pairs*

| Cat. No. Value | Cyl. No. | Control | Perf. Type 2 | 2A | Cyl. No. | Perf. Type 2A |
|---|---|---|---|---|---|---|
| CC1 | | | | | | |
| 1¼d. | 8 | U 34 | 1·75 | † | 8. | 2·00 |
| | 13 | V 34 | 80 | † | 13. | 80 |
| | 34 | U 34 | 1·60 | † | 34. | 2·00 |
| | 34 | V 34 | 80 | † | 34. | 80 |
| | 38 | V 34 | 1·40 | † | 38. | 1·25 |
| | 42 | V 34 | 80 | † | 42. | 80 |
| | 43 | V 34 | 1·40 | † | 43. | 1·40 |
| | 45 | V 34 | 80 | — | 45. | 80 |

Control opposite left of 19th row. Cylinder number opposite left of 20th row.

*Prices are for blocks of four*

| Cat. No. Value | Cyl. No. | Control | Perf. Type 2 | 4 | Cyl. No. | Perf. Type 2 A | 2 |
|---|---|---|---|---|---|---|---|
| CC2 | | | | | | | |
| 1d. | 1 | V 34 | 45 | 55 | 1. | 45 | † |
| | 2 | V 34 | 45 | 55 | 2. | 45 | 12·00 |
| | 5R | V 34 | 45 | 60 | 5R. | 45 | † |
| | 6R | V 34 | 45 | 65 | 6R. | 45 | † |
| | *9R | V 34 | † | † | *9R. | † | — |
| | 10R | V 34 | 15·00 | † | 10R. | 15·00 | † |
| | 11R | V 34 | 45 | 55 | 11R. | 45 | † |
| | 14 | V 34 | 4·00 | † | 14. | 4·00 | † |
| | 15 | V 34 | 5·00 | 4·00 | 15. | 4·00 | † |

Cylinder Nos. 1, 2, 5R, 11 R and 15 are known with watermark inverted.
Cylinder 6R (no dot) has a small split dot which was added in error.
Cylinder numbers bearing an asterisk are "abnormals". For explanation see note under "Printing" on page 89.

| Cat. No. Value | Cyl. No. | Control | Perf. Type 2 | 4 | 6 | Cyl. No. | Perf. Type 2A (or 6A) | 6B |
|---|---|---|---|---|---|---|---|---|
| CC3 | | | | | | | | |
| 1½d, | 17 | V 34 | 9·00 | † | † | 17. | 7·00 | † |
| | 46 | V 34 | 80 | 17·00 | 1·25 | 46. | 85 | † |
| | 47 | V 34 | 45 | 17·00 | 50 | 47. | 40 | † |
| | *49 | V 34 | 32·00 | † | † | *49. | 32·00 | † |
| | 54 | V 34 | 45 | † | † | 54. | 40 | † |
| | 55 | V 34 | 45 | † | † | 55. | 45 | † |
| | *63 | V 34 | 40·00 | † | † | *63. | † | † |
| | 68R | V 34 | 45 | 60 | † | 68R. | 45 | † |
| | 69 | V 34 | 45 | 3·50 | † | 69. | 45 | † |
| | *70 | V 34 | † | 32·00 | † | *70. | 32·00 | † |
| | 94 | V 34 | 45 | 50 | 50 | 94. | 45 | † |
| | 97 | V 34 | 60 | 50 | 45 | 97. | 45 | † |
| | 98 | V 34 | 45 | 50 | 45 | 98. | 45 | 45 |
| | 100 | V 34 | 45 | 50 | 55 | 100. | 45 | 55 |
| | 101 | V 34 | 45 | 50 | 45 | 101. | 45 | 40 |
| | 102 | V 34 | 60 | 80 | 1·25 | 102. | 60 | 1·25 |

Variety (Reverse feed). Cylinder 68R and cylinder 101 from the no dot panes, are known with Perforation Type 2A.
Cylinder 68R. dot is known with watermark inverted.
Cylinder 98 no dot is known with experimental use of Perforation Type 5.

## INTERMEDIATE FORMAT

Control opposite left of 19th row.   Cylinder number opposite left of 20th row.

*Prices are for blocks of four*

| Cat. No. Value | Cyl. No. | Control | Perf. Type 2 | 4 | 6 | Cyl. No. | 2A | 6B |
|---|---|---|---|---|---|---|---|---|
| CC4 ½d. | 3 | V 34 | 1·60 | 70 | 45 | 3. | 70 | 45 |
| | 4 | V 34 | 80 | 70 | 45 | 4. | 70 | 45 |
| CC5 1d. | 20 | V 34 | 3·25 | † | 2·00 | 20. | 2·00 | — |
| | 24 | V 34 | 2·00 | 2·20 | 1·50 | 24. | 1·25 | 90 |
| | 25 | V 34 | 1·50 | 1·50 | 1·00 | 25. | 90 | 90 |
| | 28 | V 34 | † | 14·00 | 12·00 | 28. | 14·00 | 12·00 |

Variety (Reverse feed).  Cylinder 25 no dot exists with Perforation Type 2A

| Cat. No. Value | Cyl. No. | Control | Perf. Type 2 | 4 | 6 | Cyl. No. | 2A | 6B |
|---|---|---|---|---|---|---|---|---|
| CC6 1¼d. | 104 | V 34 | 2·60 | 2·40 | 2·40 | 104. | 2·40 | 2·40 |
| | 105 | V 34 | 2·40 | 8·00 | 2·60 | 105. | 2·40 | 2·60 |
| | 106 | V 34 | 2·60 | 3·75 | 2·40 | 106. | 2·60 | 2·40 |
| | 107 | V 34 | † | — | 4·00 | 107. | — | 4·00 |

Cylinder 104 no dot is known with experimental use of Perforation Type 5

Control opposite left of 18th row.   Cylinder number opposite left of 20th row.

*Prices are for blocks of six*

| Cat. No. Value | Cyl. No. | Control | Perf. Type 2 | 5 | 6 | Cyl. No. | 2A | 5 | 6B |
|---|---|---|---|---|---|---|---|---|---|
| CC7 ½d. | 4 | W 35 | 4·75 | 1·00 | 85 | 4. | 4·75 | 1·00 | 85 |

Cylinder 4. dot is known with Perforation Type 3C (£10).

| Cat. No. Value | Cyl. No. | Control | Perf. Type 2 | 5 | 6 | Cyl. No. | 2A | 5 | 6B |
|---|---|---|---|---|---|---|---|---|---|
| CC8 1d. | 24 | W 35 | † | 7·00 | 7·00 | 24. | † | 7·00 | 7·00 |

Control and cylinder number both opposite left of 18th row

*Prices are for blocks of six*

| Cat. No. Value | Cyl. | Control | Perf. Type 2 | 5 | 6 | Cyl. No. | 2A (or 6A) | 5 | 6B |
|---|---|---|---|---|---|---|---|---|---|
| CC9 1¼d. | 113 | V 34 | † | † | 9·00 | 113. | — | † | 9·00 |
| CC10 2d. | 5 (i) | V 34 | † | † | 1·60 | 5. (i) | 4·50 | † | 2·00 |
| | 5 (i) | W 35 | † | 1·40 | 1·60 | 5. (i) | † | 1·40 | 2·00 |
| | 5 (ii) | W 35 | 6·00 | † | 1·40 | 5. (ii) | 8·00 | † | 1·60 |

Cylinder 5 exists in two states: (i) 5 very faint; (ii) the 5 has been re-etched to appear bolder and larger.

## SMALL FORMAT

Control and cylinder number both opposite left of 18th row.

*Prices are for blocks of six*

| Cat. No. Value | Cyl. No. | Control | Perf. Type 2 | 5 | 6 | Cyl. No. | 2A | Perf. Type 5 | 6B |
|---|---|---|---|---|---|---|---|---|---|
| CC11 ½d. | 11 | W 35 | 1·20 | 90 | 40 | 11. | 1·20 | 90 | 40 |
| | 12 | W 35 | † | † | † | *12. | — | † | † |
| | 13 | W 35 | 1·40 | 1·75 | 35 | 13. | 1·40 | 1·75 | 35 |
| | 18 | W 35 | † | 45 | 55 | 18. | † | 45 | 55 |
| | 22 | W 35 | 1·20 | 35 | 35 | 22. | 1·20 | 35 | 35 |
| | *24 | W 35 | † | † | † | *24. | 12·00 | † | † |
| | 25 | W 35 | † | 35 | 40 | 25. | 7·00 | 35 | 40 |
| | 27 | W 35 | † | 1·50 | 1·50 | 27. | † | 1·50 | 1·50 |
| | 30 | X 35 | † | 35 | 35 | 30. | † | 35 | 35 |
| | 31 | X 35 | † | 40 | 35 | 31. | † | 40 | 35 |
| | 32 | X 35 | † | 35 | 35 | 32. | † | 35 | 35 |
| | 36 | X 35 | 1·65 | 35 | 35 | 36. | 1·65 | 35 | 35 |
| | 39 | X 35 | 1·65 | 35 | 35 | 39. | 1·65 | 35 | 35 |
| | 39 | Y 36 | † | 35 | 35 | 39. | † | 35 | 35 |
| | 40 | X 35 | † | 35 | † | 40. | † | 35 | † |
| | 41 | X 35 | 4·25 | 35 | 35 | 41. | † | 35 | 35 |
| | 41 | Y 36 | † | 70 | † | 41. | † | 70 | † |
| | 42 | X 35 | — | 35 | 35 | 42. | † | 35 | 35 |
| | 42 | Y 36 | 4·25 | 35 | 35 | 42. | 6·00 | 35 | 35 |
| | 44 | Y 36 | † | 35 | † | 44. | † | 35 | † |
| | 45 | Y 36 | † | 35 | † | 45. | 8·00 | 35 | † |
| | 48 | Y 36 | † | 35 | † | 48. | † | 35 | † |
| | 48 | Z 36 | † | 40 | † | 48. | † | 40 | † |
| | 49 | Y 36 | † | 35 | 60 | 49. | † | 35 | 60 |

The only known example of cylinder 12. dot is a single specimen with attached control.

| | | | | | | | | | |
|---|---|---|---|---|---|---|---|---|---|
| CC12 1d. | 32 | W 35 | 8·00 | † | 7·00 | 32. | † | 8·00 | 7·00 |
| | 34 | X 35 | † | 35 | 45 | 34. | † | 35 | 45 |
| | 35 | X 35 | † | 35 | † | 35. | † | 35 | — |
| | 39 | X 35 | † | 35 | 40 | 39. | † | 35 | 40 |
| | 40 | X 35 | † | † | † | *40. | † | — | † |
| | 41 | X 35 | † | † | 75 | 41. | † | † | 75 |
| | 42 | X 35 | — | 35 | 45 | 42. | † | 35 | 45 |
| | 44 | X 35 | † | 3·00 | 3·50 | 44. | † | 3·00 | 3·50 |
| | 45 | X 35 | † | 5·00 | — | 45. | † | 5·00 | † |
| | 46 | X 35 | 2·00 | 35 | 40 | 46. | 2·00 | 35 | 40 |
| | 50 | X 35 | 2·00 | 35 | 40 | 50. | 2·00 | 35 | 40 |
| | 50 | Y 36 | 1·75 | 35 | † | 50. | 1·75 | 35 | † |
| | 53 | Y 36 | 1·75 | 35 | 75 | 53. | 1·75 | 35 | 75 |
| | 54 | Y 36 | 2·50 | 35 | † | 54. | 3·00 | 35 | † |

| | | | | | | | | | |
|---|---|---|---|---|---|---|---|---|---|
| CC13 1½d. | 116 | W 35 | 1·50 | 2·00 | 1·50 | 116. | 80 | 1·25 | 50 |
| | 119 | W 35 | 1·50 | † | 1·50 | 119. | 80 | — | 50 |
| | 124 | W 35 | † | 50 | 60 | 124. | † | 50 | 60 |
| | 127 | X 35 | † | 70 | 50 | 127. | † | 70 | 50 |
| | 128 | X 35 | † | † | 50 | 128. | † | † | 50 |
| | 130 | X 35 | † | 50 | 50 | 130. | † | 50 | 50 |
| | 132 | X 35 | 4·00 | 50 | 50 | 132. | 4·00 | 50 | 50 |
| | 133 | X 35 | † | 50 | † | 133. | † | 50 | † |
| | 135 | X 35 | 4·00 | 50 | † | 135. | 4·00 | 50 | † |
| | 135 | Y 36 | † | 50 | † | 135. | † | 55 | † |
| | 137 | X 35 | † | 50 | † | 137. | 4·00 | 50 | † |
| | 137 | Y 36 | † | 50 | † | 137. | 2·00 | 50 | † |
| | 139 | Y 36 | † | 1·00 | † | 139. | † | 1·00 | † |
| | 140 | Y 36 | † | 50 | † | 140. | † | 50 | † |
| | 141 | X 35 | † | 50 | † | 141. | † | 50 | † |
| | 141 | Y 36 | † | 50 | † | 141. | † | 50 | † |
| | 143 (i) | Y 36 | † | 60 | † | 143. | 5·00 | 70 | † |
| | 143 (ii) | Y 36 | † | 1·50 | † | | | | |
| | 144 | Y 36 | 2·00 | 60 | 3·00 | 144. | 2·75 | 50 | 3·00 |
| | 144 | Z 36 | 4·00 | 60 | † | 144. | 4·00 | 50 | † |
| | 146 | Y 36 | 5·50 | 60 | † | 146. | 5·50 | 50 | † |
| | 148 | Y 36 | 2·00 | 60 | † | 148. | 2·00 | 50 | † |
| | 149 | Y 36 | † | 60 | † | 149. | 3·50 | 50 | † |
| | 149 | Z 36 | 4·00 | 60 | † | 149. | 4·00 | 50 | † |
| | 153 | Z 36 | 3·50 | 60 | † | 153. | 3·50 | 50 | † |

*Varieties:*

Cylinder 116 known Perforation Type 5 with extension hole missing (£15).
Cylinder 139. (Reverse feed) Perforation Type 2 (£15).
Cylinder 149. (Reverse feed) Perforation Type 2 (£10).
Cylinder 143 no dot exists in two states.   The second state shows a large flaw in the margin opposite the
19th row and retouching to the base of figures 36 of the control.

## SMALL FORMAT—continued

**CC14 2d.**

| Cyl. No. | Control | 2 | 5 | 6 | Cyl. No. | 2A | 5 | 6B |
|---|---|---|---|---|---|---|---|---|
| 8 | X 35 | | 2·00 | 2·00 | 8. | † | 1·50 | 1·50 |
| 10 | X 35 | † | 1·20 | 1·20 | 10. | † | 1·20 | 1·30 |
| 10 | Y 36 | † | 1·20 | † | 10. | † | 1·20 | † |
| 10 | Z 36 | 3·00 | 1·30 | 1·20 | 10. | † | 1·30 | 1·30 |
| 12 | X 35 | † | 1·20 | 1·30 | 12. | † | 1·20 | 1·30 |
| 12 | Y 36 | † | 1·20 | † | 12. | † | 1·20 | † |
| 12 | Z 36 | 4·00 | 1·20 | † | 12. | † | 1·20 | † |
| 12 | A 37 | † | 1·20 | † | 12. | † | 1·20 | † |
| 13 | Z 36 | 5·00 | 1·20 | 1·30 | 13. | 4·50 | 1·20 | 1·30 |
| 13 | A 37 | † | 1·20 | † | 13. | † | 1·60 | † |

*Variety:*
Cylinder 10. dot known Perforation Type 3 with control Y 36 (£20.).

**CC15 2½d.**

| Cyl. No. | Control | 2 | 5 | 6 | Cyl. No. | 2A | 5 | 6B |
|---|---|---|---|---|---|---|---|---|
| 6 | W 35 | 4·50 | 2·00 | † | 6. | 4·50 | 2·00 | † |
| 7 | W 35 | 4·50 | 2·00 | † | 7. | 4·50 | 2·00 | † |
| 8 | Y 36 | 6·00 | 3·00 | † | 8. | 6·00 | 3·00 | † |
| 9 | Y 36 | 10·00 | 5·00 | † | 9. | † | 6·00 | † |

**CC16 3d.**

| Cyl. No. | Control | 2 | 5 | 6 | Cyl. No. | 2A | 5 | 6B |
|---|---|---|---|---|---|---|---|---|
| 1 | W 35 | 2·50 | † | † | 1. | 2·50 | † | † |
| 2 | W 35 | 2·75 | † | † | 2. | 2·75 | † | † |
|  | W 35 | | | | *3. | £150 | † | † |
| 6 | X 35 | † | 2·50 | 2·50 | 6. | † | 2·50 | 2·50 |
| 12 | Y 36 | † | 2·75 | † | 12. | † | 2·75 | † |
| 13 | Y 36 | † | 2·50 | † | 13. | † | 2·50 | † |
| 14 | Y 36 | 4·50 | 2·50 | † | 14. | 4·50 | 2·50 | † |
| 14 | Z 36 | 4·50 | 2·50 | † | 14. | 4·50 | 2·50 | † |
| 14 | Z 36 bar — | † | 2·50 | 2·60 | 14. bar — | † | 2·50 | 2·75 |
| 14 | Z 36 bars ⌊ | † | 2·50 | † | 14. bars ⌊ | † | 2·50 | † |

*Variety:*
Cylinder 1. dot known Perforation Type 3.

**CC17 4d.**

| Cyl. No. | Control | 2 | 5 | 6 | Cyl. No. | 2A | 5 | 6B |
|---|---|---|---|---|---|---|---|---|
| 3 | W 35 | 2·00 | † | † | 3 | — | † | † |
| 8 | X 35 | † | 2·50 | — | 8. | † | 2·50 | — |
| 9 | X 35 | † | 7·00 | † | 9. | † | 7·00 | † |
| 11 | X 35 | 6·00 | 2·25 | 2·40 | 11. | 6·00 | 2·25 | 2·40 |
| 11 | Y 36 | † | 2·00 | † | 11. | † | 2·00 | † |
| 11 | Y 36 bar — | † | 2·00 | 2·00 | 11. bar — | † | 2·00 | 2·40 |
| 11 | Y 36 bars ⌊ | † | 2·00 | 4·00 | 11. bars ⌊ | † | 2·00 | 3·00 |
| 11 | Y 36 bars □ | † | 2·00 | † | 11. bars □ | † | 2·00 | † |
| 11 | Y 36 bars □ | † | 2·00 | † | 11. bars □ | † | 2·00 | † |

Cylinder 3 in Perforation Type 2A has no dot, presumably omitted in error.

**CC18 5d.**

| Cyl. No. | Control | 2 | 5 | 6 | Cyl. No. | 2A | 5 | 6B |
|---|---|---|---|---|---|---|---|---|
| 5 | X 35 | † | 20·00 | † | 5. | † | 20·00 | † |
| 5 | Y 36 | 8·00 | 3·00 | † | 5. | 8·00 | 3·00 | † |
| 5 | Z 36 | † | † | 3·00 | 5. | † | † | 3·00 |
| 5 | Z 36 bar — | † | 3·00 | 3·00 | 5. bar — | 8·00 | 3·00 | 3·00 |
| 5 | Z 36 bars ⌊ | † | † | 3·25 | 5. bars ⌊ | † | † | 3·25 |
| 5 | Z 36 bars □ | † | 3·25 | † | 5. bars □ | † | 3·25 | † |
| 5 | Z 36 bars □ | † | 3·25 | † | 5. bars □ | † | 3·25 | † |

**CC19 9d.**

| Cyl. No. | Control | 2 | 5 | 6 | Cyl. No. | 2A | 5 | 6B |
|---|---|---|---|---|---|---|---|---|
| 15 | X 35 | † | 12·00 | 12·00 | 15. | † | 12·00 | 12·00 |
| 15 | X 35 bar — | † | † | 12·00 | 15. bar — | † | † | 12·00 |
| 15 | X 35 bars ⌊ | † | 14·00 | † | 15. bars ⌊ | † | 14·00 | † |
| 15 | X 35 bars □ | † | 14·00 | † | 15. bars □ | † | 14·00 | † |
| 15 | X 35 bars □ | † | † | 15·00 | 15. bars □ | † | † | 15·00 |

**CC20 10d.**

| Cyl. No. | Control | 2 | 5 | 6 | Cyl. No. | 2A | 5 | 6B |
|---|---|---|---|---|---|---|---|---|
| 3 | Y 36 | † | 18·00 | † | 3. | † | 18·00 | † |
| 3 | Y 36 bar — | 25·00 | 19·00 | † | 3. bar — | † | 19·00 | † |
| 3 | Y 36 bars ⌊ | † | 19·00 | † | 3. bars ⌊ | † | 19·00 | † |
| 3 | Y 36 bars □ | † | 20·00 | † | 3. bars □ | † | 19·00 | † |
| 3 | Y 36 bars □ | † | † | 20·00 | 3. bars □ | † | † | 20·00 |

Cylinder 3. Y 36—exists also with Perforation Type 2.

**CC21 1s.**

| Cyl. No. | Control | 2 | 5 | 6 | Cyl. No. | 2A | 5 | 6B |
|---|---|---|---|---|---|---|---|---|
| 3 | Y 36 | † | 30·00 | † | 3. | † | 30·00 | † |
| 4 | Y 36 | † | 30·00 | † | 4. | † | 30·00 | † |
| 5 | Z 36 | † | 32·00 | † | 5. | † | 32·00 | † |
| 5 | Z 36 bar — | † | 32·00 | — | 5. bar — | † | 32·00 | — |
| 5 | Z 36 bars ⌊ | † | 34·00 | † | 5. bars ⌊ | † | 34·00 | † |
| 5 | Z 36 bars □ | † | 34·00 | † | 5. bars □ | † | 34·00 | † |
| 5 | Z 36 bars □ | † | † | 35·00 | 5. bars □ | † | † | 35·00 |

On cylinder 5 both panes show an erased " 1 " before the " 5 ".

# King Edward VIII

**½d. GREEN, No. P1.**  Perforation Type 5 on both dot and no dot cylinders

| Cyl. No. | Control | No dot Cyl. | Dot Cyl. | Cyl. No. | Control | No dot Cyl. | Dot Cyl. | Cyl. No. | Control | No dot Cyl. | Dot Cyl. |
|---|---|---|---|---|---|---|---|---|---|---|---|
| *2 | A 36 | † | — | 12 | A 36 | 30 | 75 | 21 | A 37 | 40 | 40 |
| 4 | A 36 | 1·00 | 1·00 | 13 | A 36 | 40 | 40 | 22 | A 37 | 30 | 30 |
| 5 | A 36 | 60 | 60 | 15 | A 36 | 40 | 40 | 24 | A 37 | 40 | 40 |
| 7 | A 36 | 30 | 80 | 16 | A 36 | 30 | 30 | 25 | A 37 | 40 | 40 |
| 10 | A 36 | 30 | 80 | | | | | 26 | A 37 | 30 | 30 |

Perforation Types 2 (no dot cylinder) and 2A (dot cylinder)

| 7 | A 36 | 2·50 | 2·50 | 10 | A 36 | 2·50 | 2·50 |
|---|---|---|---|---|---|---|---|

**1d. SCARLET, No. P2.**  Perforation Type 5 on both dot and no dot cylinders

| 2 | A 36 | 30 | 30 | 5 | A 36 | 60 | 60 | 13 | A 37 | 60 | 60 |
|---|---|---|---|---|---|---|---|---|---|---|---|
| 3 | A 36 | 30 | 30 | 6 | A 36 | 30 | 30 | 14 | A 37 | 65 | 65 |
| 4 | A 36 | 30 | 30 | | | | | | | | |

Perforation Types 2 (no dot cylinder) and 2A (dot cylinder)

| 3 | A 36 | † | — | 5 | A 36 | † | 10·00 | *7 | A 36 | — | † |
|---|---|---|---|---|---|---|---|---|---|---|---|
| 4 | A 36 | — | † | 6 | A 36 | — | — | | | | |

**1½d. RED-BROWN, No. P3.**  Perforation Type 5 on both dot and no dot cylinders

| 2 | A 36 | 35 | 35 | 12 | A 36 | 35 | 35 | 16 | A 36 | 35 | 35 |
|---|---|---|---|---|---|---|---|---|---|---|---|
| 4 | A 36 | 35 | 35 | 12 | A 37 | 3·00 | 3·00 | 16 | A 37 | 40 | 40 |
| 6 | A 36 | 35 | 35 | 13 | A 36 | 35 | 35 | 17 | A 37 | 40 | 40 |
| 8 | A 36 | 35 | 35 | 13 | A 37 | 35 | 35 | *18 | A 37 | — | † |
| 9 | A 36 | 35 | 35 | 15 | A 36 | 1·50 | 1·50 | 20 | A 37 | 30 | 30 |
| | | | | 15 | A 37 | 35 | 35 | | | | |

Perforation Types 2 (no dot cylinder) and 2A (dot cylinder)

| 2 | | † | — | 8 | | † | 6·50 | 12 | A 36 | 2·50 | 2·50 |
|---|---|---|---|---|---|---|---|---|---|---|---|
| 4 | | † | 2·50 | 9 | | — | † | | | | |

Perforation Types 6 (no dot cylinder) and 6B (dot cylinder)

| 15 | A 37 | — | — | 20 | A 37 | 1·00 | 1·00 |
|---|---|---|---|---|---|---|---|

Cylinder 12. (A 36) is known with Perforation Type 2 (Reverse feed)

**2½d. BLUE, No. P4.**  Perforation Type 5 on both dot and no dot cylinders

| 2 | A 36 | 60 | 60 | 2 | A 36 bar — | 50 | 50 |
|---|---|---|---|---|---|---|---|

# King George VI

**½d. GREEN, No. Q1.**    Without pick up bar.    Perforation Type 5

| Cyl. No. | Control | No dot | Dot | Cyl. No. | Control | No dot | Dot | Cyl. No. | Control | No dot | Dot |
|---|---|---|---|---|---|---|---|---|---|---|---|
| 2 | A 37 | 30 | 30 | 6 | A 37 | 30 | 30 | 11 | A 37 | 40 | 40 |
| 2 | B 37 | 55 | 55 | 8 | A 37 | 30 | 30 | 12 | A 37 | 40 | 40 |
| 3 | A 37 | 30 | 30 | 8 | B 37 | 30 | 30 | 12 | B 37 | 40 | 40 |
| 4 | A 37 | 30 | 30 | 10 | A 37 | 30 | 30 | | | | |

Perforation Type 2A

| 6 | A 37 | † | 5·00 |
|---|---|---|---|

Perforation Type 6 (no dot) and 6B (dot)

| 2 | A 37 | 40 | 40 |
|---|---|---|---|

With pick up bar.    Perforation Type 5

| Cyl. No. | Control | No dot | Dot | Cyl. No. | Control | No dot | Dot | Cyl. No. | Control | No dot | Dot |
|---|---|---|---|---|---|---|---|---|---|---|---|
| 2 | B 37 | 45 | 45 | 58 | C 38 | 60 | 60 | 90 | F 39 | 50 | 50 |
| 12 | B 37 | 40 | 40 | 58 | D 38 | 45 | 45 | 93 | E 39 | 45 | 45 |
| 16 | B 37 | 30 | 30 | 59 | C 38 | 45 | 45 | 95 | E 39 | 40 | 40 |
| 17 | B 37 | 30 | 30 | 61 | C 38 | 35 | 35 | 98 | E 39 | 40 | 40 |
| 18 | B 37 | 30 | 30 | 64 | D 38 | 35 | 35 | 99 | E 39 | 35 | 35 |
| 19 | B 37 | 35 | 35 | 67 | D 38 | 30 | 30 | 100 | E 39 | 40 | 40 |
| 20 | B 37 | 7·00 | 9·00 | 68 | D 38 | 30 | 30 | 100 | F 39 | 1·25 | 1·25 |
| 22 | B 37 | 40 | 40 | 68 | E 39 | 50 | 50 | 101 | E 39 | 55 | 55 |
| 24 | B 37 | 45 | 45 | 69 | D 38 | 45 | 45 | 101 | F 39 | 45 | 45 |
| 25 | B 37 | 30 | 30 | 70 | D 38 | 45 | 45 | 104 | F 39 | 30 | 30 |
| 31 | B 37 | 30 | 30 | 72 (i) | D 38 | 1·00 | 1·00 | 105 (i) | F 39 | 2·00 | 1·00 |
| 32 | B 37 | 35 | 35 | 72 (ii) | D 38 | 45 | 45 | 105 (ii) | F 39 | † | 1·50 |
| 35 | C 38 | 35 | 35 | 73 | D 38 | 30 | 30 | 105 (iii) | F 39 | 1·50 | 2·00 |
| 37 | C 38 | 35 | 35 | 74 | D 38 | 40 | 40 | 106 (i) | F 39 | 45 | 45 |
| 40 | C 38 | 30 | 30 | 76 | D 38 | 45 | 45 | 106 (ii) | F 39 | 65 | 65 |
| 42 | C 38 | 35 | 35 | 76 | E 39 | 45 | 45 | 108 | F 39 | 70 | 70 |
| 43 (i) | C 38 | 45 | 45 | 77 | E 39 | 45 | 45 | 110 | F 39 | 65 | 65 |
| 43 (ii) | C 38 | 45 | 45 | 78 | E 39 | 30 | 30 | 113 | F 39 | 30 | 30 |
| 52 | C 38 | 45 | 45 | 81 | D 38 | 45 | 45 | 119 | G 40 | 70 | 65 |
| 53 | C 38 | 30 | 30 | 81 | E 39 | 45 | 45 | 120 | G 40 | 30 | 30 |
| 55 | C 38 | 30 | 30 | 82 | D 38 | 40 | 40 | 120 | I 41 | 70 | 30 |
| 56 | C 38 | 35 | 35 | 90 | E 39 | 45 | 45 | | | | |

Perforation Type 6 (no dot) and 6B (dot)

| Cyl. No. | Control | No dot | Dot | Cyl. No. | Control | No dot | Dot | Cyl. No. | Control | No dot | Dot |
|---|---|---|---|---|---|---|---|---|---|---|---|
| 58 | D 38 | 60 | 60 | 72 (i) | D 38 | 1·10 | 1·10 | 76 | E 39 | 45 | 45 |
| 67 | D 38 | 50 | 50 | 72 (ii) | D 38 | 50 | 50 | 81 | E 39 | 40 | 40 |
| 68 | D 38 | 55 | 55 | 73 | D 38 | 60 | 60 | 82 | D 38 | 40 | 40 |
| 69 | D 38 | 55 | 55 | 74 | D 38 | 60 | 60 | 101 | F 39 | 1·10 | 1·10 |
| 70 | D 38 | 50 | 50 | 76 | D 38 | 50 | 50 | | | | |

*Varieties:*

Cylinder 43 exists in two states:

> State (i) both dot and no dot panes show " 43 " engraved over " 23 ", the " 2 " showing clearly.
> State (ii) retouch on both panes, the " 2 " no longer visible.   The base of figure " 38 " of control has been retouched.

Cylinder 72 exists in two states:

> State (i) both dot and no dot panes show a very weak control
> State (ii) both controls retouched.

Cylinder 105 dot exists in three states:

> State (i) Without retouch.
> State (ii) " 3 " of control lightly retouched at base.
> State (iii) Control completely retouched.

Cylinder 105 no dot exists in two states:

> State (i) Pale control.
> State (iii) Control strongly retouched.

Cylinder 106 exists in two states:

> State (i) both dot and no dot panes show trace of a previous control.   The F 39 control has been lightly retouched.
> State (ii) The control has been further retouched, and the " shadow control " almost completely removed.

Retouched controls

The following F 39 controls were retouched before the cylinders were put to press: 90, 100, 101, 101., 104

"Shadow" controls

Distinct traces of a previous control are seen on the following:

E 39　Cyl. 68, 68., 81, 81. (D 38)　　　　　G 40　Cyl. 119, 119., 120, 120. (F 39)
F 39　Cyl. 90, 101, 104., 108, 110. (E 39)　　I 41　Cyl. 120, 120. (F 39)

## ½d. PALE GREEN, No. Q2.　Perforation Type 5

| Cyl. No. | Control | No dot | Dot | Cyl. No. | Control | No dot | Dot | Cyl. No. | Control | No dot | Dot |
|---|---|---|---|---|---|---|---|---|---|---|---|
| 124 | J 41 | 1·50 | 1·50 | 129 | P 44 | 75 | 50 | 141 | U 47 | 40 | 40 |
| 124 | K 42 | 30 | 30 | 130 | N 43 | 30 | 30 | 142 | S 46 | 30 | 30 |
| 124 | L 42 | 30 | 30 | 130 | P 44 | 30 | 30 | 142 | T 46 | 30 | 30 |
| 125 | J 41 | 30 | 30 | 132 | P 44 | 30 | 30 | 143 | U 47 | 30 | 30 |
| 125 | K 42 | 30 | 30 | 134 | Q 45 | 30 | 30 | 146 | None | 30 | 30 |
| 128 | M 43 | 30 | 30 | 134 | S 46 | 30 | 30 | 150 | None | 30 | 30 |
| 128 | N 43 | 30 | 30 | 135 | R 45 | 30 | 30 | 151 | None | 40 | 40 |
| 128 | O 44 | 40 | 40 | 135 | S 46 | 30 | 30 | 152 | None | 30 | 30 |
| 129 | M 43 | 40 | 40 | 137 | None | 30 | 30 | 153 | None | 40 | 40 |
| 129 | O 44 | 30 | 30 | 141 | T 46 | 30 | 30 | | | | |

### Perforation Type 6

| | | No dot 6 | 6B | Dot 6 | | | No dot 6 | 6B | Dot 6 | | | No dot 6 | 6B | Dot 6 |
|---|---|---|---|---|---|---|---|---|---|---|---|---|---|---|
| 124 | J 41 | 75 | 1·00 | 1·00 | 125 | J 41 | 30 | 30 | 30 | 132 | P 44 | 40 | 40 | † |
| 124 | L 42 | 30 | 30 | 30 | 130 | P 44 | 30 | 30 | † | | | | | |

### Perforation Type 5AE.　No dot cylinder only

| 129 | P 44 | 40 | 132 | P 44 | 40 | 134 | Q 45 | 40 |
|---|---|---|---|---|---|---|---|---|
| 130 | P 44 | 30 | | | | | | |

## ½d. ORANGE, No. Q3.　Perforation Type 5

| 151 | None | 30 | 30 | 153 | None | 30 | 30 | 155 | None | 30 | 30 |
|---|---|---|---|---|---|---|---|---|---|---|---|
| 152 | None | 30 | 30 | 154 | None | 30 | 30 | | | | |

## 1d. SCARLET, No. Q4.　Without pick up bar.　Perforation Type 5

| 1 | A 37 | 14·00 | † | 7 | A 37 | 40 | 40 | 9 | A 37 | 14·00 | † |
|---|---|---|---|---|---|---|---|---|---|---|---|
| 3 | A 37 | 40 | 40 | 8 | A 37 | 40 | 40 | 10 | A 37 | 50 | 50 |
| 4 | A 37 | 40 | 40 | 8 | B 37 | 50 | 50 | 11 | B 37 | 45 | 45 |

### Perforation Type 6 (no dot) and 6B (dot)　Perforation Type 2A

| 7 | A 37 | 45 | 45 | 11 | B 37 | † | 8·00 |
|---|---|---|---|---|---|---|---|

### With pick up bar.　Perforation Type 5

| 8 | B 37 | 50 | 50 | 27 | E 39 | 40 | 40 | 45 | H 40 | 40 | 40 |
|---|---|---|---|---|---|---|---|---|---|---|---|
| 11 | B 37 | 60 | 60 | 30 | F 39 | 3·25 | 3·25 | 46 | H 40 | 45 | 45 |
| 12 | B 37 | 40 | 40 | 33 | F 39 | 40 | 40 | 47 | H 40 | 50 | 50 |
| 12 | C 38 | 50 | 50 | 39 | F 39 | 70 | 70 | 48 | H 40 | 50 | 50 |
| 15 | C 38 | 40 | 40 | 39 | G 40 | 50 | 50 | 48 | I 41 | 50 | 40 |
| 16 | C 38 | 40 | 40 | 40 | G 40 | 50 | 50 | 49 | H 40 | 50 | 50 |
| 18 | C 38 | 40 | 40 | 40 | H 40 | 45 | 45 | 49 | I 41 | 50 | 40 |
| 19 | D 38 | 60 | 60 | 41 | G 40 | 40 | 40 | 51 | H 40 | 60 | 60 |
| 22 | D 38 | 45 | 45 | 41 | H 40 | 50 | 50 | 51 | I 41 | 40 | 40 |
| 23 | D 38 | 60 | 60 | 42 | F 39 | 50 | 50 | 53 | I 41 | 40 | 40 |
| 24 | D 38 | 40 | 40 | 43 | H 40 | 50 | 50 | 54 | I 41 | 40 | 40 |
| 26 | D 38 | 40 | 40 | 44 | H 40 | 50 | 50 | 61 | I 41 | 40 | 40 |
| 26 | E 39 | 60 | 50 | 45 | G 40 | 50 | 50 | | | | |

### Perforation Type 6 (no dot) and 6B (dot)

| 26 | E 39 | 60 | 40 | 30 | F 39 | 50 | 50 | 39 | F 39 | 50 | 50 |
|---|---|---|---|---|---|---|---|---|---|---|---|
| 27 | E 39 | 40 | 40 | 31 | F 39 | 50 | 50 | 42 | F 39 | 50 | 50 |
| 27 | F 39 | 70 | 70 | 33 | F 39 | 50 | 50 | | | | |

Cylinder 31 exists only with Type 6 perforation.

On cylinder 19 (both panes), the tail of the "9" was originally engraved short and close to the loop. Before being put to press, the tail was re-engraved long and wide of the loop.

"Shadow" controls

Distinct traces of the previous control are seen on the following:

E 39　Cyl. 26, 26. (D 38)
I 41　Cyl. 48, 49 (H 40)

## 1d. PALE SCARLET, No. Q5.   Type I.   Perforation Type 5

| Cyl. No. | Control | No dot | Dot | Cyl. No. | Control | No dot | Dot | Cyl. No. | Control | No dot | Dot |
|---|---|---|---|---|---|---|---|---|---|---|---|
| 66 | J 41 | 35 | 35 | 95 | N 43 | 75 | 75 | 125 | S 46 | 30 | 30 |
| 69 | J 41 | 30 | 30 | 95 | O 44 | 50 | 50 | 127 | S 46 | 30 | 30 |
| 70 | J 41 | 35 | 30 | 96 | M 43 | 35 | 35 | 127 | T 46 | 35 | 35 |
| 71 | J 41 | 35 | 35 | 96 | N 43 | 35 | 35 | 129 | S 46 | 35 | 35 |
| 72 | J 41 | 30 | 35 | 97 | N 43 | 35 | 35 | 129 | T 46 | 35 | 35 |
| 72 | K 42 | 30 | 30 | 98 | O 44 | 30 | 30 | 130 | S 46 | 35 | 35 |
| 72 | L 42 | 40 | 40 | 99 | N 43 | 40 | 40 | 132 | T 46 | 30 | 30 |
| 73 | J 41 | 30 | 30 | 100 | N 43 | 75 | 75 | 133 | T 46 | 30 | 30 |
| 73 | K 42 | 30 | 30 | 100 | O 44 | 30 | 30 | 134 | T 46 | 30 | 30 |
| 74 | J 41 | 40 | 40 | 101 | P 44 | 35 | 35 | 136 | T 46 | 30 | 30 |
| 74 | K 42 | 45 | 45 | 102 | O 44 | 45 | 45 | 139 | T 46 | 30 | 30 |
| 75 | K 42 | 30 | 30 | 102 | P 44 | 30 | 30 | 140 | T 46 | 35 | 35 |
| 76 | K 42 | 30 | 30 | 105 | O 44 | 45 | 45 | 141 | T 46 | 30 | 30 |
| 76 | L 42 | 45 | 45 | 105 | P 44 | 30 | 30 | 142 | T 46 | 30 | 30 |
| 76 | M 43 | 35 | 35 | 106 | P 44 | 80 | 35 | 143 | T 46 | 30 | 30 |
| 78 | L 42 | 30 | 30 | 106 | Q 45 | 30 | 30 | 145 | None | 30 | 30 |
| 80 | M 43 | 30 | 30 | 107 | P 44 | 30 | 30 | 146 | U 47 | 30 | 30 |
| 81 | L 42 | 30 | 30 | 107 | Q 45 | 35 | 35 | 148 | U 47 | 30 | 30 |
| 82 | L 42 | 35 | 35 | 112 | P 44 | 35 | 35 | 149 | U 47 | 30 | 30 |
| 82 | M 43 | 40 | 40 | 113 | Q 45 | 35 | 35 | 150 | None | 30 | 30 |
| 86 | M 43 | 40 | 40 | 113 | Q 45 | 40 | 40 | 153 | U 47 | 30 | 30 |
| 90 | N 43 | 35 | 35 | 118 | Q 45 | 30 | 30 | 155 | U 47 | 30 | 30 |
| 90 | O 44 | 45 | 35 | 118 | R 45 | 30 | 30 | 156 | None | 35 | 35 |
| 91 | N 43 | 45 | 35 | 120 | Q 45 | 30 | 30 | 157 | None | 35 | 35 |
| 91 | O 44 | 50 | 45 | 120 | R 45 | 30 | 30 | 160 | None | 30 | 30 |
| 91 | P 44 | 70 | 70 | 121 | Q 45 | 30 | 30 | 166 | None | 30 | 30 |
| 92 | M 43 | 40 | 40 | 122 | Q 45 | 35 | 35 | 167 | None | 30 | 30 |
| 92 | N 43 | 30 | 30 | 122 | R 45 | 30 | 30 | 169 | None | 30 | 30 |
| 93 | M 43 | 30 | 30 | 123 | R 45 | 30 | 30 | 171 | None | 30 | 30 |
| 94 | N 43 | 40 | 40 | 124 | S 46 | 30 | 30 | 172 | None | 30 | 30 |
| 94 | O 44 | 50 | 40 | 125 | R 45 | 35 | 35 | | | | |

### Perforation Type 6 (no dot) and 6B (dot)

| Cyl. No. | Control | No dot | Dot | Cyl. No. | Control | No dot | Dot | Cyl. No. | Control | No dot | Dot |
|---|---|---|---|---|---|---|---|---|---|---|---|
| 72 | L 42 | 35 | 35 | 125 | R 45 | 30 | 30 | 153 | U 47 | 35 | 35 |
| 76 | L 42 | 45 | 45 | 125 | S 46 | 30 | 30 | 171 | None | 1·50 | 1·50 |
| 121 | Q 45 | 35 | 35 | 127 | S 46 | 35 | 35 | 172 | None | 35 | 35 |
| 123 | S 46 | 50 | 50 | 129 | S 46 | 35 | 35 | | | | |
| 124 | S 46 | 35 | 35 | 150 | U 47 | 45 | 45 | | | | |

### Perforation Type 5AE (no dot cylinder only)

| Cyl. No. | Control | No dot | Cyl. No. | Control | No dot | Cyl. No. | Control | No dot |
|---|---|---|---|---|---|---|---|---|
| 90 | O 44 | 40 | 98 | O 44 | 35 | 106 | P 44 | 40 |
| 91 | N 43 | 50 | 100 | O 44 | 35 | 106 | Q 45 | 45 |
| 91 | O 44 | 60 | 101 | P 44 | 40 | 107 | P 44 | 50 |
| 91 | P 44 | 70 | 102 | O 44 | 50 | 107 | Q 45 | 1·00 |
| 94 | N 43 | 40 | 102 | P 44 | 50 | 112 | P 44 | 50 |
| 94 | O 44 | 40 | 105 | O 44 | 50 | 113 | P 44 | 50 |

## Type II.   Perforation Type 5

| Cyl. No. | Control | No dot | Dot | Cyl. No. | Control | No dot | Dot | Cyl. No. | Control | No dot | Dot |
|---|---|---|---|---|---|---|---|---|---|---|---|
| 174 | None | 35 | 35 | 180 | None | 35 | 35 | 186 | None | 40 | 40 |
| 175 | None | 35 | 35 | 181 | None | 35 | 35 | 189 | None | 35 | 35 |
| 178 | None | 45 | 45 | 182 | None | 35 | 35 | 190 | None | 50 | 50 |
| 179 | None | 35 | 35 | 183 | None | 40 | 40 | | | | |

### Perforation Type 6 (no dot) and 6B (dot)

| Cyl. No. | Control | No dot | Dot | Cyl. No. | Control | No dot | Dot |
|---|---|---|---|---|---|---|---|
| 174 | None | 45 | 45 | 180 | None | 45 | 45 |
| 179 | None | 45 | 45 | 181 | None | 45 | 45 |
| | | | | 185 | None | 35 | 35 |
| | | | | 190 | None | 80 | 80 |

Cylinder 124 sometimes shows a dot after the number.  Printings from the no dot pane may always be recognised by the presence of a cut in the rule under the first stamp, bottom row.
Cylinder 185 only exists with perforation Type 6.

## 1d. ULTRAMARINE, No. Q6.   Perforation Type 5

| Cyl. No. | Control | No dot | Dot | Cyl. No. | Control | No dot | Dot | Cyl. No. | Control | No dot | Dot |
|---|---|---|---|---|---|---|---|---|---|---|---|
| 190 | None | 30 | 30 | 191 | None | 30 | 30 | 192 | None | 50 | 35 |

### Perforation Type 6 (no dot) and 6B (dot)

| Cyl. No. | Control | No dot | Dot | Cyl. No. | Control | No dot | Dot |
|---|---|---|---|---|---|---|---|
| 191 | None | 35 | 35 | 192 | None | 30 | 30 |

## 1½d. RED-BROWN, No. Q7. Perforation Type 5. Without pick up bar

| Cyl. No. | Control | No dot | Dot | Cyl. No. | Control | No dot | Dot | Cyl. No. | Control | No dot | Dot |
|---|---|---|---|---|---|---|---|---|---|---|---|
| 1 | A 37 | 50 | 50 | 18 | B 37 | 40 | 40 | 33 | B 37 | 5·00 | † |
| 12 | A 37 | 50 | 50 | 22 | B 37 | 40 | 40 | 35 | B 37 | † | 20·00 |
| 14 | A 37 | 50 | 50 | 30 | B 37 | 40 | 40 | | | | |
| 17 | B 37 | 40 | 40 | 32 | B 37 | 40 | 40 | | | | |

### With pick up bar

| Cyl. No. | Control | No dot | Dot | Cyl. No. | Control | No dot | Dot | Cyl. No. | Control | No dot | Dot |
|---|---|---|---|---|---|---|---|---|---|---|---|
| 38 | B 37 | 40 | 40 | 84 | C 38 | 50 | 50 | 123 | E 39 | 40 | 40 |
| 42 | B 37 | 40 | 40 | 85 | C 38 | 50 | 50 | 124 | E 39 | 40 | 40 |
| 45 | B 37 | 40 | 40 | 86 | C 38 | 40 | 40 | 125 | E 39 | 40 | 40 |
| 46 | B 37 | 40 | 40 | 88 | C 38 | 50 | 50 | 126 | E 39 | 40 | 40 |
| 48 | B 37 | 40 | 40 | 89 | C 38 | 2·00 | 20·00 | 128 | E 39 | 40 | 40 |
| 49 | B 37 | 40 | 40 | 90 | C 38 | 50 | 50 | 135 | E 39 | 40 | 40 |
| 50 | B 37 | 40 | 40 | 91 | C 38 | 55 | 55 | 136 | E 39 | 70 | 70 |
| 51 | B 37 | 40 | 40 | 92 | C 38 | 40 | 40 | 138 | E 39 | 80 | † |
| 52 | B 37 | 70 | 70 | 93 | C 38 | 50 | 50 | 139 | E 39 | 70 | 70 |
| 54 | B 37 | 40 | 40 | 93 | D 38 | 50 | 50 | 141 | F 39 | 50 | 50 |
| 55 | B 37 | 40 | 40 | 95 | C 38 | 50 | 50 | 144 | E 39 | 50 | 50 |
| 56 | B 37 | 50 | 50 | 96 | C 38 | 50 | 80 | 145 | E 39 | 50 | 50 |
| 59 | B 37 | 40 | 40 | 98 | C 38 | 40 | 40 | 148 | E 39 | 50 | 50 |
| 60 (i) | B 37 | 50 | 50 | 102 | D 38 | 40 | 40 | 148 | F 39 | 70 | 70 |
| 60 (ii) | B 37 | 50 | 50 | 104 | C 38 | 80 | 80 | 149 | F 39 | 70 | 70 |
| 61 | B 37 | 55 | 55 | 104 | D 38 | 80 | 40 | 150 | E 39 | 70 | 70 |
| 64 | B 37 | 40 | 40 | 106 | D 38 | 40 | 40 | 150 | F 39 | 70 | 70 |
| 65 | B 37 | 40 | 40 | 107 | D 38 | 40 | 40 | 151 | E 39 | 50 | 50 |
| 68 | B 37 | 50 | 50 | 108 | D 38 | 40 | 40 | 152 | E 39 | 50 | 50 |
| 68 | C 38 | 50 | 50 | 109 | D 38 | 40 | 40 | 153 | F 39 | 40 | 40 |
| 69 | C 38 | 45 | 45 | 110 | D 38 | 40 | 40 | 154 | E 39 | 45 | 45 |
| 70 | C 38 | 40 | 40 | 112 | D 38 | 40 | 40 | 156 | E 39 | 45 | 45 |
| 71 | B 37 | 40 | 40 | 113 | D 38 | 40 | 40 | 159 | F 39 | 40 | 40 |
| 71 | C 38 | 50 | 50 | 116 | D 38 | 40 | 40 | 161 | F 39 | 45 | 45 |
| 74 | C 38 | 40 | 40 | 120 | D 38 | 70 | 70 | 164 | F 39 | 80 | 80 |
| 76 | C 38 | 40 | 40 | 120 | E 39 | 40 | 40 | 165 | G 40 | 80 | 80 |
| 77 | C 38 | 40 | 40 | 121 | D 38 | 70 | 70 | 167 | F 39 | 50 | 50 |
| 81 | C 38 | 40 | 40 | 122 | D 38 | 50 | 50 | 173 | G 40 | 40 | 40 |
| 83 | C 38 | 50 | 50 | 122 | E 39 | 40 | 40 | | | | |

In cylinder 98 the figure " 9 " is retouched.

### Perforation Type 6 (no dot) and 6B (dot)

| | | | | | | | | | | | |
|---|---|---|---|---|---|---|---|---|---|---|---|
| 83 | C 38 | 75 | 75 | 145 | E 39 | 2·00 | 2·00 | 161 | F 39 | 1·50 | 1·50 |

### Perforation Type 2A

| | | | | | | | | |
|---|---|---|---|---|---|---|---|---|
| 106 | D 38 | † | 7·00 | 135 | E 39 | † | 18·00 | |

*Varieties:*

Cylinder 60 exists in two states. In state (ii) the cylinder has been rechromed, and the control on both panes is weak and irregular in depth.

The left pane of cylinder 12 has a tiny dot after the " 12.".

The right pane of cylinder 110 was without dot. It may be distinguished by the pick up bar under the first stamp, which has a nick in base at left.

Retouched controls

The following controls were retouched before the cylinders were put to press

E 39 Cyl. 120. dot
F 39 Cyl. 141, 141. and 149

" Shadow " controls

Distinct traces of F 39 are seen on control G 40 cyl. 165 and 165.

## 1½d. PALE RED-BROWN, No. Q8. Perforation Type 5

| Cyl. No. | Control | No dot | Dot | Cyl. No. | Control | No dot | Dot | Cyl. No. | Control | No dot | Dot |
|---|---|---|---|---|---|---|---|---|---|---|---|
| 174 | N 43 | 50 | 50 | 183 | O 44 | 50 | 50 | 186 | S 46 | 50 | 50 |
| 175 | L 42 | 50 | 50 | 184 | S 46 | 50 | 55 | 187 | U 47 | 55 | 55 |
| 175 | N 43 | 55 | 55 | 185 | S 46 | 50 | 50 | 187 | None | 50 | 50 |
| 176 | L 42 | 50 | 50 | 185 | U 47 | 50 | 50 | 191 | None | 50 | 50 |
| 179 | Q 45 | 50 | 50 | 185 | None | 75 | 75 | 192 | None | 65 | 50 |
| 183 | N 43 | 50 | 50 | 186 | R 45 | 50 | 50 | | | | |

## Perforation Type 6

| Cyl | Control | No dot 6 | 6B | Dot 6 | | Cyl | Control | No dot 6 | 6B | Dot 6 | | Cyl | Control | No dot 6 | 6B | Dot 6 |
|---|---|---|---|---|---|---|---|---|---|---|---|---|---|---|---|---|
| 178 | O 44 | 50 | 55 | 50 | | 178 | P 44 | 50 | 50 | † | | 183 | O 44 | 55 | 65 | 50 |

## Perforation Type 5AE, no dot cylinder only

| 179 | Q 45 | 1·20 |
|---|---|---|

On cylinder 183 the control O 44 has been retouched on both panes.
Cylinder 178 exists Perforation Type 6 only.

## 1½d. GREEN, No. Q9.  Perforation Type 5

| Cyl. No. | Control | No dot | Dot | | Cyl. No. | Control | No dot | Dot | | Cyl. No. | Contro | No dot | Dot |
|---|---|---|---|---|---|---|---|---|---|---|---|---|---|
| 190 | None | 30 | 30 | | 194 | None | 30 | 30 | | 197 | None | 30 | 30 |
| 192 | None | 4·50 | 30 | | 195 | None | 30 | 30 | | 199 | None | 40 | 40 |
| 193 | None | 30 | 30 | | 196 | None | 30 | 30 | | | | | |

### Perforation Type 6 (no dot) and 6B (dot)

| 195 | None | 40 | 40 | | 197 | None | 40 | 40 |
|---|---|---|---|---|---|---|---|---|

## 2d. ORANGE, No. Q10.  Perforation Type 5

| Cyl | Control | No dot | Dot | | Cyl | Control | No dot | Dot | | Cyl | Control | No dot | Dot |
|---|---|---|---|---|---|---|---|---|---|---|---|---|---|
| 1 | B 37 | 1·50 | 1·50 | | 11 | F 39 | 2·00 | 2·00 | | 15 | G 40 | 1·50 | 1·50 |
| 1 | C 38 | 4·00 | 4·00 | | 11 | G 40 | 2·00 | 2·00 | | 15 | H 40 | 3·00 | 3·00 |
| 7 | D 38 | 1·50 | 1·50 | | 12 | E 39 | 1·50 | 1·50 | | 17 | H 40 | 1·50 | 1·50 |
| 8 | D 38 | 1·50 | 1·50 | | 12 | G 40 | 1·50 | 1·50 | | 17 | I 41 | 1·50 | 1·50 |
| 10 | E 39 | 1·50 | 1·50 | | 14 | G 40 | 1·50 | 1·50 | | 20 | I 41 | 2·50 | 2·50 |
| 11 | E 39 | 1·50 | 1·50 | | 14 | H 40 | 2·00 | 2·00 | | | | | |

### Perforation Type 6 (no dot) and 6B (dot)

| 10 | E 39 | 2·00 | 2·00 | | 11 | F 39 | 2·00 | 2·00 | | 12 | F 39 | 1·70 | 1·70 |
|---|---|---|---|---|---|---|---|---|---|---|---|---|---|
| 11 | E 39 | 2·00 | 2·00 | | 12 | E 39 | 2·00 | 2·00 | | | | | |

## 2d. PALE ORANGE, No. Q11.  Perforation Type 5

| Cyl | Control | No dot | Dot | | Cyl | Control | No dot | Dot | | Cyl | Control | No dot | Dot |
|---|---|---|---|---|---|---|---|---|---|---|---|---|---|
| 23 | M 43 | 70 | 70 | | 34 | P 44 | 60 | 60 | | 47 | U 47 | 60 | 60 |
| 24 | J 41 | 60 | 60 | | 36 | Q 45 | 60 | 60 | | 49 | U 47 | 60 | 60 |
| 24 | K 42 | 60 | 60 | | 38 | P 44 | 60 | 60 | | 50 | U 47 | 60 | 60 |
| 25 | J 41 | 60 | 60 | | 39 | P 44 | 60 | 60 | | 52 | None | 60 | 60 |
| 25 | K 42 | 60 | 60 | | 39 | Q 45 | 60 | 60 | | 54 | None | 60 | 60 |
| 25 | L 42 | 60 | 60 | | 40 | Q 45 | 60 | 60 | | 55 | None | 70 | 70 |
| 25 | M 43 | 60 | 60 | | 40 | R 45 | 75 | 75 | | 58 | None | 60 | 60 |
| 26 | L 42 | 70 | 70 | | 41 | R 45 | 60 | 60 | | 59 | None | 60 | 60 |
| 30 | M 43 | 60 | 60 | | 42 | S 46 | 60 | 60 | | 60 | None | 60 | 60 |
| 30 | N 43 | 60 | 60 | | 42 | U 47 | 60 | 60 | | 61 | None | 60 | 60 |
| 32 | N 43 | 60 | 60 | | 45 | R 45 | 60 | 60 | | 62 | None | 60 | 60 |
| 32 | O 44 | 75 | 75 | | 45 | T 46 | 60 | 60 | | 67 | None | 70 | 70 |
| 33 | O 44 | 60 | 60 | | 47 | T 46 | 60 | 60 | | 68 | None | 1·00 | 1·00 |

### Perforation Type 6 (no dot) and 6B (dot)

| 25 | J 41 | 70 | † | | 47 | T 46 | 60 | 60 | | 61 | None | 60 | 60 |
|---|---|---|---|---|---|---|---|---|---|---|---|---|---|
| 25 | L 42 | 60 | 70 | | 52 | None | 60 | 60 | | 62 | None | 70 | 70 |
| 34 | P 44 | 60 | † | | 53 | None | 70 | 70 | | 64 | None | 60 | 60 |
| 38 | P 44 | 60 | 60 | | 55 | None | 60 | 60 | | 67 | None | 75 | 75 |
| 45 | S 46 | 60 | 60 | | 58 | None | 70 | 70 | | 68 | None | 2·00 | 2·00 |
| 45 | T 46 | 60 | 60 | | 59 | None | 70 | 70 | | | | | |

### Perforation Type 6 (dot)

| 25 | J 41 | 70 | | 34 | P 44 | 60 | | 38 | P 44 | 60 |
|---|---|---|---|---|---|---|---|---|---|---|
| 25 | L 42 | 60 | | | | | | | | |

### Perforation Type 5AE, no dot cylinder only

| 39 | P 44 | — |
|---|---|---|
| 40 | Q 45 | — |

Cylinders 53 and 64 only exist with Type 6 perforation.
On cylinder 47 the control U 47 has been retouched on both panes.

## 2d. RED-BROWN, No. Q12. Perforation Type 5

| Cyl. No. | Control | No dot | Dot | Cyl. No. | Control | No dot | Dot | Cyl. No. | Control | No dot | Dot |
|---|---|---|---|---|---|---|---|---|---|---|---|
| 67 | None | 1·00 | 1·00 | 71 | None | 75 | 75 | 75 | None | 80 | 80 |
| 68 | None | 75 | 75 | 72 | None | 75 | 75 | | | | |
| 69 | None | 75 | 75 | 73 | None | 75 | 75 | | | | |

### Perforation Type 6 (no dot) and 6B (dot)

| | | | | | | | | | | | |
|---|---|---|---|---|---|---|---|---|---|---|---|
| 69 | None | 75 | 75 | 70 | None | 1·50 | 1·50 | 71 | None | 80 | 80 |

Cylinder 70 only exists with perforation Type 6.

## 2½d. ULTRAMARINE, No. Q13. Perforation Type 5. Without pick up bar

| | | | | | | | | | | | |
|---|---|---|---|---|---|---|---|---|---|---|---|
| 1 | A 37 | 16·00 | 16·00 | 2 | B 37 | 1·00 | 1·00 | 2 | D 38 | 2·50 | 2·50 |
| 2 | A 37 | 1·00 | 1·00 | | | | | | | | |

### Perforation Type 6 (no dot) and 6B (dot)

| | | | | | | | |
|---|---|---|---|---|---|---|---|
| 2 | A 37 | 1·00 | 1·00 | 2 | D 38 | 1·00 | 1·00 |

### With pick up bar. Perforation Type 5

| | | | | | | | | | | | |
|---|---|---|---|---|---|---|---|---|---|---|---|
| 3 | E 39 | 1·00 | 1·00 | 22 | H 40 | 1·00 | 1·00 | 44 | I 41 | 1·50 | 1·50 |
| 3 | G 40 | 1·50 | 1·50 | 23 | H 40 | 2·00 | 2·00 | 45 | I 41 | 1·00 | 1·00 |
| 6 (i) | G 40 | 1·50 | 1·50 | 25 | H 40 | 1·00 | 1·00 | 48 | I 41 | 1·00 | 1·00 |
| 6 (ii) | G 40 | 2·50 | 2·50 | 28 | H 40 | 1·00 | 1·00 | 53 | I 41 | 1·00 | 1·00 |
| 6 | H 40 | 1·00 | 1·00 | 30 | H 40 | 2·00 | 2·00 | 56 | I 41 | 1·00 | 1·00 |
| 7 | G 40 | 1·25 | 1·25 | 34 | H 40 | 1·25 | 1·00 | 57 | I 41 | 1·00 | 1·00 |
| 10 | G 40 | 1·25 | 1·25 | 36 | H 40 | 1·25 | 1·00 | 58 | I 41 | 1·00 | 1·00 |
| 10 | H 40 | 4·00 | 4·00 | 40 | H 40 | 1·50 | 1·50 | 59 | I 41 | 1·25 | 1·25 |
| 13 (i) | G 40 | 1·25 | -- | 41 | H 40 | 1·25 | 1·25 | 61 | I 41 | 1·00 | 1·00 |
| 13 (ii) | G 40 | 2·00 | 2·00 | 41 | I 41 | 1·00 | 1·00 | 62 | I 41 | 1·50 | 1·50 |
| 15 | G 40 | 2·00 | 2·00 | 43 | H 40 | 2·00 | 2·00 | 63 | I 41 | 1·25 | 1·25 |
| 15 | H 40 | 2·00 | 2·00 | 43 | I 41 | 1·50 | 1·50 | 64 | I 41 | 1·50 | 1·50 |
| 20 | H 40 | 1·50 | 1·50 | 44 | H 40 | 1·00 | 1·00 | 65 | I 41 | 1·50 | † |

### Perforation Type 6 (no dot) and 6B (dot)

| | | | | | | | | | | | |
|---|---|---|---|---|---|---|---|---|---|---|---|
| 6 (i) | G 40 | 1·25 | 1·25 | 20 | H 40 | 1·50 | 1·50 | 30 | H 40 | 1·00 | 1·00 |
| 6 (ii) | G 40 | 1·50 | 1·50 | 22 | H 40 | 3·00 | 3·00 | 41 | H 40 | 3·00 | 3·00 |
| 8 | G 40 | 1·75 | 1·75 | 23 | H 40 | 1·50 | 1·50 | | | | |
| 10 | H 40 | 1·50 | 1·50 | 25 | H 40 | 2·00 | 2·00 | | | | |

*Varieties:*

Cylinder 8 exists only with perforation Type 6
Cylinder 6 Control G 40 exists in two states:
    (i) Control faint
    (ii) Control heavily retouched
Cylinder 6 Control H 40 exists with traces of " G 40 "
Cylinder 13 exists in two states:
    (i) Control faint
    (ii) Control heavily retouched
The control G 40 on cylinder 7 was retouched before being put to press

## 2½d. LIGHT ULTRAMARINE, No. Q14.    Perforation Type 5

| Cyl. No. | Control | No dot | Dot | Cyl. No. | Control | No dot | Dot | Cyl. No. | Control | No dot | Dot |
|---|---|---|---|---|---|---|---|---|---|---|---|
| 69 | J 41 | 50 | 50 | 135 | M 43 | 50 | 50 | 203 | S 46 | 50 | 50 |
| 70 | J 41 | 50 | 50 | 135 | N 43 | 50 | 50 | 203 | T 46 | 50 | 50 |
| 72 | J 41 | 50 | 50 | 136 | N 43 | 50 | 50 | 204 | T 46 | 50 | 50 |
| 73 | J 41 | 10·00 | † | 138 | N 43 | 50 | 50 | 204 | U 47 | 50 | 50 |
| 75 | J 41 | 2·00 | 2·00 | 142 | N 43 | 50 | 50 | 205 | S 46 | 50 | 50 |
| 77 | J 41 | 50 | 50 | 142 | O 44 | 60 | 60 | 205 | T 46 | 50 | 50 |
| 80 | J 41 | 50 | 50 | 143 | N 43 | 70 | 70 | 206 | S 46 | 50 | 50 |
| 80 | K 42 | 50 | 50 | 144 | N 43 | 50 | 50 | 209 | U 47 | 50 | 50 |
| 81 | J 41 | 50 | 50 | 145 | N 43 | 50 | 50 | 210 | T 46 | 50 | 50 |
| 81 | K 42 | 60 | 60 | 145 | O 44 | 50 | 50 | 211 | U 47 | 50 | 50 |
| 82 | J 41 | † | 10·00 | 146 | N 43 | 70 | 70 | 212 | U 47 | 50 | 50 |
| 83 | J 41 | 50 | 50 | 146 | O 44 | 50 | 50 | 213 | U 47 | 50 | 50 |
| 83 | K 42 | 60 | 60 | 147 | O 44 | 50 | 50 | 216 | U 47 | 50 | 50 |
| 84 | J 41 | 50 | 50 | 148 | O 44 | 50 | 50 | 217 | U 47 | 50 | 50 |
| 84 | K 42 | 50 | 50 | 149 | O 44 | 50 | 50 | 219 | None | 1·50 | 1·50 |
| 84 | L 42 | 60 | 60 | 150 | O 44 | 50 | 50 | 220 | U 47 | 50 | 50 |
| 86 | K 42 | 50 | 50 | 151 | P 44 | 50 | 50 | 222 | None | 50 | 50 |
| 87 | K 42 | 50 | 50 | 152 | O 44 | 50 | 50 | 223 | None | 50 | 50 |
| 90 | K 42 | 50 | 50 | 152 | P 44 | 50 | 50 | 224 | None | 50 | 50 |
| 92 | K 42 | 50 | 50 | 153 | O 44 | 50 | 50 | 225 | U 47 | 50 | 50 |
| 95 | K 42 | 50 | 50 | 154 | O 44 | 50 | 50 | 225 | None | 1·25 | 1·25 |
| 95 | L 42 | 50 | 50 | 155 | O 44 | 55 | 55 | 226 | None | 75 | 75 |
| 96 | K 42 | 55 | 55 | 155 | P 44 | 50 | 50 | 227 | U 47 | 50 | 50 |
| 96 | L 42 | 1·25 | 1·25 | 156 | P 44 | 50 | 50 | 228 | None | 50 | 50 |
| 97 | L 42 | 50 | 50 | 157 | P 44 | 50 | 50 | 229 | None | 50 | 50 |
| 99 | L 42 | 50 | 50 | 159 | P 44 | 50 | 50 | 230 | None | 50 | 50 |
| 100 | L 42 | 80 | 80 | 162 | P 44 | 50 | 50 | 231 | None | 50 | 50 |
| 101 | L 42 | 50 | 50 | 164 | P 44 | 50 | 50 | 234 | None | 50 | 50 |
| 104 | L 42 | 50 | 50 | 165 | P 44 | 50 | 50 | 235 | None | 50 | 50 |
| 110 | L 42 | — | † | 166 | P 44 | 1·00 | 1·00 | 236 | None | 50 | 50 |
| 110 | M 43 | 50 | 50 | 168 | P 44 | 50 | 50 | 238 | None | 50 | 50 |
| 111 | L 42 | 50 | 50 | 172 | P 44 | 50 | 50 | 239 | None | 50 | 50 |
| 111 | M 43 | 50 | 50 | 172 | Q 45 | 50 | 50 | 240 | None | 50 | 50 |
| 113 | L 42 | 50 | 50 | 173 | Q 45 | 55 | 55 | 241 | None | 50 | 50 |
| 113 | M 43 | 50 | 50 | 174 | P 44 | 50 | 50 | 244 | None | 80 | 80 |
| 114 | L 42 | 50 | 50 | 174 | Q 45 | 55 | 55 | 245 | None | 50 | 50 |
| 117 | L 42 | 50 | 50 | 177 | Q 45 | 50 | 50 | 246 | None | 55 | 55 |
| 117 | M 43 | 50 | 50 | 178 | Q 45 | 50 | 50 | 247 | None | 50 | 50 |
| 118 | M 43 | 50 | 50 | 184 | Q 45 | † | — | 248 | None | 50 | 50 |
| 119 | M 43 | 50 | 50 | 186 | Q 45 | 50 | 50 | 249 | None | 50 | 50 |
| 120 | M 43 | 50 | 50 | 186 | R 45 | 50 | 50 | 250 | None | 50 | 50 |
| 121 | M 43 | 50 | 50 | 187 | Q 45 | 50 | 50 | 252 | None | 50 | 50 |
| 121 | N 43 | 50 | 50 | 187 | R 45 | 50 | 50 | 253 | None | 50 | 50 |
| 124 | M 43 | 50 | 50 | 190 | Q 45 | 50 | 50 | 254 | None | 50 | 50 |
| 127 | M 43 | 50 | 50 | 190 | R 45 | 50 | 50 | 255 | None | 50 | 50 |
| 130 | M 43 | 50 | 50 | 194 | R 45 | 50 | 50 | 256 | None | 50 | 50 |
| 131 | M 43 | 50 | 50 | 195 | S 46 | 50 | 50 | 260 | None | 50 | 50 |
| 131 | N 43 | 60 | 60 | 197 | S 46 | 50 | 50 | 261 | None | 60 | 60 |
| 132 | M 43 | 50 | 50 | 201 | S 46 | 60 | 60 | 263 | None | 60 | 60 |
| 132 | N 43 | 60 | 60 | 201 | T 46 | 50 | 50 | 266 | None | 75 | 75 |
| 133 | M 43 | 60 | 60 | 202 | S 46 | 50 | 50 | | | | |
| 133 | N 43 | 60 | 60 | 202 | T 46 | 60 | 60 | | | | |

## Perforation Type 6 (no dot) and 6B (dot)

| Cyl. No. | Control | No dot | Dot | Cyl. No. | Control | No dot | Dot | Cyl. No. | Control | No dot | Dot |
|---|---|---|---|---|---|---|---|---|---|---|---|
| 111 | L 42 | 1·25 | 1·25 | 164 | P 44 | 50 | 50 | 195 (i) | R 45 | 50 | 50 |
| 135 | M 43 | 60 | † | 165 | P 44 | 50 | 50 | 195 (ii) | R 45 | 3·50 | 3·50 |
| 138 | N 43 | 50 | 75 | 167 | P 44 | 70 | 60 | 196 | R 45 | 50 | 50 |
| 144 | N 43 | 50 | 50 | 172 | P 44 | 50 | 50 | 236 | None | 50 | 50 |
| 146 | N 43 | 65 | † | 173 | Q 45 | 50 | 50 | 238 | None | 50 | 50 |
| 148 | O 44 | † | 75 | 179 | Q 45 | 85 | 85 | 239 | None | 50 | 50 |
| 151 | N 43 | 50 | † | 184 | Q 45 | 50 | 50 | 240 | None | 50 | 50 |
| 151 | O 44 | 50 | 50 | 187 | Q 45 | 70 | 50 | 246 | None | 1·25 | 1·25 |
| 152 | O 44 | 50 | 55 | 187 | R 45 | 70 | 70 | 260 | None | 50 | 50 |
| 156 | P 44 | 55 | † | 190 | Q 45 | 75 | 75 | 261 | None | 75 | 75 |
| 161 | P 44 | 50 | 50 | 194 | R 45 | 50 | 50 | 263 | None | 50 | 50 |

## Perforation Type 6 (dot)

| Cyl. No. | Control | Dot | Cyl. No. | Control | Dot | Cyl. No. | Control | Dot |
|---|---|---|---|---|---|---|---|---|
| 135 | M 43 | 60 | 151 | O 44 | 60 | 165 | P 44 | 50 |
| 138 | N 43 | 50 | 152 | O 44 | 60 | 167 | P 44 | 60 |
| 144 | N 43 | 70 | 156 | P 44 | 60 | 173 | Q 45 | 50 |
| 146 | N 43 | 70 | 161 | P 44 | 50 | 184 | Q 45 | 60 |
| 151 | N 43 | 50 | 164 | P 44 | | | | |

## Perforation Type 5AE, no dot cylinder only

| Cyl. No. | Control | No dot | Cyl. No. | Control | No dot | Cyl. No. | Control | No dot |
|---|---|---|---|---|---|---|---|---|
| 142 | O 44 | 75 | 156 | P 44 | 3·50 | 184 | Q 45 | 45 |
| 145 | O 44 | 50 | 162 | P 44 | 50 | 186 | Q 45 | 50 |
| 146 | N 43 | 75 | 164 | P 44 | 50 | 219 | None | 2·25 |
| 148 | O 44 | 75 | 165 | P 44 | 50 | 223 | None | 65 |
| 149 | O 44 | 60 | 172 | P 44 | 50 | 248 | None | 65 |
| 150 | O 44 | 50 | 172 | Q 45 | 60 | 249 | None | 2·00 |
| 152 | O 44 | 65 | 174 | Q 45 | 50 | | | |
| 154 | O 44 | 50 | 177 | Q 45 | 50 | | | |

Cylinders 161, 167, 179 and 196 only exist with perforation Type 6.

*Varieties:*

Cylinder 100 had the L and fraction bar engraved by hand.
On cylinder 146 the control N 43 has been heavily retouched on both panes. The retouches show as an outline of heavy dots.
Cylinder 195 exists in two states. In state (ii) the control has been heavily retouched.
The U 47 controls have been retouched on cylinder 212 (dot pane) and cylinder 217 (no dot pane).

Errors of engraving

Cylinder 144 (both panes) were originally engraved " 141 ". Cylinder 166 dot pane was originally engraved " 116.", and cylinder 204 (no dot pane) was originally engraved " 104 ".

" Shadow " controls

Distinct traces of the previous control are seen on L 42 cylinder 96 dot (K 42) a·d on O 44 cylinder 146 both panes (N 43).

## 2½d. SCARLET, No. Q15. Perforation Type 5

| Cyl. No. | Control | No dot | Dot | Cyl. No. | Control | No dot | Dot | Cyl. No. | Control | No dot | Dot |
|---|---|---|---|---|---|---|---|---|---|---|---|
| 259 | None | 75 | 75 | 268 | None | 60 | 60 | 275 | None | 60 | 60 |
| 261 | None | 65 | 65 | 269 | None | 60 | 60 | 276 | None | 60 | 60 |
| 264 | None | 1·75 | 1·75 | 270 | None | 60 | 60 | 277 | None | 60 | 60 |
| 266 | None | 65 | 65 | 273 | None | 60 | 60 | 279 | None | 60 | 60 |
| 267 | None | 60 | 60 | 274 | None | 60 | 60 | | | | |

## 3d. VIOLET, No. Q16. Perforation Type 5

| | Control | | | | | Control | | | | Control | | |
|---|---|---|---|---|---|---|---|---|---|---|---|---|
| 3 | C 38 | 3·00 | 3·00 | 9 | D 38 | 3·50 | 3·50 | 17 | G 40 | 8·00 | 8·00 |
| 5 (i) | C 38 | 3·00 | 3·00 | 11 | E 39 | 3·50 | 3·50 | 18 | G 40 | 3·50 | 3·50 |
| 5 (ii) | C 38 | † | 3·00 | 12 | E 39 | 3·50 | 3·50 | 18 | H 40 | 3·50 | 3·50 |
| 9 | C 38 | 4·00 | 4·00 | 14 | G 40 | 3·50 | 3·50 | | | | |

Perforation Type 6 (no dot) and 6B (dot)

| 11 | E 39 | 3·50 | 3·50 | 12 | E 39 | 3·50 | 3·50 |
|---|---|---|---|---|---|---|---|

*Varieties:*

Cylinder 5 exists in two states:
    (i) No dot after " 5 ".
    (ii) added dot after " 5 ".
Both states show a white dot in " 3 " of the control, not present in the no dot pane.

## 3d. PALE VIOLET, No. Q17. Perforation Type 5

| 21 | J 41 | 1·50 | 1·50 | 25 | N 43 | 1·50 | 1·50 | 28 | Q 45 | 1·50 | 1·50 |
|---|---|---|---|---|---|---|---|---|---|---|---|
| 21 | K 42 | 1·50 | 1·50 | 25 | O 44 | 1·50 | 1·50 | 30 | None | 2·00 | 2·00 |
| 21 | L 42 | 1·50 | 1·50 | 26 | N 43 | 1·50 | 1·50 | 32 | None | 2·25 | 2·25 |
| 22 | L 42 | 2·00 | 2·00 | 26 | O 44 | 1·50 | 1·50 | 34 | None | 1·50 | 1·50 |
| 22 | M 43 | 1·50 | 1·50 | 27 | R 45 | 2·50 | 1·50 | | | | |
| 22 | N 43 | 2·00 | 2·00 | 27 | None | 2·50 | 1·50 | | | | |

Perforation Type 6

| | | No dot 6 | Dot 6B | 6 | | | No dot 6 | Dot 6B | 6 | | | No dot 6 | Dot 6B | 6 |
|---|---|---|---|---|---|---|---|---|---|---|---|---|---|---|
| 21 | J 41 | 1·50 | 1·50 | 2·00 | 22 | L 42 | 3·00 | 3·00 | † | 29 | O 44 | 1·50 | 1·50 | † |
| 21 | L 42 | 3·00 | 3·00 | † | 28 | P 44 | 1·50 | 1·50 | † | 29 | P 44 | 2·00 | 2·00 | † |

Perforation Type 2A

| 30 | None | † | — |
|---|---|---|---|

Perforation Type 5AE, no dot cylinder only

| 25 | O 44 | 1·50 |
|---|---|---|
| 28 | Q 45 | 2·00 |

Cylinder 29 only exists with perforation Type 6.

" Shadow " control

Distinct traces of the previous control are seen on K 42 cylinder 21 dot (J 41).

**4d. GREY-GREEN, No. Q19.**  Single Pane cylinder.  Perforation Type 6B

| Cyl. No. | Control | No dot | Dot | Cyl. No. | Control | No dot | Dot | Cyl. No. | Control | No dot | Dot |
|---|---|---|---|---|---|---|---|---|---|---|---|
| 1 | D 38 | 1·50 | | 1 | I 41 | 1·50 | | 1 | K 42 bars ⌐ | 1·50 | |
| 1 | E 39 | 1·50 | | 1 | K 42 | 2·00 | | | | | |
| 1 | G 40 | 1·50 | | 1 | K 42 bar — | 1·50 | | | | | |

Perforation Type 6 (no dot)
1   I 41   2·00

Double Pane cylinder.   Perforation Type 6 (no dot) and 6B (dot)

| 6 | None | 1·50 | 1·50 | 9 | O 44 bar — | 1·50 | 1·50 | 9 | O 44 bars ☐ | 1·50 | 1·50 |
| 9 | O 44 | 1·50 | 1·50 | 9 | O 44 bars ⌐ | 1·50 | 1·50 | | | | |

**4d. ULTRAMARINE, No. Q20.**   Perforation Type 5
13   None   2·00   2·00

Perforation Type 6 (no dot) and 6B (dot)
13   None   2·00   2·00

Perforation Types 2 (no dot) and 3 (dot)
13   None   3·00   3·00

**5d. BROWN, No. Q21.**   Single Pane cylinder.   Perforation Type 6B

| 1 | D 38 | 1·25 | 1 | G 40 | 1·25 | 1 | K 42 | i·50 |
| 1 | E 39 | 1·25 | 1 | I 41 | 1·25 | | | |

Perforation Type 6 (no dot)
1   I 41   5·00

Double Pane cylinder.   Perforation Type 5

| 3 | L 42 | 20·00 | 20·00 | 3 | L 42 bars ⌐ | 1·25 | 1·50 | 3 | L 42 bars ☐ | 1·50 | 1·50 |
| 3 | L 42 bar — | 1·50 | 1·50 | 3 | L 42 bars ☐ | 1·50 | 1·50 | | | | |

Perforation Type 6 (no dot) and 6B (dot)
3   L 42 bars ☐   1·25   1·25
4   K 42   †   3·00

Perforation Type 5AE, no dot cylinder only
3   L 42 bars ⌐   3·50

**6d. PURPLE, No. Q22.**   Typographed control.   Single pane cylinder.   Perforation Type

| 1 | D 38 | 1·50 | 25 | L 42 | 1·00 | 36 | T 46 | 1·00 |
| 1 | E 39 | 90 | 30 | M 43 | 1·00 | 36 | U 47 | 1·00 |
| 10 | F 39 | 1·20 | 32 | L 42 | 1·00 | 36 | None | 1·00 |
| 10 | G 40 | 1·20 | 32 | M 43 | 1 25 | 37 | T 46 | 1·50 |
| 10 | H 40 | 1·50 | 32 | N 43 | 1·00 | 37 | None | 1·20 |
| 21 | H 40 | 2·00 | 33 | O 44 | 1·00 | 39 | None | 1·00 |
| 25 | J 41 | 1·00 | 33 | Q 45 | 1·00 | 41 | None | 1·20 |
| 25 | K 42 | 1·00 | 33 | T 46 | 3·00 | | | |

Perforation Type 6B (no dot)
1   D 38   1·50
25   L 42   4·00

Perforation Type 6 (no dot)
1   D 38   3·00
37   None   2·75

Perforation Type 3
25   K 42   3·50
32   N 43   2·00

## 7d. EMERALD-GREEN, No. Q23.   Single Pane cylinders.   Perforation Type 6B

| Cyl. No. | Control | No dot | Dot | Cyl. No. | Control | No dot | Dot | Cyl. No. | Control | No dot | Dot |
|---|---|---|---|---|---|---|---|---|---|---|---|
| 1 | E 39 bar — | 1·50 | | 2 | E 39 bars □ | 1·75 | | 3 | E 39 bars ⌐ | | 1·50 |
| 1 | E 39 bars ⌐ | 1·50 | | 2 | E 39 bars □ | 1·50 | | 3 | E 39 bars □ | | 1·50 |
| 2 | E 39 | 1·50 | | 2 | E 39 bars |□ | 1·50 | | 3 | E 39 bars □ | | 1·50 |
| 2 | E 39 bar — | 1·50 | | 3 | E 39 bars ⌐ | 1·50 | | | | | |

Perforation Type 6 (no dot)

| | Control | | |
|---|---|---|---|
| 1 | E 39 bar — | 2·00 | |
| 2 | E 39 bars □ | 1·50 | |
| 3 | E 39 bars ⌐ | 1·50 | |

Double Pane cylinders.   Perforation Type 5

| 9 | None | 2·50 | 2·50 |
|---|---|---|---|
| 10 | S 46 | 2·00 | 2·00 |
| 10 | None | 2·00 | 2·00 |
| 12 | None | 2·00 | 2·00 |

Perforation Type 6 (no dot) and 6B (dot)

| 9 | None | 4·00 | 4·00 |
|---|---|---|---|
| 10 | S 46 | 2·00 | 2·00 |
| 10 | None | 2·25 | 2·25 |
| 12 | None | 2·25 | 2·25 |

## 8d. CARMINE, No. Q24.   Single Pane cylinders.   Perforation Type 6B

| 1 | E 39 | 1·75 | | 1 | E 39 bars ⌐ | 1·50 | | 3(i) O 44 | 1·50 |
|---|---|---|---|---|---|---|---|---|---|
| 1 | E 39 bar — | 1·75 | | 1 | E 39 bars □ | 1·50 | | 3(ii) O 44 | 1·50 |
| 1 | E 39 bars ⌐ | 1·50 | | 1 | E 39 bars □ | 1·50 | | 3   O 44 bar — | 1·75 |

Double Pane cylinders.   Perforation Type 5

| 6 | S 46 | 1·50 | 1·50 |
|---|---|---|---|
| 9 | None | 1·50 | 1·50 |

Perforation Type 6 (no dot) and 6B (dot)

| 6 | S 46 bar — | 1·50 | 1·50 |
|---|---|---|---|
| 9 | None | 1·75 | 1·75 |

*Varieties:*

The control O 44 exists in two states:
  (i) Control very faint
  (ii) Control retouched with heavy outline

## 9d. OLIVE-GREEN, No. Q25.   Typographed control.   Single Pane cylinders.   Perforation Type 2

| 2 | I 41 | 1·50 | | 2 | O 44 | 1·50 | | 3 | G 40 | 1·50 |
|---|---|---|---|---|---|---|---|---|---|
| 2 | K 42 | 1·50 | | 2 | P 44 | 1·50 | | 3 | H 40 | 1·50 |
| 2 | L 42 | 1·50 | | 2 | R 45 | 1·50 | | 3 | N 43 | 1·50 |
| 2 | N 43 | 1·50 | | 3 | E 39 | 1·50 | | | | |

Perforation Type 3 (no dot)

| 2 | R 45 | — |
|---|---|---|

Double Pane cylinders.   Perforation Type 5

| 5 | None | 1·50 | 1·50 |
|---|---|---|---|

Perforation 5AE (no dot cylinder only)

| 5 | None | 5·00 |
|---|---|---|

| Perforation Type 6 (no dot) and 6B (dot) | | | | Perforation Type 2 (no dot) and 2A (dot) | | | |
|---|---|---|---|---|---|---|---|
| 5 | None | 1·50 | 1·50 | 5 | None | 2·50 | 2·50 |

**10d. TURQUOISE-BLUE, No. Q26.**   Typographed control.   Single Pane cylinder.   Perforation 2

| Cyl. No. | Control | No dot | Dot | Cyl. No. | Control | No dot | Dot | Cyl. No. | Control | No dot | Dot |
|---|---|---|---|---|---|---|---|---|---|---|---|
| 1 | E 39 | 2·00 | | 1 | J 41 | 2·00 | | 1 | N 43 | 2·00 | |
| 1 | F 39 | 2·00 | | 1 | K 42 | 2·00 | | 1 | O 44 | 2·00 | |
| 1 | H 40 | 2·00 | | 1 | L 42 | 2·00 | | | | | |
| 1 | I 41 | 2·00 | | 1 | M 43 | 2·00 | | | | | |

Double Pane cylinders.   Perforation Type 6 (no dot) and 6B (dot)

| | | | | | | | | | | | |
|---|---|---|---|---|---|---|---|---|---|---|---|
| 5 | Q 45 | 2·00 | 2·00 | 5 | U 47 | 2·00 | 2·00 | 6 | Q 45 | † | 4·00 |
| 5 | T 46 | 2·00 | 2·00 | 5 | None | 2·00 | 2·00 | 7 | None | — | — |

Perforation Type 5

| | | | |
|---|---|---|---|
| 7 | None | 2·00 | 2·00 |

**11d. PLUM, No. Q27.**   Double Pane cylinders.   Perforation Type 5

| | | | |
|---|---|---|---|
| 1 | None | 2·00 | 2·00 |

Perforation Type 6 (no dot) and 6B (dot)

| | | | |
|---|---|---|---|
| 1 | None | 2·25 | 2·25 |

**1s. BISTRE-BROWN, No. Q28.**   Photogravure control.   Single Pane cylinders.   Perforation Type 6B

| | | |
|---|---|---|
| 7 | E 39 | 2·25 |
| 7 | G 40 | 2·25 |

Typographed control.   Single Pane cylinders.   Perforated Type 6B

| | | | | | | | | |
|---|---|---|---|---|---|---|---|---|
| 6 | H 40 | 2·25 | 6 | K 42 | 2·25 | 6 | O 44 | 2·25 |
| 6 | J 41 | 2·25 | 6 | M 43 | 2·25 | 7 | H 40 | 2·25 |

Perforation Type 6 (no dot)

| | | |
|---|---|---|
| 6 | J 41 | 2·25 |
| 6 | M 43 | 2·25 |

On cylinder 6 the number was originally engraved in reverse.   This was corrected before the cylinder was put to press.

Double Pane cylinders.   Perforation Type 6 (no dot) and 6B (dot)

| | | | | | | | | | | | |
|---|---|---|---|---|---|---|---|---|---|---|---|
| 13 | Q 45 | 2·25 | 2·25 | 16 | U 47 | 2·25 | 2·25 | 19 | None | 2·75 | 2·75 |
| 14 | None | — | † | 16 | None | 2·25 | 2·25 | | | | |
| 16 | S 46 | 2·25 | 7·50 | 17 | None | 2·25 | 2·25 | | | | |

Perforation Type 5

| | | | |
|---|---|---|---|
| 16 | None | 2·25 | 2·25 |
| 17 | None | 2·25 | 2·25 |
| 19 | None | 2·25 | 2·25 |

# Bibliography

*British Philatelist, The* (Formerly monthly). Charles Nissen & Co., Ltd., London.

*British Postage Stamp Varieties*, by R. C. Alcock and C. W. Meredith. Published by R. C. Alcock Ltd., 1949.

*Great Britain. A Study of the Cracked Units of the De La Rue One Penny Stamp, 1902–1910*, by H. S. Doupé. Published by the Great Britain Philatelic Society, London, 1962.

*Great Britain. The Coronation Stamp, 1937*, by L. Birch. Published by the Midland Stamp Co., Birmingham.

*Encyclopaedia of British Empire Postage Stamps, The: Vol. I: Great Britain and the Empire in Europe*. Republished by Robson Lowe Ltd., 1952.

*G.B. Journal, The* (Bi-monthly). Published by the Great Britain Philatelic Society, London.

*King Edward VIII. A Study of the Stamps of the Reign of King Edward VIII*, by J. B. M. Stanton. Published by the Great Britain Philatelic Society, London, 1958.

*King George V. A Study of the Provisional Issues of 1934 and 1935*, by J. B. M. Stanton and K. G. Rushworth. Published by Stanley Gibbons Ltd., London, 1959.

*Postage Stamps of Great Britain, The, Part III, The Embossed Issues, The Surface-Printed Issues of Queen Victoria and King Edward VII*, edited by K. M. Beaumont and John Easton. Published by the Royal Philatelic Society, London, 1964.

*Postage Stamps of Great Britain, The, Part IV, The Issues of King George V*, by K. M. Beaumont and J. B. M. Stanton. Published by the Royal Philatelic Society, London, 1957.

*Stamps of Great Britain, The*, by Stanley Phillips. Published by Stanley Gibbons Ltd., London, 1921.

# INDEX (References are to page numbers)

| | KING EDWARD VII | | | | KING GEORGE V | | | | | | | | | | | | KING EDWARD VIII | | | KING GEORGE VI | | | | | | | | |
| | De La Rue | Harrison | Somerset House | Plate Identification | Downey Heads | | | | Simple Cypher | | | Block Cypher | | Photogravure | | | | | | Original Colours | | | Lighter Colours | | | Change of Colour | | |
| | | | | | Plate 1A | Plate 1B | Re-engraved | Plate Identification | Postal Issues | Watermark Varieties | Plate Identification | Postal Issues | Plate Identification | Postal Issues | Booklet Panes/Cylinder Nos. | Cylinder Nos., Controls & Perfs. | Postal Issues | Booklet Panes/Cylinder Nos. | Cylinder Nos., Controls & Perfs. | Postal Issues | Booklet Panes/Cylinder Nos. | Cylinder Nos., Controls & Perfs. | Postal Issues | Booklet Panes/Cylinder Nos. | Cylinder Nos., Controls & Perfs. | Postal Issues | Booklet Panes/Cylinder Nos. | Cylinder Nos., Controls & Perfs. |
| ½d. | 25 | 26 | .. | 142 | 54 | 55 | 56 | 169 | 61 | 132 | 171 | 81 | 180 | 91 | 243 | 250 | 105 | 244 | 253 | 106 | 245 | 254 | 107 | 245 | 255 | 107 | 245 | 255 |
| 1d. | 27 | 29 | .. | 150 | 57 | 58 | 59 | 170 | 63 | 132 | 184 | 82 | 195 | 90 | 243 | 249 | 105 | 244 | 253 | 108 | 245 | 255 | 108 | 248 | 256 | 109 | 245 | 256 |
| 1½d. | 30 | .. | 31 | 159 | .. | .. | .. | .. | 66 | 132 | 198 | 83 | 203 | 90 | 243 | 249 | 105 | 244 | 253 | 110 | 246 | 257 | 111 | 248 | 257 | 111 | 246 | 258 |
| 2d. | 32 | .. | 32 | 160 | .. | .. | .. | .. | 67 | 132 | 208 | 84 | 212 | 91 | .. | 250 | 105 | .. | 253 | 111 | 246 | 258 | 112 | 246 | 258 | 112 | 246 | 259 |
| 2½d. | 34 | 33 | .. | 160 | .. | .. | .. | .. | 69 | 132 | 214 | 84 | 215 | 92 | .. | 252 | .. | .. | .. | 112 | .. | 259 | 113 | 247 | 260 | 113 | .. | 261 |
| 3d. | 35 | 35 | .. | 161 | .. | .. | .. | .. | 70 | 132 | 217 | 85 | 219 | 92 | .. | 252 | 105 | .. | 253 | 113 | .. | 261 | 113 | .. | 261 | 114 | 247 | 262 |
| 4d. | 37 | 36 | 37 | 161 | .. | .. | .. | .. | 72 | 132 | 220 | 85 | 221 | 92 | .. | 252 | .. | .. | .. | 114 | .. | 262 | .. | .. | .. | .. | .. | .. |
| 4½d. | 38 | .. | 39 | 162 | .. | .. | .. | .. | 73 | 132 | 222 | 86 | 223 | 92 | .. | 252 | .. | .. | .. | 114 | .. | 262 | .. | .. | .. | .. | .. | .. |
| 5d. | 40 | .. | 40 | 163 | .. | .. | .. | .. | 74 | 132 | 224 | .. | .. | .. | .. | .. | .. | .. | .. | 114 | .. | 262 | .. | .. | .. | .. | .. | .. |
| 6d. | 40 | .. | 41 | 164 | .. | .. | .. | .. | 75 | 132 | 224 | .. | .. | .. | .. | .. | .. | .. | .. | 114 | .. | 262 | .. | .. | .. | .. | .. | .. |
| 7d. | .. | .. | 43 | .. | .. | .. | .. | .. | 76 | 132 | 224 | 87 | 224 | .. | .. | 252 | .. | .. | .. | 114 | .. | 263 | .. | .. | .. | .. | .. | .. |
| 8d. | 41 | .. | .. | 165 | .. | .. | .. | .. | 77 | 132 | 225 | 87 | 225 | .. | .. | 252 | .. | .. | .. | 115 | .. | 263 | .. | .. | .. | .. | .. | .. |
| 9d. | .. | .. | .. | 165 | .. | .. | .. | .. | 79 | 132 | 225 | 87 | 225 | 92 | .. | 252 | .. | .. | .. | 115 | .. | 263 | .. | .. | .. | .. | .. | .. |
| 10d. | 43 | .. | 44 | 166 | .. | .. | .. | .. | 80 | 132 | 225 | .. | 225 | 92 | .. | 252 | .. | .. | .. | 115 | .. | 264 | .. | .. | .. | .. | .. | .. |
| 11d. | .. | .. | .. | 166 | .. | .. | .. | .. | .. | 132 | 226 | .. | 226 | .. | .. | .. | .. | .. | .. | 115 | .. | 264 | .. | .. | .. | .. | .. | .. |
| 1s. | 44 | .. | 44 | 167 | .. | .. | .. | .. | .. | .. | .. | .. | .. | 92 | .. | 252 | .. | .. | .. | 115 | .. | 264 | .. | .. | .. | 114 | .. | 262 |
| 2/6 | 44 | .. | 44 | 167 | 96 (Waterlow) | | 96 (De La Rue) | | | | | 98 (Bradbury Wilkinson) | | 99 (Re-engraved) | | | | | | 116 Brown | | | | | | 118 Green *(Change of Design)* | | |
| 5s. | 44 | 45 | 45 | 167 | 98 | | 98 | | | | | 98 | | 99 | | | | | | 116 Red | | | | | | 118 Red | | |
| 10s. | 45 | 45 | 45 | 168 | 98 | | 99 | | | | | 98 | | 99 | | | | | | 116 Dark Blue | | | 116 Ultramarine | | | 118 Ultram. | | |
| £1 | 45 | 45 | 45 | 168 | 99 | | 99 | | | | | 99 | | 99 | | | | | | 116 Brown | | | | | | 118 Brown | | |

*Change of Colour — 116 Green*

# ROMANO HOUSE

*Stanley Gibbons' special salon*
*for the Connoisseur of Rare Stamps*

Only 30 yards from our Shop at 391 Strand is Romano House, Stanley Gibbons' Rare Stamp Department.

Here, in luxurious surroundings, the connoisseur can examine at his leisure the cream of the world's finest stock with the aid of an experienced staff, led by **Les Hallam** (for Great Britain), **John Farthing** (British Commonwealth), and **Steven Kander** (Foreign Countries).

**Romano House, 399 Strand, London WC2**

**Please address correspondence to:**
**Stanley Gibbons Ltd.,**
**391 Strand, London, WC2R OLX**

# Three Fine Blank Albums
# To House Your G.B. Collection . . .

## THE EXETER

Peg-fitting at its cheapest. The fine matt white cartridge leaves are supplied either groove-fluted or double linen-hinged leaves size $10\frac{3}{8} \times 9\frac{3}{4}$ in.; the fine quality hard-wearing Rexine binder is available in Red, Blue or Green, neat and tidy without lettering.

| Item No. | U.K. | ABROAD |
|---|---|---|
| **3828** with 75 groove-fluted leaves | **49/10 (£2.49)** | 40/– (£2.00) |
| **3830** with 50 double linen-hinged leaves | **71/6  (£3.58)** | 57/6 (£2.88) |
| **3832** with 50 double linen-hinged transparent faced leaves | **77/10 (£3.89)** | 62/6 (£3.13) |

## THE DEVON

The really large capacity album—at a breathtakingly economic price! 250 pages size, $10\frac{3}{8} \times 9\frac{3}{4}$ in.; and room for a few more to be added. An album that lets you spend more on your stamps, yet it is one you will be proud to own. Peg-fitting binder in Red, Blue, Green or Black.

| | | |
|---|---|---|
| **3834** Devon album complete with 250 leaves | **56/– (£2.80)** | 45/– (£2.25) |

## THE PLYMOUTH

A distinguished setting for your stamps—at moderate cost. Modern in concept, it will not 'date' with the passing years. The cover, of finest quality hardwearing Rexine over heavy board, is blind-blocked and has no outside lettering; there is a choice of four colours: Maroon, Blue, Green and Black. Inside are 75 double linen-hinged leaves, size $10\frac{3}{8} \times 9\frac{3}{4}$ in., of special matt white cartridge paper, available with or without attached transparent interleaving.

| | | |
|---|---|---|
| **391** Plymouth Album complete in case with 75 leaves | **£6.10.8 (£6.54)** | £5.5.0 (£5.25) |
| **392** Plymouth Album complete in case with 75 transparent-faced leaves | **£7.3.2 (£7.16)** | £5.15.0 (£5.75) |

All prices " postage extra "

# THE ORIEL

**THE WORLD'S FINEST COLLECTIONS ARE HOUSED IN 'ORIELS'**

The 'ORIEL' is luxuriously bound with red leather back and corners, and cloth sides, finished in gold with space on back of cover for lettering. The gilt-edged leaves are of the finest mould-made paper, overall size $10\frac{3}{8}$ x $9\frac{3}{4}$ in., feint quadrillé ruled, and double-linen-hinged. The special telescopic fitting means that it is possible to remove any single leaf or batch of leaves without disturbing the others.

The complete album is supplied with strong cloth-cover lined drop-in case.

| Item No.<br>395 | Complete Album<br>with 50 leaves | *£17* U.K. (including tax)<br>Abroad £13.6.8 (13·34)<br>Postage extra |
|---|---|---|

# *Parting is such sweet sorrow . . .*

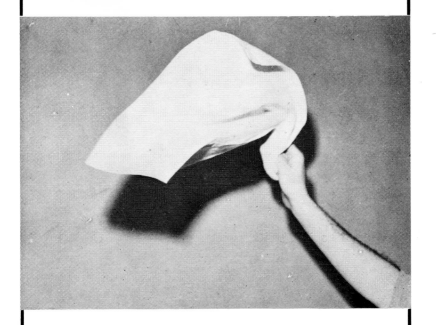

but not to the same extent when you sell your specialised or really first-class collection to Stanley Gibbons. We'll sooth those sorrowful parting pangs with our century-old remedy— A COMPLETELY SATISFACTORY TRANSACTION!

And since our customers include many of the world's most famous names in philately you know that your precious material will fall into discerning hands.

Each year we travel hundreds of thousands of miles all over the world to obtain good collections. We may not be visiting you just yet, so don't wait for us, contact in the first instance *Barry Peachey now at 391, Strand, London WC2R OLX or ring him on 01–836 9707.*